The Intext Series in **BASIC MATHEMATICS**

under the consulting editorship of

RICHARD D. ANDERSON
Louisiana State University

ALEX ROSENBERG
Cornell University

Modern
Intermediate
Algebra

Modern
Intermediate
Algebra

SAMUEL M. SELBY
Hiram College

WILLIAM H. BEYER
University of Akron

INTEXT EDUCATIONAL PUBLISHERS
College Division of Intext

Scranton   San Francisco   Toronto   London

ISBN 0-7002-2352-5

Library of Congress Catalog Card Number 77-160679

COPYRIGHT © 1971, BY INTERNATIONAL TEXTBOOK COMPANY

Preface

Higher education has recognized the tremendous growth and popular acceptance of junior college and technical school programs which now serve a vast number of newly created curricula that demand a return to basic courses of mathematics.

This text, titled *Modern Intermediate Algebra*, is intended particularly for the student who, for reasons such as inadequate previous training or the immaturity of youth, must learn algebra from a reasonable beginning based on a knowledge of arithmetic and at a pace slower than that expected from the typical college freshman. The text is not encyclopedic in character but it is the feeling of the authors that most of the important concepts classified as being "modern" have been covered adequately for the consumption of the student at this level.

The basic orientation is to provide a background where the student gains manipulative skills in problem solving. Mathematical elegance and extreme rigor are not most appealing to the learner at this level but a challenge to his intuition supported by reasonably complete and accurate proofs should serve his purposes more adequately. The authors have responded to these reactions by continually introducing and reinforcing ideas and concepts with numerous examples and illustrations. The contents are designed to serve a three-to five-hour course patterned either on a semester or quarter basis. The vast amount of problem material should give the instructor ample opportunity and freedom to gear his course to any level of competence desired.

The descriptive term "modern" as contained in the title of this text is merited since special emphasis has been given to topics such as set notation, the real number line, order properties of the real number system, absolute value, inequalities, matrices, logic, mathematical induction, and linear programming.

To reiterate, the authors desire to point out the following special features of the text, namely:

1. The illustrative examples are numerous and carefully selected to cover typical cases.
2. The fact that in algebra the rules of arithmetic are applied to letters instead of numbers is emphasized by frequent use of at least two illustrative examples, one of which is purely arithmetic in character. This encourages the student to check procedures, rules, and results by use of numbers chosen from his arithmetic experience.
3. Many common errors caused by inexperience are pointed out and discussed before the student is challenged with them in the exercise material. It will be noted that in certain of the problems, the sole question to be considered is whether a given operation is or is not valid.
4. In a text at this level, the primary objective is clarity based on intuition rather than mathematical rigor. The use of set notation as a communication medium is employed where it helps to promote understanding of an idea and not as an end-all for its own sake.
5. There are approximately 3,000 problem exercises which provide ample drill and a means of creating manipulative skills in problem solving.
6. The printing of only half of the answers in any mathematics text usually cuts down the available problem list by almost one-half. This is due to the fact that most instructors assign for homework those problems for which answers appear in the text. On the other hand, some problems without answers are necessary for the purpose of an extra challenge wherein the student acquires self reliance by learning to check results on his own. If both these situations are taken into account, it seems advisable to include most but not all of the answers. This text includes answers to approximately 4/5 of the problems, with the remaining answers not even printed in pamphlet form since copies eventually reach unintended hands.
7. The guiding principle throughout this text has been to maintain, so far as the subject matter allows, a consistent upward-sloping degree of difficulty.

Because of limitations of space, it was decided not to include topics such as permutations and combinations, probability, and an introduction to statistics. The feeling of the authors was that these topics could better be handled in courses following those for which this text was intended.

The authors dedicate this text "Modern Intermediate Algebra" to Professor Ralph S. Underwood, formerly of Texas Tech University, and the late Professor Thomas R. Nelson of Texas A&M University. Permission to use materials which were originally prepared by them but modified to serve present needs, is gratefully appreciated. Several others are responsible for suggestions and recommendations, and to these thanks are in order. They include Professors Roy A. Mazzagatti and David L. Howard of Miami-Dade Junior College, Professor James W. Mettler of The Pennsylvania State University, and Professor Ernest A. Kuehls of The University of Akron.

Special mention is due Mr. Charles J. Updegraph, Mathematics Editor at Intext, for his excellent services, and the joint efforts in preparation and typing rendered by Mrs. William Beyer, Miss Carole Blanchard, and Mrs. Vernon Boger.

SAMUEL M. SELBY
WILLIAM H. BEYER

Akron, Ohio
May, 1971

Contents

CHAPTER 9   EXPONENTS AND RADICALS . . . 183

CHAPTER 10   THE NUMBER SYSTEM . . . 210

CHAPTER 11   QUADRATIC EQUATIONS . . . 222

chapter **1**

Introduction to Sets

1-1. SETS

A *set* is any well-defined collection, aggregate, group, or class of distinct objects; the objects being called *elements* or *members* of the set. From a mathematical point of view both the concept of a set, and that of an object belonging to it, are postulated notions and accepted as existing without being formally defined. Intuitional experience guides us in building of sets. Examples of sets are:

1. The digits in the decimal number system, namely $0, 1, 2, 3, \ldots, 9$.
2. The names in the Akron telephone directory for the year 1969.
3. The vowels of the alphabet a, e, i, o, and u.
4. The nations which form the United Nations Assembly.
5. The real number values of x that make $2x + 5 = 3x - 1$, which is 6.
6. The people living on the moon.

The sets in 1, 3, and 5 are defined by the actual listing of their elements, while those in 2, 4, 6 are defined by a statement of some property, or rule, which makes it possible to tell whether or not a particular object is or is not an element of the set.

It is noted that the elements of a set are objects of varying natures, such as numbers, letters, people, abstract ideas, and the like. It is possible that the elements of a set are sets themselves. In example 4, each nation constitutes a people, who in turn can be subdivided into other sets of individuals in accord with some special means of selection. It is possible for a set to contain some elements that are themselves sets and some that are not.

This important concept and postulated idea of a set has significantly affected modern mathematics. It will provide us with a means of expressing clarity, consistency, and effectiveness for communicating principles that involve numbers, or ideas whether they be concrete or abstract, as we proceed onward in this text.

1-2. NOTATION

A customary symbolism for designating a set is to list its elements in enclosed braces { }. The braces where the elements are listed, and where order of listing is unimportant is then designated by either capital letters $A, B, C, \ldots$ or otherwise, depending on the type of discussion in which the set finds itself. This manner of denoting a set of elements is referred to as the *roster method.*

The symbol $\in$ means "is an element of" or "is a member of" or "belongs to." Accordingly, "$x \in S$" means "x is an element of S," "x is a member of S" or "x belongs to the set S." The symbol $\notin$ implies noninclusion of an element in a set S, or that the element does not belong to the set S. Examples for use of $\in$ and $\notin$ are:

1. If $S = \{1,2,3,4\}$, then $1 \in S$, and $7 \notin S$, The City of Washington $\notin S$; etc.
2. If $A = \{$Elsie, Dee, Bill, Sam$\}$, then Tom $\notin A$; $5 \notin A$, Dee $\in A$.

1-3. EQUAL SETS OR WHEN ARE SETS CONSIDERED EQUAL TO ONE ANOTHER?

Two sets designated by distinct letters, say A and B, are equal if every element of A is an element of B and if every element of B is an element of A. We designate such equality by the notation $A = B$. The order in which elements are listed within braces in no way affects the decision as to whether a set A is or is not equal to a set B. The importance of specifying equality dictates that the contained elements of one set are those contained by the other, and vice versa.

For example, the following sets are obviously equal.

$$\{\text{Tom, Dick, Harry}\} = \{\text{Dick, Tom, Harry}\} = \{\text{Dick, Harry, Tom}\}$$
$$= \{\text{Tom, Harry, Dick}\} = \{\text{Harry, Dick, Tom}\}$$
$$= \{\text{Harry, Tom, Dick}\}.$$

1-4. WHAT DO WE MEAN BY THE EMPTY SET—NULL SET—VOID SET?

In order to deal with sets on a manipulative basis, it is convenient to define the "empty," "null," or "void" set as being one that possesses no elements. It is designated by the symbol ϕ, or braces with no elements included within, namely { }. Examples of this set are:

1. The set of all human beings 50 feet tall.
2. The set of those elements common to $\{a,b,c\}$ and $\{4,3,2,0\}$.
3. The solution in integers that will make $3x + 5 = x$.

1-5. SUBSETS

A set T is considered to be a subset of a set S if each of the elements of T are also elements of a set S. The symbol "$\subseteq$" denotes this property of being a subset. $T \subseteq S$ implies that T is a subset of S. If T is not a subset of S, the notation $T \nsubseteq S$ is used. For example:

1. If $S = \{3,5,8,10\}$ and $T = \{3,10\}$, then $T \subseteq S$.
2. If $S = \{$cat, mouse, pig, horse$\}$ and $T = \{$elephant$\}$, then $T \nsubseteq S$.

Definition of a "Proper Subset"

If a set T is a nonempty subset of S where at least one of the elements of S is not in T, then T is called a *proper subset* of S. To indicate that this nonempty subset T is a proper subset of S, we use if desired the modified symbolism $T \subset S$. But it certainly is still correct to write $T \subseteq S$, as will be pointed out in what follows. The empty set ϕ is a proper subset of every nonempty set S. This follows from the fact that if ϕ is not a subset of S, it must possess at least one distinct element not contained in S. But ϕ has no elements, and as a consequence a contradiction arises. It follows that ϕ is a subset of every nonempty set, and is proper since S is nonempty.

The empty set is *unique*, since if there were at least two distinct empty sets, namely ϕ_1, and ϕ_2, one of these would have to contain an element not contained in the other. But an empty set contains no elements, and thus ϕ_1 cannot be distinct from ϕ_2. When one speaks of the empty set, it should be referred to as "*the* empty set," and not as "*an* empty set." The word "an" gives one the impression several such sets exist, which is not the case.

Every set S is considered to be a subset of itself. In other words, $S \subseteq S$. The set S cannot be a proper subset of itself, since if it were, at least one of its elements would be lacking from among its members, which is evidently impossible.

As already shown the empty set is a proper subset of every nonempty set S, but cannot be considered a proper subset of itself. In summary, the empty set ϕ is unique, is a subset of itself, and does not contain itself as a proper subset. In other words, $\phi \subseteq \phi$ is considered correct notation but $\phi \subset \phi$ is incorrect. In fact, any set, whether empty or otherwise, permits the notation $S \subseteq S$. As presented in this section it would be incorrect to write $S \subset S$, since S is not a proper subset of itself. It will be found that some mathematicians permit the notation $S \subset S$ in place of $S \subseteq S$, but in accord with the discussion given here, the authors of this text feel that $S \subset S$ is ambiguous and causes unnecessary concern relative to the meaning of a proper subset.

EXERCISE 1-1

List within braces { } the elements for each set as described in Probs. 1–5.

1. The letters in the word "mathematics."
2. The last three presidents of the United States.
3. The positive integers less than 5.
4. The positive odd integers between 2 and 20.
5. The months of the year having 31 days.

Describe each of the sets in Probs. 6–10 by a "word statement."

6. {Superior, Erie, Huron, Michigan, Ontario}.
7. {1,3,5,7,9,8,6,4,2}.
8. {a,e,i,o,u}.
9. {1,3,5,7,9}.
10. {Monday, Tuesday, Wednesday, Thursday, Friday, Saturday, Sunday}.

If P is the set of individuals who have served as president of the United States, Q the set {2,4,6,8}, and R = {a,e,i,o,u}, determine in Probs. 11–15 which of the following hold.

11. $5 \notin Q$.
12. Andrew Jackson $\in P$.
13. $u \in R$.
14. Robert E. Lee $\notin P$.
15. $0 \in Q$.

If $A = \{1,3,4,\{6,9\}\}$, $B = \{3,\{6,9\}\}$, $C = \{1,\{2\},5\}$, and $D = \{2,5,7,8\}$ then determine in Probs. 16–25 which of the following hold.

16. $B \subset A$.
17. $B = C$.
18. $5 \in C$.
19. $\{2\} \in C$.
20. $\emptyset \subset B$.
21. $6 \subset A$.
22. $B \subseteq A$.
23. $0 \in A$.
24. $C \nsubseteq A$.
25. $\{\{2\},5\} \subset D$.

Let $A = \{1,2,3\}$, $B = \{1,3,5,7\}$, and $C = \{1,2,3,4,5,6,7\}$. Complete the following statements in Probs. 26–35 by placing in the blank space, the appropriate symbol chosen from the set $\{\in, \notin, =, \neq, \subseteq, \nsubseteq\}$.

26. 2 ____ A Ans.: $2 \in A$.
27. 4 ____ B.
28. 0 ____ A.

29. A ____ B.   33. B ____ C.

30. $\{\ \ \}$ ____ ϕ.   34. ϕ ____ A.

31. $\{3,1,2\}$ ____ A.   35. $\{7,3,5,1\}$ ____ B.

32. A ____ C.

1-6. EQUIVALENT SETS

If the elements of two sets A and B can be paired in such a way so that to each one of the elements of either set, there is a unique partner element associated from the other, then a one-to-one correspondence exists between these two sets A and B. This is symbolically represented as $A \leftrightarrow B$, and the two sets are said to be equivalent one to the other. Two sets may possess equivalence and yet not be equal to one another. However, all equal sets are of necessity equivalent or saying it another way, every set is equivalent to itself. The examples which follow illustrate equivalence.

$$\text{Let } A = \{\alpha,\beta,\gamma,\delta\},$$
$$B = \{\text{peanut, apple, orange, pear}\},$$
$$C = \{\gamma,\delta,\beta,\alpha\}.$$

Here one pairing of the elements in A with those in B is

α	β	γ	δ
$\updownarrow$	$\updownarrow$	$\updownarrow$	$\updownarrow$
apple	peanut	orange	pear

and $A \leftrightarrow B$. It is obvious that A and B are not equal. There are twenty-four pairings* which might have been used, but it is only necessary to show that at least one such pairing exists between A and B to establish equivalence. It is also noted that if $A \leftrightarrow B$, then $B \leftrightarrow A$.

If A is studied in relationship to C, a matching such as

$\alpha \in A$	$\beta \in A$	$\delta \in A$	$\gamma \in A$
$\updownarrow$	$\updownarrow$	$\updownarrow$	$\updownarrow$
$\gamma \in C$	$\alpha \in C$	$\beta \in C$	$\delta \in C$

indicates that $A \leftrightarrow C$ or that $C \leftrightarrow A$. It is evident that $A = C$, which was not the case for A when associated with B.

*Other pairings might have been

α	β	γ	δ		α	β	γ	δ	
$\updownarrow$	$\updownarrow$	$\updownarrow$	$\updownarrow$	or	$\updownarrow$	$\updownarrow$	$\updownarrow$	$\updownarrow$	etc.
pear	apple	peanut	orange		orange	pear	peanut	apple	

1-7.   CARDINALITY FOR EQUIVALENT SETS

The Natural Numbers

$N = \{1,2,3,4,5,\ldots\}$ and the nonnegative integers $W = \{0,1,2,3,\ldots\}$ are well known to all of us and will be used as a starting point for exploring and exploiting our experiences with number ideas. The order in which each number element follows the other in sets N and W is of vast importance in what follows. The set of natural numbers N is essential for purposes of establishing "a counting process," or for "telling how many" elements a set possesses. There are an endless number of proper subsets that belong to N. For example, $\{1,2,3\}$, $\{1,2,3,4,5\}$, etc., are proper subsets of N. We are particularly concerned with those proper subsets of N which start with the element 1 followed in sequence by the other elements up to a desired natural number element. The proper subsets so formed are employed to carry out "a counting process," as shown in the example.

If sets $A = \{3,1,2,8\}$,

$\quad\quad\quad\quad B = \{\alpha,\beta,\gamma,\delta\}$,

$\quad\quad\quad\quad C = \{$Earth, Moon, Mars, Jupiter$\}$

are paired with the proper subset $\{1,2,3,4\} \subset N$ where the order of the elements in $\{1,2,3,4\}$ is kept intact, then sets A, B, and C are all equivalent to one another and in turn to $\{1,2,3,4\}$. These sets are said to have the same *cardinality*, or cardinal number. The cardinal number associated with these sets is defined to be the counting number designated as the natural number 4, the last element in the proper subset $\{1,2,3,4\} \subset N$.

Since the empty set ϕ possesses no elements, an equivalence between a proper subset of N and those of ϕ is meaningless, and by agreement the nonnegative integer 0 (which is not a natural number) is accepted as representing the cardinality of ϕ.

The counting number, or the indication of "how many" elements are in a set, is symbolized as $n(A)$ if the set is A. In the preceding example $n(A) = n(B) = n(C) = 4$. It should be observed that the counting numbers are independent of the type of objects constituting the make-up of a set. In other words, all sets that are equivalent to one another have the same cardinality and the same counting number, irrespective of the type of objects involved as elements of the sets.

1-8.   THE MEANING OF "MORE THAN" AND "LESS THAN"

If a and b represent counting numbers, then "a less than b," written as "$a < b$," means that a is the cardinality of a set T that is equivalent to a proper subset of a second set S whose cardinality is b. If $a < b$, we sometimes for convenience rephrase the associated statement "a less than

b" and say that "b is more than a" or that "b is greater than a" and write "$b > a$." For example, if

$$S = \{2,4,8,10\}$$

and

$$T = \{a,b\},$$

$n(S) = 4$, and $n(T) = 2$. Hence $4 > 2$ or $2 < 4$. Here "2 is less than 4" or "4 is greater than 2." It is evident that set T is equivalent to a proper subset of S. For example $\{8,10\} \subset S$ and $\{a,b\}$ is equivalent to it.

1-9. THE MEANING OF FINITE AND INFINITE SETS

All the definitions and examples in Sec. 1-6, 1-7, and 1-8 relate to sets that are defined as being finite. The property which determines whether a set is finite or infinite is illustrated in what follows:

If a proper subset of N as described in Sec. 1-7, can be paired with a given set S, then S is referred to as a finite set and possesses a finite counting number. If this is not the case, then S is an infinite set. It is noted that ϕ, by definition, is considered to be a finite set, and possesses the finite counting number 0.

An example of an infinite set is the set of natural numbers $N = \{1,2,3,4,5,...\}$ which can be matched with one of its many proper subsets such as $\{3,6,9,12,15,18,...\}$ in the following manner:

$$
\begin{array}{cccc}
1 & 2 & 3 & 4 \\
\updownarrow & \updownarrow & \updownarrow & \updownarrow \quad \text{etc.} \\
3 & 6 & 9 & 12
\end{array}
$$

Hence N itself is an infinite set.

An infinite set can be matched from an equivalence standpoint with proper subsets of itself. This is absolutely not true for finite sets.

Sets such as $M = \{m,2m,3m,4m,...\}$, where $m \in N$, are examples of infinite sets. If $m = 4$, $M = \{4,8,12,16,...\}$. If $m = 5$, $M = \{5,10,15,20,...\}$. Here each element of the set M is a multiple of m and is divisible by m. The natural number multiplier m is called a *factor* of each of the elements of M.

1-10. PRIME NUMBERS AND COMPOSITE NUMBERS

For convenience all natural numbers with the exception of the number 1, are described either as prime numbers or otherwise as composite numbers in accord with the following understanding.

Any natural number p not equal to unity is a *prime* number if it is not divisible by any natural number other than p or 1.

If a natural number n is not unity and not prime, it is composite. A composite number can always be represented as a product of two or more prime numbers other than itself. A composite number with respect to N possesses unique representation in terms of its primes except for the order in which they appear in the product. For example:

  1. 2,3,5,7,11,... are prime numbers.
  2. $6 = 2 \cdot 3 = 3 \cdot 2, 8 = 2 \cdot 2 \cdot 2$ are composite numbers.

The natural number 1 is referred to as "the unit" for the set of natural numbers N.

EXERCISE 1-2

1. Set up in three distinct ways a one-to-one correspondence between {1,2,3} and {a,b,c}.

2. Show by pairing that the set of primary directions namely North, South, East, West on a compass is equivalent to the set of seasons of the year. Are these sets equal?

3. Pair A = {a,e,i,o,u} with two distinct subsets of N. Find $n(A)$.

4. Let B = {1,2,3,4}.
    (a) List all subsets of B that have cardinality 2. Call this set of subsets C.
    (b) List all subsets of B that have cardinality 3. Call this set of subsets D.
    (c) Is it possible to set up a matching between the sets C and D?
    (d) Find $n(C)$ and $n(D)$.
    (e) Determine the validity of the following.
        (i) $C \leftrightarrow D$.
        (ii) $B \leftrightarrow D$.
        (iii) $B = C$.

5. Classify the following sets in accordance as to whether they are finite or infinite:
    (a) N = the set of all natural numbers.
    (b) D = the set of all days of the week.
    (c) E = the set of all even numbers.
    (d) ϕ.
    (e) $\{\phi, N\}$.
    (f) $\{\phi,1,2,3,4\}$

6. Let A = {1,2,3,4} and B = {3,4,5,6,7}. Set up a matching to prove that $n(A) < n(B)$.

7. Show that A = {1,4,9,16,25,...} is infinite.

8. Show that $B = \left\{ \dfrac{6}{1}, \dfrac{6 \cdot 5}{1 \cdot 2}, \dfrac{6 \cdot 5 \cdot 4}{1 \cdot 2 \cdot 3}, \ldots \right\}$ is finite. Assume that factors in the numerator are members of the set of integers: positive, negative, or zero.

9. The following numbers are either prime or composite. For those which are composite specify the corresponding unique representation in terms of primes:

$$3,9,11,24,29,36,47,60.$$

1-11. REPLACEMENT SETS AND SET-BUILDER NOTATION

Certain elements of a set S are sometimes selected because of some special property they may possess, and as a consequence a subset of S containing these elements is obtained. At other times substitution for a set S by a set T is desirable and still other changes may result as one set is created from another. When such operations are performed upon given sets various questions arise as to whether set T is actually the same as S or in what way it may be different. In order to answer questions of this character it is convenient to introduce some new symbolism and nomenclature. The examples which follow describe more clearly what is involved.

1. If $A = \{2,3,6,8,7,9\}$, and if special emphasis is placed on the elements 2, 6, and 8, a statement such as "x is an even natural number" can be made to indicate this attention. This statement is called an "open sentence*," and x is referred to as a variable or placeholder. The sentence is not precise until an appropriate x is chosen from elements of A, called the replacement set, which then makes the open sentence either true or false. Here x can be replaced by either 2, 6, 8, but not 3, 7, or 9. The set $\{2,6,8\}$, which is a proper subset of the set A is called a "truth set" for the open sentence "x is an even natural number." The truth set is also referred to as the "solution set" for this open sentence. If the open sentence had been "x is a natural number larger than 18," the "truth set" or "solution set" would have been the empty set ϕ.

2. If $A = \{$Elsie, Sam, Bill, Dee$\}$, the open sentence "x is 10 years old," is not the type of open sentence that is meaningful since A lacks precise details. Insufficient information is given about the constituent members so as to tell from the set A alone how to judge respective ages. Adequate information must always be included in order to produce solution sets for open sentences.

Other ways of describing "solution sets" for "open sentences" brings into usage a notation and symbolism which is referred to as "set-builder" notation. For example, if $A = \{1,2,5,7,9\}$, then a truth set or a solution set described as $B = \{x \in A : x$ is an even integer$\}$ makes good sense. In English, this reads "the set of all x belonging to A such that x is an even

---

*The term *open sentence*, as used in mathematics, is also referred to as a defining condition, and will be used in this sense throughout this text.

integer." The desired solution set is thus described by B, and results in $B = \{2\}$. In B, this set-builder notation employs the following symbolism which should be noted carefully and translated into English when necessary.

Braces { } used to enclose the basic descriptive features of a set, and read in English as "the set of"

$\in$ used in $x \in A$ and read in English as "all x belonging to A," where A is the replacement set

Semicolon ":" or bar " | " and read in English as "such that"

Following the semicolon or bar, precise information is given as to how elements of the solution set are to be chosen.

For example, let $A = \{2,4,6,8,10\}$ and $B = \{x \in A : x$ is divisible by $4\}$. In English, B is read "B is the set of all elements x belonging to A such that x is divisible by four." Here $B = \{4,8\}$.

If $C = \{x \in A : x$ is an odd integer$\}$, then $C = \emptyset$, or $C = \{\ \}$. The set A from which the choices for the placeholder x were obtained is referred to not only as the replacement set but also as the universal set for the discussion at hand. If at the beginning of a discussion, the universal set is clearly understood from the context, for convenience it is omitted from the "set-builder notation."

For example if the universal set is understood to be N, the set of the natural numbers, then $S = \{x : x < 5\}$ reads S is "the set of all x belonging to the natural numbers such that $x < 5$." Here $S = \{1,2,3,4,\}$.

EXERCISE 1-3

Let $A = \{2, 4, 6, 8, 10\}$ be the universal set. Obtain in Probs. 1 to 5 the respective solution sets for the following open sentences where $x \in A$.

1. x is an even number.
2. x is an odd number.
3. $x - 2 \in A$.
4. $x + 4 \in A$.
5. $x \neq 2$.

Let $B = \{3,4,7,9,13\}$ be the universal set. List the elements of the sets described in Probs. 6–15.

6. $\{x \in B \mid x > 5\}$.
7. $\{x \in B : x$ is an even number$\}$.
8. $\{x \in B : x + 4 = 13\}$.
9. $\{x \in B \mid x$ is a 2-digit number$\}$.
10. $\{x \in B \mid x$ is the sum of two numbers of $B\}$.
11. $\{x \in B \mid x \neq 3$ and $x \neq 13\}$.
12. $\{x \in B : x > 7\}$.
13. $\{x \in B : x < 9\}$.
14. $\{x \in B \mid 3 \cdot x \notin B\}$.
15. $\{x \in B \mid x$ is the difference of two numbers of $B\}$.

Let $N = \{1,2,3,4,5,\ldots\}$ = the set of all natural numbers, be the universal set. Use set-builder notation in Probs. 16–20 to describe the listed sets.

16. $\{1,2,3,4\}$.

17. $\{1,3,5,7,9,\ldots\}$.

18. $\{1,4,9,16,25,\ldots\}$.

19. $\{3\}$.

20. $\{\ \} = \phi$.

1-12.   OPERATIONS WITH SETS

Two basic operations, namely "union," symbolized as $\cup$, and "intersection," symbolized as $\cap$, operate on sets to produce other sets from them. The operations will now be defined.

If A and B are two sets, their union is symbolized as $A \cup B$. $A \cup B$ includes those elements that belong to A or to B or to both. It follows from this definition that if either $x \in A$ or if $x \in B$, or if x is common to both A and B, then $x \in (A \cup B)$. Hence $A \cup B = \{x : x \in A \text{ or } x \in B\}$. The "or" used here is the and/or and means "either" or "both." The intersection of A and B, symbolized as $A \cap B$ includes only those elements which are common to both A and B. This definition is symbolically written as $A \cap B = \{x : x \in A \text{ and } x \in B\}$. The "and" as used here means "both" or "at the same time."

Examples of the operations of union and intersection are as follows:

If $A = \{\alpha,1,3,M\}$,

$\qquad B = \{1,M,5,\beta\}$, and

$\qquad C = \{\text{Harry, Sam, William}\}$

then $A \cup B = \{\alpha,1,3,M,5,\beta\}$;

$A \cap B = \{1,M\}$; $A \cap C = \phi$.

Note that $A \cup B = B \cup A$ and $A \cap B = B \cap A$; $A \cup A = A$; $A \cap A = A$.

The operations of $\cup$ and $\cap$ are called *binary operations*, since they operate on two sets at a time.

One should observe that just because $A \cup B$ might equal $A \cup C$, the conclusion that $B = C$ doesn't necessarily follow. An example to emphasize this point follows.

If $A = \{1,2,3\}$; $B = \{1\}$, $C = \{2,3\}$, then $A \cup B = A \cup C$ and yet $B \neq C$.

If the intersection set of two sets A and B is the empty set, written $A \cap B = \phi$, then sets A and B are said to be *disjoint sets*.

1-13.   OPERATION OF COMPLEMENTATION

As pointed out previously, if a set A and several subsets related to it are being considered in the same problem, then the set A is referred to as the universal set. It is usually represented as $\mathcal{U}$ and should not be confused with the operation $\cup$ (union). During any given discussion, the $\mathcal{U}$

may change into subsets of itself as convenience suggests from new sets that are formed. If a subset B is formed from the elements of $\mathcal{U}$, an operation called *complementation* results for set B with respect to $\mathcal{U}$. This complement of B is designated as B' and is made up of those elements in $\mathcal{U}$ which are not in B. For example,

If $\mathcal{U} = \{1,3,5,7,9,10\}$ and if $B = \{1,5,7\}$, $C = \{\ \}$, $D = \{1,3,5,7,9,10\}$, then $B' = \{3,9,10\}$; $\mathcal{U}' = \phi$; $C' = \mathcal{U}$; $D' = \phi$.

EXERCISE 1-4

If $\mathcal{U} = N$ is the set of natural numbers, $A = \{1,3,4,6,9\}$, $B = \{3,6,9\}$, $C = \{1,2,5\}$, and $D = \{2,5,7,8\}$, determine the validity for the statements in Probs. 1–10.

1. $C \subset A'$
    Ans.: $C = \{1,2,5\}$.
    $\qquad A' = \{2,5,7,8,10,11,\ldots\}$.
    Thus C is not a subset of A' and the statement is false.

2. $A' \subseteq D$.

3. $A' = D$.

4. $C \subseteq B'$.

5. $B = C$.

6. $C \subset B'$.

7. $\phi \subset C'$.

8. $\{8\} \in A'$.

9. $0 \in A'$.

10. $\phi \subseteq A$.

If $A = \{0,1,2,3,4,5\}$, $B = \{0,1,3,4\}$, and $C = \{4,5,6,7\}$, enclose within braces the elements for the statements in Probs. 11–25.

11. $A \cap B$.
    Ans.: $A = \{0,1,2,3,4,5\}$.
    $\qquad B = \{0,1,3,4\}$.
    $\qquad A \cap B = \{0,1,3,4\}$.

12. $A \cup B$.

13. $A \cup C$.

14. $B \cap B$.

15. $C \cup C$.

16. $A \cup \phi$.

17. $B \cap \phi$.

18. $A \cup (B \cap C)$. *Hint:* Perform $B \cap C$ first, and then combine result with A in union.

19. $A \cup (B \cup C)$.

20. $A \cap (B \cup C)$.

21. $A \cap (B \cap C)$.

22. $A \cup (B \cap \phi)$.

23. $(A \cup B) \cap (A \cup C)$. (See hint given in Prob. 18 above.)

24. $(A \cap B) \cup (A \cap C)$.

25. $(A \cup B) \cap (A \cap C)$.

Find the solution set in Probs. 26–30 (a) using set-builder notation, and (b) listing the elements.

26. $\{x \in N : 0 < x < 6\} \cap \{x \in N : 2 < x < 8\}$.
    Ans.: (a) $\{x \in N : 2 < x < 6\}$.
         (b) $\{3,4,5\}$.
27. $\{2,4,5\} \cup \{y \in N \mid 4 < y\}$.
28. $\{x \in N \mid x < 8\} \cup \{x \in N \mid x > 9\}$.
29. $\{x \in N \mid x < 8\} \cap \{x \in N \mid x > 9\}$.
30. $\{1,2,3\} \cap \{x \in N \mid 1 < x < 3\}$.

If A and B are disjoint sets and $n(A) = a$ and $n(B) = b$, then the sum of a and b may be defined as $a + b = n(A) + n(B) = n(A \cup B)$. In Probs. 31–36, let $A = \{1,2,3\}$, $B = \{4,5,6,7\}$ and $C = \{6,7,8,9\}$.

31. Find $n(A)$, $n(B)$, and $n(C)$.
32. Find $n(A \cup B)$.
33. Does $A \cap B = \phi$?
34. Show that $n(A \cup B) = n(A) + n(B)$.
35. Explain why $n(B) + n(C) \neq n(B \cup C)$
36. Find $n(B \cup C)$.

1-14. VENN DIAGRAMS

The understanding of operations with sets is aided by a verification process employing visual characteristics. Sets are represented by either circles, rectangles, or other geometric figures which enclose areas. Points on the interior of these geometrical configurations are used to indicate elements belonging to represented sets. The use of parentheses are employed in expressions which involve set operations so as to clarify the order in which operations are to be performed. For example:

    1. $A \cap (B \cup C)$ implies that one finds $B \cup C$ first and then proceeds to determine the intersection of A and $B \cup C$.

    2. $[A \cap (B \cup C)]'$ means that one performs the operations indicated in (1) and then obtains the resultant set by taking the complement of $A \cap (B \cup C)$ with respect to its universe $\mathcal{U}$.

Geometrical figures representing sets are referred to as Venn diagrams, named after John Venn (1834–83) who studied logical thinking by this means. Examples of Venn diagrams are illustrated in the material that follows.

    1. The heavy line around the outside boundary of the joined areas of circles A and B graphically represents $A \cup B$. The points in the interior of the upper circle represents the elements of A and those points in the interior of the lower circle the elements of B. The union of A and B consists of all those points representing elements in A or B or in both A and B. This is indicated by the shaded area in Fig. 1-1.

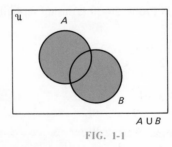

FIG. 1-1

2.   The set $A \cap B$ can be represented as the points which correspond to elements common to both A and B in the interior of the
shaded area in Fig. 1-2.

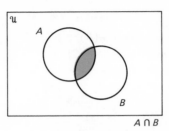

FIG. 1-2

3.   In Fig. 1-3 $A \cup B$ represents the interior points of circle A
together with those interior points of circle B. Here $A \cap B = \phi$, the
empty set. Sets A and B are thus disjoint.

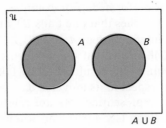

FIG. 1-3

EXERCISE 1-5

In Figs. 1-4, 1-5, 1-6, and 1-7, segments of circle areas are described in numbers. If these numbered areas are called regions, denote in Probs. 1–13 what
regions are involved.

1. A'.   4. $A \cup B$.
2. B'.   5. $\mathfrak{U}$.
3. $A \cap B$.

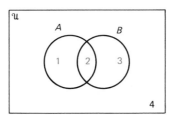

FIG. 1-4

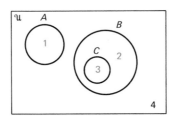

FIG. 1-5

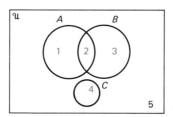

FIG. 1-6

For Fig. 1-7, show that Probs. 6-13 are true.

6. $(A \cup B)' = A' \cap B'$.
    Solution: $A \cup B = 1, 2, 3, 4, 5, 6$
                   $(A \cup B)' = 7, 8$
                   $A' = 3, 6, 7, 8$
                   $B' = 1, 4, 7, 8$
               $A' \cap B' = 7, 8$
    Therefore, $(A \cup B)' = A' \cap B'$
7. $(A \cap B) \cap C = A \cap (B \cap C)$.
8. $(A \cup B) \cup C = A \cup (B \cup C)$.
9. $A \cap (B \cup C) = (A \cap B) \cup (A \cap C)$.
10. $A \cup (B \cap C) = (A \cup B) \cap (A \cup C)$.

11. $(A \cap B)' = A' \cup B'$.
12. $A \cup B = B \cup A$.
13. $A \cap B = B \cap A$.

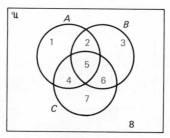

FIG. 1-7

If $Q = \{a,2,3\}$, $R = \{5,6,2,7,8\}$, $S = \{a,b,3,2\}$ and $T = \{1,3,5,9\}$, determine the validity for the statements made in Probs. 14–25.

14. $3 \in (R \cup Q \cap S)$.
15. $2 \in (Q \cap R \cap S)$.
16. $5 \in (Q \cap T)$.
17. $b \in (S \cup T)$.
18. $(S \cap T) \subset (S \cap Q)$.
19. $(S \cup Q) = S$.
20. $[R \cap (T \cap Q)] \neq \phi$.
21. $[(S \cap T) \cap R] \neq \phi$.
22. $[(Q \cap R) \cup (S \cap T)] = \{2,3\}$.
23. $[(Q \cup T) \cap S] \neq \phi$.
24. S and T are disjoint sets.
25. $(R \cap Q)$ and $(R \cap S)$ are disjoint sets.
26.   If $A = \{1,2,3\}$, $B = \{5,2,7,8\}$, $C = \{1,4,6,3,8\}$, show that statements in Probs. 6–13 hold for these sets. Assume that $\mathfrak{U} = N$, the set of natural numbers.

chapter 2

Algebra
As a Language
and a Tool

2-1. THE RELATION BETWEEN ALGEBRA AND ENGLISH

As applied, algebra is a method of solving problems by the use of numbers, letters, symbols, and expressions containing them.

As written and as read, algebra is a brief and useful international language. One must learn to read it, at least in part, before any calculations can be initiated. Fortunately for the beginning student, many of its symbols are the familiar ones of arithmetic. Others may be learned as they occur in the text.

This language of algebra is usually much briefer than English. For example, the English phrase, "the number which is 3 less than 4 times itself" becomes, in algebra, simply "$4x - 3$." Again, the statement that "twice a number plus 5 is equal to the sum of the number and 4" is written in algebra as the *equation*

(1) $$2x + 5 = x + 4,$$
where x represents the number.

When certain numbers are always related in a given manner, this fact is expressed conveniently in an algebraic *statement* or *formula*. For instance, the distance d traveled by a body moving at uniform speed equals the product of its rate r and the time t. The area A of a rectangle is equal to the product of its length l and its width w. Facts such as these lead to statements

(2) $$d = rt$$
(3) $$A = lw.$$

The problems in Exercise 2-1 test one's ability to translate English phrases or sentences into algebraic statements.

EXERCISE 2-1

If x represents any number, express in terms of x the described numbers in Probs. 1–6.

1. The triple of x.
2. The number which is 3 greater than x.
3. Three more than one-half of x.
4. Two less than 4 times x.
5. One-third of the number which is 2 less than x.
6. Five times the product of x by its triple.
7. A man walks toward a point 45 miles away at 3 mph. How far has he traveled, and how far has he to go, after $x + 1$ hours?
8. If apples and oranges sell for 8¢ and 10¢ each, respectively, what is the selling price of $2x$ apples and $4y$ oranges?
9. A and B, 40 miles apart, walk toward each other. After A has walked x miles and B has walked y miles, how far apart are they?
10. Work Prob. 9 if A and B go in the same direction, with A behind B.

Write as formulas or algebraic statements the facts stated in Probs. 11–25.

11. The area P of a parallelogram equals the product of its base b by its altitude h.
12. The area T of a triangle equals one-half the product of its base b by its altitude h.
13. The circumference C of a circle equals twice the product of its radius r by the constant π, which is approximately equal to 3.1416.
14. Simple interest I is the product of the principal P by the rate r by the time t.
15. Three times the number x, plus 7, equals one-third the sum of x and 8.
16. Two more than three times x is 2 greater than 3 times x.
17. One-third the sum of x and twice y is half the sum of y and thrice x.
18. Five less than twice the sum of x and 1 is 4 more than half the number which exceeds x by 3.
19. The sum of two numbers is 20. (*Ans.:* x and $20 - x$.)
20. The difference of two numbers is 7.
21. One number is one-third of another number.
22. One number is 5 less than three times another number.
23. One number is 3 more than two-fifths of another number.
24. If one has x dimes and 3 times as many nickels as dimes, find the value in cents of what he has.
25. If a man is x years old now, how old was he 10 years ago? How old will he be in 20 years? How old will he be in y years from now?

2-2. THE RELATION BETWEEN ALGEBRA AND ARITHMETIC

It should be observed that algebra is a method of solving problems by the use of letters, symbols or expressions involving letters which stand for numbers. Arithmetic, on the other hand, involves the computation with particular numbers. The result of an algebraic problem often can be applied to many instances by simply assigning different number values to the letters, whereas an arithmetic result applies only to the one problem under consideration.

2-3. NUMBERS

The concept of what is meant by a number and its symbolic representation develops and changes as one studies mathematics. Illustrations of certain types of numbers rather than a definition of numbers in general are herewith presented.

Most easily understood are the *whole numbers*, or *integers*, such as 1, 2, 3, etc. Then there are *fractions*, such as $\frac{1}{2}, \frac{3}{5}, \frac{9}{4}$, etc. Integers and fractions may be *positive*, such as $1, 2, \frac{1}{2}, \frac{3}{5}$, etc., or *negative*, such as -3, $-11, -\frac{2}{3}$, etc. Negative numbers are useful in various situations, as when we say that the temperature is $-30°$ (thirty degrees below zero) or that a river level is -5 feet, meaning that its surface is 5 feet below normal.

The numbers mentioned thus far are called real numbers. There are still many types of numbers which are real that have not yet been discussed but will be explored more thoroughly in Sec. 9-3. Examples of such numbers are $\sqrt{2}, \sqrt[3]{5}, 2 + \sqrt{3}$, etc.

Along with real numbers are a class of numbers called *imaginary numbers*. Examples of this kind are $\sqrt{-4}, 2 + \sqrt{-9}, \sqrt{3} + 4i$, where $i = \sqrt{-1}$, etc. This type of number will be examined in Sec. 10-1.

As a consequence a number is either real or imaginary, but not both. We shall for the present concentrate on the real numbers, and even though numbers like $\sqrt{2}, \sqrt{5}$, etc. haven't yet been discussed, an intuitive appreciation will be assumed for them in what follows.

All real numbers may be represented conveniently as points on a line, referred to as the real number line and shown in Fig. 2-1.

FIG. 2-1

The real number line calls attention to the very special number *zero*, written 0, which separates the negative and positive numbers and is considered neither positive nor negative. The number 0 may be classed with either group. It can be represented as $0 = +0 = -0$ without impairing its properties. The special rules for computation with zero are discussed in Sec. 2-7.

If a real number is represented by a symbol, letter, or expression, then this number is one and only one of the following: namely, *positive*, *negative*, or *zero*. If it is positive, it is to the right of the number zero on the real number line. If it is negative, it is to the left of the number zero. For example, if the expression $\dfrac{a - b}{3}$ represents a real number and is to the right of zero on the number line, it is positive (as illustrated in Fig. 2-1). If $(-a)$ represents a real number and is placed on the real number line as indicated in Fig. 2-1, then $(-a)$ is a positive number, in spite of the fact that it is represented by the symbol $-a$. Associated with every positive real number is a unique counterpart called its *additive inverse* which is a negative real number. It is defined in such a way that the sum of the positive real number and its additive inverse is the zero number. For example, -3 is the additive inverse for 3, -7 for 7, etc. Correspondingly, the additive inverse for a negative number is a unique positive number such that their sum is zero. For example, 5 is the additive inverse for -5, $\dfrac{2}{3}$ is the additive inverse for $-\dfrac{2}{3}$. The additive inverse for zero is itself or saying it another way, -0 is the additive inverse for 0, and vice versa. If a letter such as x represents the number and if x is positive, the additive inverse of x is negative and is by agreement represented as $-x$. However, if x is negative, its additive inverse is positive and still would be represented by $-x$. It is evident that the symbolic representation of a number may be misleading and tempt one to describe same as a negative number when it truly is positive, or vice versa. This will be explained in what will follow in reference to the real number line.

Every *positive real number* has a unique counterpart called its *multiplicative inverse*. By definition this multiplicative inverse is also *positive* and is a number such that when multiplied by its original results in the number unity. For example, the multiplicative inverse for 5 is $\dfrac{1}{5}$, for $\dfrac{2}{3}$ is $\dfrac{3}{2}$, etc. If the number is *negative*, its multiplicative inverse is *negative* and satisfies the preceding definition. For example, the multiplicative inverse for $-\dfrac{1}{2}$ is -2, for -5 is $-\dfrac{1}{5}$, etc. *Zero has no multiplicative inverse.*

In other words, the multiplicative inverse for 0 is not $\frac{1}{0}$, and 0 multiplied

by $\frac{1}{0}$ is not 1. This will be explained in a later section.

The stroke " − " in front of a number like 5 produces the number − 5 and should be read in English as "minus five," in preference to "negative five." Thus it seems more reasonable to say "minus five is a negative number" than to say "negative five is a negative number." This observation is made so that more care is taken when the use of words like minus, negative, plus, positive, etc. are used to describe numbers. For example, it was pointed out that $-x$ might under certain circumstances represent a positive number. It is less ambiguous to say in English "minus x represents a positive number" than to say "negative x represents a positive number."

The terms *additive inverse* and *multiplicative inverse* are sometimes replaced by the terms "opposite" and "reciprocal" respectively.

2-4. ALGEBRA AS A DEDUCTIVE SYSTEM

Algebra is called a *deductive* system because it is based on a set of postulates and rules performed on numbers from which other numbers arise. The results obtained by this type of reasoning are permanent (do not change) so long as the rules and postulates are kept intact. The set of real numbers here designated as R_e and its corresponding real-number line with two basic operations called addition and multiplication form the foundation from which algebra emanates. The symbol " + " is read "plus" or "add," and denotes the operation of addition, and the symbols " · " or " × " is read "multiply" and denotes multiplication. As a consequence if $a, b \in R_e$, then "$a + b$" is the real number resulting from carrying out the operation of addition, and "$a \cdot b$" or "$a \times b$" or just "ab" the result of carrying out multiplication between the real numbers a and b in that order. The resulting numbers obtained are referred to, respectively, as the sum and product of a and b.

The operations of subtraction " − " and division " ÷ " are handled by use of the concept of additive and multiplicative inverses for numbers. For example, to "subtract the number 5 from 9" is defined as "sum of 9 and the additive inverse of 5," or $9 + (-5)$, which becomes $9 - 5 = 4$, as will be discussed more fully later. To "divide 9 by 3" is transformed into the "product of 9 by the multiplicative inverse of 3" which becomes

$$9 \times \left(\frac{1}{3}\right) = 9\left(\frac{1}{3}\right) = 3.$$

For brevity, the use of the word *number* throughout this material shall indicate "real number" unless otherwise specified.

We use the sign of equality "$=$" with numbers to denote "sameness" or "identity." When we say that $a = b$, it implies that a and b represent the same number, or that an equation $a = b$ has been created.

When we use an equality sign, it is assumed that it possesses the following properties for all numbers $a, b, c, \ldots, \in R_e$, namely:

1. $a = a$ (reflexive property).
2. If $a = b$, then $b = a$ (symmetric property).
3. If $a = b$ and $b = c$, then $a = c$ (transitive property).
4. If $a = b$ and $c = d$, then $a + c = b + d$ (additive property).
5. If $a = b$ and $c = d$, then $ac = bd$ (multiplicative property).

The assumptions made for the equality sign seem quite reasonable. The first assumption, which states that a number is equal to itself seems quite plausible. In the equation $a = b$ the replacement of a by its equal b and correspondingly b by its equal a results in the symmetric property $b = a$. This second assumed property makes it possible for any number to be replaced by an equal one. This creates a powerful technique of carrying out substitutions. Properties 3, 4, and 5 follow from this principle of substitution. For example, starting with the sum $a + c$, the replacement of "a by its equal b" and "c by its equal d" results in $a + c = b + d$.

If in properties 4 and 5, with $c = c$ used in place of $c = d$, the resulting equalities become $a + c = b + c$ and $ac = bc$. In everyday English this produces the important conclusions: the same number may be added to both members of an equation, and both members of an equation may be multiplied by the same number. To reiterate, it implies that whatever truth was involved in the original equation of necessity it will be retained in the newly formed equation when such operations as described in our conclusions are performed.

2-5. ABSOLUTE VALUE—ALGEBRAIC AND NUMERICAL COMPARISON OF REAL NUMBERS

In Sec. 2-3 we agreed to associate points to the right of zero on the real-number line with positive numbers and those to the left of zero with negative numbers. To indicate that a real number a is positive, we write $a > 0$ and say in English "a is greater than zero," while if a is negative, we write $a < 0$ and accordingly say "a is less than zero."

If a and b are any two real numbers, then we say that "b is less than a" if $a - b$ is a positive number. We symbolize this fact by writing $b < a$. Another way of saying that $b < a$ is to show that a positive number c exists such that $a = b + c$. The statement "$b < a$" implies the statement

"$a > b$"; that is, if b is less than a, then a is larger than b. The operational symbols ">" and "<" are read "greater than" and "less than," respectively. If $b > a$, it should be observed that on the real-number line, the point representing b is to the right of the point representing a. If $b < a$, the point representing b is to the left of a.

When a point is to the right of another point, then the number representing the one to the right is said to be *algebraically* larger than the one to the left. For example, the number 0 is algebraically larger than any negative number and algebraically smaller than any positive number. "$-2 > -3$" states that -2 is algebraically larger than -3, since -2 is to the right of -3 on the number line. It is also true that $-2 - (-3) = -2 + 3 = 1$, which is positive.

Statements such as $a \geq b$ and $a \leq b$ are read "a is equal to or greater than b" and correspondingly, "a is equal to or less than b."

Statements employing symbols $>$, $<$, $\geq$, $\leq$ are referred to as *inequalities*.

Every real number has an *absolute value*. If a is a real number, its absolute value is written as $|a|$ and is defined as follows:

$$|a| = \begin{cases} a \text{ if } a \text{ is a positive number} \\ 0 \text{ if } a \text{ is zero} \\ -a \text{ if } a \text{ is a negative number} \end{cases}$$

In other words, the absolute value of a equals itself if it is *positive* or *zero*, and its *additive inverse* if negative. The *absolute value* of a real number is never negative. The absolute value of both the real number and its additive inverse are equal, i.e., $|a| = |-a|$.

If $|a| > |b|$, we say that "a is numerically larger than b." If $|a| < |b|$, we say that "a is numerically smaller than b." For example, since $5 > 3$, $|5| > |3|$, it follows 5 is both numerically and algebraically larger than 3.

Another interesting example is to consider $-2 > -3$, and $|-3| > |-2|$. It follows that -2 is algebraically larger than -3, but numerically smaller than -3.

We note that $|-2| = |2|$, $|0| = |-0|$. For future use it is observed that if $|2x - 1|$ is involved in an expression and $2x - 1$ represents a real number, then

$$|2x - 1| = \begin{cases} 2x - 1 \text{ if } 2x - 1 \text{ is positive or zero} \\ -(2x - 1) \text{ if } 2x - 1 \text{ is negative} \end{cases}$$

2-6. OPERATIONS WITH POSITIVE AND NEGATIVE NUMBERS

When negative numbers are taken into account the ordinary operations of arithmetic must be explained anew. The rules for addition and subtraction are as follows:

1. To add two numbers with like signs (both positive or both negative) add their absolute values and prefix their common sign.
2. To add two numbers with unlike signs, subtract the smaller absolute value from the larger one and prefix the sign of the numerically larger number. If the numbers are numerically equal, their sum is zero.
3. To subtract one number from another, change the sign of the number subtracted and then add.

These operations are illustrated in column form in the examples below.

Addition

(a) 3   (b)   3   (c) -3 (d) -3
     5   -5 5 -5
     —   ——   —   ——
     8   -2 2 -8

Subtraction

(e) 3   (f)   3   (g) -3 (h) -3
     5   -5 5 -5
     ——   —   ——   —
    -2 8 -8 2

The operations above may be written on single lines by observing the rule that when parentheses are removed the signs enclosed are changed if and only if the sign before the parentheses is minus. Thus $-(+8) = -8$; $-(-8) = +8$ (or just 8); $+(+8) = 8$; and $+(-8) = -8$. Accordingly, (d) and (h), for example, become

(d) $(-3) + (-5) = -3 - 5 = -8$
(h) $(-3) - (-5) = -3 + 5 = 2$

For multiplication and division of positive and negative numbers a single rule suffices:

4. The product, and also the quotient, of two positive numbers or two negative numbers is positive. The product, and also the quotient, of a positive number by a negative number or a negative number by a positive number is negative.

Thus $(+4)(+5) = 4 \cdot 5 = 20$; $(-4)(-5) = 20$; $(+4)(-5) = -20$; and $(-4)(+5) = -20$. Also, $10 \div 2 = 5$; $(-10) \div (-2) = 5$; $10 \div (-2) = -5$; and $(-10) \div 2 = -5$.

We reemphasize that the representation of a real number by a letter or symbol or expression does not determine whether the number is positive or negative. For example, the symbol $(-a)$ and the symbol $(-b)$, when multiplied, give the symbol $+ab$. As to whether the number ab is positive or negative depends upon what type of numbers $-a$ and $-b$ were originally. If $-a$ is positive and $-b$ is negative, then their product ab is negative. What if $-a$ and $-b$ are both negative?

It should be noted that when numbers are represented by signed symbols such as $-a$, a, b, $-b$, etc., we have assumed that they represent real numbers, but we haven't dictated that they must be positive, negative, or zero. As a consequence, we shall accept without proof the rule of signs for symbolic representation of numbers by such signed symbols. This rule was used in the preceding paragraph. We now state this rule and ask that special emphasis be given it.

The product and also the quotient of two numbers represented by *like signed symbols* produces "a plus-signed symbol for the resulting product or quotient number"; of two numbers represented by *unlike signed symbols*, produces "a minus-signed symbol for the *resulting product or quotient number.*"

For example, $(-a)$ multiplied by $(-b)$ produces the symbol $+ab$ or just ab for convenience. This does not mean that ab is necessarily a positive number nor that it is a negative number. To be able to tell, one must know what type of numbers $(-a)$ and $(-b)$ represented with respect to positive and negative as already pointed out.

This is a very important fact, and a student must recognize that there are *two rules* of sign for multiplication and division of numbers: one that deals with whether the numbers are positive or negative and the other that deals with the signed symbols that represent these numbers.

As shown in the above example, multiplication of positive numbers may be indicated by dots instead of parentheses, provided that the dots are centered vertically to avoid confusing them with decimal points. In the case of letters representing numbers, the omission of a sign between them indicates multiplication, so that, for example, ab means "a times b." This practice, of course, would not do for numbers themselves. Why not?

Division is indicated by use of a horizontal bar, or the symbol $\div$. For example, $10 \div 5 = \dfrac{10}{5} = 2$. Accordingly, $\dfrac{a+b}{c+d} = (a+b) \div (c+d)$, and not $a + b \div c + d$. Parentheses must be inserted between the dividend and the divisor. The horizontal bar should be regarded as a type of parentheses as well as implying division.

2-7. OPERATIONS WITH ZERO

The rules for operations with zero are as follows.

The value of a number is unchanged when zero is added to it or subtracted from it.

1. $0 + 6 = 6 + 0 = 6$; $0 - 7 = -7 + 0 = -7$; $0 + 0 = 0$.

2. $5 - 0 = -0 + 5 = 5$; $-3 - 0 = -0 - 3 = -3$; $0 - 0 = 0$; $a + 0 = a$; $0 + a = a$; $-a + 0 = -a$; $(a+b) + 0 = a+b$.

The product of any number and zero is zero.

3. $0 \cdot 4 = 4 \cdot 0 = 0;\ 0(-4) = (-4)0 = 0;\ 0 \cdot a = 0;\ 0(-a) = 0;$
$0(a + b) = 0;\ (a + b)0 = 0.$

The quotient obtained by dividing zero by any number other than zero is zero.

4. $\dfrac{0}{1} = \dfrac{0}{-1} = 0;\ \dfrac{a}{b} \cdot 0 = 0,\ (b \neq 0).$

5. $\dfrac{8}{0}$ and $\dfrac{-8}{0}$ *are not solvable*, in terms of finite real numbers. It
is a postulate of the real number system that division of any real number by the real number zero does not lead to a finite real number. That is, *it is impossible to divide any number by zero.*

To see that the statements in (4) and (5) are reasonable, notice that the value of $\dfrac{8}{2}$, or 4, is "the number of 2's which will add up to 8." Similarly, $\dfrac{8}{0}$ asks "how many zeros will add up to 8?"*   Evidently, there exists no unique real number which meets this condition, since the sum of any number of zeros is zero. Similarly, if $\dfrac{8}{0}$ = (some definite number), then 0 times that number should equal 8; but this is certainly impossible, as seen from statement (3).

EXERCISE 2-2 (ORAL)

1.   Arrange the following numbers so that, as read from left to right, they increase algebraically: $-1,\ -15, 0, 6, \dfrac{2}{3}, -4, -5, -\dfrac{1}{2}, 5, -2.$

2.   Arrange the numbers of Prob. 1 so that, as read from left to right, they increase numerically, or in absolute values.

Perform the additions and subtractions as indicated in Probs. 3–14.

3. $3 + (-7).$ 4. $(-6) + 3.$ 5. $-8 + (-5).$
6. $-15 + (+5).$ 7. $-9 - (-2).$ 8. $8 - (-4).$
9. $6 - 11.$ 10. $(13) - (8).$ 11. $-7 - 0.$
12. $0 + (-17).$ 13. $0 - (-32).$ 14. $-15 - (-0).$

Perform the additions as indicated in Probs. 15–26.

*It might be thought that by this test the value of $\dfrac{8}{0}$ must be one, since "one zero adds up to zero"; but so do two zeros, three zeros, etc. The rule stated in (5) holds in *all* cases.

15.	$\begin{array}{r} 5 \\ 8 \\ \hline \end{array}$	16.	$\begin{array}{r} -8 \\ 4 \\ \hline \end{array}$	17. $\begin{array}{r} -8 \\ -1 \\ \hline \end{array}$ 18. $\begin{array}{r} 1 \\ -8 \\ \hline \end{array}$

15. $\begin{array}{r} 5 \\ 8 \\ \hline \end{array}$ 16. $\begin{array}{r} -8 \\ 4 \\ \hline \end{array}$ 17. $\begin{array}{r} -8 \\ -1 \\ \hline \end{array}$ 18. $\begin{array}{r} 1 \\ -8 \\ \hline \end{array}$

19. $\begin{array}{r} -5 \\ 8 \\ \hline \end{array}$ 20. $\begin{array}{r} -2 \\ -6 \\ \hline \end{array}$ 21. $\begin{array}{r} 3 \\ 0 \\ \hline \end{array}$ 22. $\begin{array}{r} 0 \\ -5 \\ \hline \end{array}$

23. $\begin{array}{r} 0 \\ 10 \\ \hline \end{array}$ 24. $\begin{array}{r} -17 \\ 0 \\ \hline \end{array}$ 25. $\begin{array}{r} 0 \\ -20 \\ \hline \end{array}$ 26. $\begin{array}{r} 31 \\ 0 \\ \hline \end{array}$

27–38. Subtract the lower from the upper numbers in Probs. 15–26.

39–50. Multiply the numbers in Probs. 15–26.

Perform the indicated multiplications in Probs. 51–62.

51. $6(-7)$. 52. $(-15)(0)$. 53. $0(100)$.
54. $9(-4)(-5)$. 55. $(-0)(28)$. 56. $(-5)(6)$.
57. $+7(-3)$. 58. $-(-1)(-1)$. 59. $4(-1)$.
60. $-(2)(-3)$. 61. $-0(-15)$. 62. $(+7)(-2)$.

Express as integers the quotients indicated in Probs. 63–71.

63. $20 \div 4$. 64. $(-21) \div (7)$. 65. $14 \div (-2)$. 66. $(-20) \div 2$.
67. $\dfrac{12}{-6}$. 68. $\dfrac{12}{2}$. 69. $\dfrac{-15}{3}$. 70. $\dfrac{6}{-3}$. 71. $\dfrac{-25}{-5}$.

Which of the quotients indicated in Probs. 72–87 are true numbers? Find the values of these numbers.

72. $\dfrac{0}{17}$. 73. $\dfrac{0}{-25}$. 74. $\dfrac{13}{-0}$. 75. $\dfrac{-26}{0}$.

76. $\dfrac{-0}{14}$. 77. $\dfrac{-0}{-1}$. 78. $\dfrac{0}{1}$. 79. $\dfrac{0}{0}$.

80. $\dfrac{0-4}{4}$. 81. $\dfrac{0(-4)}{0-4}$. 82. $\dfrac{0-8}{0(-8)}$. 83. $\dfrac{4+0}{4-0}$.

84. $\dfrac{0-4}{0-2}$. 85. $\dfrac{4(+0)}{4-0}$. 86. $\dfrac{-6+0}{-6-0}$. 87. $\dfrac{-6(+0)}{-6+0}$.

2-8. ALGEBRAIC EXPRESSIONS

A single number or letter, or a group of them, is called an *algebraic expression*.

Examples: $4; x; 3x; 2x - 1; \dfrac{1}{x}; \dfrac{2-x}{3}$.

An expression with no plus or minus or equality signs between its parts is called a *term*.

Examples: $7; -2; a; xy; xyz; \dfrac{2}{x}; -2ab^3$.

The term $-2ab^3$ stands for "-2 times a times b^3," where -2 is the *numerical coefficient*, a and b are *literal* numbers, or letters standing for

numbers, and b^3 (read "b cubed" or "the third power of b") means bbb, or
b taken 3 times as a factor. Here b is the *base* and 3 is the *exponent* of b.
Thus, if $a = 3$ and $b = 2$, then $-2ab^3 = -2 \cdot 3 \cdot 2 \cdot 2 \cdot 2 = -48$.

Terms differing only in numerical coefficients, such as $3x^2$ and $-2x^2$,
or as^3, $4as^3$, and $-3as^3$, are called *like* terms. An expression of one term
is called a *monomial*; of two terms, a *binomial*; of three terms, a *trinomial*;
and of two or more terms, a *polynomial*. The terms of a polynomial are
connected by plus or minus signs, as in the example:

$$2x^5 - 3x^4 + 5x^2 - 3ax + 2a + b.$$

The sign in front of the leading term $2x^5$ is understood to be plus, while
the coefficient of the last term b is understood to be 1.

2-9. ADDITION AND SUBTRACTION OF POLYNOMIALS

Here it is convenient to state in the form of *laws* certain unproved
but reasonable assumptions about numbers represented by letters. Such
assumptions are called *postulates*.

1. *The commutative law of addition:* The sum of two or more terms
in an algebraic expression is not changed by changing their order. In
other words, the order in which we carry out addition upon a and b results in the same number $a + b$ or $b + a$.

Thus, just as $4 + 5 = 5 + 4$, so does $x + y = y + x$, no matter what
number values we assign to x and y.

2. *The associative law of addition:* The sum of any number of terms
in an algebraic expression is the same, however grouped.*

That is, just as $4 + 9 + 5 = (4 + 9) + 5 = 4 + (9 + 5) = 18$, so, in
general, $x + y + z = (x + y) + z = x + (y + z)$.

3. *The distributive law:* The sum of the product of one term by an
algebraic expression made up of two or more terms is the product of this
term by each of the individual terms in the algebraic expression. That is,

$$a(b + c + d) = ab + ac + ad.$$

This equation should be verified for various special number values of the
letters, such as $a = 2$, $b = 3$, etc. Once granted, it enables us to combine
the like terms of a polynomial. Thus $2x^3 + 5x^3 = x^3(2 + 5) = 7x^3$, and
$ax^2 + 7ax^2 = ax^2(1 + 7) = 8ax^2$.

This enables us to add or subtract polynomials by combining like
terms. For example,

$$(x^3 - 2x^2 + x + 7) + (3x + 4x^3 - 5 + 6x^2)$$
$$= (x^3 - 2x^2 + x + 7 + 3x + 4x^3 - 5 + 6x^2)$$

(by the associative law)

---

*The phrase "however grouped" follows since it is assumed that the commutative
law for addition holds.

$$= (x^3 + 4x^3 - 2x^2 + 6x^2 + x + 3x + 7 - 5)$$
$$\text{(by the commutative law)}$$
$$= (x^3 + 4x^3) + (-2x^2 + 6x^2) + (x + 3x) + (7 - 5)$$
$$\text{(by the associative law)}$$
$$= 5x^3 + 4x^2 + 4x + 2.$$
$$\text{(by the distributive law)}$$

In subtracting one polynomial from another note that $-(a + b - c) =$ $(-1)(a + b - c) = (-1)a + (-1)b + (-1)(-c) = -a - b + c.$ This indicates that *when parentheses preceded by a minus sign are removed, the signs of all terms which had been inside the parentheses are changed.* Thus

$$(x^3 - 2x^2 + x + 7) - (3x + 4x^3 - 5 + 6x^2)$$
$$= x^3 - 2x^2 + x + 7 - 3x - 4x^3 + 5 - 6x^2$$
$$= -3x^3 - 8x^2 - 2x + 12.$$

This work is also shown in column form below.   For convenience, the terms are arranged in the order of descending powers of x.   Both forms are essential and conversion from one to the other is many times desirable.

Addition	*Subtraction*

$$
\begin{array}{ll}
\begin{array}{r}
x^3 - 2x^2 + \ \ x + 7 \\
4x^3 + 6x^2 + 3x - 5 \\
\hline
5x^3 + 4x^2 + 4x + 2
\end{array}
&
\begin{array}{r}
x^3 - 2x^2 + \ \ x + \ \ 7 \\
4x^3 + 6x^2 + 3x - \ \ 5 \\
\hline
-3x^3 - 8x^2 - 2x + 12
\end{array}
\end{array}
$$

2-10. REMOVAL AND INTRODUCTION OF SYMBOLS OF AGGREGATION

It has already been noted that the signs of terms within parentheses when preceded by a minus sign are changed when removal of such parentheses is desired but remain unchanged when the parentheses was preceded by a plus sign. Similar statements hold when other symbols of aggregation are used. This enables us to simplify expressions containing such symbols of aggregation (parentheses, brackets, braces) by removing them one pair at a time, beginning with the innermost ones. This procedure is then continued on all new expressions formed from the original one until all such grouping symbols have been removed and like terms collected.

Example.

$$2x + \{3x - [2x - 5(x - 1)]\}$$
$$= 2x + \{3x - [2x - 5x + 5]\}$$
$$= 2x + \{3x - 2x + 5x - 5\}$$
$$= 2x + 3x - 2x + 5x - 5$$
$$= 8x - 5.$$

When parentheses or other symbols of aggregation are introduced into an expression, the signs of the terms within are not changed if the sign preceding the grouping is plus, but are changed if the sign preceding is minus. This statement may be verified by removing the grouping symbols in accordance with the preceding rules.

Example 1.

$$3x + 2y + z - w = (3x + 2y) + (z - w)$$
$$= (3x + 2y) - (-z + w).$$

Example 2.

$$3x - 2y - z = 3x + (-2y - z) = 3x - (2y + z).$$

Example 3.

$$2x - y - (a + b) = 2x + [-y - (a + b)]$$
$$= 2x - [y + (a + b)].$$

It is important to notice that the same terms can be enclosed within parentheses preceded by either a plus or a minus sign. The above examples illustrate how the last two terms in each are enclosed with either sign preceding.

Example 4. We can replace lengthy statements by use of parentheses, and then simplify same accordingly. For example, "subtract $5x^2 - 2x$ from $3x^3 + 2x^2 - 1$ and add the result to $-2x^3 - 3x^2 + 1$" can be replaced by $[(3x^3 + 2x^2 - 1) - (5x^2 - 2x)] + (-2x^3 - 3x^2 + 1)$. To simplify same we proceed as follows:

$$[(3x^3 + 2x^2 - 1) - (5x^2 - 2x)] + (-2x^3 - 3x^2 + 1)$$
$$= [3x^3 + 2x^2 - 1 - 5x^2 + 2x] - 2x^3 - 3x^2 + 1$$
$$= 3x^3 - 3x^2 + 2x - 1 - 2x^3 - 3x^2 + 1$$
$$= x^3 - 6x^2 + 2x.$$

EXERCISE 2-3

1. Write three like terms involving x, y, and z.
2. Write two examples of monomials; of binomials; of trinomials.

Add the polynomials in Probs. 3–12, both in row fashion as well as in column fashion.

3. $4x - 7; 2x + 3$.
4. $2x + 3; 4 - 7x$.
5. $2ax^2 + 3x - 2; ax^2 - 5x + 3$.
6. $3ax^2 - 2x + 4; 2ax^2 - 3x + 5$.
7. $x^3 - 5x^2 + ax - 2; 3x^3 + 2x^2 - 3ax + 1$.
8. $x^3 - 2x^2 - 3ax + 1; 2x^3 + 2x^2 - 3ax + 1$.

9. $x - 5x^4 + 3x^2 - 2a; 2x^4 - 2x^2 - 1 + 3x$.

10. $4x + 3x^3 - x^4 + 3; 2x + x^4 + 4a - 3x^2$.

11. $2; x^3 - x + 7; 3x^2 + 4 - 2x$.

12. $x - 2; x^4 - 3x + x^2 - 1; 6 + x^2$.

13–16. Verify the additions in Probs. 3–6 when x and a are replaced by 1 and 0 respectively.

17–20. Verify the additions in Probs. 3–6 when x and a are replaced by 2 and -3 respectively.

21. If the arithmetic results obtained in Probs. 13–20 do not expose any errors in the algebraic sums obtained in Probs. 3–6, does this prove that these sums are correct?

22–29. Subtract the second from the first polynomial in each of Probs. 3–10, both in row fashion as well as in column fashion.

30–37. Subtract the first from the second polynomial in each of Prob. 3–10.

In Probs. 38–47 remove the symbols of aggregation and simplify.

38. $2a - (b + 3a - d)$.

39. $3x - (2y - 4x + 1)$.

40. $2 - 3(x - y) + 2(x + y)$.

41. $4 + 2(a - 2b) - 3(2a - b)$.

42. $2a + [3a - (2b + 1) - c] + 1$.

43. $3c + [2b - (a - c) + 4] - 3$.

44. $2 - \{3x - [x - (2x - 1) + 2] - 2\}$.

45. $3a - \{2b - [3a - 2(2b - 1)] + 3\}$.

46. $-\{2x^2 - [(3ax + 3b)x + x^2]\}$.

47. $-\{3x^2 - [x - (2ax - 1)x]\}$.

Insert parentheses preceded by a minus sign which will include all but the first term in each of Probs. 48–51.

48. $2x - 3a + b$.

49. $4x - 2a - 3y$.

50. $a + 2b - c + 2$.

51. $3a + 4b - c - 1$.

52. To the sum of $b - 2c + 3a$ and $-6a - 2b + 3c$ add the result of subtracting $b + 4c$ from $3a - b - 2c$, (a) in row and column fashion, (b) proceed as in Example 4, Sec. 2-10.

53. Subtract $3x^2$ from $5x^3 - 2x^2 + 7x - 2$ and add the result to $-3x^3 + 4x^2 - 1$, (a) in row and column fashion, (b) in same manner as in Example 4, Sec. 2-10.

54. Take $2a^2 - 4ab$ from $-5a^2 + 6ab + 3$ and add the remainder to $4a^3 + 2ab - 3a^2$.

55. To what expression must $2a^2 - 3ab + 6$ be added to give 0? *Hint:* Let x be the unknown expression, then $x + [2a^2 - 3ab + 6] = 0$, etc.

2-11. MULTIPLICATION AND DIVISION OF POLYNOMIALS

In order to discuss the multiplication and division of polynomials, the commutative and associative laws of multiplication are restated for emphasis.

1. *The commutative law of multiplication.* The product of two or more algebraic expressions is not changed by changing their order.

That is, just as $2 \cdot 3 = 3 \cdot 2$, so it is true that $ab = ba$ in all cases.

2. *The associative laws of multiplication.* The product of three or more algebraic expressions is not changed by grouping them in different ways.*

Since $(2 \cdot 3)4 = 2(3 \cdot 4)$, for example, so in general we assume that $(ab)c = a(bc)$.

Two of the *laws of exponents*, which are discussed at length in Chapter 9, will be needed in what follows:

3. $a^m a^n = a^{m+n}$.

Examples: $2^2 2^3 = 2^5$; $x^4 x^7 = x^{11}$; $aa^2 a^7 = a^1 a^2 a^7 = a^{10}$.

4. $\dfrac{a^m}{a^n} = a^{m-n}$ when $m > n$.

Examples: $\dfrac{3^5}{3^2} = 3^{5-2} = 3^3$; $\dfrac{a^9}{a^2} = a^7$.

The following product law which is treated more fully in Chapter 4 is used in what follows.

5. $\left(\dfrac{a}{b}\right)\left(\dfrac{c}{d}\right) = \dfrac{ac}{bd}$.

Example:

$$\left(\frac{2}{5}\right)\left(\frac{3}{7}\right) = \frac{2 \cdot 3}{5 \cdot 7} = \frac{6}{35}$$

Algebraic terms may be multiplied or divided by making use of the five laws stated in this section.

Example 1.

$$
\begin{aligned}
(2ax^3)(3a^2x^4) &= 2 \cdot 3aa^2 x^3 x^4 & \text{by (1)} \\
&= (2 \cdot 3)(aa^2)(x^3 x^4) & \text{by (2)} \\
&= 6a^3 x^7 & \text{by (3)}
\end{aligned}
$$

Example 2.

$$\frac{10a^8 x^4}{2a^3 x} = \left(\frac{10}{2}\right)\left(\frac{a^8}{a^3}\right)\left(\frac{x^4}{x}\right) \quad \text{by (5)}$$

*The phrase "different ways" follows since it is assumed that the commutative law of multiplication holds.

$$= 5a^{8-3}x^{4-1} \qquad \text{by (4)}$$
$$= 5a^5x^3.$$

The multiplication of two polynomials, such as is indicated in the expression $(x^3 - 2x^4 + x + 3x^2 - 1)(x - 3x^3 + 2)$, can be accomplished conveniently by arranging the polynomials in terms of descending powers of x and then employing law (3), as in the following example.

$$
\begin{array}{l}
-2x^4 + x^3 + 3x^2 + x - 1 \qquad \text{(first algebraic expression or factor)}\\
 - 3x^3 + x + 2 \qquad \text{(second algebraic expression or factor)}\\
\hline
6x^7 - 3x^6 - 9x^5 - 3x^4 + 3x^3\\
 - 2x^5 + x^4 + 3x^3 + x^2 - x\\
 - 4x^4 + 2x^3 + 6x^2 + 2x - 2\\
\hline
6x^7 - 3x^6 - 11x^5 - 6x^4 + 8x^3 + 7x^2 + x - 2 \quad \text{(product)}
\end{array}
$$

This can also be worked out in row fashion by writing factors on a single line and carrying out indicated operations term by term followed by collection of like terms. For example,

$$(3x^2 - 2x + 1)(2x - 5) = 6x^3 - 15x^2 - 4x^2 + 10x + 2x - 5$$
$$= 6x^3 - 19x^2 + 12x - 5.$$

An indicated division, such as

$$\frac{5x^3 - 5x^4 + x^5 + x + 5}{x^2 - 3x - 2} = (5x^3 - 5x^4 + x^5 + x + 5) \div (x^2 - 3x - 2)$$

may be carried out as here shown. The fraction line separating the numerator from the denominator acts as a parentheses, which should be inserted as shown. When used in this sense the fraction line is regarded as a symbol of grouping called a *vinculum*. However, it still retains its implied meaning of division between the numerator and the denominator. The explanation of the steps involved are given just below the actual division.

$$
\begin{array}{r}
x^3 - 2x^2 + x - 1 \quad \text{(Quotient*)}\\
x^2 - 3x - 2 \overline{\smash{)}\,x^5 - 5x^4 + 5x^3 + x + 5}\\
\underline{x^5 - 3x^4 - 2x^3}\\
-2x^4 + 7x^3 + x + 5\\
\underline{-2x^4 + 6x^3 + 4x^2}\\
x^3 - 4x^2 + x + 5\\
\underline{x^3 - 3x^2 - 2x}\\
-x^2 + 3x + 5\\
\underline{-x^2 + 3x + 2}\\
3 \quad \text{(remainder)}
\end{array}
$$

(divisor) $x^2 - 3x - 2$ ... (dividend)

*The word "quotient" is often used with two different meanings. We shall use it with a small "q" to mean the total result of an indicated division. Thus the "quotient" of 27 divided by 5 is $5\frac{2}{5}$, while the "Quotient" is 5.

Explanation

The first step is to arrange the dividend and divisor in the order of the descending powers of the same letter. Here the dividend, divisor, and Quotient, so arranged with respect to the powers of x, are respectively $x^5 - 5x^4 + 5x^3 + x + 5$, $x^2 - 3x - 2$, and $x^3 - 2x^2 + x - 1$. The first term (x^3) of the Quotient is obtained by dividing the first term (x^5) of the dividend by the first term (x^2) of the divisor. The result, (x^3), is then multiplied by the divisor, and the product is subtracted from the dividend. The remainder thus obtained forms the new dividend, $-2x^4 + 7x^3 + x + 5$. To obtain the second term $(-2x^2)$ of the Quotient, the procedure above is repeated, with x^2 being divided into $-2x^4$. Succeeding terms of the Quotient are thus obtained until either a zero remainder is reached or one in which the exponent of the letter upon which the original arrangement is based (in this case, x) is less than the largest exponent it has in the divisor. The final result shows that

$$\frac{x^5 - 5x^4 + 5x^3 + x + 5}{x^2 - 3x - 2} = x^3 - 2x^2 + x - 1 + \frac{3}{x^2 - 3x - 2}$$

In general,

$$\frac{\text{dividend}}{\text{divisor}} = \text{Quotient} + \frac{\text{remainder}}{\text{divisor}}.$$

The result of a long division should always be stated in the form indicated above.

EXERCISE 2-4

Perform the multiplications or divisions as indicated in Probs. 1-7.

1. $(3x^2 a)(4a^3 x)$.   2. $5x^3(-3bx)$.   3. $(-4x)(2ax)(-3a^2 x^3)$.

4. $\dfrac{12a^3 y^4}{-2a^2 y}$.   5. $\dfrac{6a^7 b^6 c^3}{-3a^2 bc}$.   6. $\dfrac{-6xy^2 z^3}{2y^2 z^3}$.   7. $\dfrac{-8x^4 y^7 z^2}{-2x^3 y^2 z^2}$

8. Verify that $[(x + 1)(x - 1)](2x + 1) = (x + 1)[(x - 1)(2x + 1)]$.

Multiply the pairs of polynomials in Probs. 9–21 (a) in row fashion and (b) in column fashion.

9. $(6x^7 + 11x^2 - x - 5)$; $(2x)$.
10. $(3x^5 - 11x^4 + 7x^2 - 5x + 2)$; $(3x)$.
11. $(3x^4 - 7x^3 + 2x^2 - 9x + 3)$; $(3x - 1)$.
12. $(2x^4 - 5x^3 + 5x - 2)$; $(x^2 - 3x + 2)$.
13. $(6x^4 + 7x^3 - 10x^2 - 5x + 2)$; $(2x^2 + 3x - 1)$.
14. $(x^5 + x^4 - 5x^3 + 5x^2 + 4x - 2)$; $(x^2 - 3x + 1)$.
15. $(6x^5 - 5x^3 + 4x + 4x^4 + 5x^2 - 2)$; $(-1 + 2x + 2x^2)$.

16. $(4 + 2x - x^2 - 4x^3 + 6x^4); (x + 3x^2 - 1)$.
17. $(3x^3 + 8x^2 - 3 + 2x); (x^2 - 1 + 2x)$.
18. $(8 - 12x + 4x^3); (3x + 2x^2 - 2)$.
19. $(13x - 6x^2 - 11x^3 + 3x^4); (3x - 1 + x^2)$.
20. $(5x^2 + 1 - 5x + 4x^3); (1 + 4x^2 - 3x)$.
21. $(-x + 6x^3 - 3 + 11x^2); (x - 2 + 3x^2)$.

22–34. Divide the first polynomial by the second one in each of Probs. 9–21.

35. Divide $3x^5 + 2x^2 - 3x^3 + 1$ by $2x^2 - 3x + 1$.
36. Divide $a^3 + b^3$ by $a + b$. Arrange in descending powers of a; in powers of b.
37. Divide $a^3 - b^3$ by $a - b$.
38. Divide $27ax^2 - 25a^3 + 20a^2x - 18x^3$ by $6x - 5a$.

If $A = 3x^2 - 2x + 4$, $B = 3x^2 - x - 1$, and $C = -3x + 1$, find the values of the quantities in Probs. 39–41. In 42–45 simplify by carrying out the ultimate divisions.

39. $2A - 3B$.
40. $BC + AB$.
41. $(A + 2B) \div C$.
42. $A \div (2B + C)$.
43. $\dfrac{2A + 3B - C}{A - B}$.
44. $\dfrac{BC + AB}{2A - 3B}$.
45. $\dfrac{2B + C}{A}$.

REVIEW EXERCISES

If x represents a number, write the numbers indicated in Probs. 1–7.

1. Four times the number.
2. Three-fourths of it.
3. 20 percent of it.
4. The difference between the number and 7. (Two answers.)
5. Eight more than the number.
6. Nine less than three times the number.
7. The excess of 5 over 2.5 times the number.

If x and y represent the tens' digit and the units' digit respectively in a number of two digits, write the numbers indicated in Probs. 8–11.

8. The number.
9. The number when the digits are reversed.
10. The sum of the digits divided by 3.

11.   Twice the number, increased by 36.

If x represents the width in yards of a rectangular field, express in terms of x the length, perimeter, and area of the field under the conditions stated in Probs. 12 and 13.

12.   The length is four times the width.
13.   The length is nine yards less than twice the width.

If A walks x feet per second and B walks two feet a second faster, write the quantities described in Probs 14–16.

14.   The distance A travels in ten minutes.
15.   The distance B travels in half an hour.
16.   The distance traveled by both in one hour.

Write as formulas the statements in Probs. 17–26.

17.   The volume V of a sphere is equal to the product of $\frac{4}{3}$, π, and the cube of the radius R.
18.   The area A of a trapezoid is equal to the product of the altitude h by one-half the sum of the parallel sides, a and b.
19.   The cost T in dollars for a telegram of 50 words is computed at the rate of m cents for each of the first ten words and x cents for each of the others.
20.   At p dollars each, x books would cost C dollars.
21. D is the difference between twice x and y. (Two formulas.)
22.   A man's age is x now and was y ten years ago.
23.   On \$5000 at x percent $\left(x\% = \dfrac{x}{100}\right)$ the yearly interest is I dollars.
24.   The yearly interest on R dollars at 7 percent is I dollars.
25.   The cost in cents of s pounds of nuts at 50¢ per pound and y pounds of candy at 75¢ per pound is C.
26.   The distance in feet traveled in x hours at the rate of five miles per hour is x.

Evaluate the number expressions in Probs. 27–34.

27. $(-4)(-2)(3)$.   28. $-(-3)^2$.   29. -3^2.
30. $[(-1) - (-3)][4 - (-2)]$.   31. $-20 + 0$.
32. $\dfrac{-20 + 0}{0(-20)}$.   33. $\dfrac{20 - 20}{20 + 20}$.   34. $\dfrac{20 + 20}{20 - 20}$.

Find the missing number in each of Probs. 35 to 40.

35. $7 + (?) = -11$.   36. $-8 - (?) = 10$.
37. $(-2) \times (?) = 16$.   38. $-25 + (?) = 5$.
39. $(?) - 8 = -10$.   40. $3 \times (?) = -15$.

If $a = 3$, $b = -2$, and $c = 1$, find the value of the expressions in Probs. 41–46.

41. $-3a^2 + 2b - c$.

42. $\dfrac{a + b + c}{2bc}$

43. $3a^3c - 5$.

44. $(a + b)(b + c)$.

45. $a + b(b + c)$.

46. $\dfrac{-a - b(b - c)}{b + c}$.

Add the expressions in each of Probs. 47–51.

47. $-3b^2$
    $2b^2$
    $-7b^2$

48. $3y^2$
    $-2y^2$
    $-y^2$

49. $-3(a + b)$
    $-2(a + b)$
    $7(a + b)$

50. $4x^2 - y^2 + z$
    $ - 2y^2 - 3z$
    $3x^2 + 2z$

51. $2x - y + 3$
    $-3x + 3y - 1$
    $x + y - 2$

52. Add: $4a^2 - 3ab + 6c$; $4ab - 2a^2 - 3c$; $-2c - 10ab + 6a^2$, (a) in column fashion, (b) by method of Example 4, Sec. 2-10.

53. Add: $7mn - 3n^2 + 6$; $-5n^2 - 7mn - 2$; $6 - mn$, (a) in column fashion, (b) by method of Example 4, Sec. 2-10.

Subtract the lower from the upper expression:

54. $4a - 7b - c$
    $-2a + 3b - 2c$

55. $3x^2 + 4xy - y^2$
    $ - 5xy + 2y^2$

56. Subtract $4x - y + 2z$ from $3x + y - 4z$, (a) in column fashion, (b) by method of Example 4, Sec. 2-10.

57. To the sum of $-4x^2 + 3xy - 2$ and $-5xy - 7 + 8x^2$ add the excess of $4xy - 2$ over $2x^2 - 8xy + 6$, (a) in column fashion, (b) by method of Example 4, Sec. 2-10.

58. How much must be added to the sum of $3ab + 7c^2 - 2d$ and $-6 + 3c^2$ to give $-5ab - c^2$?

Remove the symbols of aggregation and collect like terms:

59. $4 - [2x - 1 - (3x - 1)]$.

60. $-[(2x^2 - 3y^2) + y] - [-x^2 + (2y - x)]$.

61. $-3(a - 2b) + 6\{-4 - [b - 2(4 + b)]\}$.

62. $(3x + y + 6) - [(2x - y - 4) - (3y - 2)]$.

Insert parentheses preceded by a minus sign which will include all but the first two terms:

63. $-3x^2 - y - 2x + z - 3w$.   64. $a^2 - b^2 + 4a^4 - 2a^2b^2$.

65. $x^2 + 2xy + 3y^2 + 4$.   66. $-5 + y - x - 3z^2$.

Carry out the indicated multiplications:

67. $(-3x)(2y)$.   68. $(-3x^2y)(-xy^2)(7x^4y^3)$.

69. $-(-3mn^2)(-5m^2n)$.   70. $3x^2(2xy - y^2)$.

71. $-5mn(2m^2n - 3m + 2n)$.   72. $(3x^2 - y + 6x)(-x + y - x^2)$.

73. $\begin{array}{r} 4a - 2b \\ a + 7b \end{array}$ 74. $\begin{array}{r} x^2 + y^2 \\ x - y \end{array}$

75. $\begin{array}{r} 2x^2 - 2xy - y^2 \\ 3x - y \end{array}$ 76. $\begin{array}{r} x^3 + x^2y - 2y \\ 3x^2 - 2xy + y \end{array}$

77. $(x + 4)(x + 3)$.   78. $(x - 5)(x - 2)$.

79. $(x + 7)(x - 3)$.   80. $-(x + 2)(x - 3)$.

81. $-3(a - 1)(a + 1)$.   82. $(2a + 3)(a - 4)$.

83. $(3a - 2)(2a - 5)$.   84. $-2(5a - 1)(3a + 1)$.

85. $-3(2 - x)(3x - 1)$.   86. $(2x + y)(2x - y)$.

87. $(-3x + y)(y + 3x)$.   88. $-(2x - y)(2x + y)$.

89. $-5(3x^2 - y)(3x^2 + y)$.   90. $(2x^2 + 7)(2x^2 + 7)$.

91. $(3 - 2x)(3 - 2x)$.   92. $-2(4 - x)(4 - x)$.

93. $-3(x + 2)^2$.   94. $(10x + 3)^2$.

95. $-(5x - 4y)^2$.   96. $(4x + 5y)^2$.

Note. When the multiplications in Probs. 77–96 have been carried out by the methods given in this chapter, the student should study Secs. 3-2 and 3-3 and then do the problems orally.

Perform the indicated divisions.

97. $\dfrac{-64xy^2}{8xy}$.   98. $\dfrac{-125m^3}{-5m^2}$.

99. $18a^2b^4 \div 2ab^2$.   100. $(-12x^2y^3z) \div (-4x^2y^2)$.

101. $(6x^3 - 2x + x^2 + 3) \div (2x - 1)$.

102. $(9x^2 - 24xy + 16y^2) \div (3x - 4y)$.

103. $(3x^2 - 5x + 2x^3 - 1) \div (3x + 1)$.

chapter 3

Type Products and Factoring

3-1. THE FACTORING RULE

In arithmetic, since $18 = 3 \cdot 3 \cdot 2 = 9 \cdot 2 = 6 \cdot 3 = 1 \cdot 18$, it is convenient to consider the positive integral divisors of 18 which are 1, 2, 3, 6, 9 and 18 and refer to these as being factors of 18. This means that if the integer 18 is divided by any one of these factors, 1, 2, 3, 6, 9, and 18 a resultant integer is obtained. Of these factors, only 2 and 3 are prime numbers.

When dealing with algebraic expressions it is possible to make use of a similar factoring rule. In order to explain factoring procedures for algebraic expressions certain definitions will be needed.

A polynomial which is the sum of terms such as $5x^3y^4$, in which all exponents of x and y are *positive integers*, is said to be *integral* and *rational* in x and y. In this chapter only integral rational polynomials will be considered, including in this general description not only expressions with two or more terms, such as $3x + 5$ and $3x^2 - 5xy + 4$, but even single terms such as $3x$ and 5.

When a polynomial is expressed as the product of two or more integral rational polynomials, it is said to be *factored*, and the parts which are multiplied together are the *algebraic factors*.

In this chapter we shall bar factoring which introduces coefficients that are fractions or types of numbers not yet discussed in this text. Thus when we write $x^2 - 1 = (x - 1)(x + 1)$ and $3x + 6 = 3(x + 2)$, we say that $x^2 - 1$ and $3x + 6$ have been factored. Each of the four factors $x - 1$, $x + 1$, 3, and $x + 2$ are considered as prime factors. Even though it is correct to write $x + 2 = 2\left(\dfrac{x}{2} + 1\right)$, and $x^2 - 2 = (x - \sqrt{2})(x + \sqrt{2})$, where $(\sqrt{2})^2 = 2$, the expressions $x + 2$ and $x^2 - 2$ will be considered here as prime or more convenient in their original forms than in terms of the factors which introduce fractions and irrational-number coefficients. When this occurs we shall say that the original expression is in factored form unless permitted otherwise for desired coefficients.

When a polynomial is completely factored, it is expressed as the product of its prime factors. For example, $x^3 - x = x(x^2 - 1)$ is not completely factored since $x^2 - 1$ is not prime. Here

$$x^3 - x = x(x - 1)(x + 1).$$

3-2. USEFUL IDENTITIES

Certain operations involving algebraic expressions are repeated so often that memorization in type forms becomes important. This is especially true for the following, which should be memorized both in symbols and as statements in words.

1. $a(b + c) = ab + ac.$
2. $(a + b)^2 = a^2 + 2ab + b^2.$
3. $(a - b)^2 = a^2 - 2ab + b^2.$
4. $(a - b)(a + b) = a^2 - b^2.$

These results should be considered as multiplications when read from left to right and as factorization when read from right to left.

The student should check these results by multiplication, and should verify them for various special values of the letters, such as $a = 4$, $b = 2$, etc. For example, statement (3) in words would be, "A quantity made up as a difference of two numbers when squared is equal to the square of the first number minus twice the product of the first number and second number plus the square of the second number."

Statements (1) to (4) are examples of *algebraic identities*. An identity is an equation which is satisfied by all the values of the letters for which the members of the equation are defined. A value is permissible if it makes each side of the equation a finite number. In the identity

$$\frac{2x}{x^2 - 4} = \frac{1}{x - 2} + \frac{1}{x + 2}$$

the values 2 and -2 for x are not permissible. Why?

Also useful from the standpoint of factoring are the identities:

5. $a^3 - b^3 = (a - b)(a^2 + ab + b^2).$
6. $a^3 + b^3 = (a + b)(a^2 - ab + b^2).$

Illustrative Examples

A. Type products

1. $3(2x^2 - 3x + 1) = 3(2x^2) - 3(3x) + 3 \cdot 1$
$$= 6x^2 - 9x + 3.$$

2. $(2x + 3y)^2 = (2x)^2 + 2(2x)(3y) + (3y)^2$
$$= 4x^2 + 12xy + 9y^2.$$

3. $(3x - 2)^2 = (3x)^2 - 2(3x)(2) + 2^2$
$$= 9x^2 - 12x + 4.$$

4. $(5x - 4)(5x + 4) = (5x)^2 - (4)^2$
$$= 25x^2 - 16.$$

One should observe carefully the construction from left to right, and with practice, should be able to omit intermediate steps and write end results. In other words, the result of squaring $(3x - 2)$ should be written directly as

$$(3x - 2)^2 = 9x^2 - 12x + 4.$$

B. Examples in factoring

5. $2ax^2 - 6ax + 2a = 2a(x^2 - 3x + 1).$

6. $4x^2 - 9 = (2x)^2 - 3^2 = (2x - 3)(2x + 3).$

7. $4x^2 + 4ax + a^2 - y^2 + 2yb - b^2$
$$= (4x^2 + 4ax + a^2) - (y^2 - 2yb + b^2)$$
$$= (2x + a)^2 - (y - b)^2$$
$$= [(2x + a) - (y - b)][(2x + a) + (y - b)]$$
$$= (2x + a - y + b)(2x + a + y - b).$$

8. $8x^3 - 27 = (2x)^3 - 3^3$
$$= (2x - 3)[(2x)^2 + (2x)(3) + 3^2]$$
$$= (2x - 3)(4x^2 + 6x + 9).$$

9. $27y^3 + 1 = (3y)^3 + 1^3$
$$= (3y + 1)[(3y)^2 - (3y)(1) + 1^2]$$
$$= (3y + 1)(9y^2 - 3y + 1).$$

10. $9x^2 + 24xy + 16y^2 = (3x + 4y)^2.$

11. $4a^2 - 20a + 25 = (2a - 5)^2.$

C. Examples for learning identities (1) to (6)
    Supply the missing factor so as to make the equality correct.

12. $(3x - 2)(\ ?\ ) = 6x^2 - x - 2.$ Ans.: $2x + 1.$

13. $(3x - 2)(\ ?\ ) = 6x^2 - 7x + 2.$

14. $(2x + 1)(\ ?\ ) = 4x^2 - 1.$

15. $(1 - 3x)(\ ?\ ) = -6x^2 - x + 1.$

16. $[2x - (3 + y)][\ ?\ ] = 4x^2 - (3 + y)^2.$

17. $(x - 2y)(\ ?\ ) = x^3 - 8y^3.$ Ans.: $x^2 + 2xy + y^2.$

18. $(2x + y)(\ ?\ ) = 8x^3 + y^3.$

19. $(3x - y)(\ ?\ ) = 9x^2 - 6xy + y^2.$

20. $(\ ?\ )(4x^2 + 2xy + y^2) = 8x^3 - y^3.$

21. $[1 - (x - y)][\ \ ?\ \ ] = 1 - (x - y)^2.$
22. $[(x + 2y) - 1][\ \ ?\ \ ] = (x + 2y)^2 - 1.$
23. $(\ \ ?\ \ )(9y^2 - 6yz + 4z^2) = 27y^3 + 8z^3.$
24. $[a - (b - c)][\ \ ?\ \ ] = a^2 - (b - c)^2.$
25. $[(a - b) - c][\ \ ?\ \ ] = (a - b)^2 - c^2.$
26. $[\ \ ?\ \ ][x^2 + x(y + z) + (y + z)^2] = x^3 - (y + z)^3$
27. $[(r - s) + (y + t)][\ \ ?\ \ ] = (r - s)^2 - (y + t)^2.$
28. $a(x + y) + b(x + y) = (x + y)(\ \ ?\ \ ).$
29. $a(x + y) - (x + y) = (x + y)(\ \ ?\ \ ).$
30. $-a(x + y) - (x + y) = (x + y)(\ \ ?\ \ ).$

EXERCISE 3-1

1. State each of the identities (1), (2), (3), (4), (5), and (6), Sec. 3-2, in English.

2. Write a trinomial involving x which is (a), rational and integral in x, (b), not rational and integral in x.

   By use of the proper type products perform (orally when possible) the multiplications indicated in Probs. 3–29.

3. $5x(2x - a - 1).$
4. $-3y(y - 2xy).$
5. $4a^2b(b^3 - ab).$
6. $-2x^2(3x - 2ax + b + 2).$
7. $6a(-2x - a).$
8. $3p(p^2 + q^2).$
9. $(x + 5)^2.$
10. $(2x^2 + 4)^2.$
11. $-(3xy + 2)^2.$
12. $-2(3m^2 + 2n)^2.$
13. $(2a^2 - b)^2.$
14. $(4m^2 - 3x)^2.$
15. $-2(-3y + x)^2.$
16. $(2 - y^2)^2.$
17. $(3a^2c - \frac{1}{2})^2.$
18. $(3x - 2y)(3x + 2y).$
19. $(2x^2 + 4y^2)(2x^2 - 4y^2).$
20. $-(2x^3 - y^3)(2x^3 + y^3).$

21. $\left(\dfrac{a}{b} + \dfrac{b}{a}\right)\left(\dfrac{a}{b} - \dfrac{b}{a}\right).$
22. $[(x + a) - 2][(x + a) + 2].$

23. $(3x - 2 - 3y)(3x - 2 + 3y).$
    Hint: $3x - 2 - 3y = [(3x - 2) - 3y].$
24. $[(x + y) - (2r - s)][(x + y) + (2r - s)].$
25. $(x + y)(x^2 - xy + y^2).$
26. $(3a + b)(9a^2 - 3ab + b^2).$
27. $(2p^2 + 3mp)(4p^4 - 6mp^3 + 9m^2p^2).$
28. $-(y - a)(y^2 + ay + a^2).$
29. $-3(2a - b)(4a^2 + 2ab + b^2).$
30. Prove the identity $(a + b + c)^2 = a^2 + b^2 + c^2 + 2ab + 2ac + 2bc$ both by direct multiplication and by writing the left member in the form $[(a + b) + c]^2.$

31. State the identity in Prob. 30 in a suitable form for oral problems.

Use the statement obtained in Prob. 31 to find the squares indicated in Probs. 32–34.

32. $(x + y + 2z)^2$.   33. $(3x - 2y + z)^2$.   34. $(2a - b - 3c)^2$.

Factor the expressions in Probs. 35–60.

35. $6ax^2 + 2ax - 4a$.   36. $x(a + b) + x$.
37. $2ay^2 - y$.   38. $4x^2 + 4x + 1$.
39. $x^2 - 6xy + 9y^2$.   40. $4x^2 - 9y^2$.
41. $4y^2 - 1$.   42. $(a + b)^2 - (c + d)^2$.
43. $1 - (2x - y)^2$.   44. $8 - 27y^3$.
45. $27x^3 + 1$.   46. $27x^6 - 8y^6$.
47. $(a + b)^3 - 8$.   48. $64 - (x + 2y)^2$.
49. $(x + y)^2 - (x + y)$.   50. $1 - 16y^4$.
51. $x^6 - y^6$.   52. $x^6 + y^6$.
                                        Hint: $x^6 + y^6 = (x^2)^3 + (y^2)^3$.
54. $(x - y)^2 - (a + b)^2$.   55. $(m - n)^2 - 16$.
56. $(k + 1)^2 - (x - y)^2$.   57. $100x^5y^3 - 25x^3y$.
58. $12a^4b^5 - 36$.   59. $64x^3y^5 - 16xy^3$.
60. $72a^4b^2 - 9ab^2$.

3-3. FACTORING A TRINOMIAL

The identities

(1) $$(x + a)(x + b) = x^2 + (a + b)x + ab$$

and

(2) $$(ax + b)(cx + d) = acx^2 + (ad + bc)x + bd$$

should not be memorized for their own sake; but should suggest a practical method for multiplying two monomials and thereby aid in the factoring of a trinomial. To illustrate the technique involved for finding the product $(2x + 3)(3x - 2)$ mentally, the following procedure should be noted. The first term of the product is $(2x)(3x) = 6x^2$. The second term is the sum of the products of "inside terms" and "outside terms," or $3(3x) + (2x)(-2) = 9x - 4x = 5x$. The third term is $3(-2) = -6$. Hence the product is $6x^2 + 5x - 6$. Practice for proficiency in this direction is essential.

To factor the trinomial $6x^2 + 11x - 2$, for example, we experiment with binomial factors whose first terms are $6x$ and x or $3x$ and $2x$, and whose second terms are factors of -2. Among the possibilities for factorization are $(6x + 1)(x - 2)$, $(6x - 1)(x + 2)$, $(6x + 2)(x - 1)$,

$(6x - 2) (x + 1)$, $(3x + 1) (2x - 2)$, etc. An alert inspection of "inside plus outside products" (the key to the whole method) yields $x - 12x = -11x, - x + 12x = 11x$, and the final result can now be written as $6x^2 + 11x - 2 = (6x - 1) (x + 2)$. When using this method, one should *always* check the middle term in the product of the trial factors before accepting them as correct.

The method is unchanged but shorter when the coefficient of x^2 is 1. When factoring $x^2 + x - 12$ for example, we seek two numbers whose product is -12 and whose sum is 1, the coefficient of x. These are readily found to be 4 and -3. Write the factors $(x + 4) (x - 3)$ and check the inside and outside products. It is most important for the student to become accustomed to this check as part of a method for factorization of trinomial expressions.

EXERCISE 3-2

Do orally Probs. 77–96 in the Review Exercises of Chapter 2.

Factor the following trinomials.

1. $x^2 + 2x + 1$.	2. $4x^2 + 12x + 9$.	3. $16x^2 + 40x + 25$.
4. $a^2 - 10a + 25$.	5. $9k^2 + 6k + 1$.	6. $x^2 - 4x + 4$.
7. $9x^2 - 12x + 4$.	8. $25x^2 - 40x + 16$.	9. $4m^2 - 4m + 1$.
10. $36r^2 - 24rs + 4s^2$.	11. $x^2 - 5x + 6$.	12. $x^2 - 2x - 3$.
13. $x^2 + 3x + 2$.	14. $x^2 - 5x - 6$.	15. $x^2 + 6x - 7$.
16. $x^2 + 5x - 6$.	17. $x^2 - 3x + 2$.	18. $x^2 - 6x - 7$.
19. $x^2 + x - 2$.	20. $x^2 - x - 2$.	21. $x^2 - 11x + 30$.
22. $x^2 - 11x - 12$.	23. $x^2 + 11x - 12$.	24. $x^2 - 4x - 5$.
25. $x^2 + 4x - 5$.	26. $x^2 - 10x + 21$.	27. $x^2 + 12x + 32$.
28. $x^2 + 12x - 13$.	29. $x^2 - 12x - 13$.	30. $x^2 + 10x - 11$.
31. $2x^2 + 5x + 2$.	32. $2x^2 - 3x - 2$.	33. $3x^2 + 5x - 2$.
34. $5x^2 - 3x - 2$.	35. $4x^2 - x - 3$.	36. $6x^2 + 5x - 6$.
37. $6x^2 - 5x - 6$.	38. $10x^2 - 11x + 3$.	39. $10x^2 - x - 3$.
40. $8x^2 - 14x - 15$.	41. $6x^2 + 13x + 5$.	42. $15x^2 - 19x + 6$.
43. $9x^2 - 3x - 2$.	44. $9x^2 + 15x - 6$.	45. $14x^2 + 11x - 15$.
46. $24x^2 + 7x - 6$.	47. $27x^2 - 6x - 8$.	48. $20x^2 + 16x + 3$.
49. $36x^2 + 9x - 10$.	50. $27x^2 + 3x - 2$.	

3-4. FACTORING BY GROUPING TERMS

In general, it is more difficult to perform factorization on algebraic expressions than it is to carry out multiplication, since there is no single routine method which can always be applied for the factoring process.

Yet there are devices which often prove useful toward performing factoring. One of these is that of grouping terms, which will now be illustrated.

Since $cx + dx = x(c + d)$, by the distributive law of multiplication, it follows that, if x is replaced by $(a + b)$,

(1) $$c(a + b) + d(a + b) = (a + b)(c + d).$$

That is, if the terms of an expression can be arranged in groups connected by plus and/or minus signs in such a way that a certain common quantity appears as a factor of each group, then that common quantity is a factor of the whole expression.

Certain frequently made errors will be avoided if one studies the following examples carefully.

Illustrative Examples

1. $2ax + 3ay + 4bx + 6by = (2ax + 3ay) + (4bx + 6by)$
    $$= a(2x + 3y) + 2b(2x + 3y)$$
    $$= (2x + 3y)(a + 2b).$$

2. $12ac - 8bc - 3ad + 2bd = (12ac - 8bc) - (3ad - 2bd)$
    $$= 4c(3a - 2b) - d(3a - 2b)$$
    $$= (3a - 2b)(4c - d).$$

3. $3\,ax + x - y + 3az + z - 3ay = 3ax - 3ay + 3az + x - y + z$
    $$= (3ax - 3ay + 3az) + (x - y + z)$$
    $$= 3a(x - y + z) + 1(x - y + z)$$
    $$= (x - y + z)(3a + 1).$$

If a common factor does not appear after several experimental groupings of the terms, it may be possible to rearrange the terms of the original algebraic expression, so that the expression becomes factorable as the differences of two squares. This is illustrated in Examples 4 and 5.

Illustrative Examples

4. $4x^2 - 9y^2 + 6y - 1 = 4x^2 - (9y^2 - 6y + 1)$
    $$= (2x)^2 - (3y - 1)^2$$
    $$= [(2x) - (3y - 1)][(2x) + (3y - 1)]$$
    $$= (2x - 3y + 1)(2x + 3y - 1).$$

5. $4xy - 1 + 4y^2 + x^2 = (x^2 + 4xy + 4y^2) - 1$
    $$= (x + 2y)^2 - 1^2$$
    $$= [(x + 2y) - 1][(x + 2y) + 1]$$
    $$= (x + 2y - 1)(x + 2y + 1).$$

For emphasis note that a definite procedure is indicated for factoring, or attempting to factor, a polynomial of four terms. The "two-two" grouping will aid in exposing any common binomial factor if one such exists. If this fails and if there is at least one perfect square term in the expression, the "three-one" grouping may be tried. At best, proficiency in factoring procedures can only be gained through constant practice.

A binomial or trinomial containing two perfect square terms can many times be changed to a perfect square by the addition and subtraction of a term. If the term thus added is itself a perfect square, the original expression may be factored, as in the examples below.

Illustrative Examples

6. $x^4 + 4 = (x^4 + 4x^2 + 4) - 4x^2$
$$= (x^2 + 2)^2 - (2x)^2$$
$$= (x^2 + 2 - 2x)(x^2 + 2 + 2x).$$

7. $x^4 + x^2 + 1 = (x^4 + 2x^2 + 1) - x^2$
$$= (x^2 + 1)^2 - x^2$$
$$= (x^2 + 1 - x)(x^2 + 1 + x).$$

EXERCISE 3-3

Factor the following expressions.

1. $a(x - y) + b(x - y)$.
2. $b(x + y) - c(x + y)$.
3. $x(a + b) + y(a + b)$.
4. $m(k - 1) - n(k - 1)$.
5. $-h(r + s) + k(r + s)$.
6. $ax + ay + bx + by$.
7. $bx - by + cx - cy$.
8. $x^3 - 2x^2 + x - 2$.
9. $2x^3 + 3x^2 - 2x - 3$.
10. $ax^2 + ax - bx - b$.
11. $x^2 - y^2 + x - y$.
12. $x^2 - y^2 - x + y$.
13. $4x^2 - 9y^2 + 2x - 3y$.
14. $9x^2 - 16y^2 - 3x - 4y$.
15. $16x^2 - 25y^2 + 8ax - 10ay$.
16. $4x^2 + 2y - 1 - y^2$.
17. $x^2 + y^2 + 2xy - 9$.
18. $16 + 2xy - x^2 - y^2$.
19. $x^2 + y^2 - 2xy - 25$.
20. $16 - 8x + x^2 - y^2$.
21. $y^2 - x^2 + 2y + 1$.
22. $4x^2 - y^2 - 4x + 1$.
23. $x^2 - y^2 - 6x + 9$.
24. $x^2 + a^2 - b^2 - 2ax + 2b - 1$.
25. $x^2 - y^2 - c^2 - 4x + 2cy + 4$.
26. $x^8 + x^4 + 1$.
27. $x^4 - 3x^2 + 1$.
28. $x^4 + 3x^2 + 4$.
29. $x^4 + 5x^2 + 9$.
30. $x^4 - 5x^2 + 4$.
31. $x^4 - 7x^2 + 9$.
32. $x^4 + 2x^2 + 9$.
33. $x^4 + 4x^2 + 16$.
34. $4x^4 + 3x^2 + 1$.
35. $ax + by + bx + ay$.
36. $x + y - x^2 + y^2$.
37. $4x^2 - y^2 + 4y - 4$.
38. $4x^4 + 1$.
39. $25x^4 + x^2 + 1$.
40. $9x^4 + 2x^2 + 1$.
41. $9x^4 - 10x^2 + 1$.
42. $9x^4 - 40x^2 + 16$.

3-5. DEFINITIONS

The *degree* of an integral rational term in any letters is the sum of the exponents of these letters in that term. Its degree in a given letter is the exponent of that letter. Thus $3x^2y^3$ is of degree 5 in x and y, of degree 2 in x, and of degree 3 in y.

The degree of a polynomial is the same as that of its term of highest degree. For example, $x^3y + xy^5 - 1$ is a sixth-degree polynomial in x and y and is of degree 3 in x and of degree 5 in y.

A polynomial A is a *multiple* of a polynomial B if B is a factor of A. To illustrate, 5, 10, 15x, and 25 $(x + y)$ are multiples of 5, while $x - 1$ and $x^2 - 1$ are multiples of $x - 1$.

A multiple of each of two or more polynomials is called a common multiple. For instance, $25x^3y^2$ is a *common multiple* of 5, x and y^2.

3-6. LOWEST COMMON MULTIPLE

The lowest common multiple (L.C.M.) *of two or more polynomials is the common multiple of lowest degree and with the smallest possible numerical coefficients.* It is found by multiplying the distinct prime factors of all the polynomials and assigning to each the largest exponent with which it appears in any of the polynomials under consideration. Prime factors such as $x - y$ and $y - x$, which differ only in sign, are considered as being alike in character when forming the L.C.M. This is illustrated in Example 3.

Example 1. The L.C.M. of 6, 9, and 12, or $2 \cdot 3$, $3 \cdot 3$, and $2^2 \cdot 3$, is $2^2 \cdot 3^2$, or 36.

Example 2. The L.C.M. of 6x, $9(y + 1)^3$, and $12x^2(y + 1)$ is $36x^2(y + 1)^3$.

Example 3. The L.C.M. of $x - y$ and $y^2 - x^2$ may be considered either as $y^2 - x^2$ or $x^2 - y^2$, and not $(x - y)(y^2 - x^2)$. (Note that as a consequence there are two correct forms of the L.C.M., one being the negative or additive inverse of the other.)

3-7. HIGHEST COMMON FACTOR

The highest common factor (H.C.F.) *of two or more polynomials is the common factor of highest degree and with the largest possible numerical coefficients.* It is found by multiplying the common factors, and assigning to each of these the smallest exponent with which it appears in any one polynomial.

Example 1. The H.C.F. of 30, 12, 18, when represented in terms of its prime factors, namely $2 \cdot 3 \cdot 5$, $2^2 \cdot 3$, and $2 \cdot 3^2$, is $2 \cdot 3$ or 6.

Example 2.   The H.C.F. of $30x^3(x - y)^4$, $12x^2(x - y)$, and $18x^4(y - x)^3$ is $6x^2(x - y)$, or may be considered as $6x^2(y - x)$.

EXERCISE 3-4

Find the H.C.F. and L.C.M. of the polynomials in each group.

1. 9, 12, 15.   2. 12, 18, 24.   3. 18, 27, 36.

4. 14, 21, 36.   5. 20, 35, 50.   6. 30, 45, 75.

7. 80, 32, 96.   8. 54, 36, 90.   9. 65, 91, 104.

10. $x^2, 3x^3y, 4x^4y^3$.   11. $5a^3x^2, 15a^2x^3, 10a^4x^4$.

12. $12x^3y^2, 15x^2y^3, 9x^4y^4$.   13. $(x - y), (x^2 - y^2), (x^2 - xy)$.

14. $(x^2 + xy), (x + y), (x^2 - y^2)$.

15. $(x^2 - 2xy + y^2), (x^2 - y^2), (x^3 - x^2y)$.

16. $(x^2 + 2xy + y^2), (x^2 - y^2), (x^3 + x^2y)$.

17. $(x^2 - 3x + 2), (x^2 - 4), (x^2 - 5x + 6)$.

18. $(2x^2 - 3x + 1), (2x^2 + 5x - 3), (4x^2 - 1)$.

19. $(3x^2 + 5x - 2), (3x^2 - 4x + 1), (3x^2 + 2x - 1)$.

20. $(2x^2 - 5x - 3), (2x^2 - x - 1), (2x^2 - 3x + 1)$.

21. $(6x^2 + x - 1), (3x^2 - 4x + 1), (6x^2 - 5x + 1)$.

22. $(5x^2 - x - 4), (15x^2 + 2x - 8), (10x^2 - 7x - 12)$.

23. $(x - 2y)^2, (2y - x)^3, (x^3 - 2x^2y)$.

24. $(x - y)^3, (y - x)^3, (xy^2 - y^3)^2$.

REVIEW EXERCISES

Factor by using the type form $ab + ac = a(b + c)$

1. $4y^3 - 12y^2$.   2. $3ab^2 + 6b^3$.

3. $m^2n - mn^2$.   4. $3a^3b + 5ab^2 - ab$

5. $6x^5 - 2x^3y^3 - 2x^3y$.   6. $y(x - 3y) + 2(x - 3y)$.

7. $c(3a - b) - 2a(3a - b)$.

8. $-x^2(2m - n) - y^2(2m - n) + 3(2m - n)$.

Factor by grouping.

9. $mx + my + cx + cy$.   10. $a^4 + 2a^3 - 2a - 4$.

11. $x^3 - x^2 - x + 1$.   12. $6ab - 2a + 3b - 1$.

13. $x^3 - 4x^2y - 2xy^2 + 8y^3$.   14. $6pq - 9p + 4q - 6$.

15. $6m^3 + 12m^2n + 4mn^2 + 8n^3$ 16. $x^2 - 9y^2 + x - 3y$.

Factor the following trinomials.

17. $y^2 - y - 12$.   18. $2x^2 + 5x + 2$.

19. $x^2 + 10x + 21$.   20. $m^2n^2 - 5mn - 15$.

21. $x^2 + xy - 12y^2$.

22. $p^4 + 16p^2 - 36$.

23. $12a^2 - a - 1$.

24. $25r^2 + 10rs - 3s^2$.

25. $a^2 - 5ab - 24b^2$.

26. $12x^2 + 71x - 25$.

27. $20 + 8x - x^2$.

28. $x^8 + 4x^4y^4 + 4y^8$.

29. $4c^2 - 4cd + d^2$.

30. $9a^2 + 6a + 1$.

31. $4 - 20x + 25x^2$.

32. $9x^4 - 6x^2yz + y^2z^2$.

Factor by using the type form $a^2 - b^2 = (a - b)(a + b)$.

33. $4x^2 - 121y^2$.

34. $81 - x^4$ (three factors).

35. $16a^2 - 25b^2$.

36. $(3x - y)^2 - 9$.

37. $x^2 - (2y + z)^2$.

38. $(x + 2y)^2 - 9(m - n)^2$.

39. $1 - (x + y)^2$.

40. $4x^2 - 4xy + y^2 - z^2$.

Hint. $4x^2 - 4xy + y^2 - z^2 = (2x - y)^2 - z^2$.

41. $9 - a^2 + 8ab - 16b^2$.

42. $4x^2 - 4ax + 2by + a^2 - b^2 - y^2$.

43. $p^2 + q^2 - a^2 + 2pq$.

Factor by using the type forms $a^3 + b^3 = (a + b)(a^2 - ab + b^2)$; and $a^3 - b^3 = (a - b)(a^2 + ab + b^2)$.

44. $x^3 + 8$.

45. $m^3 - 27$.

46. $a^3y^3 + 64$.

47. $x^6 + a^6$.

48. $(2x - 1)^3 - 8$.

49. $27y^3 + (a + 2b)^3$.

50. $x^6 - y^6$.

Hint. First treat as difference of squares.

Factor as a difference of two squares by adding and subtracting a perfect square.

51. $x^4 + 64$.

52. $x^4 + 4y^4$.

53. $x^4 + x^2y^2 + y^4$.

54. $x^4 - 24x^2 + 16$. [*Hint.* $x^4 - 24x^2 + 16 = (x^2 - 4)^2 - 16$

55. $x^4 - 12x^2y^2 + 16y^4$.

56. $a^4 - 10a^2b^2 + 16b^4$.

Factor completely, using the type forms given in this chapter. Remove first any monomial divisor which exists in the given expression before factoring it further.

57. $4r^2y^2 - 25r^2$.

58. $y^6 - 8y^4 + 16y^2$.

59. $x^4 - a^4$.

60. $2a^6 - 8y^6$.

61. $a^3 + a^2 - 4a - 4$.

62. $y^4 - 2a^2y^2 + a^4$.

63. $m(n^2 - 1) - 2(n^2 - 1)$.

64. $x^3 + 27m^3$.

65. $4x^2 - 1 - 4y - 4y^2$.

66. $(2x - 4)^2 - (3y + 2)^2$.

67. $3x^2a - 2axy - ay^2$.

68. $8r^2mx - 16rm - 48r^3m^3$.

69. $(x + y) - b^2(x + y)$. 70. $2(a + b)^2 + 5(a + b) - 12$.
71. $p^2q^2 - 1$. 72. $4x^2 + 28cx + 49c^2$.
73. $x^3 - (a + 2)^3$. 74. $x^2(2x + 1) - (4x^2 - 1)$.
75. $(a + b)(x + y) - (a + b)(3x - y)$.

76. Why is it that $\dfrac{10^3 + 7^3}{10^3 + 3^3}$ can be simplified by the illegitimate operation of canceling the exponents?

77. Show that $\dfrac{(a + b)^3 + a^3}{(a + b)^3 + b^3} = \dfrac{2a + b}{a + 2b}$, and apply this result to Prob. 76.

chapter 4

Fractions

4-1. DEFINITIONS

An algebraic fraction is an indicated quotient of two algebraic expressions. The dividend and divisor are called respectively the *numerator* and *denominator*.

Examples:

$$\frac{x}{y}; \quad \frac{a+1}{\frac{a}{2}-1}; \quad \frac{2-3x}{1}; \quad \frac{2}{3}; \quad \frac{\frac{x}{a}+\frac{y}{2}}{x-\frac{y}{3}};$$

where the respective numerators and denominators are x and y; $a+1$ and $\frac{a}{2}-1$; $2-3x$ and 1; 2 and 3; $\frac{x}{a}+\frac{y}{2}$, and $x-\frac{y}{3}$.

Fractions such as $\frac{2}{3}$ and $\frac{2x+1}{2x-1}$ are called simple, since neither the numerator nor denominator of the respective fractions contain terms of the form $\frac{a}{b}$, where b is different from 1. Fractions of the type $\dfrac{2+\frac{1}{2}}{3}$ and $\dfrac{2+\frac{1}{x}}{3-\frac{1}{x}}$ are called *complex*, since terms either in the numerator or denominator or in both do contain terms of the type $\frac{a}{b}$, where b is different from 1.

As pointed out in Sec. 2-3., if the product of two numbers is 1, each is called the reciprocal or multiplicative inverse of the other. Thus the reciprocal of $\frac{a}{b}$ is $\frac{b}{a}$; and the reciprocal of $-x$ (or $\frac{-x}{1}$) is $\frac{1}{-x}$, which equals $-\frac{1}{x}$. Zero is the only number which has no reciprocal. Why? _____

4-2. REDUCTION OF A SIMPLE FRACTION TO ITS LOWEST TERMS

Law 1. *The value of a fraction is not changed when both the numerator and denominator are multiplied or divided by the same non-zero quantity.*

Two observations should be made when interpreting this law: (a) it states "when both the numerator and denominator," and "not merely one or the other," (b) it says when both numerator and denominator are "multiplied or divided by," and not merely one or the other. It certainly doesn't say that we can add or subtract the same nonzero quantity from the numerator and denominator of the fraction without changing its value.

Examples.

$$\frac{3}{6} = \frac{1}{2}; \quad \frac{2}{3} = \frac{8}{12}; \quad \frac{ax}{xy} = \frac{a}{y}; \quad \frac{a}{b} = \frac{x^2 a}{x^2 b}.$$

By virtue of this law we may reduce to lowest terms a simple fraction by factoring the numerator and denominator and dividing out all common factors other than 1 or -1 between the numerator and the denominator. This procedure is a short way of dividing both numerator and denominator by its common factor.

Example.

$$\frac{ax^2 - a}{ax^3 - a} = \frac{\overset{1}{\cancel{a}}(\overset{1}{\cancel{x-1}})(x+1)}{\underset{1}{\cancel{a}}(\underset{1}{\cancel{x-1}})(x^2 + x + 1)} = \frac{x+1}{x^2 + x + 1}.$$

A fraction is not reduced to lowest terms until all common factors of the numerator and the denominator have been divided out; or in other words, until the numerator and denominator have been divided by their highest common factor.

A fraction is said to be in *simplified form* if it is in lowest terms and if either, both, or neither of its numerator or denominator is represented in factored form. For example, any of the forms

$$\frac{2(x-y)(x+y)}{(x+2y)(x-3y)}, \quad \frac{2x^2 - 2y^2}{x^2 - xy - 6y^2},$$

$$\frac{2(x-y)(x+y)}{x^2 - xy - 6y^2}, \quad \frac{2x^2 - 2y^2}{(x+2y)(x-3y)}$$

are simplified for the same fraction. Which form is best for the fraction depends on what further manipulation is to be carried out where this fraction may be involved.

It is noted that if all of the common factors of the numerator or of the denominator or both divide out in the fraction being reduced, the factor 1 is still present in the appropriate position where this happens in the given fraction.

Example.

$$\frac{\overset{1}{\cancel{a}}}{\underset{1}{ab}} = \frac{1}{b}; \quad \frac{\overset{1}{ab}}{\cancel{a}} = \frac{b}{1} = b; \quad \frac{\overset{1}{ab}}{\underset{1}{\cancel{ab}}} = \frac{1}{1} = 1.$$

Caution: Errors due to faulty division of common factors are very numerous, and the student who is not sure of his knowledge or ability in algebra should be especially careful when he is tempted to cross out letters or expressions just because they look alike above or below a line in a fraction. The simple rule to be applied is that any algebraic expression being used in division between a numerator and a denominator of a fraction must be a *factor of the whole numerator* and also a *factor of the whole denominator*. Hence the student should make sure that the factoring of both numerator and denominator is done correctly before any simplification is carried out. For example, if the numerator is $xy + a$, then neither x nor y nor a is a factor of the whole numerator, although the expression "$xy + a$" considered as *an entity* is a factor of itself, as shown in some of the examples.

Examples in which division of factors is permissible:

$$\frac{xy + a}{b(xy + a)} = \frac{\overset{1}{\cancel{(xy + a)}}}{b\underset{1}{\cancel{(xy + a)}}} = \frac{1}{b}; \quad \frac{2x + 4}{6} = \frac{\overset{1}{\cancel{2}}(x + 2)}{\underset{1}{\cancel{2} \cdot 3}} = \frac{x + 2}{3}.$$

Examples in which division of factors is incorrect. (Decide why in each case.)

$$\frac{xy + a}{x}; \quad \frac{a + 1}{a + 2}; \quad \frac{2(x + y)}{1 - 3(x + y)}; \quad \frac{2x + y + z}{x + y + z}; \quad \frac{(a + b)(c + d)}{(a + b)c + d}.$$

In the fraction $\dfrac{a + 1}{a + 2}$ the division of a is of course not permissible since it would violate the rule about factors. But *why* is it not permissible? Note that when we divide by a factor we are actually *dividing* the numerator and denominator by that factor, whereas if we incorrectly cross out a from the fraction $\dfrac{a + 1}{a + 2}$ we are *subtracting* a from the numerator and denominator. This changes the value of a fraction, as illustrated in the case $\dfrac{2}{3} \neq \dfrac{2+1}{3+1}$ (or $\dfrac{2}{3} \neq \dfrac{3}{4}$).

It is permissible to divide $x + 2$ from the numerator and denominator of $\dfrac{3y(\overset{1}{\cancel{x+2}}) - 5(\overset{1}{\cancel{x+2}})}{(\underset{1}{\cancel{x+2}})(x-2)}$, obtaining $\dfrac{3y-5}{x-2}$, since this operation is equivalent to dividing both members of the fraction by the factor $x + 2$. However, it is a safer procedure to write this fraction as $\dfrac{(x+2)(3y-5)}{(x+2)(x-2)}$ before carrying out the division. It will help to avoid errors if both the full numerator and the full denominator of a fraction are completely factored before division is applied.

EXERCISE 4-1

1. How many *terms*, and how many prime *factors*, has each of the following expressions: (a) xyz; (b) $x^2 + x + 1$; (c) $x^2 - y^2$?

2. In which of the two following cases is reduction of a fraction to lowest terms always permissible: The numerator and denominator of a fraction have (a) a common term, (b) a common factor?

In which of Probs. 3–13 is reduction to lowest terms permissible? In these cases carry out the reduction.

3. $\dfrac{ax}{x(b+1)}$.

4. $\dfrac{x+y}{x-y}$.

5. $\dfrac{(x-y)(x+y)+1}{2(x+y)}$.

6. $\dfrac{(x-1)(x+1)}{3(x+1)}$.

7. $\dfrac{(x-1)x+1}{x+1}$.

8. $\dfrac{(x+1)a}{x+1}$.

9. $\dfrac{(x+1)a}{(x+1)+b}$.

10. $\dfrac{(x-y)(x+y)}{x-y(x+y)}$.

11. $\dfrac{a+b+c}{3(x+y)(a+b+c)}$.

12. $\dfrac{(a+b)x-y}{(a+b)(x-y)}$.

13. $\dfrac{(x-y)(x+y)}{ax+ay}$.

Explain the errors that have been made in the reduction to lowest terms for Probs. 14–17.

14. (a) $\dfrac{3(x+y) + (\overset{1}{\cancel{x-y}})}{(\cancel{x-y})(x+y)} \overset{?}{=} \dfrac{3x+3y+1}{x+y}$

(b) $\dfrac{cx + b}{c} \overset{?}{=} \dfrac{\overset{1}{\cancel{c}x} + b}{\cancel{c}} \overset{?}{=} x + b$
$\quad\;\; 1$

15. (a) $\dfrac{x + \overset{1}{\cancel{y - z}}}{\cancel{y - z}} \overset{?}{=} x + 1$
$\quad\;\; 1$

(b) $\dfrac{2a + 4}{a + 3} \overset{?}{=} \dfrac{\overset{1}{\cancel{2a + 4}}}{\cancel{a + 3}} \overset{?}{=} \dfrac{2 + 4}{1 + 3} = \dfrac{6}{4} = \dfrac{3}{2}$
$\qquad\qquad\;\; 1$

16. (a) $\dfrac{\overset{1}{\cancel{x + y}}}{\cancel{x^2 - y^2} + 3} \overset{?}{=} \dfrac{1}{x - y + 3}$
$\;\; x - y$

(b) $\dfrac{2 + 5(x + y)}{(x + y)^2} \overset{?}{=} \dfrac{2 + 5\overset{1}{\cancel{(x + y)}}}{\underset{x + y}{\cancel{(x + y)^2}}} \overset{?}{=} \dfrac{2 + 5}{x + y} = \dfrac{7}{x + y}$

17. (a) $\dfrac{\overset{(a + b)}{\cancel{(a + b)^2}} + \overset{1}{\cancel{c^2}}}{\underset{1}{\cancel{c^2}}\underset{1}{\cancel{(a + b)}}} = a + b + 1$

(b) $\dfrac{12(x^2 - y^2) + 3(x + y) + 6}{3(x^2 - y^2)(x + 2y)} \overset{?}{=} \dfrac{\overset{4}{\cancel{12}}\overset{1}{\cancel{(x^2 - y^2)}} + 3(x + y) + 6}{\underset{1}{\cancel{3}}\underset{1}{\cancel{(x^2 - y^2)}}(x + 2y)}$

$\qquad\qquad\qquad\qquad\qquad\quad \overset{?}{=} \dfrac{3x + 3y + 10}{x + 2y}$

Reduce to lowest terms:

18. $\dfrac{2}{6}$.   19. $\dfrac{66}{99}$.   20. $\dfrac{15}{35}$.   21. $\dfrac{42}{30}$.   22. $\dfrac{x^3 - 1}{x^2 - 1}$.

23. $\dfrac{36x^2}{54x}$.   24. $\dfrac{x(y - 3)}{2(y - 3)}$.   25. $\dfrac{7(x - 5)}{3(x - 5)}$.

26. $\dfrac{6(x^2 - y^2)}{5(x - y)}$.   27. $\dfrac{5x(y^2 - 1)}{2x(y - 1)}$.   28. $\dfrac{7y^2(x^2 - 9)}{3y(x - 3)}$.

29. $\dfrac{x^2 - 3x - 4}{x^2 + 5x + 4}$.   30. $\dfrac{x^2 - 3x + 2}{x^2 - x - 2}$.   31. $\dfrac{x^2 + 7x + 12}{x^2 + x - 12}$.

32. $\dfrac{x^2 - 2x - 15}{x^2 - 9}$.   33. $\dfrac{x^2 - 5x + 6}{x^2 - x - 6}$.   34. $\dfrac{x^2 + x - 6}{x^2 + 2x - 3}$.

35. $\dfrac{2x^2 + 3x - 2}{2x^2 - 3x + 1}$.   36. $\dfrac{6x^2 - x - 2}{2x^2 - x - 1}$.   37. $\dfrac{3x^2 + 2x - 1}{2x^2 + x - 1}$.

38. $\dfrac{12x^2 + 5x - 3}{8x^2 + 10x + 3}.$

39. $\dfrac{15x^2 - 2x - 8}{-12 + 7x + 10x^2}.$

40. $\dfrac{21x^2 + 43x - 14}{-21 + 5x + 6x^2}.$

41. $\dfrac{x^3 - x^2 - 4x + 4}{x^3 - x^2 - 9x + 9}.$

42. $\dfrac{x^3 - 3x^2 + x - 3}{-3x + x^2 + 3x^3 - x^4}.$

43. $\dfrac{x^3 - 5x^2 + 2x - 10}{-15 + 3x + 5x^2 - x^3}.$

44. $\dfrac{5(c - d)^3 - x(c - d)}{c^2 - d^2}.$

45. $\dfrac{r^2 - s^2 - 5r + 5s}{r^2 - 2rs + s^2}.$

46. $\dfrac{x^4 + 4y^4}{5x^2 - 10xy + 10y^2}.$

47. $\dfrac{(x + y)^2 + 11(x + y) + 24}{x^2 + 2xy + y^2 - 9}.$

40. $\dfrac{(x + y)(x - y) - 5y(x - y)}{x^3 - y^3}.$

49. $\dfrac{a^3 + 8b^3 + a^2 - 4b^2}{a^2 - 4b^2}.$

50. $\dfrac{(3x - 2y)(3x^2 + xy - 4y^2)}{(3x + 2y)(3x^2 + xy - 2y^2)}.$

4-3. RULES ABOUT FRACTIONS

In this and the next two sections we shall deal with simple fractions, such as $\dfrac{2}{3}$ or $\dfrac{3x - 1}{x + 2}.$

Rule 1. The sign before a fraction is changed when the sign of either the numerator or the denominator is changed.

For by the rule of signs [(4), Sec. 2-6], $\dfrac{a}{-b} = -\dfrac{a}{b}$, and $\dfrac{-a}{b} = -\dfrac{a}{b}.$

Rule 2. The sign before a fraction is changed when the sign of a factor of either the numerator or the denominator is changed.

For again by the rule of signs, $a(-b) = -ab$. Hence when the factor b is changed to $-b$ the sign of the whole numerator or denominator in which it appears will be changed, so that Rule 1 will apply.

Example 1.

$$\frac{1}{(-2)(-3)} = -\frac{1}{2(-3)} = \frac{1}{2 \cdot 3} = \frac{1}{6}.$$

Example 2.

$$\frac{a}{x(1 - x)} = -\frac{a}{x(-1 + x)} \quad \text{or} \quad -\frac{a}{x(x - 1)}.$$

Reminder. It is important to note here that Rule 2, as does Rule 3 below, refers to *factors* and not *terms*. For instance, in Example 2 above, when the sign of the factor $1 - x$ is changed it becomes $-1 + x$ or $x - 1$, and *not* $1 + x$.

Definition. Integers divisible by 2 are referred to as *even numbers*; all other integers are *odd.* Even numbers include, 2, 4, 6, -2, -4, etc., as well as 0; odd numbers include 1, 3, 5, -1, -3, etc.

Rule 3. The sign before a fraction is or is not changed according as the number of factors whose signs are changed is odd or even. The altered factors may be all in the numerator or in the denominator, or they may be in both.

Example:

$$\frac{(1 - x)(2 - x)(x - 3)}{(x - 1)(x - 2)(3 - x)} = -\frac{(x - 1)(x - 2)(x - 3)}{(x - 1)(x - 2)(x - 3)} = -1.$$

Here the minus sign is inserted before the fraction in the second step because the number of factors there changed in sign is 3, which is odd.

Rule 4. To add or subtract fractions with the same denominators, add or subtract the numerators and place the result over the common denominator.

Examples:

$$\frac{2}{3} + \frac{5}{3} = \frac{2 + 5}{3} = \frac{7}{3}$$

$$\frac{8}{5} - \frac{6}{5} = \frac{8 - 6}{5} = \frac{2}{5}.$$

$$\frac{6}{7} + \frac{5}{7} - \frac{8}{7} = \frac{6 + 5 - 8}{7} = \frac{3}{7}.$$

$$\frac{x}{a + 1} + \frac{x^2}{a + 1} - \frac{2}{a + 1} = \frac{x + x^2 - 2}{a + 1}.$$

$$\frac{1}{x - 1} + \frac{a}{1 - x} = \frac{1}{x - 1} - \frac{a}{x - 1} \quad \text{(by Rule 1)}.$$

$$= \frac{1 - a}{x - 1}.$$

EXERCISE 4-2

In Probs. 1–9, write each factor with a plus literal term, changing its sign where necessary. [For instance, $x - 3$ should be left unchanged, but $3 - x$ should be changed to $-(x - 3)$.] Then divide out common factors where permissible and reduce each fraction to lowest terms.

1. $\dfrac{x - 1}{1 - x}.$

2. $\dfrac{(x - 1)^2}{(1 - x)^2}.$

3. $\dfrac{(x - 1)^3}{(1 - x)^3}.$

4. $\dfrac{(x-1)(x-2)}{(1-x)(2-x)}.$

5. $\dfrac{(x-1)(2-x)(x-3)}{(1-x)(x-2)(3-x)}.$

6. $\dfrac{(3x-1)(4-x^3)(x-2)}{(2-x)(x^3-4)(3x-1)}.$

7. $\dfrac{(x-5)^2(x-6)^3}{(5-x)^2(6-x)^3}.$

8. $\dfrac{(x-1)10}{(1-x)10}.$

9. $\dfrac{(2x-3)^5(4-x)^6}{(3-2x)^5(x-4)^6}.$

Perform the operations indicated below.

10. $\dfrac{3x-1}{5}+\dfrac{x+2}{5}.$

11. $\dfrac{2x-2}{4}+\dfrac{2x+3}{4}.$

12. $\dfrac{3x+5}{6}-\dfrac{2x+3}{6}.$

13. $\dfrac{5x-7}{5}+\dfrac{3x+2}{5}.$

14. $\dfrac{7x+2}{8}-\dfrac{3x+3}{8}.$

15. $\dfrac{6x-5}{7}-\dfrac{5x-6}{7}.$

16. $\dfrac{x-3}{x+1}+\dfrac{2x+4}{x+1}.$

17. $\dfrac{3x+7}{2x-1}-\dfrac{2x+6}{2x-1}.$

18. $\dfrac{4x+5}{x-9}-\dfrac{3x-2}{9-x}.$

19. $\dfrac{3x-5}{1+x}+\dfrac{2x-1}{x+1}.$

20. $\dfrac{10x+3}{5x^2-6}+\dfrac{3+10x}{6-5x^2}.$

21. $\dfrac{15x-7}{3x^2-5}-\dfrac{7-15x}{5-3x^2}.$

4-4.   ADDITION AND SUBTRACTION OF SIMPLE FRACTIONS

By use of Law 1, Sec. 4-2, two or more simple fractions may be written with a common denominator.

Example 1.

Write the numbers 4 (or $\dfrac{4}{1}$), $\dfrac{2}{3}$, $\dfrac{5}{6}$, and $\dfrac{16}{15}$ as fractions with a lowest common denominator (L.C.D.).

Solution. The L.C.D. of the fractions is the L.C.M. (30) of the denominators 1, 3, 6, and 15. Now, $\dfrac{4}{1}=\dfrac{4\cdot30}{1\cdot30}=\dfrac{120}{30};\dfrac{2}{3}=\dfrac{2\cdot10}{3\cdot10}=\dfrac{20}{30};$ $\dfrac{5}{6}=\dfrac{5\cdot5}{6\cdot5}=\dfrac{25}{30};$ and $\dfrac{16}{15}=\dfrac{16\cdot2}{15\cdot2}=\dfrac{32}{30}.$

Example 2.

Write the fractions $\dfrac{a}{3x(x-2)}$ and $\dfrac{5}{6(2-x)}$ with an L.C.D.

Solution. $\dfrac{5}{6(2-x)}=-\dfrac{5}{6(x-2)}$ by Rule 1, Sec. 4-3. The L.C.D. of the fractions is then $6x(x - 2)$. We now write

$$\frac{a}{3x(x - 2)} = \frac{2a}{6x(x - 2)}$$

and

$$\frac{-5}{6(x - 2)} = -\frac{5x}{6x(x - 2)}.$$

In view of Rule 4, Sec. 4-3, we have

Rule 1. *To add or subtract fractions, write them with a common denominator (their L.C.D.), add or subtract the numerators as indicated, and put the result over the L.C.D.*

Example 1.

$$2 + \frac{1}{2} - \frac{5}{6} = \frac{2}{1} + \frac{1}{2} - \frac{5}{6} = \frac{12}{6} + \frac{3}{6} - \frac{5}{6} = \frac{12 + 3 - 5}{6} = \frac{10}{6} = \frac{5}{3}.$$

Example 2.

$$\frac{x + 2}{x + 1} + \frac{2 + x^2}{1 - x^2} + x = \frac{x + 2}{x + 1} - \frac{x^2 + 2}{x^2 - 1} + \frac{x}{1}$$

$$= \frac{(x + 2)(x - 1)}{(x + 1)(x - 1)} - \frac{x^2 + 2}{x^2 - 1} + \frac{x(x^2 - 1)}{x^2 - 1}$$

$$= \frac{(x + 2)(x - 1) - (x^2 + 2) + x(x^2 - 1)}{x^2 - 1}$$

$$= \frac{x^2 + x - 2 - x^2 - 2 + x^3 - x}{x^2 - 1}$$

$$= \frac{x^3 - 4}{x^2 - 1}.$$

From Rule 1 we get the simple results: $\dfrac{a}{b} + \dfrac{c}{d} = \dfrac{ad + bc}{bd}$ and $\dfrac{a}{b} - \dfrac{c}{d} = \dfrac{ad - bc}{bd}$. But note that these results are not efficient as *formulas* when b and d have some factors in common. For example, if we use the method indicated by these results we have:

$$\frac{1}{x + 1} + \frac{1}{x^2 - 1} = \frac{(x^2 - 1) + (x + 1)}{(x + 1)(x^2 - 1)} = \frac{x^2 + x}{(x + 1)(x^2 - 1)}$$

$$= \frac{x(x + 1)}{(x + 1)(x^2 - 1)} = \frac{x}{x^2 - 1},$$

whereas the method of Rule 1 gives the simplified answer at once.

Exercise. Find the blunder in the following incorrect addition:

$\dfrac{1}{1} - \dfrac{x + 2}{3} = \dfrac{3}{3} - \dfrac{x + 2}{3} = \dfrac{3 - x + 2}{3} = \dfrac{5 - x}{3}$. This typical error is so common that it should be thoroughly understood and then carefully avoided. A second common blunder is the omission of the denominator. The student should cultivate the habit of writing the denominator *first* to avoid forgetting it when the computation of the numerator is long.

EXERCISE 4-3

In each problem below, combine the given quantities into a single fraction and reduce it to lowest terms.

1. $\dfrac{1}{2} + \dfrac{1}{3}$

2. $\dfrac{1}{3} + \dfrac{3}{5}.$

3. $\dfrac{3}{4} + \dfrac{1}{5}.$

4. $\dfrac{2}{7} + \dfrac{2}{3}.$

5. $\dfrac{3}{2} - \dfrac{5}{7}.$

6. $\dfrac{3}{5} + \dfrac{2}{3} - \dfrac{1}{4}.$

7. $\dfrac{3}{8} - \dfrac{4}{7} + \dfrac{1}{5}.$

8. $\dfrac{7}{5} - \dfrac{3}{4} + \dfrac{3}{8}.$

9. $\dfrac{8}{9} - \dfrac{1}{4} + \dfrac{2}{3}.$

10. $\dfrac{x + 1}{1 - x} + \dfrac{3x}{x - 1}.$

11. $\dfrac{x + 3}{x - 2} + \dfrac{2x + 3}{2 - x}.$

12. $\dfrac{3x - 5}{2x - 3} - \dfrac{x - 2}{3 - 2x}.$

13. $\dfrac{x}{2} + \dfrac{2x}{3} - \dfrac{1}{4}.$

14. $\dfrac{3x}{5} - \dfrac{x}{4} + \dfrac{2}{3}.$

15. $\dfrac{2x}{7} + \dfrac{x}{5} - \dfrac{3}{7}.$

16. $\dfrac{4x}{9} + \dfrac{2x}{3} - \dfrac{5}{6}.$

17. $\dfrac{5x}{4} - \dfrac{4x}{5} - \dfrac{3}{2}.$

18. $\dfrac{7x}{5} - \dfrac{3x}{2} + \dfrac{3}{5}.$

19. $\dfrac{2}{x} - \dfrac{x}{3} - \dfrac{5}{6}.$

20. $\dfrac{x}{5} + \dfrac{3}{x} - 3.$

21. $\dfrac{3}{2x} - \dfrac{x}{3} + 1.$

22. $\dfrac{3x}{5} - \dfrac{3}{5x} + 3.$

23. $\dfrac{7}{4x} - 5 + \dfrac{3x}{2}.$

24. $\dfrac{6x}{7} - 4 + \dfrac{3}{7x}.$

25. $\dfrac{3x - 1}{x + 2} + \dfrac{x - 3}{x - 2}.$

26. $\dfrac{3x + 2}{x - 3} + \dfrac{2x - 3}{x + 3}.$

27. $\dfrac{5x + 6}{2x - 1} + \dfrac{3x + 2}{3x + 2}.$

28. $\dfrac{3x + 5}{2x + 3} - \dfrac{2x + 3}{3x - 2}.$

29. $\dfrac{4x - 5}{3x - 4} - \dfrac{2x - 7}{2x + 3}.$

30. $\dfrac{9x - 4}{4x + 2} + \dfrac{3x + 5}{x - 3}.$

31. $\dfrac{7x + 3}{2x - 1} + \dfrac{x - 2}{4x^2 - 1}.$

32. $\dfrac{5x - 9}{x + 3} - \dfrac{4x - 3}{x + 1}.$

33. $\dfrac{6x^2 + 7}{3x^2 - 2x - 1} + \dfrac{2x - 5}{3x + 1}.$

34. $\dfrac{8x^2 - 5x + 3}{6x^2 + 5x - 6} - \dfrac{4x + 7}{3x - 2} + \dfrac{x + 5}{2x + 3}.$

35. $\dfrac{4x + 3}{2x - 5} + \dfrac{2x - 5}{3x + 4} - \dfrac{9x^2 + 6x + 10}{6x^2 - 7x - 20}.$

36. $\dfrac{10x - 11}{3x - 1} - \dfrac{5x + 9}{2x + 5} + \dfrac{x^2 - 3x + 5}{6x^2 + 13x - 5}.$

37. $\dfrac{2x - y}{3x - 2y} - \dfrac{x - 2y}{2y - 3x} + 2.$

38. $\dfrac{4x + 7y}{5x - 7y} - \dfrac{3x + 4y}{7y - 5x} - 3.$

39. $\dfrac{4x - 5y}{3x - y} + 3 + \dfrac{x + 7y}{y - 2x}.$

40. $\dfrac{7x + 2y}{3x - 5y} + \dfrac{2x - 3y}{5y - 3x} - 2.$

41. $\dfrac{5x - 3y}{2y - 3x} - \dfrac{3x + 5y}{3x - 2y}.$

42. $\dfrac{9x - 4y}{7x - y} - 5 + \dfrac{7x - 5y}{y - 7x}.$

43. $\dfrac{5}{x + y} - \dfrac{2x - 3y}{x^2 - xy + y^2} + 1.$

44. $\dfrac{7}{x - y} - \dfrac{4x + 2y}{x^2 + xy + y^2} + 1.$

45. $\dfrac{x + (2x - 3)}{x} - \dfrac{3x + 5}{2x - 7}.$

46. $\dfrac{2x - (x - 3)}{3x} - \dfrac{5x - 6}{5x}.$

47. $\dfrac{(2x - 3) - 4x}{5x} + \dfrac{3x - 2}{3x}.$

48. $\dfrac{(x + 5) - 3x}{3x} - \dfrac{2 - 3x}{2}.$

49. $\dfrac{(6x - 5) - 4x}{4x} - \dfrac{2x - 5}{3}.$

4-5. MULTIPLICATION AND DIVISION OF SIMPLE FRACTIONS

Rule 1. The product of two or more simple fractions is the product of the numerators divided by the product of the denominators.

Example 1.

$$(2) \quad \left(\frac{5}{3}\right)\left(\frac{1}{3}\right) = \left(\frac{2}{1}\right)\left(\frac{5}{3}\right)\left(\frac{1}{3}\right) = \frac{2 \cdot 5 \cdot 1}{1 \cdot 3 \cdot 3} = \frac{10}{9}.$$

Example 2.

$$(a) \quad \left(\frac{b}{c}\right)\left(\frac{d}{e}\right)\left(\frac{f}{g}\right) = \left(\frac{a}{1}\right)\left(\frac{b}{c}\right)\left(\frac{d}{e}\right)\left(\frac{f}{g}\right) = \frac{abdf}{ceg}.$$

Rule 2. To divide one fraction by another, multiply the first one by the reciprocal (or multiplicative inverse) of the second.

Example 1.

$$\frac{3}{5} \div \frac{4}{7} = \left(\frac{3}{5}\right)\left(\frac{7}{4}\right) = \frac{21}{20}.$$

Example 2.

$$\frac{x}{x - 1} \div \frac{x^2}{x^2 - 1} = \left(\frac{x}{x - 1}\right)\left(\frac{x^2 - 1}{x^2}\right) = \frac{x(x - 1)(x + 1)}{x^2(x - 1)}$$

$$= \frac{x + 1}{x}.$$

Note. As in the cases of addition and subtraction, the rules for multiplication and division of fractions are postulates which may be observed to be true in all arithmetic cases. For example, since $\frac{8a}{2a} = 4$, where a can be anything except zero, $\frac{8 \text{ thirds}}{2 \text{ thirds}} = 4$. By Rule 2, $\frac{8}{3} \div \frac{2}{3} = \left(\frac{8}{3}\right)\left(\frac{3}{2}\right) = 4$.

Also, $\quad \dfrac{a}{b} \div \dfrac{c}{d} = \dfrac{\dfrac{a}{b}}{\dfrac{c}{d}} = \dfrac{\dfrac{a}{b} \cdot bd}{\dfrac{c}{d} \cdot bd} = \dfrac{ad}{bc} = \left(\dfrac{a}{b}\right)\left(\dfrac{d}{c}\right).$

EXERCISE 4-4

Perform the indicated multiplications and leave answers in simplified form.

1. $(3)\left(\dfrac{15}{9}\right)$.

2. $(5)\left(\dfrac{14}{25}\right)$.

3. $(-2)\left(\dfrac{-4}{3}\right)$.

4. $\left(\dfrac{-12}{35}\right)\left(\dfrac{14}{15}\right)$.

5. $\left(\dfrac{-2}{3}\right)\left(\dfrac{9}{16}\right)\left(\dfrac{4}{15}\right)$.

6. $\left(\dfrac{3}{4}\right)\left(\dfrac{8}{21}\right)\left(\dfrac{-12}{16}\right)$.

7. $\left(\dfrac{-4}{5}\right)\left(\dfrac{-25}{24}\right)\left(\dfrac{9}{35}\right)$.

8. $(5)\left(\dfrac{3}{7}\right)\left(\dfrac{-21}{15}\right)$.

9. $\left(\dfrac{-7}{8}\right)\left(\dfrac{48}{84}\right)(-3)$.

10. $(-11)\left(\dfrac{57}{110}\right)\left(\dfrac{-15}{19}\right)$.

11. $(2x)\left(\dfrac{x-1}{x+2}\right)$.

12. $(-3x)\left(\dfrac{2x+3}{9x-6x}\right)$.

13. $\left(\dfrac{5x+2}{3x-1}\right)(3x-2)$.

14. $\left(\dfrac{3x-7}{2x+1}\right)(4x+2)$.

15. $\left(\dfrac{6x-5}{3x+2}\right)(6x+4)$.

16. $\left(\dfrac{15x-3}{5x-1}\right)(2x-3)$.

17. $\left(\dfrac{13x+3}{7x-1}\right)(21x-3)$.

18. $\left(\dfrac{17x-3}{15x-3}\right)(5x-1)(x)$.

19. $\left(\dfrac{13x-2}{21x-7}\right)(1-3x)(x)$.

20. $\left(\dfrac{15x-5}{1-3x}\right)(3x+1)(-3x)$.

21. $\left(\dfrac{7x-3}{2x^2-3x+1}\right)(1-x)(-3x)$.

22. $\left(\dfrac{6x+4}{6x^2+x-2}\right)(1-2x)(-5x)$.

23. $\left(\dfrac{6 - 10x}{5x^2 + 7x - 6}\right)(x + 2)(-x).$

24. $\left(\dfrac{12 - 8x}{6x^2 - 19x + 15}\right)(5 - 3x)\left(\dfrac{1}{4}\right).$

25. $\left(\dfrac{16 - 4x}{3x^2 - x - 14}\right)(7 - 3x)\left(\dfrac{3}{2}\right).$

26. $\left(\dfrac{6x^2 - 19x + 10}{2 - x - 3x^2}\right)\left(\dfrac{x + 1}{5 - 2x}\right)(3).$

27. $\left(\dfrac{3x^2 + x - 2}{6x^2 - 13x + 6}\right)\left(\dfrac{2 - 3x}{5 - x}\right)(15).$

28. $\left(\dfrac{3x - 1}{2x - 5}\right)\left(2 - \dfrac{5}{x}\right).$

29. $\left(\dfrac{3x - 2}{2x + 3}\right)\left(2 + \dfrac{3}{x}\right).$

30. $\left(\dfrac{2x - 5}{3x - 4}\right)\left(3 - \dfrac{4}{x}\right).$

31. $\left(\dfrac{5x - 7}{6x - 2}\right)\left(\dfrac{1}{x} - 3\right).$

32. $\left(\dfrac{4x + 3}{5x - 20}\right)\left(\dfrac{4}{x} - 1\right).$

33. $\left(\dfrac{3x - 2}{x + 3}\right)\left(\dfrac{2x - 3}{x - 3}\right).$

34. $\left(\dfrac{5x + 7}{x - 5}\right)\left(\dfrac{2x - 3}{x + 7}\right).$

35. $\left[\dfrac{x - (2x - 3)}{x}\right]\left(\dfrac{-x}{2 + 3x}\right).$

36. $\left[\dfrac{2x - (x + 3)}{2x}\right]\left(\dfrac{x^2 - 3x}{x^2 - 9}\right).$

EXERCISE 4-5

Perform the indicated divisions and leave answers in simplified form.

1. $\dfrac{2x - 3}{3x - 4} \div (2x - 3).$

2. $\dfrac{3x - 3}{5x + 3} \div (x - 1).$

3. $\dfrac{4x + 12}{7x + 10} \div (x + 3).$

4. $\dfrac{2x - 4}{2x + 3} \div (x - 2).$

5. $\dfrac{6x + 15}{3x + 5} \div (2x + 5).$

6. $\dfrac{x^2 - 4}{x^2 + 4} \div (2 - x).$

7. $\dfrac{x^2 - x - 2}{x^2 + x - 2} \div (x + 1).$

8. $\dfrac{2x^2 + 3x - 2}{2x^2 - x - 3} \div (x + 2).$

9. $\dfrac{12x^2 - 7x - 12}{12x^2 + 7x - 12} \div (3x - 1).$

10. $\dfrac{3x^2 + 2x - 1}{3x^2 - 2x - 1} \div (3x - 1).$

11. $(3x - 2) \div \dfrac{x - 2}{x + 3}.$

12. $(2x + 5) \div \dfrac{3x - 2}{x - 2}.$

13. $(5x - 3) \div \dfrac{x + 4}{2x - 5}.$

14. $(7x + 2) \div \dfrac{2 + 7x}{5 - 3x}.$

15. $(3x - 5) \div \dfrac{5 - 3x}{7x + 2}.$

16. $(6x + 5) \div \dfrac{6x^2 - x - 5}{6x^2 - 5x - 6}.$

17. $(3 + 2x) \div \dfrac{6x^2 + 5x - 6}{6x^2 - 11x - 2}.$

18. $\dfrac{(3x^2 + 2x - 1)}{6x^2 - 7x - 3} \div \dfrac{3x^2 - 4x + 1}{2x^2 - x - 3}.$

19. $(2x^2 + 3x - 2) \div \dfrac{2x^2 - x - 3}{3x^2 + 2x - 1}.$

20. $(12x^2 - 7x - 12) \div \dfrac{12x^2 + 25x + 12}{6x^2 - x - 12}.$

21. $\dfrac{y - 3}{(x - 2)^2} \div \dfrac{3 - y}{x - 2}.$

22. $\dfrac{2x - 5}{3y + 7} \div \dfrac{5 - 2x}{14 + 6y}.$

23. $x \div \dfrac{1}{x}.$

24. $(y + 1) \div \dfrac{2}{3y}.$

25. $(2x - 1) \div \dfrac{1}{2}.$

26. $(3x + 2) \div \dfrac{2}{3}.$

27. $(6x^2 - 9x + 3) \div \dfrac{3}{4}.$

28. $(5x^2 + 10x - 5) \div \dfrac{5}{7}.$

29 $= \dfrac{-(3x - 2)}{5x + 7} \div \dfrac{2 - 3x}{14 + 10x}.$

30. $\dfrac{x^2 - 3xy - 4y^2}{2x^2 + 3xy - 2y^2} \div \dfrac{-2y - x}{2x - y}.$

31. $\dfrac{1 - 9x^2}{x - 1} \div \dfrac{3x^2 + 2x - 1}{1 + 2x - 3x^2}.$

32. $\dfrac{y^2 - 2xy - 3x^2}{y^2 + 2xy - 3x^2} \div \dfrac{3x^2 + 5xy + 2y^2}{3x^2 + 4xy + y^2}.$

33. $\dfrac{2x^2 + xy - y^2}{2y^2 - 6xy + 4x^2} \div \dfrac{2x^2 + xy - y^2}{2x^2 - xy - y^2}.$

34. $\dfrac{6x^2 - 13xy + 6y^2}{xy - 3x + 2y - 6} \div \dfrac{3y^2 - 5xy + 2x^2}{6 - 2y + xy - 3x}.$

35. $\dfrac{2x^2 - 5xy + 2y^2}{2y^2 + 3xy - 2x^2} \div \dfrac{2y^2 - 3xy - 2x^2}{2x^2 - xy - y^2}.$

36. $\dfrac{xy - x - 2y + 2}{xy - 2x + y - 2} \div \dfrac{xy + x - 2y - 2}{xy + x + y + 1}.$

4-6. SIMPLIFICATION OF COMPLEX FRACTIONS

We have seen that a fraction is complex if either the numerator or the denominator contains a fraction. In this case we shall speak of the *minor denominators*. For example, in the complex fraction $\dfrac{1 + \dfrac{a}{2} + \dfrac{3}{b}}{\dfrac{1}{b} - \dfrac{1}{2}},$ the minor denominators are 2 and b.

To simplify a complex fraction we reduce it to a simple fraction in its lowest terms.

When neither the numerator A nor the denominator B of a complex fraction itself contains a complex fraction, there are two methods of simplifying $\frac{A}{B}$.

Method 1. Multiply both the numerator and the denominator by the L.C.M. of the minor denominators. (See Law 1, Sec. 4-2.)

Example 1.

$$\frac{1 + \frac{1}{2} + \frac{2}{3} - \frac{1}{12}}{\frac{5}{6} - \frac{2}{3} + 1} = \frac{\left(1 + \frac{1}{2} + \frac{2}{3} - \frac{1}{12}\right)12}{\left(\frac{5}{6} - \frac{2}{3} + 1\right)12} = \frac{12 + 6 + 8 - 1}{10 - 8 + 12} = \frac{25}{14} .$$

Example 2.

$$\frac{\frac{a}{2} - \frac{b}{x}}{\frac{c}{x^2} + \frac{1}{2}} = \frac{\left(\frac{a}{2} - \frac{b}{x}\right)2x^2}{\left(\frac{c}{x^2} + \frac{1}{2}\right)2x^2} = \frac{ax^2 - 2bx}{2c + x^2} .$$

Method 2. Reduce the numerator and likewise the denominator to a simple fraction, and then apply Rule 2, Sec. 4-5.

Example 1.

$$\frac{2 + \frac{1}{2} - \frac{1}{3}}{3 - \frac{1}{3}} = \frac{\frac{12}{6} + \frac{3}{6} - \frac{2}{6}}{\frac{9}{3} - \frac{1}{3}} = \frac{\frac{13}{6}}{\frac{8}{3}} = \left(\frac{13}{6}\right)\left(\frac{3}{8}\right) = \frac{13}{16} .$$

Example 2.

$$\frac{\frac{1}{x - 1} + 2}{1 + \frac{1}{1 - x^2}} = \frac{\frac{1}{x - 1} + \frac{2(x - 1)}{x - 1}}{\frac{1 - x^2}{1 - x^2} + \frac{1}{1 - x^2}} = \frac{\frac{2x - 1}{x - 1}}{\frac{2 - x^2}{1 - x^2}}$$

$$= \left(\frac{2x - 1}{x - 1}\right)\left(\frac{1 - x^2}{2 - x^2}\right) = \left(\frac{2x - 1}{x - 1}\right)\left(\frac{x^2 - 1}{x^2 - 2}\right)$$

$$= \frac{(2x - 1)(x + 1)}{x^2 - 2} .$$

In general, Method 1 is shorter and more efficient when the minor denominators are single terms; otherwise Method 2 is preferable.

When either the numerator or the denominator of a complex fraction is itself a complex fraction, the latter fraction must be simplified first. The same rule applies to the latter fraction, and so on.

   Example.

$$\cfrac{1}{1 + \cfrac{1}{1 + \cfrac{1}{1 + \cfrac{1}{x}}}} = \left\{ \cfrac{1}{1 + \left[\cfrac{1}{1 + \left(\cfrac{1}{1 + \cfrac{1}{x}} \right)} \right]} \right\}.$$

Here we simplify successively the fractions within parentheses, brackets, and braces, thus:

$$\left\{ \cfrac{1}{1 + \left[\cfrac{1}{1 + \cfrac{x}{x + 1}} \right]} \right\} = \left\{ \cfrac{1}{1 + \cfrac{x + 1}{2x + 1}} \right\} = \frac{2x + 1}{3x + 2}.$$

EXERCISE 4-6

Simplify the following fractions.

1. $\dfrac{\dfrac{1}{x}}{\dfrac{1}{y}}.$

2. $\dfrac{x + \dfrac{1}{y}}{x - \dfrac{1}{y}}.$

3. $\dfrac{1 - \dfrac{1}{x}}{1 + \dfrac{1}{x}}.$

4. $\dfrac{\dfrac{1}{x + y} + 1}{\dfrac{1}{x + y} - 1}.$

5. $\dfrac{\dfrac{1}{x - y} - 1}{\dfrac{1}{x + y} + 1}.$

6. $\dfrac{\dfrac{x}{x + y} - 1}{\dfrac{y}{x + y}}.$

7. $\dfrac{\dfrac{y}{y - x} - 1}{\dfrac{x}{y - x}}.$

8. $\dfrac{\dfrac{a}{x} - \dfrac{b}{y}}{\dfrac{bx - ay}{xy}}.$

9. $\dfrac{\dfrac{x}{y} - \dfrac{y}{x}}{\dfrac{1}{y} - \dfrac{1}{x}}.$

10. $\dfrac{\dfrac{1}{x} + \dfrac{1}{y}}{\dfrac{x}{y} + \dfrac{y}{x}}.$

11. $\dfrac{\dfrac{6x^2 - 13xy + 6y^2}{xy - 3x + 2y - 6}}{\dfrac{3y^2 - 5xy + 2x^2}{6 - 2y - 3x + xy}}.$

12. $\dfrac{\dfrac{2x^2 - 5xy + 2y^2}{2x^2 - 3xy - 2y^2}}{\dfrac{2y^2 - 3xy - 2x^2}{2x^2 - xy - y^2}}.$

13. $$\dfrac{\dfrac{2x^2 + xy - y^2}{2y^2 - 6xy + 4x^2}}{\dfrac{2y^2 + xy - x^2}{2x^2 - xy - y^2}}.$$

14. $$\dfrac{\dfrac{3x^2 + 2xy - y^2}{3x^2 - 2xy - y^2}}{\dfrac{4xy - 3x^2 - y^2}{4xy + 3x^2 + y^2}}.$$

15. $$\dfrac{\dfrac{2y^2 - xy - 3x^2}{2y^2 - 3xy + x^2}}{\dfrac{6x^2 + 5xy - 6y^2}{6x^2 - 11xy - 2y^2}}.$$

16. $$\dfrac{\dfrac{x^3 - y^3}{(x - y)^3}}{\dfrac{x^2 - y^2}{(x - y)^2}}.$$

17. $$\dfrac{\dfrac{-3(x - y)}{6(x - y)}}{\dfrac{5(x - y)^2}{3(x - y)^3}}.$$

18. $$\dfrac{1 - \dfrac{x + y}{x}}{1 - \dfrac{x - y}{x}}.$$

19. $$\dfrac{2 - 3\left(\dfrac{x - y}{y}\right)}{3 + 2\left(\dfrac{x + y}{y}\right)}.$$

20. $$\dfrac{3x - \dfrac{2 - y}{x}}{\dfrac{3y - x}{x} - x}.$$

21. $$\dfrac{\dfrac{2x - y}{y - x} - (x - y)}{\dfrac{2y - x}{x - y} - (y - x)}.$$

22. $$\dfrac{\dfrac{3}{x} - 4 + x}{\dfrac{12}{x} - 7 + x}.$$

23. $$\dfrac{\dfrac{6}{x} + x - 5}{1 - \dfrac{x + 2}{x^2}}.$$

24. $$\dfrac{\dfrac{-4}{x} - 1 + 6x}{2 - \dfrac{x + 1}{x^2}}.$$

25. $$\dfrac{2 - \dfrac{3x + 2}{x}}{2 - \dfrac{3x - 1}{x}}.$$

26. $$2 + \dfrac{3}{1 + \dfrac{1}{x}}.$$

27. $$1 - \dfrac{1}{1 - \dfrac{1}{x}}.$$

28. $$\dfrac{1}{2x - 1} - \dfrac{3}{1 + \dfrac{1}{x}}.$$

29. $$\dfrac{2}{2x + 1} + \dfrac{1}{2 - \dfrac{1}{x + 1}}.$$

30. $$\dfrac{1}{3x + x} - \dfrac{1}{3 - \dfrac{1}{x + 1}}.$$

REVIEW EXERCISES

Reduce the fractions in Probs. 1–6 to lowest terms.

1. $$\dfrac{4a^2 + 6ab - 4b^2}{a^2 - ab - 6b^2}.$$

2. $$\dfrac{9x^2 - 12xy + 4y^2}{27x^3 - 8y^3}.$$

3. $\dfrac{(x + 2y)^3 + z^3}{(x + 2y)^2 - z^2}.$

4. $\dfrac{3mn + 6kn + mc + 2kc}{3mn + 6kn - mc - 2kc}.$

5. $\dfrac{p^4 - q^4}{p^6 - q^6}.$

6. $\dfrac{(2x - y)^3 - 5(2x - y)}{4x^2 - y^2}.$

Carry out the indicated operations and express the answer to each as a simple fraction in lowest terms.

7. $\dfrac{3x - 1}{3} - \dfrac{5x + 2}{4} + \dfrac{x - 1}{8}.$

8. $\dfrac{3y + a}{4y} - \dfrac{2y - a}{3y} - \dfrac{4}{3}.$

9. $\dfrac{3x - y}{4y^2} + \dfrac{2xy - 1}{3xy} - \dfrac{2x + 1}{4x^2} - \dfrac{1}{2x}.$

10. $-\dfrac{a^2 + 5b^2}{a^3 - b^3} + \dfrac{a - b}{a^2 + ab + b^2} - \dfrac{3}{a - b}.$

11. $\dfrac{3x}{x^2 - y^2} + \dfrac{2x + 1}{(x - y)^2}.$

12. $\dfrac{a}{(a - b)(b - c)} - \dfrac{b}{(c - a)(b - a)} + \dfrac{c}{(b - c)(a - c)}.$

13. $\dfrac{3x - 5}{x - 3} - 2x - 1.$

14. $\dfrac{x + 1}{4x - 4} - \dfrac{x + 2}{3x + 3} + \dfrac{x}{2(x + 1)}.$

15. $\dfrac{4x - 3}{x - 2} - 2.$

16. $1 - \dfrac{x(x - y)}{1 - xy}.$

17. $\dfrac{ab - 3b^2}{3a - b} + a - 2b.$

18. $\dfrac{x^2 - y^2}{9z^2} \cdot \dfrac{18z}{(x - y)^3}.$

19. $\dfrac{a^2b^2 + 3ab}{9b^2 - 1} \cdot \dfrac{3b + 1}{ab + 3}.$

20. $\dfrac{x^2 + xy - 12y^2}{x^2 - xy - 6y^2} \cdot \dfrac{x^2 - 5xy - 14y^2}{x^2 + 11xy + 28y^2}.$

21. $\dfrac{x^3 - x^2 + 4x - 4}{2x^2 - x} \cdot \dfrac{2x^2 + x - 1}{x^2 + 4}.$

22. $\dfrac{a(a + 2b)}{a^4 + 4b^4} \cdot \dfrac{ab - 2b^2}{a^2 - 4b^2} \div \dfrac{1}{a^2 - 2ab + 2b^2}.$

23. $\left(\dfrac{a^3}{4} - 2\right)\left(1 + \dfrac{a}{2}\right).$

24. $\left(\dfrac{4x^2}{y^2} - 1\right)\left(\dfrac{y}{2x - y} + 1\right).$

25. $\left(\dfrac{3ab - b^2}{1 - 3ab} + 1\right)\left(3a - \dfrac{a^2 + ab}{1 - b}\right).$

26. $\left(x - 1 + \dfrac{2}{x + 1}\right)\left(x + 1 - \dfrac{3}{x - 1}\right).$

27. $\dfrac{\dfrac{3x}{1 - x} + 1}{\dfrac{2}{1 - x}}.$

28. $\dfrac{2 - \dfrac{3}{a - 1}}{\dfrac{3}{1 - a} - 1 + \dfrac{2}{a^2 - 1}}.$

29. $\dfrac{x + \dfrac{3}{y - x}}{-\dfrac{1}{x - y} + \dfrac{2}{(y - x)^2}}.$

30. $\dfrac{\dfrac{m - n}{m - p} - \dfrac{m - p}{m - n}}{\dfrac{1}{m - p} - \dfrac{1}{m - n}}.$

31. $\dfrac{\dfrac{x^2}{y^2} - 1}{\dfrac{x^2}{y^2} - \dfrac{2x}{y} + 1}.$

32. $\dfrac{\dfrac{1}{a - b}}{1 + \dfrac{ab + 2b^2}{a^2 - b^2}}.$

33. $3 - \dfrac{1}{2 - \dfrac{1}{a + b}}.$

34. $3 - \dfrac{1}{2 - \dfrac{1}{a} - \dfrac{1}{b}}.$

35. $\dfrac{2(x^2 - 4)(2x - 3) - 2x(2x - 3)^2}{(2x - 3)^2}.$

36. $\dfrac{3(a^2 + 4)(a^2 + 5) - (a^2 + 5)^2}{(a^2 + 4)^2}.$

37. $\left(-\dfrac{2}{x + 1} + \dfrac{3}{x + 2} - \dfrac{1}{x + 3}\right) \cdot \dfrac{(x + 3)^2(x + 1)}{(x + 2)}.$

38. $\dfrac{(u + 2)^2(-3u^2) - 2u(u + 2)}{(u + 2)^3}.$

39. $\dfrac{a - b}{(a - b)^2 - c^2} - \dfrac{a + b}{(a - c)^2 - b^2}.$

40. $\dfrac{(a - b)^2 - c^2}{a^2 - (b - c)^2} \cdot \dfrac{(a + b)^2 - c^2}{a^2 - (b + c)^2}.$

41. $\left[\dfrac{a^3 - b^3}{a^3} \cdot \dfrac{b^2 - a^2}{(b - a)^2}\right] \div \dfrac{a^2b + ab^2 + b^3}{a^2 + 2ab + b^2}.$

42. $\dfrac{a + b}{a - b} - \dfrac{a - b}{a + b} - \dfrac{a - 2b}{b^2 - a^2}.$

43. $\left(1 - \dfrac{m^2}{n^2}\right)\left(\dfrac{n}{m - n} - 1\right) - \left(1 - \dfrac{m^3}{n^3}\right)\left(1 - \dfrac{mn + n^2}{m^2 + mn + n^2}\right).$

44. $\left[\dfrac{(a + b)^2 - c^2}{a^2 + ab - ac} \cdot \dfrac{a^2 b^2 c^2}{a^2 + ab + ac}\right] \div \dfrac{a^2 c^2}{abc}.$

GENERAL REVIEW EXERCISES

Which of the following in (a) to (l) is true or false? If false, explain why.

1. (a) $\dfrac{a + 2(a - b)}{3(a - b)} = \dfrac{a + 2}{3}.$

(b) $\dfrac{x}{y} - 2a = x - 2ay.$

(c) $\dfrac{x}{y} + \dfrac{w}{z} = \dfrac{xz + yw}{yz}.$

(d) $\dfrac{r}{s} + \dfrac{a}{b} = \dfrac{r + a}{s + b}.$

(e) $\dfrac{(a - b)^2}{a^2 - b^2} = \dfrac{a - b}{a + b}.$

(f) $\dfrac{c}{d} \cdot \dfrac{d}{c} = 0.$

(g) $\dfrac{\frac{3}{1}}{\frac{1}{5}} = 15.$

(h) $5\left(\dfrac{c}{d}\right) = \dfrac{5c}{5d}.$

(i) $\dfrac{1}{3}\left(\dfrac{x + y}{2}\right) = \dfrac{x + y}{6}.$

(j) The factors $\dfrac{x^2}{y^2} - 4x^2 = (x - 2xy)(x + 2xy).$

(k) If $.03y = 6$, then $y = 200.$

(l) $\dfrac{.02a + .3}{.7x} = \dfrac{2a + 30}{70x}.$

2. Carry out indicated operations and leave answers in simplified form.

(a) $\dfrac{3}{y} + \dfrac{2}{y - 1}.$

(b) $\dfrac{5x}{2x + 1} - \dfrac{3x}{2x - 1}.$

(c) $\dfrac{5x}{x + 1} - \dfrac{2}{x^2 - 1}.$

(d) $\dfrac{3x}{x-1} - \dfrac{2}{x^2+1}.$

(e) $\dfrac{1}{3} - \dfrac{2}{x-4} + \dfrac{3x}{x-2}.$

(f) $2 - \dfrac{3}{x-3} + \dfrac{x}{x+3}.$

(g) $\dfrac{5x}{2x-1} - \dfrac{3x}{1-2x}.$

(h) $\dfrac{3}{9x^2-4} + \dfrac{2}{3x+2} - \dfrac{3x}{2-3x}.$

(i) $\dfrac{3}{x^3-8} + \dfrac{x}{x^2+2x+4} + \dfrac{1}{2-x}.$

3. Carry out the indicated operations and leave answers in simplified form.

(a) $\dfrac{3x}{x-2} \cdot \dfrac{x^2-4}{x^2}.$

(b) $\dfrac{3y+1}{2y-5} \cdot \dfrac{2y^2-5y}{3y^2-1}.$

(c) $\dfrac{9x-3}{2x^2} \cdot \dfrac{3x}{9x^2-1} \cdot \dfrac{3x+1}{9}.$

(d) $\dfrac{c^2-9d^2}{c+2d} \div \dfrac{c^2+6cd+9d^2}{c^2-cd-6d^2}.$

(e) $\left(\dfrac{a}{z} + \dfrac{z}{a}\right) \div \dfrac{a^2+z^2}{3az}.$

(f) $\left(\dfrac{1}{x^2} - \dfrac{1}{y^2}\right) \div \dfrac{(x+y)^2}{xy^2+x^2y}.$

(g) $\dfrac{x^3-z^3}{x+z} \cdot \dfrac{x^2-z^2}{x^2-2xz+z^2} \cdot \dfrac{5xz}{x^2+xz+z^2}.$

(h) $\dfrac{2x+y}{\dfrac{1}{2x} + \dfrac{1}{y}}.$

(i) $1 + \dfrac{1}{1 + \dfrac{1}{2 + \dfrac{1}{3}}}.$

(j) $\dfrac{\dfrac{x^2}{y^2} - \dfrac{y^2}{x^2}}{1 - \dfrac{x^4}{y^4}}.$

4. Supply the missing term in each of the following fractions.

(a) $\dfrac{2xy}{x - 3y} = \dfrac{?}{9xy - 3x^2}$.

(b) $\dfrac{bz + by}{z^2 - y^2} = \dfrac{?}{z - y}$.

(c) $\dfrac{5x - 2}{15x^2 - x - 2} = \dfrac{?}{1 + 3x}$.

(d) $\dfrac{2c - d}{4c^2 + 2cd + d^2} = \dfrac{?}{8c^3 - d^3}$.

5. Find each of the following products.

(a) $(3x - 1)(5x + 1)$.

(b) $(3z - 2y^2)(3z + 2y^2)$.

(c) $(5x - 2y)(3x + 2y)$.

(d) $(7x - 2)^2$.

(e) $(3x^2 + 2y^3)^2$.

(f) $(x + y + z)(x - y - z)$.

(g) $[(a - b) + c]^2$.

(h) $(98)(102)$.

(i) $(x + 2y)(x^2 - 2xy + 4y^2)$.

(j) $(1 - x)(x^2 + x + 1)$.

6. Factor completely.

(a) $49z^3 - 121z$.

(b) $64a^6 - 1$.

(c) $x^2 - x^4$.

(d) $c^3 - c^2d - 12cd^2$.

(e) $5m^2 - 2mn - 3n^2$.

(f) $(3a + b)^2 - 4z^2$.

(g) $2x^3 + 9x^2 - 8x - 15$.

(h) $75a^3c - 90a^2c^2 + 27ac^3$.

(i) $4x^2 - 4xy + y^2 - a^2$.

(j) $2s(c - d) + r(d - c)$.

7. Simplify.

(a) $(3a - 2b + c) + (5a - b - c) - [(2a - 3b) - 5(a + b)]$.

(b) $6x^2 - 4x(2x - 1) - 3x[-2x - (-3x - 1) - 10x]$.

8. Perform the indicated operations and simplify.

(a) $(4a^2b)(-3ab^3)$.

(b) $(-2a^2b)(-3b^2)^2(-2ab)$.

(c) $(x^2 + x^6) \div x^2$.

(d) $(9z^3 - 18z^2 + 8z) \div (-2z)$.

chapter **5**

Linear Equations in One Unknown

5-1. INTRODUCTION

In Chapters 2 to 4 we have dealt with the problem of converting a given algebraic expression to an equivalent expression which possessed a specified form. In this chapter the study under which two algebraic expressions are equal will be investigated. For example, we shall explore methods for finding the required replacement for x so that a mathematical expression such as $2x + 1 = 3$ becomes true. An expression or defining condition of this type is called an *equation*. The student should keep in mind that such equations are variable sentences (or open sentences), for which we endeavor to find under what conditions they are true—that is, we are searching for their solution sets, which will consist of those values of the open variable x that makes them true.

We shall borrow from Chapter 1 certain communication symbols and terms that were used with "sets." Terms such as "open sentence," "defining condition," and "equation" will be used interchangeably as convenience dictates. So will it be with the terms "variable," "open variable," and "unknown." "Replacement set" or "universal set" will be used to mean one and the same set. By using this nomenclature in different forms, the student will become acquainted with various ways of expressing himself in English.

5-2. MATHEMATICAL STATEMENTS INVOLVING ONE VARIABLE

As previously stated, an equation is an open sentence or defining condition which states that two expressions, at least one of which contains one or more variables, are designated as equal. For example,

(1) $$5x - 3 = x + 5$$

is an equation, and is a true statement when x is replaced by 2, where the universal set for x is the real number system. It is not a true statement when x is replaced by $-1, 0, 1$, or any number other than 2. The solution set here would be $\{2\}$. The original problem could have been stated in set notation as $\{x \in R_e \mid 5x - 3 = x + 5\}$, which in English reads "the set of all x belonging to the real number system such that $5x - 3 = x + 5$."

Certain other equations are true statements regardless of the number values that may be substituted for the variable. For example, the equation

(2) $$2x + x = 3x$$

that is,

$$\{x \in R_e \mid 2x + x = 3x\} = R_e$$

is such since it is true if x is replaced by any real number. Its solution set is the real-number system.

Still another possibility is that of an equation that produces a false statement for all replacement values chosen for the variable. For example,

(3) $$x + 1 = x + 3$$

is obviously false, since the sum of any given number and 1 cannot be equal to the sum of the same number and 3. In set notation this could be stated as $\{x \in R_e \mid x + 1 = x + 3\} = \phi$. The separate expressions appearing on either side of the equality sign are called the *members*, or *sides*, of the equation. If the equation produces a true statement after the open variable is replaced by a specific number chosen from a prescribed universal set, then that number is called a *root* or *solution* of that equation. It is said to satisfy the equation and becomes a listed element of the solution set. Accordingly, the set of all roots of a given equation is called the solution set of the equation.

The defining conditions specified by (1), namely $5x - 3 = x + 5$, and (3), namely $x + 1 = x + 3$, are called *conditional equations*, whereas (2), namely, $2x + x = 3x$, is called an *identical equation*, or *identity*. In summary: An open sentence (defining condition), in one or more variables such as $x, y, z, \ldots$, etc., involving an equality is called an *equation*. An equation which becomes a false statement for some or all of the elements of the universal set chosen as replacement values for $x, y, z, \ldots$, etc., is called a *conditional equation*. An equation which is a true statement for every element of the universal set chosen as replacement values for $x, y, z, \ldots$, etc., is called an *identity*. For example, if the replacement set (universal set) is R_e,

(4) $$\frac{1}{x - 1} - \frac{1}{x + 2} = \frac{3}{(x - 1)(x + 2)}$$

is not defined for $x = 1$ or $x = -2$. In this situation we consider equation (4) an identity for all values of $x \in R_e$ except when $x = 1$ or $x = -2$.

The solution set for a conditional equation is either the empty set or a set containing a finite integral number of elements.

The solution set for an identity is the set of all permissible real numbers that make the equation true. When it is desired to emphasize the fact that an equation is an identity, the equality sign may be replaced by the symbol $\equiv$, read "is identically equal to." Thus

$$x - 1 \equiv -(1 - x); \; x^2 - y^2 \equiv (x - y)(x + y).$$

The process of finding the solution set of an equation is called *solving the equation.*

The objective in solving an equation in a single variable (many times referred to as the unknown) is to find a replacement for same from a given or agreed universal set that satisfies it. In finding the solution sets of equations in general, we make use of two basic principles which follow as simple intuitive consequences from what we understand the equality sign to mean between algebraic expressions.

1. *The additive principle of equations* states that the addition (or subtraction) of an algebraic expression to both members (sides) of an equation will not affect the solution set of the original equation.

It should be noted that an expression such as $\dfrac{1}{x - 1}$ when added to both sides of an equation must take into account the fact that the new equation formed excludes a choice for $x = 1$.

2. *The multiplicative principle of equations* states that the multiplication (or division) of both members of an equation by a nonzero algebraic expression* will not affect the solution set of the original equation.

In other words, the equation resulting when either or both of these principles are applied is *equivalent to the original equation.* To reiterate, the original equation and the new equation will have the same solution set. We will now illustrate these principles by example.

Example.
Solve the equation $3x - 4 = x + 8$.

Solution. The problem here is to produce a listing of the elements for the set

$$f = \{x \in R_e \mid 3x - 4 = x + 8\}.$$

In reality, f is a form of the solution set in implicit form. We desire a more explicit form of f by a roster or listing representation for x. To find these elements, we have at our command only the additive and the multiplicative principles to use as tools. By using these principles, the original description of f would be converted to the equivalent form

*For example, if the algebraic expression used is $(x - 1)(x - 2)$, then it is a nonzero algebraic expression for all values of x except $x = 1$ or $x = 2$.

$$f = \{x \in R_e \mid x = \cdots\}$$
$$= \{\text{listing of precise } x\text{'s}\}.$$

The computation can be arranged in the following manner:

$3x - 4 = x + 8$	Original equation
$3x - 4 + 4 = x + 8 + 4$	Add 4 to both members
$3x = x + 12$	
$3x + (-x) = x + 12 + (-x)$	Add $-x$ to both members
$2x = 12$	
$\frac{1}{2}(2x) = \frac{1}{2}(12)$	Multiply both sides by $\frac{1}{2}$
$x = 6$	

Hence the solution set is

$$f = \{x \in R_e \mid x = 6\} = \{6\}.$$

To test an element of the solution set of an equation, we substitute it for the *open variable* in the *original equation*. If this substitution produces a true statement, then this element is a root; if not, the element is not a root unless an error has been committed either in the checking procedure or in the mathematics.

In the example above, the number 6 satisfies the equation $3x - 4 = x + 8$, since the replacement of x by 6 resulted in the true statement $14 = 14$.

5-3. INTEGRAL RATIONAL EQUATIONS

An integral rational equation is one in which two integral rational polynomials in the unknowns (or open variables) are equated. Thus the unknowns appear either without exponents (since the exponent 1 is usually omitted) or with the exponents 2, 3, etc.

Example 1.

$$3x - 4 = 5x.$$

Here the unknown (or open variable) is x, and the value sought for it is -2, as may be verified by trial.

Example 2.

$$ay - by = c.$$

Here the unknown is y, which stands for the expression $\dfrac{c}{a - b}$, $a \neq b$, since this value substituted for y produces a true statement. Examples 1 and 2 could have been expressed in set notation as

$$f = \{(x \in R_e \mid 3x - 4 = 5x\} = \{-2\}$$

and

$$g = \{(y \in R_e | ay - by = c\} = \left\{\frac{c}{a - b} \quad \text{where } a \neq b\right\},$$

respectively.

As we shall see, many practical problems lead to integral rational equations.

5-4. LINEAR EQUATIONS OR LINEAR DEFINING CONDITIONS

An integral rational equation in which the unknowns appear to the first degree in each term containing them is called a first degree, or linear* equation.

Example 1.

$$3x - 7 = 4. \qquad \text{(Linear in } x\text{)}$$

Example 2.

$$5a^2y - 7b^2y = c. \qquad \text{(Linear in } y\text{)}$$

Example 3.

$$5x + 2y = 4. \qquad \text{(Linear in } x \text{ and } y\text{)}$$

It should be noted that in the equation of Example 3, we may regard $5x + 2y = 4$ as being linear in x alone or in y alone when such consideration is necessary.

Hereafter in this chapter we shall consider only linear equations in one unknown (say x), which are standardized to the form $ax + b = 0$, $a \neq 0$. The solution set for such a linear equation is the set

$$f = \{x \in R_e | ax + b = 0, a \neq 0\} = \{-\frac{b}{a}\},$$

which is discussed in Sec. 5-5.

5-5. SOLVING A LINEAR EQUATION IN ONE UNKNOWN

An equation is solved by finding a succession of equivalent equations, the last one of which exposes the root of all of them. The problem here is to find the solution set of the linear equation

$$ax + b = 0, a \neq 0.$$

Addition of the quantity $(-b)$ to both members gives

$$ax = -b.$$

*We shall see that a first degree equation in not more than two variables may be represented graphically by a straight line in a rectangular system of coordinates—hence the adjective "linear."

Since $a \neq 0$, multiplication of both members by the constant $\dfrac{1}{a}$ gives

$$x = -\frac{b}{a}.$$

Hence the solution set of any linear equation of the form $ax + b = 0$, $a \neq 0$ is the set

$$f = \left\{ -\frac{b}{a} \right\}.$$

It can be proved that every linear equation of the form $ax + b = 0$, $a \neq 0$, a and b constant, has one and only one root, namely the root $-\dfrac{b}{a}$.

The simple rule that a term may be transposed from one side of the equation to the other side by changing its sign may be used in practice in place of the addition principle, but the reason for the rule should be understood. The student should be aware that he is actually forming a new equation from the original one and that addition (or subtraction) was performed to both members of the original equation.   When the term "transpose" or "transposition" is used in this text, it shall mean just this.

The essential process in solving any linear equation may be described as follows:

Step 1.   Simplify all complex fractions involved.

Step 2.   Remove parentheses, carrying out indicated multiplications.

Step 3.   Clear the equation of fractions by multiplying both members by the L.C.M. of the denominators.

Step 4.   Transpose the terms containing the unknown variables to the left side of the equality sign, and all other terms to the right side.

Step 5.   Factor the left member, expressing it as the product of the unknown variable by a second factor. This latter factor is called the *coefficient of the unknown.*

Step 6.   Divide both members of the equation by the coefficient of the unknown, which must be different from zero.

Example: Solve the equation

$$\frac{3\left(\dfrac{x}{2} + 3\right)}{\dfrac{1}{2} + 2} = \frac{6x}{7} + 4.$$

The problem here is to list the elements in the set

$$f = \left\{ x \in R_e \;\middle|\; \frac{3\left(\dfrac{x}{2} + 3\right)}{\dfrac{1}{2} + 2} = \frac{6x}{7} + 4 \right\}.$$

If the above steps are applied to this equation the following equivalent equations are obtained in succession:

$$\frac{3(x+6)}{1+4} = \frac{6x}{7} + 4$$

$$\frac{3x+18}{5} = \frac{6x}{7} + 4$$

$$21x + 126 = 30x + 140|$$

$$21x - 30x = 140 - 126$$

$$(-9)x = 14$$

$$x = \frac{14}{(-9)} = -\frac{14}{9}$$

Thus the solution set is $f = \left\{ x \in R_e \mid x = -\frac{14}{9} \right\} = \left\{ -\frac{14}{9} \right\}$.

To check $x = -\frac{14}{9}$ as a root, we substitute this value for x in the left member of the original equation and obtain

$$\frac{3\left(\frac{x}{2}+3\right)}{\frac{1}{2}+2} = \frac{3\left(-\frac{7}{9}+3\right)}{\frac{1}{2}+2} = \frac{\left(-\frac{7}{3}+9\right)(6)}{\left(\frac{5}{2}\right)(6)}$$

$$= \frac{-14+54}{15} = \frac{40}{15} = \frac{8}{3}$$

We now substitute $x = -\frac{14}{9}$ into the right-hand member of the equation and obtain

$$\frac{6x}{7} + 4 = \left(\frac{\overset{2}{\cancel{6}}}{\cancel{7}}\right)\left(-\frac{\overset{(-2)}{\cancel{14}}}{\underset{3}{\cancel{9}}}\right) + 4 = -\frac{4}{3} + 4 = \frac{8}{3}$$

Since the left- and right-hand members agree, it follows that $x = -\frac{14}{9}$

is a root or an element in the solution set.

As a suggestion to the student, it is wise to check each side of the equation separately for substituted values and then compare results, rather than work both sides of the equation at the same time.

The student can easily avoid blunders which are often made if he will keep in mind the following simple rule:

> *Whatever is done to the left member must be done to the right member.*

For example, if $2x = 5$, we would be wrong in concluding that $x = 5 - 2 = 3$, because no rule exists that permits division of the left member by 2 and subtraction of 2 from the right member, as is done in this in-correct "solution."

EXERCISE 5-1

Remove all signs of aggregation according to the rules, multiplying factors as indicated, and then determine which of the following equations are identities and which are conditional equations. It is noted here that each of Probs. 1–34 can be stated in set notation. For example, Prob. 13 can be stated as

$$f = \left\{ x \in R_e \left| \frac{\frac{x}{2} - \frac{x}{3}}{\frac{1}{2} - \frac{3}{4}} = \frac{1}{4} \right. \right\} .$$

Find the solution sets for each of the following. For practice write the original problems in set notation and check as directed by instructor.

1. $3x = 15$.
2. $5x + 20 = 0$.
3. $x(x - 1) = x^2 - x$.
4. $7x - 10 = x + 2$.
5. $2x^2 - 3x = x(2x - 3)$.
6. $4x - 3 = 5x - 5$.
7. $(x - 1)^2 = x^2 - 2x + 1$.
8. $3 - 2x = 7 + 2x$.
9. $5x^2 + 3x - 1 = x(5x + 3) - 1$.
10. $1 - 3x = 5x + 4$.
11. $x + 2 + 3x - 1 = 4x + 1$.
12. $3 + 4x = 6x - 7$.
13. $\dfrac{\dfrac{x}{2} - \dfrac{x}{3}}{\dfrac{1}{2} - \dfrac{3}{4}} = \dfrac{1}{4}$.
14. $\dfrac{2x - \dfrac{3}{4}}{2} = 2 + \dfrac{3x}{4}$.
15. $x - \dfrac{2x - \dfrac{1}{3}}{4} = 5$.
16. $3x - 10 = 10 - 3x$.
17. $1.5x - .7x = .6x + .7$.
18. $.5x + .07 = .8 + .06x$.
19. $3x + (5 - 2x) = 4x - 5$.

20. $7 - (5x + 3) + 6x = 10 - (3x + 5)$.
21. $8x - (3 + 4x) + 5 = 7x - (3 + x)$.
22. $(9 - 7x) + (3 + x) = (15 - 8x) + 4$.
23. $10x + 5 - (3x - 4) = 4x - 3$.
24. $-2(5x - 7) + (3x + 2) = 4x - 2(3 + x)$.
25. $5(2 + x) - [3(7 - 3x) - 3] = 7x + 5$.
26. $5(2 + x) - [3(x - 7) + 4(2x - 3)] = x$.
27. $8(2 - x) - 5(3 + x) = -[2(x - 1) + 3x]$.
28. $7(x - 3) - 2(3 + x) = 5[(1 - 3x) - 4]$.

29. $x - 2 - \dfrac{3x - 2}{2} = \dfrac{1}{2} + x$.   30. $\dfrac{x + 2}{2} - \dfrac{3x - 2}{2} = \dfrac{x}{2} + 1$.

31. $\dfrac{2x - 3}{3} - \dfrac{3x - 2}{3} = \dfrac{2x + 2}{\frac{3}{4} - 2}$.   32. $4 - 3x + \dfrac{2x - 3}{5} = \dfrac{4x + 5}{2}$.

33. $\dfrac{\dfrac{3x - 2}{4} - \dfrac{2x - 3}{4}}{2} = \dfrac{\dfrac{3x + 5}{4}}{6}$.   34. $\dfrac{2(2x - 5)}{3} - \dfrac{\dfrac{6x + 5}{2}}{3} = \dfrac{4x - 7}{6}$.

35. What number added to 3 is twice as much as the number minus 1?

36. If when 1 is subtracted from 3 times a certain number, the result is 5 more than the original number, what is that number?

37. If a number is multiplied by 5, the product is 2 less than twice the sum of the number and 7. Find the number.

38. One child is twice as old as another. Two years ago he was 3 times as old. Find their ages.

39. Fred has 3 times as many marbles as Bob. If he gives Bob one he will have twice as many. How many has each?

40. The quotient obtained by dividing a certain number by 3 is 5 less than twice the number. Find the number.

41. A man invested one sum at 6 percent and double that sum at 5 percent, receiving $80 interest in one year. How much was invested at each rate?

42. An airplane traveling 200 mph starts at noon after a transport which left at 10 a.m. and travels 150 mph. When will the plane overtake the transport?

5-6.   OPERATIONS WHICH YIELD EQUIVALENT EQUATIONS

When terms are transposed in an equation, or when both members are multiplied or divided by the same number, excluding zero, the resulting equation is equivalent to the first one. All of the operations required in Exercise 5-1 were of this nature.

5-7. OPERATIONS WHICH MAY NOT YIELD EQUIVALENT EQUATIONS

Multiplication of both members of an equation by zero yields the identity $0 = 0$. While this of course is true, it is not equivalent to the first equation. Division of both members by zero is not allowable, as we have seen.

Again, when we multiply both members of an equation by an expression containing the unknown, the new equation may have roots not satisfying the first one. These roots are called *extraneous*.

Example 1. The equation $x - 2 = 0$ has the root 2. If both members of the equation are multiplied by $x - 3$, the equation $(x - 2)(x - 3) = 0$ is obtained. This equation has the roots 2 and 3. However, the root 3 does not satisfy the original equation and hence is extraneous.

Example 2. Consider the equation

$$\frac{1}{(x - 1)(x - 2)} = \frac{2}{x - 2} - \frac{1}{x - 1}.$$

Multiplying both members by $(x - 1)(x - 2)$ to clear fractions, we obtain $1 = 2(x - 1) - (x - 2)$, or $x = 1$. This has the root 1. But 1 does not satisfy the first equation, since it calls for the nonpermissible division by zero. Hence 1 is extraneous, and the given equation has no root. The solution set here is the empty set ϕ.

Finally, if we divide both members by an expression containing the unknown, we usually lose one or more roots of the original equation.

Example 3. The equation $x(x - 1) = 3(x - 1)$ is satisfied by $x = 1$ or $x = 3$, as may be verified by substitution. Dividing both members by $x - 1$, we obtain $x = 3$, the root 1 being lost.

Summing up, we find that *when the members of an equation are multiplied or divided by an expression containing the unknown, the resulting equation may or may not be equivalent to the first one.*

When operations of this sort are necessary in solving equations, as in Example 2 above, the solution is not complete until the roots found have been tested in the original equation, and the extraneous roots have been rejected.

EXERCISE 5-2

The following equations may be reduced to linear ones and then solved. Where extraneous roots may have been introduced the answers must be tested. Each of these problems can be stated in set notation. For Prob. 11 the notation would be $\left\{ x \in R_e \left| \frac{3}{x} - \frac{x - 2}{x - 3} = \frac{4 - x}{x - 3} \right. \right\}$. It is suggested that the student write several of these in set notation as directed by the instructor.

1. $\dfrac{1}{x-1} + \dfrac{2}{x+1} = \dfrac{3}{x-1}.$

2. $\dfrac{3}{x-2} + \dfrac{1}{x+2} = \dfrac{8}{x^2-4}.$

3. $\dfrac{3}{x-3} - \dfrac{1}{x+2} = \dfrac{5}{x^2-x-6}.$

4. $\dfrac{4}{x+2} - \dfrac{3}{x+3} = \dfrac{8}{x^2+5x+6}.$

5. $\dfrac{3}{x+3} + \dfrac{4}{x-4} = \dfrac{28}{x^2-x-12}.$

6. $\dfrac{2x-1}{3x+2} = \dfrac{1}{2}.$

7. $\dfrac{5x+3}{2x-1} = \dfrac{1}{3}.$

8. $\dfrac{3-2x}{5-4x} = \dfrac{2}{3}.$

9. $\dfrac{3x+5}{6x-7} = \dfrac{3}{4}.$

10. $\dfrac{5-4x}{2-3x} = \dfrac{5}{4}.$

11. $\dfrac{3}{x} - \dfrac{x-2}{x-3} = \dfrac{4-x}{x-3}.$

12. $\dfrac{2}{x} - \dfrac{3x+2}{x+1} = \dfrac{2-3x}{x+1}.$

13. $\dfrac{2}{x} + \dfrac{x+3}{x-2} = \dfrac{x+5}{x-2}.$

14. $\dfrac{3x-5}{3x-2} = \dfrac{x+7}{x+3}.$

15. $\dfrac{3x-4}{3x+1} = \dfrac{2x+5}{2x-1}.$

16. $\dfrac{5x+3}{2x-1} = \dfrac{4+5x}{2x-3}.$

17. $\dfrac{4x+1}{2x+3} = \dfrac{2x-1}{x+2}.$

18. $\dfrac{6x+5}{2x+7} = \dfrac{3x-6}{x+3}.$

19. $\dfrac{3-x}{x-4} = \dfrac{2}{x} - \dfrac{5+x}{x-4}.$

20. $\dfrac{2x-5}{x+2} = \dfrac{7}{x} + \dfrac{2x+3}{x+2}.$

21. $\dfrac{x-1}{2} - \dfrac{x+2}{2} + \dfrac{3x-1}{2} = -\dfrac{1}{2}.$

22. $\dfrac{3x+2}{5} - \dfrac{x-3}{5} + \dfrac{2}{5} = \dfrac{4x+9}{5}.$

23. $\dfrac{2x-5}{3} + \dfrac{4}{3} - \dfrac{x+3}{3} = -\dfrac{x}{3}.$

24. $\dfrac{4x-3}{6} - \dfrac{5}{6} - \dfrac{6x-3}{6} = -2x.$

25. $\dfrac{3x+1}{7} + \dfrac{5}{7} - \dfrac{6x-2}{7} = 3x+1.$

26. $\dfrac{2}{x-3} - \dfrac{3}{x+3} = \dfrac{5}{x^2-9}.$

27. $\dfrac{3x+1}{x+2} - \dfrac{2x-1}{x-3} = \dfrac{x^2+7}{x^2-x-6}.$

28. $\dfrac{3}{x-5} + \dfrac{2}{x+3} = \dfrac{5-x}{x^2-2x-15}.$

29. $\dfrac{5}{x+5} - \dfrac{4}{x+1} = \dfrac{3x+10}{x^2+6x+5}.$

30. $\dfrac{4}{2x-3} - \dfrac{5}{3x-2} = \dfrac{5x-7}{6x^2-13x+6}.$

31. $\dfrac{1}{3x - 2} + \dfrac{2}{4x - 1} = \dfrac{5x - 7}{12x^2 - 11x + 2}.$

32. $\dfrac{3}{5x + 1} - \dfrac{2}{x - 1} = \dfrac{5x - 7}{5x^2 - 4x - 1}.$

33. $\dfrac{2}{3x + 1} - \dfrac{4}{2x - 1} + \dfrac{10}{6x^2 - x - 1} = 0.$

5-8. LITERAL COEFFICIENTS

If P is the perimeter of a rectangle of length l and width w, the relation between P, l, and w is evidently expressed by the formula:

(1) $$P = 2l + 2w.$$

Solving (1) for l, we have

(2) $$-2l = 2w - P; \quad 2l = P - 2w; \quad l = \frac{P - 2w}{2}.$$

Similarly,

(3) $$w = \frac{P - 2l}{2}.$$

Results (1), (2), and (3) are different versions of the same equation, solved respectively for P, l, and w in terms of the remaining letters. In such equations any one of the letters may be considered as the unknown. Thus if the perimeters and widths of many different rectangles were given, and we were asked to get the various lengths, the most efficient way would be to use (2) as a formula. If $P = 100$ and $w = 6$, $l = \dfrac{100 - 2 \cdot 6}{2} = 44$; if $P = 90$ and $w = 10$, $l = \dfrac{90 - 2 \cdot 10}{2} = 35$, etc. Similarly (1) and (3) are formulas for P and w respectively.

Whenever an equation contains other letters than the unknown, those letters will usually appear in the root of the equation. For example, given

(4) $$ax + b = 0, a \neq 0,$$

the root is evidently $-\dfrac{b}{a}$.

Such equations are said to have *literal* coefficients. It should be understood that the coefficients in an equation include not only multipliers of the unknown, as a in (4), but also the terms, such as b in (4), which do not contain the unknown.

Any linear equation in the unknown x may be represented by (4) as was pointed out in Sec. 5-5. For example, in

(5) $$2cx - 3y = 0,$$

the a of (4) stands for $2c$, and the b for $-3y$. Since the root of (4) is $-\dfrac{b}{a}$, which represents a single number for any given set of values for the literal coefficients, we can conclude that:

A linear equation has exactly one root.

Clearly an equation with literal coefficients represents infinitely many particular equations with numerical coefficients. Special cases of (4), for example, are $3x + 2 = 0$, $5x - 17 = 0$, etc. An equation like (4) is said to be more *general* than the ones with numerical coefficients. In algebra, and in fact in all mathematics, it is often desirable to have problems and solutions as general as possible, thus covering many cases in a single operation.

In solving an equation with literal coefficients, the steps of Sec. 5-5 may still be used.

Example 1. Solve

(6)
$$\frac{\frac{ax}{2}}{b} - \frac{c}{3d} + x + 1 = 2.$$

Solution.

Step 1.
$$\frac{ax}{2b} - \frac{c}{3d} + x + 1 = 2.$$

Step 2. Not needed in this case.

Step 3.
$$\left(\frac{ax}{2b} - \frac{c}{3d} + x + 1\right) 6bd = 2\,(6bd),$$

or
$$3axd - 2bc + 6bdx + 6bd = 12bd.$$

Step 4.
$$3axd + 6bdx = 2bc - 6bd + 12bd.$$

Step 5.
$$x\,(3ad + 6bd) = 2bc + 6bd.$$

Step 6.
$$x = \frac{2bc + 6bd}{3ad + 6bd}, \quad \text{or} \quad \frac{2b\,(c + 3d)}{3d\,(a + 2b)}.$$

A complete check, of course, would require the substitution of the literal root in the original equation. By way of a brief and practical partial check, however, we may substitute specific numbers for a, b, c, and d. For instance, if $a = b = c = d = 1$, then (6) becomes $\dfrac{x}{2} - \dfrac{1}{3} + x + 1 = 2$, with the root $\frac{8}{9}$. Also $\frac{2bc + 6bd}{3ad + 6bd}$ becomes $\frac{8}{9}$. Or let $a = c = 0$.

Then $x + 1 = 2$ or $x = 1$, while the root being tested becomes $\frac{6bd}{6bd} = 1$.

The partial check which is shortest, when permissible, is to replace all letters except the unknown by zero. Why not set $a = b = c = d = 0$ in the case above?

EXERCISE 5-3

Solve the following equations with literal coefficients. The unknown to be solved for is in each case either x, y, z, u, v, or w.

1. $\dfrac{3x - a}{b} = 3 + \dfrac{cx}{2}$.

2. $\dfrac{\left(2a + \dfrac{c}{2}\right)x}{d} - \dfrac{3b}{5} - 2x = 0$.

3. $cy - d = a - cy$.

4. $cw - bd = bc - dw$.

5. $ac - dv = cv - ad$.

6. $au - bd = bu - ad$.

7. $ac - bx = bc - ax$.

8. $cy - ad = \dfrac{bc - dy}{m + n}$.

9. $\dfrac{u + n}{a - b} = \dfrac{u - n}{a + b}$.

10. $\dfrac{m + v}{a - b} = \dfrac{m - v}{a + b}$.

11. $\dfrac{m + n}{w - b} = \dfrac{m - n}{w + b}$.

12. $\dfrac{m + n}{a - x} = \dfrac{m - n}{a + x}$.

13. $\dfrac{2r - n}{y + 2b} = \dfrac{r + 2n}{y - 2b}$.

14. $\dfrac{2r - n}{a + 2z} = \dfrac{r + 2n}{a - 2z}$.

15. $\dfrac{2u - n}{a + 2b} = \dfrac{u + 2n}{a - 2b}$.

16. $\dfrac{2r - v}{a + 2b} = \dfrac{r + 2v}{a - 2b}$.

17. $\dfrac{w - 2r}{2m - 3n} = 2rw$.

18. $\dfrac{2m - 3x}{2m + 3x} = m + n$.

19. $y = \dfrac{2y - 3a}{b}$.

20. $\dfrac{z - 2r}{a - 2b} = az$.

Solve each of the following formulas for the letters indicated.

21. $l = a + (n - 1)d$, for a; for n; for d.

22. $E = I\left(R + \dfrac{r}{n}\right)$, for r; for R; for n.

23. $\dfrac{1}{f} = \dfrac{1}{p} + \dfrac{1}{q}$, for q; for p; for f.

24. $\dfrac{1}{R} = \dfrac{1}{R_1} + \dfrac{1}{R_2}$, for R_1; for R_2; for R.

25. $P = A(1 - dt)$, for d; for A; for t.

26. $\dfrac{a}{v} = \dfrac{m}{M + m}$, for m;   for M;   for v.

27. $S = \dfrac{rl - a}{r - 1}$, for l;   for a;   for r.

28. $F = \dfrac{KmM}{d^2}$, for m;   for M.

29. $v = v_0 + gt$, for t;   for v_0;   for g.

30. $s = \dfrac{1}{2} at^2$, for a.

31. $A = \dfrac{1}{2} h(a + b)$, for h;   for b.

32. $V = r^2(a - b)$;   for a.

33. $\dfrac{W - W_1}{W - W_2} = a$, for W;   for W_2.

34. One boy is $2a$ years old and a second boy is $2b$ years old. What is their average age?

35. One child is a years old, and a second one is $2b$ years older than the first. What is their average age?

36. Henry had a marbles. After buying 10 more he had half as many as John. How many had John?

37. A boy who had x dimes in his pocket found half a dollar and then gave half of the money he had with him to his mother. What was the value of her share in cents?

38. A man who owed a dollars paid x dollars on the debt and then owed $\dfrac{1}{3}$ of the original amount. Find x.

39. In making a trip a man averaged a miles per hour going and b miles per hour on his return. If he was c hours on the road, how far from home did he go?

40. How many pounds of cream testing x percent butter fat must be added to y pounds of milk testing z percent butter fat to give milk testing w percent butter fat?

41. If oranges cost c cents per dozen, how many oranges can one buy for a dollars?

EXERCISE 5-4

Solve the following stated problems involving fractions.

1. If a certain number is divided by 4 the Quotient is 3 and the remainder is 3. Find the number. *Note.* In this and succeeding problems we use the relation (Sec. 2-11)

$$\frac{\text{dividend}}{\text{divisor}} = \text{Quotient} + \frac{\text{remainder}}{\text{divisor}}.$$

Observe the distinction here made between "Quotient" and "quotient." For example, the Quotient of 13 divided by 4 is 3, while the quotient, or total result of the division, is $3\frac{1}{4}$.

2. What number is divided by 7 if the Quotient is 3 and the remainder is 2?

3. If 2 is added to a certain number and this sum is divided by 3 the Quotient is 4 and the remainder is 2. Find the number.

4. One number is 3 more than another. If the first one is divided by the second the quotient is $\frac{3}{2}$. Find the numbers.

5. One number is 2 less than another. If the first one is divided by the second the quotient is $\frac{2}{3}$. Find the numbers.

6. The difference between two numbers is 3. If the larger is divided by the smaller the quotient is $\frac{4}{3}$. Find the numbers.

7. If x is added to both the numerator and denominator of $\frac{1}{5}$, the new fraction formed equals $\frac{1}{2}$. Find the value of x.

8. Find the number which must be added to both the numerator and denominator of $\frac{1}{3}$ to make the new fraction equal to $\frac{3}{4}$.

9. What number must be subtracted from both the numerator and denominator of $\frac{15}{17}$ to yield the fraction $\frac{3}{5}$?

10. If a certain number is added to the numerator and subtracted from the denominator of $\frac{1}{8}$, the new fraction equals $\frac{4}{5}$. Find the number.

11. The numerator of a fraction is 2 less than the denominator. If 1 is added to both numerator and denominator, the resulting fraction is $\frac{2}{3}$. Find the original fraction.

12. The denominator of a fraction is 2 more than the numerator. If 11 is added to both numerator and denominator, the new fraction can be reduced to $\frac{14}{15}$. Find the original fraction.

13. The denominator of a fraction is 1 more than 3 times the numerator. If 3 is added to both numerator and denominator, the new fraction equals $\frac{1}{2}$. Find the original fraction.

5-9. GEOMETRIC PROBLEMS

Many problems that are geometric in character occur in one's normal experience. They vary widely and include lengths, areas, volumes, relative sizes of angles, etc.

Example 1.   A 5-foot string is cut into two pieces, one of which is $\frac{4}{5}$ of the other. Find the length of each piece.

Solution.   Let

$$x = \text{number of feet in the longer piece}$$

Then

$$\frac{4x}{5} = \text{number of feet in the shorter piece}$$

$$x + \frac{4x}{5} = 5,$$

since the sum of the parts of anything equals the whole of it. Solving, we have

$$x = \frac{25}{9}, \text{ the number of feet in the greater length}$$

$$\frac{4x}{5} = \frac{20}{9}, \text{ the number of feet in the smaller length.}$$

Example 2.   Two rectangles have the same width. One is 2 inches longer than the other and 5 inches longer than its width. If the difference in their areas is 10 square inches, find the dimensions of each.

Solution.   Let

$$x = \text{number of inches in width of each rectangle}$$
$$x + 5 = \text{number of inches in length of the longer rectangle}$$
$$x + 3 = \text{number of inches in length of the shorter rectangle}$$
$$x(x + 5) - x(x + 3) = 10.$$

Solving, we have

$$x = 5; \quad x + 5 = 10; \quad x + 3 = 8.$$

Hence the rectangles are 10 by 5 and 8 by 5 inches respectively.

Note.   The area of a circle of radius r is πr^2 square units. The volume of a right circular cylinder of radius r and height h is $\pi r^2 h$ cubic units.

Example 3.   Each of two right circular cylinders has an altitude of 10 inches. The radius of the base of the larger is two inches greater than that of the other. The difference in their volumes is 80π cubic inches. Find the radius of the base of each cylinder.

Solution.   Let

$$x = \text{number of inches in the radius}$$
$$\text{of base of smaller cylinder}$$

$$x + 2 = \text{number of inches in the radius}$$
$$\text{of base of larger cylinder}$$

$$10\pi x^2 = \text{number of cubic inches in the volume of the smaller cylinder}$$

$$10\pi(x + 2)^2 = \text{number of cubic inches in the volume of the larger cylinder}$$

Then

$$10\pi(x + 2)^2 - 10\pi x^2 = 80\pi.$$

Solving, we find that $x = 1$ and $x + 2 = 3$.

Example 4. The first angle of a triangle is equal to $\frac{1}{3}$ of the second angle and is also equal to $\frac{1}{2}$ of the third angle. Find the three angles.

Solution. Let

$$x = \text{number of degrees in the first angle}$$

Then

$$3x = \text{number of degrees in the second angle}$$
$$2x = \text{number of degrees in the third angle}$$

$$x + 3x + 2x = 180.$$

Solving, we have

$$x = 30, \quad 3x = 90, \quad 2x = 60.$$

EXERCISE 5-5

Form algebraic equations and solve the following problems.

1. A 7-foot cord is cut into two pieces so that one piece is $\frac{2}{3}$ as long as the other. Find the length of each piece.

2. A piece of wire 4 feet long is cut and the pieces are bent to form two circles. If the diameter of one circle is $\frac{3}{5}$ that of the other, find the length of each piece.

3. One string is 3 inches longer than another. If their combined length is 17 inches, find the length of each.

4. A 26-inch cord is cut into three pieces. The first is $\frac{3}{4}$ as long as the second, and the second is $\frac{2}{3}$ as long as the third. How long is each?

5. Some 12-foot boards are to be cut into two pieces to make lids for two boxes, one of which is $\frac{5}{7}$ as long as the other. How should each board be divided?

6. The width of a rectangle and the side of a square are equal. If the length of the rectangle is 5 inches more than its width, and its area is 50 square inches more than that of the square, find the dimensions of each.

7. The radius of one circle is 3 inches more than that of another, and their areas differ by 27π square inches. Find the radius of each.

8. The diameter of one circle is 4 inches more than that of another, and its area is greater by 12π square inches. Find the diameter of each.

9. Two right triangles have equal bases. The two sides of each triangle form its base and altitude. One triangle is isosceles but the altitude of the other is 4 inches longer than its base. If their areas differ by 12 square inches, find the dimensions of each.

10. The altitudes of two triangles and the base of one of them are equal. The base of the other is 6 inches more than its altitude, and the difference in the areas is 21 square inches. Find the base and altitude of each.

11. The radius of the base of one right circular cylinder is 3 inches more than that of another, and the altitude of each is 15 inches. If the difference in their volumes is 225π cubic inches, find the radius of the base of each.

12. One of the acute angles of a right triangle is 10° less than the other. Find the number of degrees in each angle.

13. The first angle of a triangle equals $\frac{1}{2}$ of the second, and the third equals the sum of the first and second. Find each angle.

14. The vertical angle of an isosceles triangle is 20° more than the sum of the equal angles. Find each angle.

15. Work problem 14 with "20° more" replaced by "4° less."

16. The first angle of a triangle is $\frac{1}{3}$ as large as the second and $\frac{1}{5}$ as large as the third. Find each angle.

5-10. PROBLEMS INVOLVING TIME, RATE, AND DISTANCE

Many problems are solved by means of the formula

$$(1) \qquad\qquad d = rt,$$

where d represents the number of units of distance, r the number of units of distance traveled in one unit of time, and t the number of units of time. For brevity, d, r, and t are called *distance*, *rate*, and *time*. It must be understood, however, that (1) holds true *only* if the rate is constant, such as it is, for instance, in a car whose speedometer needle remains fixed at the 40 mph position.

Equation (1) is used, of course, to find the distance when the rate and time are known. Solved for r and t, it takes the two alternate forms,

(2)
$$r = \frac{d}{t},$$

and

(3)
$$t = \frac{d}{r},$$

used respectively to find r and t when the other two quantities are known.

EXERCISE 5-6

Form equations and solve the following problems.

1. If one car runs 40 mph and another car runs 50 mph, in how many hours will the sum of their distances be 300 miles?

   Let
   $$x = \text{number of hours required.}$$
   Then
   $$40x = \text{number of miles first car runs. (Here } rt = 40x.)$$
   $$50x = \text{number of miles second car runs.}$$
   $$40x + 50x = 300.$$
   $$90x = 300.$$
   $$x = \frac{300}{90} = \frac{10}{3}.$$

2. A car running north at 45 mph passes point A at 12 o'clock. A second car running north at 50 mph passes A at 1:30 p.m. When will the second car overtake the first one?

3. A is 450 miles west of B. A car starts east from A at 40 mph, and at the same time another starts west from B at 45 mph. In how many hours will they meet?

4. Two men are 400 yards apart and walk straight toward each other. If one walks 80 ypm (yards per minute) and the other 90 ypm, in how many minutes will they meet?

5. Two men run in the same direction around a 440-yard track. If one runs 10 yps (yards per second) and the other $\frac{4}{5}$ as fast, in how many seconds will the faster one gain a lap?

6. One man can run 9 yps and the other can run 8 yps. If they start at the same time and run in opposite directions around a 440-yard track, in how many seconds will they meet?

7. A car starts east at 40 mph. A second car starts east from the same point one hour later at 50 mph. When will the second car be 10 miles ahead of the first one?

8. A car starts south at 40 mph. One hour later a second car starts south from the same point. If the second car overtakes the first one in three hours, find its speed.

9. A man walks toward a certain town at 2 mph. One hour later a second man starts from the same place at 3 mph. He overtakes the first man just as he reaches the town. How far was it to town and how long did each man require for the trip?

10. A train that runs 50 mph passes a station 2 hours behind a slower train and overtakes it in 3 hours. Find the speed of the slower train.

11. The current in a certain stream flows 3 mph. A crew can row twice as fast downstream as it can row upstream. How fast can it row in still water?
    Let

    $$x = \text{number of mph rowed in still water.}$$

    Then

    $$x + 3 = \text{number of mph rowed downstream.}$$

    $$x - 3 = \text{number of mph rowed upstream.}$$

    $$x + 3 = 2(x - 3).$$

    Solving, we have

    $$x = 9.$$

12. The current in a stream flows 2 mph. A crew can row $\frac{3}{2}$ times as fast downstream as it can row upstream. How fast can it row in still water?

13. The current in a stream flows 4 mph. A crew can row $\frac{2}{3}$ as fast upstream as it can row downstream. How fast can it row in still water?

14. The rate of the current is 3 mph. A crew can row 9 miles downstream in the time required for rowing 4 miles upstream. How fast can it row in still water?

15. Work Prob. 14 if the current flows 2 mph and the downstream and upstream distances are respectively 18 and 6 miles.

16. A man can row 4 mph in still water. He can row 12 miles downstream in the time required for rowing 4 miles upstream. Find the rate of the current.

17. An airplane has a cruising speed of 300 mph. On a certain day its ground speed when traveling with the wind was twice its speed against the wind. How fast was the wind blowing?

18. On a certain day the wind at 5,000 feet was blowing 50 mph, and at 10,000 feet it was blowing 20 mph in the same direction. A plane flew at 5,000 feet with the wind from *A* to *B* in 3 hours, and returned at the 10,000-feet level in 5 hours. Find its speed in still air and the distance from *A* to *B*.

5-11. PROBLEMS CONCERNING MONEY

Most practical problems about money deal with principal, interest, rate of interest, wages, profit and loss. In some other problems, usually less practical in nature, the object is to find the number or denomination of pieces of money involved.

The *principal* is the sum of money that bears interest.

The *rate* is the fraction of the principal paid for its use during a certain period of time—usually a year. Stated in percentage, it is this fraction multiplied by 100. Thus the rate of $\dfrac{06}{100}$ or .06 becomes "6 percent."

The *time* is the interval during which the principal is used. The *interest* is the total sum paid for use of the principal. The *amount* is the sum of the principal and interest.

In formulas the following notation is customary:

$$A = \text{number of dollars in the amount}$$
$$P = \text{number of dollars in the principal}$$
$$I = \text{number of dollars in the interest}$$
$$t = \text{number of interest periods in the time interval}$$
$$r = \text{rate, written as a decimal fraction}$$

We shall use the following formulas:

(1) $I = Prt.$

Solving (1) for P, r, and t successively, we have

(2) $P = \dfrac{I}{rt},$

(3) $r = \dfrac{I}{Pt},$

and

(4) $t = \dfrac{I}{Pr}.$

(5) $A = P + I,$ from the definition.

From (5) and (1),

(6) $A = P + Prt = P(1 + rt).$

When there are two or more investments, subscripts may be used to distinguish between them. For example, P_1, read "P sub one," means the first principal, P_2 the second principal, etc. Similarly, I_1 means the interest on P_1; I_2 is the interest on P_2, etc.

Example 1.   A man invests $6,000, part at 5 percent and part at 6 percent. The total interest for one year is $320. How much was each investment?

Solution.   Let the two investments be P_1 and $6000 - P_1$. For the first investment, $r = .05$ and $t = 1$; for the second, $r = .06$ and $t = 1$.

Substituting in (1) we have

$$I_1 = P_1(.05)(1) = .05 P_1,$$

and

$$I_2 = (6000 - P_1)(.06)(1) = 360 - .06 P_1.$$

But

$$I_1 + I_2 = 320, \text{ the total interest.}$$

Hence

$$.05 P_1 + (360 - .06 P_1) = 320.$$

Solving, we have

$$P_1 = 4000,$$

and

$$6000 - P_1 = 2000.$$

Example 2. What principal will yield $24 interest in 2 years at 6 percent?

Solution. Here $I = 24$, $r = .06$, $t = 2$, and P is the unknown. Using these values in (2), we have

$$P = \frac{24}{(.06)(2)} = \frac{24}{.12} = \frac{2400}{12} = 200.$$

Example 3. Two men work 6 days and receive $54 as wages. If one receives $\frac{4}{5}$ as much per day as the other, find the daily wage of each.

Solution. Let

$$x = \text{number of dollars in the daily wage of the second man}$$

Then

$$\frac{4x}{5} = \text{number of dollars in the daily wage of the first man}$$

$$x + \frac{4x}{5} = \frac{54}{6} = 9.$$

Solving, we have

$$x = 5$$

$$\frac{4x}{5} = 4.$$

EXERCISE 5-7

1. How much interest will be earned by an investment of $300 at 5 percent for 2 years?

2. An investment of $200 yields $8 interest in a year. Find the rate.

3. At what rate will $250 yield $20 interest in 2 years?

4. At what rate will $3,500 yield $350 in 3 years?

5. At what rate will $4,700 yield $282 in 2 years?

6. Find the time required for $6,500 to yield $650 at 5 percent.

7. A sum of $7,500 is invested, part at 6 percent and part at 5 percent. The annual interest on the two investments is $400. Find the two investments.

8. Part of $8,000 is invested at 4 percent and the rest at 5 percent. The 4 percent investment yields $50 more interest in a year than the other. How much is invested at each rate?

9. One part of $9,000 is invested at 4 percent and the rest at 5 percent. If the two incomes thus yielded are equal, find each investment.

10. A certain sum invested at 6 percent yields the same yearly income as an investment of $6,000 at 5 percent. What is the sum invested?

11. Two men worked 9 days and together received $144 in wages. If one man received $7 per day, how much did the other get?

12. A boy received $\frac{1}{2}$ as much pay as his father. If together they got $48 for 4 days' work, what was the daily wage of each?

13. If two common laborers and four skilled workmen receive $80 per day altogether, and if the wages for skilled labor are twice as much as for common labor, find the wage of each.

14. Ten men were employed, some at $6 per day and some at $8 per day. The total daily wages amounted to $68. Find the number employed at each wage.

15. Nine men were employed, some at $7 per day and some at $9 per day. If the total daily wages amounted to $75, find the number working at each wage.

16. $P = 325, t = 2, r = .06$. Find I.

17. $P = 450, t = 3, r = .05$. Find A.

18. $I = 18, t = 3, P = 100$. Find r.

19. $I = 60, P = 500, r = .06$. Find t.

20. $A = 770, t = 2, r = 5\%$. Find P and I.

21. $A = 690, t = 3, r = 5\%$. Find P and I.

22. $I = 80, t = 2, r = .04$. Find P.

23. A man has $1.25 in nickels and dimes. If there are three times as many nickels as dimes, find the number of each.

Let
$$x = \text{number of dimes.}$$

Then
$$3x = \text{number of nickels.}$$
$$10x = \text{value of the dimes in cents.}$$
$$5(3x) = 15x = \text{value of the nickels in cents.}$$
$$10x + 15x = 125.$$

Solving, we have
$$x = 5.$$
$$3x = 15.$$

24. A man has $3 in nickels and dimes, there being twice as many dimes as nickels. Find the number of each.

25. The sum of $1.90 is made up of quarters plus $\frac{2}{3}$ as many dimes. How many of each are there?

26. A boy has twice as many nickels as dimes and twice as many dimes as quarters. How many of each has he if the total sum is $1.30?

27. A man has $3.25 in nickels, dimes, and quarters. He has the same number of dimes as of nickels, and twice as many quarters as dimes. Find the number of each.

28. A man has $\frac{2}{3}$ as many quarters as nickels, and as many dimes as the total number of the other coins. How many of each has he if their total value is $2.30?

5-12. MIXTURE PROBLEMS

Many problems arise from the forming of mixtures of various materials. When two or more substances are mixed, an equation may be formed on the basis of the fact that the quantity of a certain substance in one material plus the quantity of this same substance in a second material is equal to the quantity of that substance in the mixture formed by combining the two materials. This same principle will extend to any mixture containing a given number of materials.

When the value of a mixture is the matter of chief interest, as in Example 2 below, we form the equation not directly on the basis of quantity but on the principle of value. When two substances are mixed we say that the value of the first plus the value of the second equals the value of the mixture.

Example 1.   How much metal that is 5 percent silver must be added to 10 pounds of metal, 2 percent of which is silver, to form a mixture having 3 percent silver?

Solution. Let

x = number of pounds of metal containing 5 percent silver.

Then

$.05x$ = number of pounds of silver in the first metal
$(.02)(10)$ = number of pounds of silver in the second metal
$(.03)(x + 10)$ = number of pounds of silver in the mixture

and

$$.05x + (.02)(10) = (.03)(x + 10).$$

Solving, we have

$$x = 5.$$

Example 2. How many pounds of coffee worth 88¢ per pound must be added to 40 pounds of coffee worth 95¢ per pound to form a mixture worth 90¢ per pound?

Solution. Let

x = number of pounds of 88¢ coffee added.
$88x$ = number of cents in the value of the 88¢ coffee
$95(40)$ = number of cents in the value of the 95¢ coffee
$90(x + 40)$ = number of cents in the value of the mixture

and

$$88x + 95(40) = 90(x + 40).$$

Solving, we have

$$x = 100.$$

EXERCISE 5-8

1. How much 10 percent copper alloy must be added to 20 pounds of 15 percent copper alloy to form a 12 percent copper alloy?

2. How many pounds of cream containing 25 percent butter fat must be added to 30 pounds of milk containing 5 percent butter fat to form a mixture containing 15 percent butter fat?

3. How much 30 percent gold alloy must be added to 25 ounces of 20 percent gold alloy to produce a 27 percent gold alloy?

4. How much pure gold must be taken from 23 ounces of 20 percent gold alloy to reduce it to a 15 percent gold alloy?

5. How much pure copper must be taken from 35 pounds of 40 percent copper alloy to reduce it to a 25 percent copper alloy?

6. How much pure silver must be taken from 45 ounces of 35 percent silver alloy to reduce it to a 20 percent silver alloy?

7. How much candy, worth 25¢ per pound, must be mixed with 20 pounds of candy worth 13¢ per pound to form a mixture of candy worth 20¢ per pound?

8. Two kinds of candy worth 15¢ and 25¢ per pound are mixed to form 30 pounds of candy worth 18¢ per pound. How much of each is used?

9. Two kinds of coffee worth 90¢ and 82¢ per pound are mixed to form 100 pounds of 85¢ per pound coffee. How much of each is used?

10. A lady bought 10 pounds of grapes for $3.35. Some of them sold for 30¢ per pound and some for 35¢ per pound. How many pounds of each kind did she buy?

11. A dealer bought 15 cases of fruit for $41.50. Some cases cost $3.00 and some $2.50. How many cases of each did he buy?

5-13.   LEVER PROBLEMS

A lever is a mechanical device by which a force applied at one point is transferred to a second point and there intensified. When we roll over a huge rock with a crowbar we apply this principle. Many problems in algebra are concerned with levers and related mechanical devices such as pulleys.

Some preliminary definitions are necessary.

The *fulcrum* is the nonmoving support upon which the lever swings when force is applied to it.

The *moment* of any force, for a given set of units, is equal to the number of units in the force multiplied by the number of units in the distance from the fulcrum to the point on the lever where the force is applied.

Question: What is the moment of a force of 10 pounds applied 5 feet from the fulcrum of a lever?

Answer: Moment = $5 \cdot 10 = 50$ foot-pounds, for the given units.

The force shown in Fig. 5-1 causes the lever to rotate about the ful-

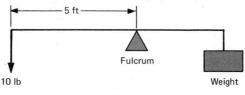

FIG. 5-1

crum in a counterclockwise direction as we view the figure. Any force acting downward on the lever to the right of the fulcrum, such as the indicated weight, would tend to rotate the lever in the opposite, or clockwise, direction.

If the sum of the moments of all forces tending to rotate the lever counterclockwise is equal to the sum of the moments of all forces tending to rotate it clockwise, the lever will be balanced and stationary. In most lever problems we calculate either the force or distance necessary to make the lever balance.

Example 1. If a force of 50 pounds is applied 5 feet from the fulcrum of a lever, where must a weight of 60 pounds be placed to balance it?

Solution. (A diagram similar to Fig. 5-1 may be drawn.) Let

$$x = \text{number of feet from the fulcrum to the weight}$$
$$5 \cdot 50 = 250 = \text{the moment of the 50-pound force}$$
$$60x = \text{the moment of the 60-pound weight}$$
$$60x = 250$$
$$x = \frac{25}{6},$$

so that the weight must be 4 feet, 2 inches from the fulcrum.

In the above example the weight of the lever is not considered. This weight may be important, however, in the case of a heavy lever such as a plank. To allow for it the lever is considered as composed of two parts called *arms*, each of which lies wholly on one side of the fulcrum. If the lever is uniform, or of the same weight for each unit of length, the moment of an arm may be found by multiplying its weight by one-half its length, as expressed in the units chosen for the problem. In other words, the moment of a lever arm equals the moment of a force equal to its weight applied at a point halfway from the fulcrum to the end of the arm.

Example 2. The fulcrum of a lever is 10 feet from one end and 4 feet from the other. If the beam weighs 8 pounds per foot, what weight must be placed at the end of the shorter arm to balance the lever?

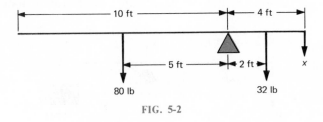

FIG. 5-2

Solution. The weights of the two arms are 80 and 32 pounds respectively. We must equate the counterclockwise (cc) and clockwise (c) moments. Let

$$x = \text{number of pounds of force applied at the}$$
$$\text{end of the shorter arm}$$

$$80 \cdot 5 = \text{moment of the left arm in the diagram (cc)}$$
$$32 \cdot 2 = \text{moment of the right arm (c)}$$
$$4x = \text{moment of the force } x \text{ (c)}$$
$$4x + 32 \cdot 2 = 80 \cdot 5.$$

Solving, we have

$$x = 84.$$

If two persons are carrying a weight swung on a pole, we may consider the weight as a fulcrum and the supporting forces as the acting ones. This is then a lever just like the others we have discussed, except that it is upside down.

Example 3. Two persons carry a weight of 100 pounds swung on a 9-foot pole. Where should the weight be placed so that one person will carry 60 pounds and the other 40 pounds?

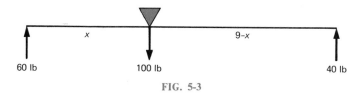

60 lb   100 lb   40 lb

FIG. 5-3

Solution. Let

$$x = \text{number of feet from weight to man carrying 60 pounds}$$
$$9 - x = \text{number of feet from weight to man carrying 40 pounds}$$
$$60x = 40 (9 - x).$$

Solving, we have

$$x = \frac{18}{5}, \quad \text{or} \quad 3\frac{3}{5}$$

$$9 - x = \frac{27}{5}, \quad \text{or} \quad 5\frac{2}{5}.$$

EXERCISE 5-9

1. A 90-pound boy and a 60-pound boy balance on a 12-foot teeter board. Where is the fulcrum?

2. What weight must be placed 6 feet from the fulcrum to balance a 70-pound weight 8 feet on the other side of the fulcrum?

3. How much weight can a 160-pound man raise with a 10-foot beam placed so that the weight is 2 feet from the fulcrum?*

*In this and subsequent problems subject to two interpretations, assume that the fulcrum is between the applied forces.

4. What force is necessary to raise a weight of 1,000 pounds with a 12-foot beam placed so that the weight is 3 feet from the fulcrum?

5. What weight must be placed 5 feet from the fulcrum to balance a 12-pound weight 4 feet on the other side of the fulcrum?

6. If the fulcrum is 4 feet from each end of a beam whose arms are uniform but unlike, weighing 75 and 40 pounds respectively, where should a 50-pound weight be placed to balance the beam?

7. Two men carry a 90-pound weight swung from a pole 8 feet long. Where must the weight be placed so that they will carry 40 and 50 pounds respectively?

8. A 12-foot beam weighs 7 pounds per foot. If the fulcrum is 4 feet from one end, what force must be applied at the end of the shorter arm to balance the beam?

9. A 14-foot beam weighs 8 pounds per foot. If the fulcrum is 6 feet from one end, what weight must be placed at the end of the shorter arm to balance the beam?

10. What force applied 7 feet from the fulcrum will balance 1,500 pounds 2 feet from the fulcrum?

11. What force applied 8 feet from the fulcrum will balance 2,000 pounds 2 feet from the fulcrum?

12. What weight placed 3 feet from the fulcrum can be balanced by a 170-pound force applied 7 feet on the opposite side of the fulcrum?

13. What weight can a 110-pound boy balance with a 12-foot lever if the weight is 2 feet from the fulcrum?

14. Two men carry a 70-pound weight swung on a 10-foot pole and placed 4 feet from one end. How much does each carry?

15. Two men carry a 120-pound weight swung 4 feet from one end of a 9-foot pole. How much does each carry if the pole itself weighs 20 pounds?

16. Two men carry a weight of 150 pounds swung on a pole. The one who is 4 feet from the weight carries 90 pounds. How long is the pole?

17. A weight of 300 pounds rests over the end of a lever 6 inches from the fulcrum. A boy weighing 60 pounds can just lift the weight. How long is the lever?

5-14. WORK PROBLEMS

Many problems involve the rate at which an action is being performed. For example, if a man can do a piece of work in 10 days, his rate of work is to do $\frac{1}{10}$ of it per day. If he works x days, he has performed $\frac{x}{10}$

of the total work. The guiding principle* in problems of this type is the fact that the product of the rate of work by the number of units of time involved is equal to the fractional amount of the work done.

Example. If A can do a piece of work in 20 days and B can do the same work in 25 days, how many days will both need to do the job when working together?

Solution. Let

$$x = \text{number of days needed for both to do the work}$$

$$\frac{1}{x} = \text{fractional part both do in one day}$$

$$\frac{1}{20} = \text{fractional part } A \text{ does in one day}$$

$$\frac{1}{25} = \text{fractional part } B \text{ does in one day}$$

$$\frac{1}{20} + \frac{1}{25} = \frac{1}{x}.$$

Clearing fractions (multiplying both members by $100x$), we have

$$5x + 4x = 100,$$
$$x = \frac{100}{9} = 11\frac{1}{9} \text{ days.}$$

EXERCISE 5-10

1. *A* can do a piece of work in 30 days and *B* can do the same job in 8 days. How long will it take for both to complete the job if they work together?

2. One pipe can fill a certain tank in 25 minutes. After this pipe has been running for 10 minutes, it is shut off and a second pipe is opened. The second pipe finishes the filling in 30 minutes. How long would it have taken the second pipe to have filled the tank alone?

3. *A* can do a certain amount of work in $\frac{1}{4}$ the time *B* requires; *B* can do the same amount in $\frac{1}{3}$ the time *C* needs. The three together can do the work in 36 days. How long will it take each of them to do the work alone?

4. A large pipe fills a tank in 12 minutes and a small pipe fills it in 18 minutes. How long will it take one large and three small pipes to fill the tank if they are all opened simultaneously?

---

*Naturally, good judgment must be used in applying the principle. For example, if one dentist can fill a tooth in one hour, it does not follow that two dentists could fill it in half an hour.

5. John started a job which ordinarily took him 5 hours, and quit after working $1\frac{1}{2}$ hours. James finished the job in 8 hours. How long would it have taken James to do the whole job by himself?

6. A can paint a house in 40 hours and B can do it in 25 hours. After A and B have been working together for 14 hours, they are joined by C and finish the job in 1 more hour. How long would it have taken C to have done the whole job alone?

7. One faucet can fill a tank in $19\frac{1}{2}$ minutes and a second in 39 minutes. How long will it take to fill three-quarters of the tank if both faucets are opened at the same time?

8. If it takes John a days to do a piece of work and James b days to do the same work, how long will it take for both to do the work together?

9. A and B together can do a piece of work in 5 days. If A works a times as fast as B, find the time each would require alone.

10. A list of names can be typed in 10 hours by one typist and in 15 hours by another. How long will it take them to complete the work together?

REVIEW EXERCISES

1. Solve the following equations.

(a) $\dfrac{5x - 1}{7} - \dfrac{3x - 2}{5} = 1.$

(b) $\dfrac{b - 4}{3 - b} = \dfrac{3 - b}{b + 4}.$

(c) $1 + \dfrac{z + 2}{2 - z} = \dfrac{z + 9}{z^2 - 3z + 2}.$

(d) $r = \dfrac{2as}{m - s}$ for s.

(e) $A = P(1 + rt)$ for t;   for r.

(f) $V = \dfrac{1}{3}\pi r^2 h$ for h.

(g) $\dfrac{V_1}{V_2} = \dfrac{P_2}{P_1}$ for V_2;   for P_2.

(h) $A = \dfrac{(b_1 + b_2)h}{2}$ for b_1;   for h.

(i) $V = \dfrac{h}{6}(b_1 + b_2 + 4M)$ for M;   for h;   for b_2.

(j) $V = \pi h^2 \left(r - \dfrac{h}{3} \right)$ for h.

(k) $C = \dfrac{In}{rn + R}$ for R;   for n;   for l.

2.   In 1 (e), find A if $P = 600$, $t = 6$, and $r = .06$.

3.   In 1 (k), find R to the nearest tenth if $C = .868$, $l = 4.12$, $n = 24$, and $r = .6$.

4.   In 1(h), find b_1 when $A = 32.1$, $b_2 = 1.7$ and $h = 2.2$.

5.   If $s = \dfrac{n}{2} [2a + (n - 1)d]$, find s if $n = 15$, $d = -4$, $a = -2$.

6.   If $s = \dfrac{n}{2} [2a + (n - 1)d]$, find d if $s = 48$, $d = -2$, $n = 20$.

7.   Translate the following into appropriate algebraic statements and solve where possible.

   (a)   What is the sum of one half of one third when added to five-sixth of three?

   (b)   How many times does $x - 2$ divide $x^3 - 8$?

   (c)   How many times does $\dfrac{a}{b}$ divide into $\dfrac{z}{y}$?

   (d)   Find the price in cents for w oranges at 65¢ per dozen.

   (e)   What is five eighths of s tenths?

   (f)   If $(x + y)$ dollars is divided among s people, how many cents will each receive?

   (g)   If a man has x dollars and y cents and spent w dollars and d cents, what does he have left in cents? In dollars?

   (h)   If 5 pears cost a cents, what is the price of b pears?

   (i)   If a man can walk at the rate of 1 mile per 15 minutes, how many miles does he walk in $(x + 2y)$ hours? How many yards?

   (j)   Sixty miles per hour is how many feet per second?

   (k)   If one third of a line length is g feet, what is the length of the line in inches?

   (l)   If one quarter of my age 4 years ago was t years, what represents my age 6 years hence?

   (m)   By how much is 75 greater than $x + y$?

   (n)   By how much is $x + y$ less than 75?

   (o)   Add $2 \cdot 3^2$ to $4 \cdot 3^2$ to $6 \cdot 3^2$ to $5 \cdot 3^2$.

8.   When working alone Harry can build a fence in 12 hours. Harry works on the construction of the fence for $2\dfrac{1}{2}$ hours after which his buddy Bill decides to help him. The fence is completed by both Bill and Harry working together an extra 8 hours. How long would it have taken Bill alone to have built the fence?

9. Jim is 24 years old. Jim is twice as old as Sam was when Jim was as old as Sam is now. How old is Sam?

10. Six boys agreed to purchase a tent, but two of them were unable to contribute towards its purchase. As a consequence, each of the others had to pay $3.00 more than had been anticipated. What was the cost of the tent?

11. A man had two investments totaling $5,000. On one, he received 6 percent interest, and on the other 5 percent. The 6 percent investment yields an annual income of $110 more than the 5 percent investment. How much has he invested at each of the rates?

chapter 6

Functions, Relations, and Their Graphs

6-1. INTRODUCTION

In Chapter 1 the concept of one-to-one correspondence between the elements of two sets was discussed. In this chapter we shall investigate a specific type of correspondence between the elements of two sets that forms the basis for the concept of a function. The idea and understanding of a function is a very important part of mathematics and will be used extensively in the remainder of this text.

6-2. ORDERED PAIRS AND CARTESIAN PRODUCTS

In many situations we are concerned with collections of objects in which the order chosen for the objects is significant. In such cases the collection of such objects is referred to by some name other than "set."

One of the simplest kinds of such collections in which the order of the objects is significant is that of an *ordered pair*. An ordered pair of objects is created when the two objects involved are such that one is identified as the first and the other, the second. If the two objects are represented by a and b, and if a is identified as the first and b the second, then we denote the ordered pair by (a,b) and call a the first element of the ordered pair and b the second element. For example, (3,2) is an ordered pair in which 3 is the first element and 2 the second element. Two ordered pairs (a,b) and (c,d) are defined as being equal *if and only if $a = c$ and $b = d$*.

The two elements of an ordered pair may be chosen from objects belonging to the same collection or each belonging to a different collection. For example, if the objects are real numbers and if $A = \{2,4\}$ and

$B = \{1,3\}$, then the ordered pairs

$$(2,1),\ (2,3),\ (4,1),\ (4,3)$$

are created which are of the form (a,b) with $a \in A$ at the same time that $b \in B$. This is an example of a Cartesian product which is now defined.

The Cartesian product of a set A and a set B (in that order) is denoted by the symbolism $A \times B = \{(a,b) \mid a \in A \wedge b \in B\}$; that is, the Cartesian product of A and B is the set of all ordered pairs (a,b) such that element a is chosen first from A and b is then chosen from B as the second element. The connective "$\wedge$" means "and" which, interpreted as used here, takes the place of the English phrase "at the same time." When used throughout this text, the implied phrase "at the same time" will usually be represented by "$\wedge$." For example, if $A = \{1,3,5\}$ and $B = \{a,b\}$, then

$$A \times B = \{(1,a),\ (1,b),\ (3,a),\ (3,b),\ (5,a),\ (5,b)\}$$

while

$$B \times B = \{(a,a),\ (a,b),\ (b,a),\ (b,b)\}.$$

It should be noted that $A \times B$ is not necessarily the same as $B \times A$.

6-3. FUNCTIONS AND RELATIONS

A *function* is a correspondence between the elements of two sets which associates with each element of the first set, a *unique element* of the second set. The first set is called the *domain D* of the function. If x is an element of the domain D of a function, then the corresponding member of the second set is called the *range* or *image value* of x. The set of all images is called the range R of the function. A unique image exists for each and every domain value if the correspondence being discussed is a function. Since a set of ordered pairs can be used effectively to represent a correspondence, a second definition for a function is also employed, namely:

A *function is a nonempty set* of ordered pairs such that no two pairs are contained in it with the first elements equal unless this is also true for the second elements. In other words, if (a,b) and (a,c) are contained in the set of ordered pairs b must equal c if we are dealing with a function.

The set of all first elements of the pairs forming the function is called its *domain D*, and the set of all second elements or images is called the *range R* of the function.

Example 1.
(a) The set of ordered pairs $\{(1,2),\ (2,3),\ (3,4)\}$ is a function. The domain of the function is the set $D = \{1,2,3\}$.

(b) The set $\{1,5),\ (2,5),\ (3,5)\}$ is a function with domain $D = \{1,2,3\}$

and range $R = \{5\}$. Note that the image of each element of the domain is the element 5, but no two ordered pairs appear with the same first element.

(c) The set $\{(1,2), (1,3), (1,4)\}$ is not a function, since it contains distinct ordered pairs having the same first element but different second elements. This set will be referred to as a *relation* in later sections, but it is not a function. In fact, it will become evident that *every function is a relation* but not every relation is a function. This is discussed more fully in Sec. 6-6.

It is many times impossible to list all the ordered pairs that constitute a function. However, it is usually possible to establish the correspondence between the elements of the domain and the range by means of defining properties designated through equations, and then by use of set notation describe the required function.

For example, consider the equation

$$x + 2y = 1, \text{ where } x \in R_e \wedge y \in R_e.$$

If x is replaced by 3 and y by -1, the equation is satisfied. Thus the ordered pair $(3,-1)$ is a solution of the given equation and belongs to the set of ordered pairs created by $x + 2y = 1$, while $(-1,3)$ is not, since the statement obtained by replacing x by -1 and y by 3 is false.

In general, an ordered pair (x,y) is a solution of an equation in two variables x and y if and only if the replacement of x by the first element of the ordered pair and of y by the second element of the ordered pair results in a true statement. The set of all solutions (x,y) of the equation $x + 2y = 1$ is called its *solution set* and is written symbolically as

$$\{(x,y) \mid x + 2y = 1\}.$$

It is understood that both x and y are elements of R_e unless otherwise specified. In English the solution set reads as follows: "The set of all ordered pairs (x,y) such that $x + 2y = 1$."

If the equation $x + 2y = 1$ is solved for y, then $y = \dfrac{1-x}{2}$. To find the various members of the solution set, we need only to substitute values of x and then calculate the corresponding values of y. Thus when $x = 1$, $y = 0$; when $x = 2$, $y = -\dfrac{1}{2}$; when $x = -1$, $y = 1$, etc. The ordered pairs $(1,0)$, $\left(2,-\dfrac{1}{2}\right)$, $(-1,1)$ are all elements of the solution set.

It is here noted that the defining condition $x + 2y = 1$ associates with each real number x a unique real number y. Therefore

$$\{(x,y) \mid x + 2y = 1\} = \left\{(x,y) \mid y = \frac{1-x}{2}\right\}$$

is a function in accord with the definition for same. This function is defined by the equation $x + 2y = 1$ or $y = \dfrac{1 - x}{2}$.

Example 2.

(a) The set $\{(x,y) \mid y = x^2\}$ is a function defined by the equation $y = x^2$. The function consists of an infinite number of ordered pairs, samples of which are $(1,1), (-1,1), (0,0), (2,4)$ and $(-2,4)$. The domain of the function is the set of real numbers R_e, while its range R is the set of non-negative real numbers.

(b) The set $\{(x,y) \mid x = y^2\}$ is not a function but is a relation, which is discussed in Sec. 6-6. Here the domain D of the set are the non-negative real numbers, and for each choice of a positive x, there are two distinct real choices of y. For example $(1,1)$ and $(1,-1)$ are both members of the solution set, and as a consequence, destroy the necessary property that in order to be a function, a distinct choice of domain value demands a unique choice of range value.

6-4. FUNCTIONAL NOTATION AND SYMBOLISM

We will generally use small letters such a f, g, or h to denote a function. For example,

$$f = \{(x,y) \mid y = x + 4\}.$$

The ordered pair (x,y) specified within the parentheses implies that x represents the elements in the domain D of f, and y represents the elements in the range R of f. These in turn are associated one with the other by the rule of correspondence (definining condition) for the function, namely $y = x + 4$, wherein each choice of $x \in R_e$ produces a unique choice of $y \in R_e$.

To designate the range value y for an associated domain value x, it is convenient to write $f(x)$, which is read either as "f of x" or "the value of the function f at x." The ordered pair produced by such a precise x can now be designated either as (x,y) or $(x,f(x))$.

In the preceding example, if desired, we can write $f(x) = x + 4$ in place of $y = x + 4$.

Example.

(a) The set $f = \{(1,2), (2,4), (3,9)\}$ is a function. The domain of f is $D = \{1,2,3\}$; the range of f is $R = \{2,4,9\}$. In the function f, the element of R that corresponds to 3 is 9; thus $f(3) = 9$. Similarly $f(1) = 2$ and $f(2) = 4$. The corresponding ordered pairs belonging to f can be represented as $(3,f(3))$, $(1,f(1))$, $(2,f(2))$ or as $(3,9)$, $(1,2)$, $(2,4)$.

(b) The set $g = \{(x,y) \mid y = g(x) = x^2 - 1\}$ is a function. The domain of g is $D = \{x \mid x \in R_e\}$. When $x = 0$, $y = -1$; when x is any number other than 0, $x^2 > 0$. Thus the range of g is $R = \{y \mid y \geq -1\}$.

Range values of a function are obtained by replacing domain values with precise choices specified by means of the symbolism $f(x)$, where x represents the value of the domain variable.

In the example $f = \{(x,y) \mid y = f(x) = x + 4\}$. Thus

$f(2) = 2 + 4 = 6$, where x is replaced by 2 in $x + 4$.
$f(-1) = -1 + 4 = 3$, where x is replaced by -1 in $x + 4$.
$f(x + h) = (x + h) + 4$, where x is replaced by $x + h$ in $x + 4$.

$$f\left(\frac{3 + w}{w}\right) = \frac{3 + w}{w} + 4$$

$$= \frac{3 + 5w}{w}, \text{ where } x \text{ is replaced by } \frac{3 + w}{w} \text{ in } x + 4.$$

Since $f(x) = x + 4$, if desirable, f can be written as

$$f = \{(x, f(x)) \mid f(x) = x + 4,\}$$
$$= \{(x, x + 4)\}$$

where (x,y) has been replaced either by $(x, f(x))$ or $(x, x + 4)$.

The *domain*, the *range*, and the *rule of correspondence* are the *three essential parts* of a function. When a function is defined by an equation, the domain and/or the range are frequently not specified explicitly. It is customary in such cases to assume that the domain of the function is either the set of real numbers or a subset of same which produces from the rule of correspondence real numbers as images. If this is not understood for the choice of the domain of the function, it is clearly spelled out for the situation being studied.

If a domain D for a function f is specifically described, then *this is it*, and it cannot be changed promiscuously. Even though values outside the prescribed domain D may create values by use of the defining conditions for the given domain D, they cannot be used.

Example. Let a function f be given by

$$f = \left\{(x,y) \mid y = f(x) = \frac{1}{x + 1}\right\}.$$

Note that the domain of f cannot contain the number -1, since $f(-1)$ is undefined. We must restrict the domain to include only those values of x for which the function is defined. Here we can write

$$D = \{x \mid x \in R_e \wedge x \neq -1\}.$$

If the domain D for f had been specified as all $x \geq 0$, then accordingly such a function implies no knowledge whatsoever when $x < 0$. It is not permissible to assume that the value of the function f, for instance is $-\dfrac{i}{2}$ when $x = -3$. In fact, so far as the studied function f is concerned, it would not exist when $x < 0$.

If a function depends on two independent variables, the function symbol should indicate both of the variables, such as in $f(x,y)$ or $g(x,y)$. The extension to any number of variables is obvious.

Example 1. The area A of a circle is a function of the radius r; thus we may write $A = f(r)$, where $f(r) = \pi r^2$. If a specific value is given to r, say $r = 6$, then $f(6) = 36\pi$. Here $f = \{(r,A) \mid A = f(r) = \pi r^2)\}$.

Example 2. The distance s that a body falls from rest is a function of the time t. We may write $s = f(t)$, where $f(t) = \dfrac{1}{2}gt^2$, $(g = 32.2)$. Here

$$f = \left\{ (t,s) \mid s = f(t) = \frac{1}{2}gt^2 \right\}.$$

Example 3. From each corner of a square sheet of cardboard 16 inches on a side, a square of side x inches is cut. The edges of the sheet are then turned up to make a box. Express the volume V of the box as a function of x.

Solution. Let $x =$ the number of inches in the side of the square cut out. Since the volume of the box can be determined for any value of x less than 8 inches, it follows that V is a function of x for the domain D, $0 < x < 8$. This is a continued inequality and reads: x is any real number greater than zero and less than 8.
Hence we may write

$$V = f(x).$$

From Fig. 6-1 it can be seen that

$$V = x(16 - 2x)^2 \text{ cu in.}$$

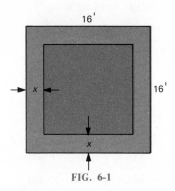

FIG. 6-1

Thus the specific algebraic expression defined by $f(x)$ is

$$f(x) = x(16 - 2x)^2.$$

In set notation,

$$f = \{(x,V) \mid V = f(x) = x(16 - 2x)^2\}.$$

Example 4. Given $f(x) = \dfrac{x}{1 + x^2}$, find $f(3), f(-2), f(0), f(a),$

$f\left(\dfrac{1}{x}\right), f(x + 1).$

Solution. $f(3) = \dfrac{3}{1 + 3^2} = \dfrac{3}{10}.$ Here the corresponding order pair

belonging to f is $(3, f(3)) = \left(3, \dfrac{3}{10}\right).$

$$f(-2) = \frac{-2}{1 + 4} = -\frac{2}{5},$$

$$f(0) = \frac{0}{1 + 0} = 0,$$

$$f(a) = \frac{a}{1 + a^2},$$

$$f\left(\frac{1}{x}\right) = \frac{\dfrac{1}{x}}{1 + \left(\dfrac{1}{x}\right)^2} = \frac{x}{1 + x^2} = f(x),$$

$$f(x + 1) = \frac{x + 1}{1 + (x + 1)^2} = \frac{x + 1}{x^2 + 2x + 2}.$$

Example 5. If $f(x) = 2x^2 + 3$, find $\dfrac{f(x_0 + h) - f(x_0)}{h}.$

Solution.

$$f(x_0) = 2x_0^2 + 3$$

$$f(x_0 + h) = 2(x_0 + h)^2 + 3$$

$$\frac{f(x_0 + h) - f(x_0)}{h} = \frac{2(x_0 + h)^2 + 3 - (2x_0^2 + 3)}{h}$$

$$= 4x_0 + 2h.$$

Example 6. If the radius and height of a right circular cylinder are represented by r and h units respectively, the total surface area S is a function of r and h. Since $S = 2\pi rh + 2\pi r^2$ square units, it follows that $f(r,h) = 2\pi rh + 2\pi r^2.$

If it had been stipulated that the volume of the right circular cylinder is 50 cubic units—that is, $\pi r^2 h = 50$, it would then be possible to express S as a function of r alone or as a function of h alone. If these functions are denoted by $F(r)$ and $G(h)$, respectively, it follows that

$$F(r) = \frac{100}{r} + 2\pi r^2$$

and

$$G(h) = 10\sqrt{2\pi h} + \frac{100}{h}.$$

Set notation would express the functions S as follows:

$$f = \{((r,h),S) \mid S = f((r,h)) = 2\pi rh + h^2\},$$

but to simplify symbolism it is agreed to drop the double parentheses and write f as

$$f = \{(r,h,S) \mid S = f(r,h) = 2\pi rh + h^2\}.$$

Example 7. If

$$f(x,y) = \frac{2x^2 - 3(x + y)}{2x - 1}$$

and

$$g(x,y) = 2xy - 3y^2,$$

find

$$\frac{3f(2,3) - g(-1,0)}{2f(-1,-2) \cdot g\left(\frac{1}{2},3\right)}.$$

Solution:

$$f(2,3) = \frac{2(2)^2 - 3(2 + 3)}{2 \cdot 2 - 1} = -\frac{7}{3}$$

$$f(-1,-2) = -\frac{11}{3}$$

$$g(-1,0) = 0$$

$$g\left(\frac{1}{2},3\right) = -24.$$

Hence

$$\frac{3f(2,3) - g(-1,0)}{2f(-1,-2) \cdot g\left(\frac{1}{2}, 3\right)} = \frac{3\left(-\frac{7}{3}\right) - 0}{2\left(-\frac{11}{3}\right)(-24)} = -\frac{7}{176}.$$

EXERCISE 6-1

Write a symbolic expression for each of the following functions and, when possible, an algebraic expression to define the function. For practice use set notation wherever convenient as directed by instructor.

1. The volume of a sphere as a function of the radius r.

2. The volume of a parallelepiped as a function of the width w if the length is twice the depth and the depth is 2 inches less than the width.

3. The weight of a boy as a function of his height h.

4. The temperature at the North Pole as a function of the time.

5. The simple interest on $100 at 5 percent as a function of the time t.

6. The surface of a cylinder of radius r if the height is equal to the diameter.
$$\text{Ans.: } S = f(r) = 4\pi r^2, f = \{(r,S) \mid S = f(r) = 4\pi r^2\}.$$

7. The area of an equilateral triangle as a function of its altitude h.

8. The volume of a gas as a function of the pressure p.

9. The area of the surface of a right circular cone in terms of its slant height s and the radius of its base r.

10. The area of the surface of a right circular cone in terms of its altitude h and the radius of its base r.

11. Given $y = 3x^2 + 7x - 4$. Find the value of y when $x = 1$; $x = 2$; $x = 0$;
$x = \dfrac{1}{2}$; $x = a$; $x = a - 1$; $x = -t$.

12. If $f(x) = 3x^2 + 7x - 4$, find $f(1)$; $f(2)$; $f(0)$; $f\left(\dfrac{1}{2}\right)$; $f(a)$; $f(z - 1)$; $f(-y)$;

$\dfrac{f(x_0 + h) - f(x_0)}{h}$. What are the corresponding ordered pairs for the values of the function f?

13. If $f(x) = \dfrac{1 - 2x}{1 - x}$, find $f(2)$; $f\left(\dfrac{1}{2}\right)$; $f(1 + x)$; $\dfrac{f(x_0 + h) - f(x_0)}{h}$.

14. If $f(x) = (x - 1)(x^2 - 1)(x^3 - 1)$, find $f(1)$; $f(0)$; $f(x + 1)$; $f(x^2)$.

15. If $f(x) = \dfrac{x^2}{1 + x}$, find $f(x) - f\left(\dfrac{1}{2}\right)$.

16. If $f(x) = \dfrac{x^3}{x^2 + 1}$, show that $f(x) + f(-x) = 0$.

17. If $f(x) = x^2 + x + 1$ and $y = x + 1$, find $f(y)$ in terms of x.

18. If $f(x) = \dfrac{2x + 3}{2x - 3}$, find $f(y) - f\left(\dfrac{1}{y}\right)$.

19. If $g(y) = \dfrac{1 - 2y^2}{2y}$, find (a) $2g(y) - g(2y)$; (b) $g\left(\dfrac{x}{2}\right) - \dfrac{1}{2}g(x)$.

20. If $f(s) = -22 - 25s + \frac{1}{2} s^2$, find (a) $3f(s) - f(3s)$; (b) $\frac{1}{3} f(s) - f\left(\frac{s}{3}\right)$.

21. If $\phi(t) = \frac{1 + 2t}{1 - 2t}$, find $\dfrac{\phi(t) - \phi(-t)}{1 + \phi(t)\,\phi(-t)}$.

22. If $X(y) = 3y^2 - 2y + 4$, find (a) $X(y_0 + h) - X(y_0)$;
    (b) $X(2y_0 + h) - X(-y_0)$.

23. If $F(x) = \dfrac{2}{3 - 5x}$, find $F(x_0 + h) - F(x_0)$.

24. If $\phi(w) = 2w^2 - \dfrac{1}{2w + 1}$, find $\dfrac{\phi(w_0 + h) - \phi(w_0)}{h}$.

25. If $S(x) = 2x^2 - 3x + 1$, find $\dfrac{S(m) - S(-p)}{S(m + p)}$.

26. If $H(y) = \dfrac{3 - 2y}{1 + 3y}$, find (a) $H(-y^2)$; (b) $H(y^{1/2})$; (c) $\dfrac{1}{H(y^2)}$; (d) $H[H(y)]$;
    (e) $[H(y)]^2$.

27. If $f(x,y) = 2x^3 - 3xy + 4y^2$, determine $f(1,2)$; $f(2,1)$; $f(-3,4)$; $f(0,5)$;
    $f(0,0)$; $f(a,b)$.

28. If $f(x,y) = 2x^2 - 4xy + 7y^2$, find $f(-2,1)$; $f(3,-1)$; $f\left(\frac{2}{3}, -\frac{1}{2}\right)$; $f(0,-3)$;
    $f(0,0)$.

29. If $f(x,y) = \dfrac{3x^2 - 2xy}{5 + x + y}$ and $g(r,h) = \dfrac{2r^2h - 3h}{r - h}$, find

    (a) $f(2,-1) \cdot g(2,-1)$;   (b) $\dfrac{f(0,0) + \frac{1}{2}g(2,1)}{3g\left(\frac{1}{2},1\right) \cdot f(-1,-2)}$.

30. A strip of copper 100 inches long and 8 inches wide is to be made into a rain gutter by turning up the edges to form a trough with a rectangular cross section. If the bent-up edge is x inches, express the volume of the trough as a function of x.

31. A farmer wishes to fence a rectangular pasture along a straight river requiring no fence. He has enough wire to build a fence 2,000 yards long. If the side bordering on the river is represented by the variable x, express the area of the pasture as a function of x.

32. A parcel-post package is in the form of a rectangular box with a square cross section. If its combined length and girth are 72 inches, and if the side of the cross section is represented by x, express the volume of the box as a function of x.

33. If a Norman window (a rectangle surmounted by a semicircle) has a perimeter of 200 inches, and if the side which is not the diameter of the semicircle is represented by x, express the area of the window as a function of x.

34. If the sum of two numbers is 100 and one of the numbers is represented by x, express (a) their product as a function of x; (b) the sum of their squares as a function of x; (c) the sum of their reciprocals as a function of x.
35. If an open-top tomato can holds 54 cubic inches, and if x represents the number of inches in the radius of the top, express the area of the surface of the can as a function of x.

6-5. PERTINENT FACTS ABOUT FUNCTIONS

Whenever an environment is such that a function can be created, it usually can be expressed in one of the following ways.

1. A chart or table of values which shows how the value of one variable changes as the values of the other variable are specified.
2. As a graph, mapping, or a chart which makes possible the reading of the value from one variable as the value of a second is located and read pictorially.
3. As a written statement which tells the required information of a function in storylike fashion.
4. As an algebraic expression, such as an equation, etc., which is really a shorthand notation for a storylike description of a function.

It is also customary that if the general representative ordered pair for a function f is symbolized as (x,y), then we say that "y is a function of x," which implies that the domain, range, and rule of correspondence are available for the creation of the function. We sometimes use the expression "the function $f(x)$," yet what really is meant is that a set of ordered pairs can be created by using the rule $f(x)$ for values of x designated by a specified domain D. It seems ambiguous to use $f(x)$ to stand for the value of the function f at x, and also to stand for all the ordered pairs which make up the function. There is a distinct difference between the value of a function f at x which is symbolized as $f(x)$, and the function f which represents all the ordered pairs. This type of description as "the function of $f(x)$" instead of "the function f" has become so embedded in mathematical environments that only experience and context material indicate clearly what is desired when one meets this terminology in a mathematics text.

6-6. RELATIONS

As pointed out in the preceding sections, for a set of ordered pairs to qualify as a function it is necessary that no two ordered pairs of the set can have the same first element and distinct second elements. Thus the set

$\{(x,y) \mid x = y^2\}$ is not a function, since a sampling of ordered pairs for

$$\{(x,y) \mid x = y^2\} = \{\ldots,(0,0), (1, -1), (1,1), \ldots\}.$$

A set such as this is called a *relation*. The student should note and re-emphasize the basic fact that every set of ordered pairs is a relation. A *function* is a special type of *relation*. The set of all first elements of the ordered pairs of the relation is the domain D of the relation, and the set of all second elements is the range R of the relation.

A relation, therefore, is any set of ordered pairs; or is merely a correspondence between two sets that associates with each element of the first set either one or more distinct elements of a second set.

If the relation satisfies the added condition that for each choice of domain value, a unique choice of range value corresponds, the produced set of ordered pairs constitutes a function.

Example 1.   The set of ordered pairs $\{(2,1),(2,2),(2,3)\}$ is a relation. The domain of the relation is $D = \{2\}$; the range is $R = \{1,2,3\}$. This set is not a function.

Example 2.   The set

$$\{(x,y) \mid y = x + 4, x \in \{0,1\}\} = \{(0,4),(1,5)\}$$

is both a relation and a function, since each element of the domain $D = \{0,1\}$ is associated with a unique element of the range $R = \{4,5\}$.

Example 3.   The set

$$\{(x,y) \mid x^2 + y^2 = -5\} = \phi$$

is not a function, but a relation. It is impossible for a sum of two positive numbers to equal a negative number. (*Hint*: The square of a nonzero real number is positive.)

6-7.   THE RECTANGULAR COORDINATE SYSTEM

The solution set, or the set of all ordered pairs which satisfy any given relation or function, may be represented by means of a graph. A rectangular coordinate system, sometimes called the Cartesian coordinate system because it was invented by the French philosopher and mathematician René Descartes (1596–1650) is a device for associating an ordered pair of numbers with a point in a plane.

The device consists of two mutually perpendicular real number lines, one horizontal and one vertical* (Fig. 6-2), drawn on a plane. The horizontal line is called the *x-axis*; the other, the *y-axis*; and, together, they are called the *coordinate axes.* The point of intersection of the two axes is called the origin and is usually denoted by O.

---

*In this statement as well as in the subsequent discussion, we assume for simplicity that the arrow on the *y*-axis points upward, as on a vertical blackboard.

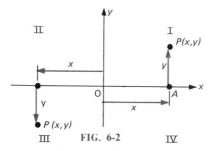

FIG. 6-2

The axes divide the plane into four regions called *quadrants*, which are numbered as shown in Fig. 6-2.

A point such as *P* is located on the plane by means of two distances —*OA* or *x*, and *AP* or *y* in the figure. The horizontal distance is the *abscissa*, the *x-distance*, or simply the *x* of *P*, and is. positive when *P* is to the right of the *y*-axis, zero when *P* is on this axis, and negative when *P* is to the left of it. This is conveniently indicated for memory purposes by the arrow on the right-hand end of the *x*-axis, which shows the positive horizontal direction. Similarly, the vertical distance is the *ordinate*, *y-distance*, or *y* of *P*, and is positive, zero, or negative according as *P* is above, on, or below the *x*-axis. The positive vertical distance is indicated by the arrow pointing upward on the *y*-axis. Together, *x* and *y* are called the *coordinates* of *P*. It is important to note that the coordinates of *P in any quadrant* are *plus x* and *plus y*, though *x* stands for a negative number in quadrants II and III, as does *y* in quadrants III and IV. The entire plane is described as the *xy*-plane and is a graphical interpretation of the totality of all ordered pairs (*x,y*) arising from the Cartesian product $R_e \times R_e = \{(x,y) \mid x \in R_e \land y \in R_e\}$.

Beginning at the origin, we mark in advance equal units of each axis on a scale to fit the problem. Then, in locating, or *plotting* a point with precise numerical coordinates, designated here as *x* and *y*, we measure *x* units to the right or left according as the *x*-value is positive or negative,

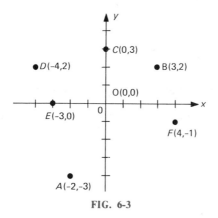

FIG. 6-3

thus reaching a point on the *x*-axis. From this point we measure *y* units upward or downward to the designated point. Thus, to plot $A(-2,-3)$ we measure 2 units to the left of the origin and then 3 units downward. Point *A*, along with others, is shown in Fig. 6-3. Note that a capital letter before the designated coordinates, while not necessary, is convenient when the point is to be referred to again. An equality sign may be inserted between the capital letter and the coordinates if desired, as $A = (-2,-3)$.

6-8. THE GRAPHS OF FUNCTIONS AND RELATIONS

By use of the rectangular coordinate system, we can obtain a geometric representation, or a geometric "picture," of a function or relation. In order to obtain this geometric representation, we require that each ordered pair (x,y) of a function or relation be the coordinates of a point in the Cartesian plane, with *x* as the abscissa and *y* as the ordinate.

This geometric representation is referred to as the *graph of a function*, or, more generally, the *graph of a relation*. It basically represents the set of all points $P(x,y)$ whose coordinates (x,y) constitute the function or relation. When a relation is defined by an equation, its graphical representation is being asked for when one uses the phraseology "graph the equation."

Many times the domain of a relation is the set of all real numbers R_e. Accordingly, the relation or function consists of an infinite number of ordered pairs, and its graph consists of an infinite number of points. Since it is impossible to plot an infinite number of points, it becomes necessary to plot a representative sample of these points and sketch in the remaining ones by connecting the plotted points in an orderly fashion by means of a "smooth" curve. The more that is known about a relation or function, the fewer the number of points are needed to obtain a good approximation of the actual graph for the relation or function.

Example.   Sketch the graph of the function

$$f = \left\{ (x,y) \mid y = f(x) = \frac{x}{2} + 1 \right\}$$

or "graph the equation $y = \frac{x}{2} + 1$."

By means of the equation $y = \frac{x}{2} + 1$ we may find the value of *y* to pair with each of several convenient values of *x*, listing them in a brief table such as:

x	−3	−2	−1	0	1	2	3
y	$-\frac{1}{2}$	0	$\frac{1}{2}$	1	$\frac{3}{2}$	2	$\frac{5}{2}$

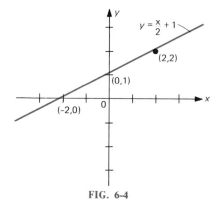

FIG. 6-4

The points whose coordinates are listed are seen in Fig. 6-4 to lie in a straight line. It can be shown that all other points obtained from the table also lie on this line. The line is said to be the graph of the function f, and also the graph or *locus* of the equation $y = \frac{x}{2} + 1$ as well as of $2y = x + 2$, obtained from the original equation by clearing fractions.

Similarly, the graph of the function

$$f = \{(x,y) \mid y = f(x) = 2x^2 - 3x\}$$

or of the equation $y = 2x^2 - 3x$ turns out to be the curve shown in Fig. 6-5.

The coordinates of the points plotted are shown in the following table.

x	-1	$-\frac{1}{2}$	0	$\frac{1}{2}$	1	$\frac{3}{2}$	2	$\frac{5}{2}$
y	5	2	0	-1	-1	0	2	5

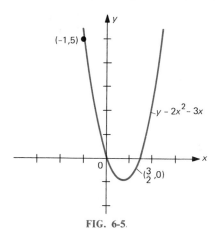

FIG. 6-5.

It is apparent that since a function is a special type of relation, not every possible set of points plotted in the Cartesian plane is the graph of a function. For example, consider the graph of $f = \{(x,y) \mid x = y^2\}$. When the value of y for each of the sample values of x has been calculated and the results tabulated, we obtain

x	0	1	1	2	2	4	4
y	0	−1	1	2	−2	2	−2

Plotting these points, and surmising in an intuitive fashion others, we obtain the graph in Fig. 6-6.

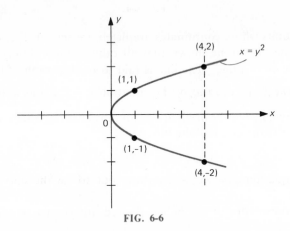

FIG. 6-6

We observe that each value of $x > 0$ is associated with two distinct values of y. Hence this is certainly not the graph of a function. The domain D of this relation is $x \geq 0$. In general, a set of points forming a relation in the Cartesian plane is the graph of a function if and only if no vertical line drawn within the domain of the relation contains more than one of these points. For example, in Fig. 6-6 the vertical line passing through $x = 2$ cuts the curve in two points and hence the set of points is not that of a function. This principle of "line testing" will be referred to as the *vertical line test* for the determination of functions from graphical representations.

EXERCISE 6-2

Plot the points having the following pairs of coordinates. (Remember that the first number is the value of x.)

1. (3,1).
2. (1,4).
3. (2,3).
4. (3,5).
5. (2,6).
6. (0,0).
7. (−2,1).
8. (3,−4).
9. (−1,−2).
10. (0,3).
11. (−2,0).
12. (0,−1).
13. (4,0).

Make a table of sample points for each of the following functions $f(x)$ in 14 to 40, where $f = \{(x,y) \mid y = f(x)\}$. What is the domain in each of the functions?

14. $x + 1$.

15. $x - 2$.

16. $x + 3$.

17. $x - 4$.

18. $2x + 1$.

19. $1 - 2x$.

20. $3x - 2$.

21. $2 - 3x$.

22. $x - \dfrac{1}{2}$.

23. $x + \dfrac{3}{4}$.

24. $\dfrac{x}{2} - 1$.

25. $\dfrac{x}{3} + 1$.

26. x^2.

27. $x^2 + 2$.

28. $x^2 - 2$.

29. $2 - x^2$.

30. $1 - 2x^2$.

31. $x^2 + x - 1$.

32. $2x^2 - 3x$.

33. $x^2 - 4x - 1$.

34. $x^2 + 2x - 2$.

35. $\dfrac{1}{x}$.

36. $\dfrac{1}{x + 1}$.

37. $\dfrac{1}{x} + 1$.

38. $\dfrac{1}{x^2}$.

39. $\dfrac{2}{x - 1}$.

40. $\dfrac{2}{x} - 1$.

41. $f = \{(x,y) \mid y = f(x) = \sqrt{x}\}$.
42. $f = \{(x,y) \mid y = f(x) = -\sqrt{x}\}$.
43. $f = \{(x,y) \mid y = f(x) = \sqrt{4 - x^2}\}$.
44. $f = \{(x,y) \mid y = f(x) = -\sqrt{4 - x^2}\}$.
45. Use the "vertical line test" to tell which of the following represent functions.

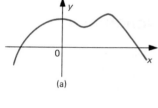

(a)

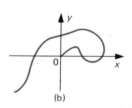

(b)

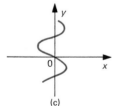

(c)

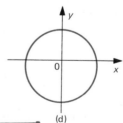

(d)

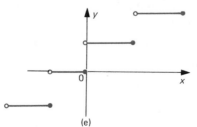

(e)

PROB. 45

6-9. VARIABLES AND CONSTANTS

If an equation in x and y is solved for y, and takes on the explicit form

$$(1) \qquad\qquad y = f(x),$$

x is not only referred to as the open variable but is also called the *independent* variable, and y, or $f(x)$, the *dependent* variable. Similarly, if the same equation were solved for x and took on the explicit form

$$(2) \qquad\qquad x = g(y),$$

y is the independent variable and x, or $g(y)$, is the dependent variable. To find corresponding pairs of values it is convenient to assign values to the independent variable and the value of the dependent variable will follow from the given equation.

A letter representing the same number throughout a precise problem is called a *constant.*

Symbols representing constants and variables are usually taken, respectively, from the first and last parts of the alphabet. By common usage and agreement some constants are frequently represented by the same number symbol irrespective of the different problems in which they may appear, such as the constant π, (the ratio of the circumference to the diameter of a circle).

6-10. THE GRAPH OF A LINEAR FUNCTION OF x

A *linear* function of x is a rational integral function of the form

$$f = \{(x,y) \mid y = f(x) = ax + b\}$$

where a and b are constants and $a \neq 0$.

Examples:

$$f = \{(x,y) \mid y = f(x) = 3x - 2\}$$

and

$$g = \left\{ (x,y) \mid y = g(x) = 5 - \frac{x}{2} \right\}$$

It is shown in the branch of mathematics called *analytic geometry* that the graph of the function

$$f = \{(x,y) \mid y = f(x) = ax + b\},$$

or of the equation

$$(1) \qquad\qquad y = f(x) = ax + b,$$

is a straight line. Evidently it crosses the y-axis at the point $(0,b)$. The second point needed to determine the line may be found by assigning any value to x at will. Thus $y = x + 1$ passes through $(0,1)$ and $(2,3)$; $y = 2x$, through $(0,0)$ and $(3,6)$.

6-11. THE GRAPH OF A LINEAR EQUATION IN ONE OR TWO VARIABLES

The general linear equation in x or y or both may be written in the form

(1)
$$ax + by = c,$$

where a, b, and c are constants and both a and b cannot be zero.

When two equations are so related that all pairs of values which satisfy one also satisfy the other, and vice versa, they are said to be *dependent*. Evidently, from the definition, two dependent equations have the same graph.

Example. $x + y = 1$ and $2x + 2y = 2$ are both satisfied by $(0,1)$, $(1,0)$, $(2,-1)$, etc.

The operations leading to dependent equations are essentially the same as those yielding equivalent equations in one variable (Sec. 5-6). That is, terms may be transposed, or both members may be multiplied or divided by any number or constant except zero. If $b \neq 0$ in (1), the solution for y, namely

(2)
$$y = -\frac{a}{b}x + \frac{c}{b},$$

involves operations of this sort, so that (2) and (1) are dependent and their graphs are the same. Since y is a linear function of x in (2), this graph is a straight line.

If $b = 0$, then $a \neq 0$ by the statement following (1), so that (1) takes the form

(3)
$$ax = c,$$

whose graph is the vertical line through $\left(\frac{c}{a},0\right)$, $\left(\frac{c}{a},1\right)$, $\left(\frac{c}{a},2\right)$, etc. For evidently the value of y is not restricted in any way by (3), while x is restricted to the one value, $\frac{c}{a}$. This graph is a straight line, but does not represent a function. Why? _____

Example. $2x = 3$, or $x = \frac{3}{2}$, is the equation of a line parallel to the y-axis and $\frac{3}{2}$ units to the right. Is this graph that of a function? _____

Similarly, if $a = 0$, so that $b \neq 0$, the graph of

(4) $$by = c$$

is a horizontal line. This graph does represent a function. Why? _____

Example. The line $y = -2$ is parallel to the x-axis and 2 units below it. Is this graph that of a function? _____

Our argument, then, leads to this conclusion:

The graph of a linear equation in x *or* y *or both is a straight line.* However, not all line graphs represent linear functions. Only those for which $b \neq 0$ in $ax + by = c$ lead to functions, where x is the domain or independent variable.

EXERCISE 6-3

Plot the graph of each of the following:

1. $f = \{(x,y) \mid x - y = 0\}$.
2. $x + y = 0$.
3. $f = \{(x,y) \mid x + y - 1 = 0\}$.
4. $x - y + 1 = 0$.
5. $f = \{(x,y) \mid 2x - y = 2\}$.
6. $3x + y - 6 = 0$.
7. $f = \{(x,y) \mid 4x - y + 4 = 0\}$.
8. $2x - 3y + 6 = 0$.
9. $f = \{(x,y) \mid 3x + 2y - 6 = 0\}$.
10. $2x - y + 4 = 0$.
11. $f = \{x,y) \mid 2x + y - 4 = 0\}$.
12. $3x + y = 5$.
13. $f = \{(x,y) \mid 2x + 3 = 0\}$. Is this a function?
14. $5y - 1 = 0$. Is this a function?
15. $f = \{(x,y) \mid x = -1\}$.
16. $y = -5$.
17. $f = \{(x,y) \mid x = 0\}$.
18. $y = 0$.

19-30. Solve each equation involved in Probs. 1–12 for y in terms of x, and then solve it for x in terms of y. Write results in set notation.

31. Given $5F - 9C = 160$, the relation between the Fahrenheit (F) and centigrade (C) temperature readings, express (a), F as a function of C; (b), C as a function of F; (c), $f(F + 40)$ as a function of C.

32. Given $I = Prt$, express (a), P as a function of I, r, and t; (b), r as a function of I, P, and t; and (c), t as a function of I, P, and r.

6-12. GRAPHS OF NONMATHEMATICAL FUNCTIONS

Often it is helpful and suggestive to make a graph showing the relation between two quantities even though it may not yet be possible to express one as a mathematical function of the other. In business, science, war, and practically every field of human activity, graphs or charts are used very extensively.

For example, the meteorologist, or "weatherman," might record the Fahrenheit temperature in a given city for every third hour of the day, getting the following result:

Time	a.m.	0	3	6	9	p.m.	12	3	6	9	12
Temperature		4	−6	−6	5		20	35	25	14	6

The graph (Fig. 6-7) with the time as the independent variable shows clearly how the temperature has changed during the day. In this case it is

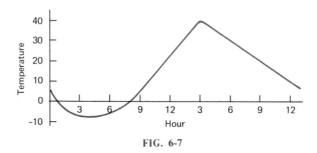

FIG. 6-7

advisable to draw a smooth curve through the plotted points to indicate that the temperature changes continuously, or from moment to moment. On the other hand, if we record quantities such as the yield per year of an acre of wheat, the smoothly curved line would be meaningless, and a broken line such as that in Fig. 6-8 is better.

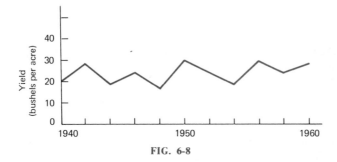

FIG. 6-8

The types of graphs used in practice are much too numerous to be shown here. Many of them, however, are based upon some modification of the coordinate system. Perhaps the most frequently used independent variable is *time*, which may be measured in seconds, minutes, hours, days, years, etc. It is interesting to note that sometimes in this type of graph, the results may be carried more or less reliably into the future.

EXERCISE 6-4

Graph the relations indicated by the data in the following problems. Use the type of curve (smooth or broken) which seems to be more appropriate for each problem.

1. Given the following readings, graph the temperature as a function of the time. Can you suggest an explanation of the unusual conditions here indicated?

Time, a.m.	4	5	6	7	8	9	10	11	12
Temp, F	60	62	65	69	75	75	65	55	55

2. Given the following data, graph the yield per year of a certain farm in bushels of corn.

Year	1920	1924	1928	1932	1936	1940	1944
Yield	600	750	600	550	510	675	790

3. Graph the indicated weight of a boy as a function of his age:

Age, years	1	2	3	4	5	6	7	8	9	10
Weight, lb	15	25	33	39	44	49	54	60	68	77

4. A river gauge registered as follows. Graph the water level as a function of the time.

Hour, a.m.	4	5	6	7	8	9	10	11	12
Level, feet	0	$\frac{5}{12}$	$\frac{5}{6}$	$\frac{5}{4}$	2	$\frac{3}{2}$	1	$\frac{1}{4}$	$-\frac{5}{12}$

5. The graph of Fig. 6-9, from the *Beacon Journal*, indicates the volume of business in Lodi for a period of one year beginning January 1:

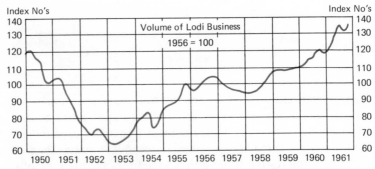

Make out a table giving approximate values of the index number corresponding to the beginning of each year during the period.

6. In 1948 the Office of Vital Statistics, Federal Security Agency, issued the following table of the expectation of life at various ages of male and female whites in the United States.

Age	Expectation of Life	
	Male	Female
0	65.5	71.0
20	49.0	53.8
40	30.7	35.0
45	26.5	30.5
50	22.4	26.2
55	18.8	22.0
60	15.4	18.1
65	12.4	14.4
70	9.8	11.2

Draw separate graphs, using the same coordinate axes, showing the expectation of life for the two sexes as a function of the age.

7. The A & B Department Store held a sale each month during the year 1969, and the following table shows the receipts for each month of the year:

Month	Receipts	Month	Receipts
January	$25,521	July	$18,020
February	19,300	August	19,200
March	21,100	September	29,300
April	27,490	October	26,395
May	28,431	November	21,400
June	21,074	December	29,906

Plot a graph showing the changes in the receipts from month to month.

chapter 7

Simultaneous Linear Equations

7-1. EQUATIONS OF THE FIRST DEGREE IN TWO VARIABLES

An equation which can be written in the form

$$(1) \qquad\qquad ax + by + c = 0,$$

where a, b, and c are real numbers and a and b are not both zero, is called a *linear equation* in the variables x and y, or an *equation of the first degree* in the variables x and y. The solution set, or simply the solution of equation (1) is the set of ordered pairs, specified by

$$(2) \; f = \{(x,y) \in R_e \times R_e \,|\, ax + by + c = 0 \wedge (a \neq 0 \vee b \neq 0)\}.$$

An ordered pair (x_1,y_1) is an element of f, or $(x_1,y_1) \in f$ if and only if $(x_1 y_1)$ has the property that equation (1) becomes an identity when x_1 is substituted for x and y_1 is substituted for y.

Two connectives have been used within the parentheses of the solution set (2), namely "$\wedge$," and "$\vee$." The connective "$\wedge$" has already been brought to our attention in Sec. 6-2. It was indicated that this symbol is read as "and" or, saying it another way, "at the same time." The symbol "$\vee$" is also an important connective and is read "or" but is not the "or" in the usual sense. It takes on the meaning of "and/or," which, interpreted another way, says "either or both," also "either but at least one." For example, in (2), the descriptive portion

$$ax + by + c = 0 \wedge (a \neq 0 \vee b \neq 0)$$

within the parentheses reads in English:

"The defining condition $ax + by + c = 0$ *at the same time* that a is *nonzero and b is zero*; or that *a is zero and b is nonzero*; or that *a is non-zero and b is nonzero*."

The *connectives* $\wedge$ and $\vee$ are conveniently used between two defining conditions to convey the meanings indicated in the preceding paragraph. They are sometimes referred to as "*conjunctive and* " ($\wedge$), and "*disjunctive or* " ($\vee$). When used in this text hereafter they will be understood to have the meanings that have been described.

We point out the similarity in meaning in Chapter 1 for "$\cap$," and "$\cup$" as used between two sets and "$\wedge$" and "$\vee$" now being used between defining conditions.

The solution set (2) for an equation of the first degree in two variables x and y is an infinite set of ordered pairs (x,y), which can be graphically represented as a straight line in the $R_e \times R_e$ space. As a consequence, an equation of the form (1) is referred to as a *linear equation*.

7-2. LINEAR SYSTEMS OF EQUATIONS

A set of m linear equations in n variables is called a linear system of equations. The solution set for such a system is the set of ordered n-tuples that are solutions to all m equations simultaneously. For example, if $n = m = 2$, and the two variables x and y are related in two separate ways by means of the defining conditions

$$3x - 5y = 12 \quad \text{and} \quad 3x - 2y = 3,$$

then the solution sets for these defining conditions may be expressed as

$$f_1 = \{(x,y) \mid 3x - 5y = 12\} \quad \text{and} \quad f_2 = \{(x,y) \mid 3x - 2y = 3\}.$$

The intersection of set f_1 with that of f_2 (i.e., $f_1 \cap f_2$) becomes the solution set for the system of simultaneous equations

$$3x - 5y = 12$$
$$\wedge$$
$$3x - 2y = 3.$$

This may be expressed in set notation as

$$f = f_1 \cap f_2 = \{(x,y) \mid 3x - 5y = 12\} \cap \{(x,y) \mid 3x - 2y = 3\}$$

or as

$$f = \{(x,y) \mid 3x - 5y = 12 \wedge 3x - 2y = 3\},$$

and in this case is the set $\{(-1,-3)\}$ made up of the singleton element $(-1,-3)$. It is a solution because when $x = -1$ and $y = -3$ are substituted into both of these equations, true statements result.

In this example the graphs of f_1 and f_2 are both straight lines, distinct and not parallel. As a consequence the solution set f is a set which consists of a single ordered pair; the graph of f is the intersection ordered pair of the graphs of f_1 and f_2.

Two simultaneous systems of equations are equivalent if and only if they possess the same solution set. Thus

$$f_1 \cap f_2 = \{(x,y) \mid x + y = 4\} \cap \{(x,y) \mid x - y = 0\}$$

and

$$g_1 \cap g_2 = \{(x,y) \mid x = 2\} \cap \{(x,y) \mid 3x - y = 4\}$$

are equivalent because $\{(2,2)\}$ is the solution set for both of these systems.

It is customary to state the problem of finding the solution set, or solution, for a system such as

$$f = \{(x,y) \mid a_1x + b_1y + c_1 = 0\} \cap \{(x,y) \mid a_2x + b_2y + c_2 = 0\}$$

by writing same in the more concise form:

$$a_1x + b_1y + c_1 = 0$$
$$\wedge$$
$$a_2x + b_2y + c_2 = 0.$$

This implies that we are seeking the common ordered pairs that satisfy both equations simultaneously.

In this chapter several methods for solving simultaneous systems of two or three linear equations, in two or three variables respectively, will be explored.

It should be noted and emphasized that if (x_1, y_1) is a solution of $a_1x + b_1y + c_1 = 0$ and $a_2x + b_2y + c_2 = 0$ simultaneously, then it is also a solution of

(3) $$a_1x + b_1y + c_1 + k(a_2x + b_2y + c_2) = 0$$

where k is any real number. For example, since $(-1,-3)$ has been obtained as the solution of $3x - 5y = 12$ and $3x - 2y = 3$, it is also a solution of $3x - 5y - 12 + k(3x - 2y - 3) = 0$, because substituting $x = -1$ and $y = -3$ into this equation results in a true statement. Thus for $k = 1$, $\frac{1}{2}$, $\sqrt{3}$, etc., (any real number), $3x - 5y - 12 + k(3x - 2y - 3) = 0$ has a solution $(-1,-3)$. This important concept will be used in the context of what follows for defining conditions like (3).

7-3.   ALGEBRAIC SOLUTIONS OF SIMULTANEOUS LINEAR EQUATIONS

The algebraic solution of a system of two simultaneous linear equations in two unknowns depends on a process called elimination. In this process, the system is reduced to a system of one equation in one unknown. The elimination procedure may be accomplished either by (A) addition and subtraction, (B) substitution, or (C) a combination of these two methods. These formal procedures will now be illustrated by examples. Let us consider the simultaneous equations involved in

(1) $$f_1 = \{(x,y) \mid 3x - 4y = 2\}$$

and

(2) $$f_2 = \{(x,y) \mid 4x + 3y = 11\}.$$

A. Addition-and-Subtraction Method

(*Note*. The meanings of the directions in parentheses below are as here indicated: (1) × 3 means that both members of the defining condition in (1) are multiplied by 3; (3) + (4) means that the corresponding members of the defining conditions in (3) and (4) are added, and so on.)

(3)	(1) × 3	$9x - 12y = 6.$
(4)	(2) × 4	$16x + 12y = 44.$
(5)	(3) + (4)	$25x = 50.$

Hence

(6)		$x = 2.$
(7)	(1) × 4	$12x - 16y = 8.$
(8)	(2) × 3	$12x + 9y = 33.$
(9)	(8) − (7)	$25y = 25.$

Hence

(10)	$y = 1.$

The solution set is {(2,1)}.

B. Substitution Method

(11) Solve (1) for y, $\qquad y = \dfrac{3x - 2}{4}.$

(12) Substitute in (2), $\qquad 4x + \dfrac{3(3x - 2)}{4} = 11.$

(13) Solve (12), $\qquad x = 2.$

(14) Substitute in (1), $\qquad 3 \cdot 2 - 4y = 2.$

Hence

$$y = 1.$$

Solution: {(2,1)}

C. Combination Method

The combination method used in solving a system of simultaneous equations consists of solving for one unknown by Method A, then substituting this value in either of the original equations to find the second unknown.

It should be kept clearly in mind that the solution of two simultaneous equations consists of a set of ordered pairs which satisfies both equations. Applying this test to our solution of (1) and (2), we have

	$3 \cdot 2 - 4 \cdot 1 = 2$	(correct)
(15)	$4 \cdot 2 + 3 \cdot 1 = 11$	(correct)

Hence the ordered pair $(2, 1)$ is a solution.

But why, it may be asked, does equation (5) give us the x-value of the equation pair? How can we add the $-12y$ of (3) to the $+12y$ of (4)

when we know from the graphs of (3) and (4) that y can have any value in either equation, so that the two y's may be representing different numbers and hence need not be equal?

The answer may be stated thus: In solving simultaneous equations the letters are considered not as variables but as unknown constants. Thus x and y are the same constants in each of equations (1) to (10), and their numerical values are exposed in equations (6) and (10).

The choice of the most efficient of the three methods for a given problem is a matter of judgment. In general, if the first unknown found is a rational number or a very simple algebraic expression such as $2a$, $3b$, etc., it is quicker to find the second unknown by substitution; otherwise, by addition and subtraction. In some trivial cases, such as $2x = 3$, $4y = 7$, none of the three methods applies; but here of course the solution $\left\{\left(\frac{3}{2}, \frac{7}{4}\right)\right\}$ is seen by inspection. When some of the coefficients are literal, Method A is usually preferable.

Example. Solve for x and y:

(16) $a_1x + b_1y = c_1,$

$\wedge$

(17) $a_2x + b_2y = c_2.$

Solution:

(18)   (16) $\times b_2$ $a_1b_2x + b_1b_2y = b_2c_1.$

(19)   (17) $\times b_1$ $a_2b_1x + b_1b_2y = b_1c_2.$

(20)   (18) $-$ (19) $a_1b_2x - a_2b_1x = b_2c_1 - b_1c_2.$

or

(21) $(a_1b_2 - a_2b_1)x = b_2c_1 - b_1c_2.$

Hence

(22) $x = \dfrac{b_2c_1 - b_1c_2}{a_1b_2 - a_2b_1}.$

(23)   (16) $\times a_2$ $a_1a_2x + a_2b_1y = a_2c_1.$

(24)   (17) $\times a_1$ $a_1a_2x + a_1b_2y = a_1c_2.$

(25   (23) $-$ (24) $a_2b_1y - a_1b_2y = a_2c_1 - a_1c_2.$

or

(26) $(a_2b_1 - a_1b_2)y = a_2c_1 - a_1c_2.$

Hence

(27) $y = \dfrac{a_2c_1 - a_1c_2}{a_2b_1 - a_1b_2}.$

The solution set is $\left\{\left(\dfrac{b_2c_1 - b_1c_2}{a_1b_2 - a_2b_1}, \dfrac{a_2c_1 - a_1c_2}{a_2b_1 - a_1b_2}\right)\right\}$. It may be checked by direct substitution in (16) and (17).

7-4. THE GRAPHICAL SOLUTION OF SIMULTANEOUS LINEAR EQUATIONS

If we graph the lines (1) and (2), Sec. 7-3, we find that they intersect at the ordered pair (2,1) as illustrated in Fig. 7-1. This ordered pair lies

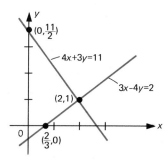

FIG. 7-1

on both lines simultaneously; that is, it is an ordered pair common to the two lines. Thus if

$$f_1 = \{(x,y) \mid a_1x + b_1y + c_1 = 0\}$$

and

$$f_2 = \{(x,y) \mid a_2x + b_2y + c_2 = 0\},$$

then $f_1 \cap f_2$ is the solution set of the system of the two linear equations. The graph of $f_1 \cap f_2$, as indicated in Sec. 7-3, will be the intersection of the graphs of f_1 and f_2, which is $\{(2,1)\}$. Since this solution set involves the single element (2,1), for brevity we sometimes say the solution set is (2,1) and omit the outside parentheses. However, this is not advisable, and it is suggested that if you refer to the point of intersection as (2,1), the parentheses may be omitted, but not when you refer to the solution set $\{(2,1)\}$.

In general, to solve graphically any two linear equations with numerical coefficients, draw the two straight lines involved and then find by inspection of the figure the coordinates of their common point, or point of intersection, if they have one. These estimated coordinates should be nearly the same as the correct solution-pair found algebraically; and of course would be exactly the same if the figure were perfectly accurate, which is impossible. Thus the graphical solution is a check on the algebraic one, and vice versa.

New light is now thrown on the algebraic difficulties that appear in some attempted solutions. Two straight lines may intersect, coincide, or be parallel, and each of these three possibilities leads to a different type of algebraic result.

If the solution set of two linear equations in two variables (a) contains exactly one solution, then the equations are called *consistent and independent* (their lines intersect in a single ordered pair—see Fig. 7-2);

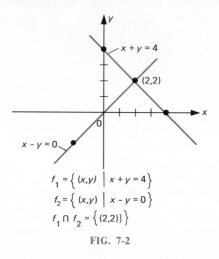

$$f_1 = \left\{ (x,y) \mid x + y = 4 \right\}$$
$$f_2 = \left\{ (x,y) \mid x - y = 0 \right\}$$
$$f_1 \cap f_2 = \left\{ (2,2) \right\}$$

FIG. 7-2

(b) is the empty set, then the equations are called *inconsistent* (their lines are parallel—see Fig. 7-3); (c) contain infinitely many solutions, then the

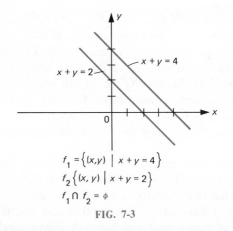

$$f_1 = \left\{ (x,y) \mid x + y = 4 \right\}$$
$$f_2 \left\{ (x, y) \mid x + y = 2 \right\}$$
$$f_1 \cap f_2 = \phi$$

FIG. 7-3

equations are called *consistent and dependent* (their lines coincide—see Fig. 7-4).

To test these possibilities graphically, of course, one merely draws the lines. A simple algebraic test is the following.

Let any two linear equations in two unknowns be written so that their right members contain all terms not involving the unknowns. Then

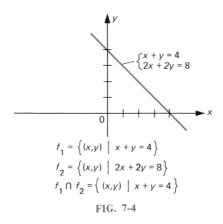

$$f_1 = \left\{ (x,y) \mid x + y = 4 \right\}$$
$$f_2 = \left\{ (x,y) \mid 2x + 2y = 8 \right\}$$
$$f_1 \cap f_2 = \left\{ (x,y) \mid x + y = 4 \right\}$$

FIG. 7-4

if their left members cannot be made identical by multiplying one equation by a constant, they are independent. When the left-hand members can be and are made identical, they are dependent when the right-hand members are then equal, and inconsistent otherwise.

Example 1. The equations

(1)
$$2x + y = 3$$

and

(2)
$$x - 3y = -2$$

are consistent and independent, since the left-hand sides cannot be made identical. The solution pair is $(1,1)$, or its solution set is $\{(1,1)\}$ when considered simultaneously.

Example 2. The equations

(3)
$$2x + y = 3$$

and

(4)
$$4x + 2y = 7$$

are inconsistent, since when the left-hand members are made identical the right-hand members are unequal. Clearly no pair of values for x and y can make $4x + 2y$ equal to both 6 and 7. The solution set here is $\emptyset$.

Example 3. The equations

(5)
$$2x + y = 3,$$

and

(6) $$4x + 2y = 6$$

considered simultaneously are consistent and dependent, since (5) can be made identical with (6) by multiplying its members by 2. Ordered pairs on the common line, or simultaneous algebraic solutions, are (0,3), (1,1), (2, – 1), etc. The solution set can be represented as either

$$\{(x,y) \mid 2x + y = 3\} \quad \text{or} \quad \{(x,y) \mid 4x + 2y = 6\}.$$

EXERCISE 7-1

By the method of addition and subtraction obtain the solution set in the following systems of equations considered simultaneously:

1. $x + 3y = 11$
   $\wedge$
   $x - 5y = -13.$

2. $3x + 4y = -1$
   $\wedge$
   $x + 5y = 7.$

3. $11x - 6y = 4$
   $\wedge$
   $4x + 15y = 53.$

4. $9x + 7y = 8$
   $\wedge$
   $8x - 9y = -69.$

5. $9x + 8y = 3$
   $\wedge$
   $9x - 8y = -77.$

6. $7x + 3y = 2$
   $\wedge$
   $8x + 7y = -2.$

7. $9x - 5y = -1$
   $\wedge$
   $10x - 8y = 5.$

8. $5x - 11y = -4$
   $\wedge$
   $6x - 8y = -10.$

9. $7x + 3y = 4$
   $\wedge$
   $8x + 7y = 26.$

10. $2x + 6y = -3$
    $\wedge$
    $3x - 5y = 6.$

11. $15x + 4y = 7$
    $\wedge$
    $6x + 14y = 9.$

12. $3x + 5y = -9$
    $\wedge$
    $4x - 3y = 17.$

13. $7x - 2y = 15$
    $\wedge$
    $6x - y = 10.$

14. $x + 3y = 9$
    $\wedge$
    $4x + 5y = 22.$

15. $2x - 3 = 5y$
    $\wedge$
    $y + 5 = 3x.$

By the substitution method obtain the solution set in the following simultaneous systems of equations:

16. $3x = 6$
    $\wedge$
    $2x - y = 7.$

17. $3y = 0$
    $\wedge$
    $3x + 2y = 6.$

18. $5x = -10$
    $\wedge$
    $3x + 4y = 2.$

19. $x + 4y = 16$
    $\wedge$
    $2x + 3y = 17.$

20. $7x + 6y = -11$
    $\wedge$
    $8x - 5y = -60.$

21. $6x - 9y = -7$
    $\wedge$
    $9x + 5y = 8.$

22. $10x + 12y = -7$
    $\wedge$
    $8x + 9y = -8.$

23. $2x - 3y = -29$
    $\wedge$
    $5x + 8y = 5.$

24. $15x - 14y = -15$
    $\wedge$
    $10x - 6y = -5.$

25. $3y = -9$
    $\wedge$
    $4x + 2y = 2.$

26. $4x = 12$
    $\wedge$
    $3x = y + 3.$

27. $2x + 9y = 13$
    $\wedge$
    $6x - 7y = -63.$

28–39. Graph the pairs of equations in Probs. 16–27, and estimate the coordinates of the points of interesection. Compare with the algebraic solutions.

Solve algebraically and obtain the solution set for the following simultaneous systems of equations.

40. $\dfrac{3}{2x - y} = \dfrac{1}{2}$
    $\wedge$
    $\dfrac{2}{x + y} = \dfrac{2}{3}.$

41. $\dfrac{1}{x + 2y} = \dfrac{1}{3}$
    $\wedge$
    $\dfrac{2}{2x - y} = \dfrac{1}{2}.$

42. $\dfrac{5}{3x + y} = \dfrac{1}{4}$
    $\wedge$
    $\dfrac{4}{x - 3y} = \dfrac{1}{3}.$

43. $\dfrac{2}{x - y} = \dfrac{1}{5}$
    $\wedge$
    $\dfrac{3}{x + y} = \dfrac{1}{3}.$

44. $\dfrac{5}{3x + 2y} = \dfrac{3}{4}$
    $\wedge$
    $\dfrac{3}{2x - 3y} = \dfrac{2}{3}.$

45. $\dfrac{5x}{y - 2} = \dfrac{7}{3}$
    $\wedge$
    $\dfrac{y}{x - 2} = \dfrac{3}{4}.$

46. $\dfrac{3}{2} = \dfrac{5y}{2x - 3}$
    $\wedge$
    $\dfrac{2}{3} = \dfrac{3x}{x + y}.$

47. $\dfrac{5}{2} = \dfrac{3x}{3 + y}$
    $\wedge$
    $\dfrac{3}{4} = \dfrac{y}{3x - 2}.$

48. $\dfrac{3y}{3y + 2} = 2$
    $\wedge$
    $\dfrac{4x}{4y - 3} = 1.$

49. $ax + by = ab$
    $\wedge$
    $bx - ay = b^2.$

50. $x + y = 2a$
    $\wedge$
    $x - y = 2b$

51. $ax + by = 2a$
    $\wedge$
    $ax - by = 2b$

52. $ax + by = 2a^2 + ab - b^2$
    $\wedge$
    $ax - by = ab + b^2.$

53. $3x = 4$
    $\wedge$
    $5y = 7$

54. $5ax = -10$
    $\wedge$
    $3by = 18.$

In Probs. 55–63, which pairs of equations produce the empty set and which have more than one ordered pair in the solution set?

55. $3x - 4y = 5$
    $\wedge$
    $6x - 8y = 20.$

56. $2x - 3y = 4$
    $\wedge$
    $4x - 6y = 8.$

57. $2x = 14 - y$
    $\wedge$
    $2y = 28 - 4x$

58. $5x = 7 - 3y$

$\wedge$

$6y = 10(1 - x).$

59. $6x - 5 = 10y$

$\wedge$

$3x - 2 = 5y$

60. $2x \quad = 1 + 3y$

$\wedge$

$6x - 9y = 3$

61. $ax + by = 5$

$\wedge$

$ax + by = 10.$

62. $ax = c - by$

$\wedge$

$3by = 3c - 3ax$

63. $ax - by = 0$

$\wedge$

$ax - by = -0$

64. $\dfrac{1}{x} + \dfrac{3}{y} = 2$

$\wedge$

$\dfrac{3}{x} - \dfrac{2}{y} = \dfrac{7}{3}$. *Hint:* Consider the unknowns as $\dfrac{1}{x}$ and $\dfrac{1}{y}$. The equations then

become: $u + 3v = 2$ and $3u - 2v = \dfrac{7}{3}$, where $u = \dfrac{1}{x}$ and $v = \dfrac{1}{y}$. Solving, we

find that $u = 1$, $v = \dfrac{1}{3}$, or $\dfrac{1}{x} = 1$, $\dfrac{1}{y} = \dfrac{1}{3}$. Hence the final solution is $x = 1$,

$y = 3$, or the solution set is $\{(1,3)\}$.

65. $\dfrac{2}{x} - \dfrac{1}{y} = 0$

$\wedge$

$\dfrac{3}{x} + \dfrac{1}{y} = \dfrac{5}{2}$

66. $\dfrac{4}{x} + \dfrac{3}{y} = 5$

$\wedge$

$\dfrac{3}{x} - \dfrac{3}{y} = 2$

67. $\dfrac{4}{x} + \dfrac{3}{y} = 5$

$\wedge$

$\dfrac{6}{x} + \dfrac{6}{y} = 5$

68. $\dfrac{2}{x} + \dfrac{1}{y} = 7$

$\wedge$

$\dfrac{1}{x} + \dfrac{2}{y} = 8.$

69. $\dfrac{1}{x} - \dfrac{3}{y} = \dfrac{5}{2}$

$\wedge$

$\dfrac{2}{x} - \dfrac{5}{y} = \dfrac{11}{2}.$

70. $\dfrac{2a}{x} + \dfrac{3b}{y} = 1$

$\wedge$

$\dfrac{2a}{x} - \dfrac{3b}{y} = 3.$

7-5. THREE EQUATIONS AND THREE UNKNOWNS

Consider the simultaneous system represented by

(1) $$f_1 = \{(x,y,z) \mid 2x + y + 2z = 1\}$$
(2) $$f_2 = \{(x,y,z) \mid 4x - y - z = 3\}$$
(3) $$f_3 = \{(x,y,z) \mid 6x + 2y + 3z = 2\}.$$

The solution set desired is $f_1 \cap f_2 \cap f_3$. In other words an ordered triple (x,y,z) is being sought which will satisfy the defining conditions in (1), (2), and (3) simultaneously. Again consider x,y,z as constants whose values are fixed in advance, so that they may be combined at will.

Here a "guiding principle" will be found helpful to avoid "working in a circle," to wit: *Eliminate one unknown at a time, using all of the equations in which it appears*, thus reducing the problem to one with fewer unknowns and fewer equations. For example, to solve the defining conditions in (1) to (3) z may be eliminated first (if so desired), thus:

(4)	(1) unchanged	$2x + y + 2z = 1.$
(5)	(2) × 2	$8x - 2y - 2z = 6.$
(6)	(4) + (5)	$10x - y = 7.$

Equation (3) must now be used, either with (1) or with (2), to eliminate the same unknown; in this case z.

(7)	(3) unchanged	$6x + 2y + 3z = 2.$
(8)	(2) × 3	$12x - 3y - 3z = 9.$
(9)	(7) + (8)	$18x - y = 11.$

There remain two equations in the same two unknowns, (6) and (9). Solving these, the values $x = \frac{1}{2}$, $y = -2$ are obtained. Substitution of these values in (1) yields $z = 1$. The tentative (or untested) solution is then the ordered triple $\left(\frac{1}{2}, -2, 1\right)$. The test is not complete until it is shown that these values satisfy all three original equations. The solution set here is $\left\{\left(\frac{1}{2}, -2, 1\right)\right\}$.

If a letter is missing in one of the simultaneous equations, it is usually advisable to eliminate this letter first. Thus, given

(10)	$2x - 3y - z = 1$
(11)	$x + 2y + 2z = 2$
(12)	$y - 3z = 2,$

x should be removed from (10) and (11), and the resulting equation can then be used with (12) to get y and z.

Thus far only equations with two and three unknowns have been considered. In general, if the number of simultaneous equations is the same as the number of unknowns, it is often (though not always) possible to find a set of values which will satisfy all of the equations. *The guiding principle* stated above equation (4) holds good in all cases.

EXERCISE 7-2

Solve the following simultaneous systems of equations and obtain the solution sets:

1. $x + y + z = 6$
    $\wedge$
    $x + y - z = 0$
    $\wedge$
    $x - y + z = 2.$

2. $x - y + z = 0$
    $\wedge$
    $x + y - z = 2$
    $\wedge$
    $x - y - z = 4.$

3. $x - y + z = 4$
   $\wedge$
   $x + y - z = 2$
   $\wedge$
   $x - y - z = -4.$

4. $x + y + z = 0$
   $\wedge$
   $x - y - z = 2$
   $\wedge$
   $x - y + z = 2.$

5. $x + 2y + z = 1$
   $\wedge$
   $2x - y - 2z = 2$
   $\wedge$
   $x - 2y + 2z = 3.$

6. $2x - 3y + z = 5$
   $\wedge$
   $x + 2y - 2z = 3$
   $\wedge$
   $3x + y - z = 2.$

7. $5x + 3y - z = 4$
   $\wedge$
   $4x - y + 2z = 3$
   $\wedge$
   $3x + 4y + z = 5.$

8. $6x - 5y + 3z = 4$
   $\wedge$
   $5x + 3y - 2z = 5$
   $\wedge$
   $3x + 2y + z = 2.$

9. $4x - 2y + 3z = 5$
   $\wedge$
   $3x + y + 2z = 3$
   $\wedge$
   $2x - 3y + 5z = 4.$

10. $2x = 3$
    $\wedge$
    $2x - y = 4$
    $\wedge$
    $3x + y - 2z = 5$
    $\wedge$
    $x + y + z + w = 6.$

11. $x + 2y = 1$
    $\wedge$
    $y + 2z = 2$
    $\wedge$
    $z + 2w = 3$
    $\wedge$
    $x + 2w = 4.$

12. $x - y + 2z = 1$
    $\wedge$
    $y + z - w = 2$
    $\wedge$
    $x - 2z + w = -1$
    $\wedge$
    $2x + y - 2w = 0.$

13. $A + 4B + C = 7$
    $\wedge$
    $A + 2B - C = 2$
    $\wedge$
    $3A - 2B + 2C = 12.$

14. $L + \dfrac{1}{3} M + \dfrac{1}{4} N = 3$
    $\wedge$
    $2L - \dfrac{5}{6} M + \dfrac{1}{2} N = \dfrac{3}{2}$
    $\wedge$
    $\dfrac{3}{2} L + \dfrac{2}{3} M - \dfrac{5}{8} N = 1.$

15. $\dfrac{x + y}{3} = \dfrac{x + z}{4} = \dfrac{y + z}{5}$
    $\wedge$
    $x + y + z = 6.$

16. $\dfrac{1}{x} + \dfrac{2}{y} + \dfrac{2}{z} = 1$
    $\wedge$
    $\dfrac{2}{x} + \dfrac{1}{y} - \dfrac{2}{z} = 1$
    $\wedge$
    $\dfrac{3}{x} + \dfrac{4}{y} - \dfrac{4}{z} = 2.$

7-6. STATED PROBLEMS WITH MORE THAN ONE UNKNOWN

Often it is more difficult to translate a problem stated in storylike fashion into a set of simultaneous equations than it is to solve the equations. Therefore, a consideration of the general principles applying to all such problems should prove helpful.

The essential steps in solving a stated problem are twofold.

1. The unknowns to be sought must be identified, designated by letters (as x, y, z, w, etc.), and described clearly.

Examples of unsatisfactory starts. Let x = time, or length, or rate, or distance, or amount, or men.

Examples of satisfactory starts:
Let x = number of minutes after 3 p.m.
Let x = number of inches in length.
Let x = number of feet per second.
Let x = number of miles in distance.
Let x = number of bushels of corn.

The idea that x represents a number and not a physical object, or a concept such as length must continually be borne in mind. The symbol x is a number that helps to measure the objective thing.

2. If there are two unknowns, two equations must be found expressing two relations between the unknowns which should be described in the problem. If there are three unknowns, three relations must be indicated, and so on. Thus as many equations as there are unknowns will be obtained, and the problem will be "set up," or ready for the formal algebraic solution.

Example. The combined age of John, Bill, and Harry is 36 years. Two years ago Bill was three times as old as John. Eight years hence Harry will be twice as old as Bill. How old is each?

Solution. In view of the question at the end we can start confidently thus: Let

$$x = \text{number of years in John's age}$$
$$y = \text{number of years in Bill's age}$$
$$z = \text{number of years in Harry's age.}$$

At this point we reread the first sentence and find that it states in English one relation between the unknowns. The statement goes into algebra thus:

(1) $$x + y + z = 36.$$

The second sentence deals with ages two years ago, which evidently are represented by $x - 2$, $y - 2$, and $z - 2$. Thus

(2) $$y - 2 = 3(x - 2).$$

Eight years hence the ages will be $x + 8$, $y + 8$, and $z + 8$. According to the third sentence,

(3) $$z + 8 = 2(y + 8).$$

Solving (1), (2), and (3) simultaneously we get $x = 4$, $y = 8$, and $z = 24$ (answer).

Not every problem has a direct question to indicate the unknowns and separate sentences to describe the conditions; but these quantities must always be described in one way or another.

It is interesting to note that impossible simultaneous conditions will be revealed algebraically by inconsistent equations; while conditions which may seem to be independent, but which really amount to the same thing, lead to dependent equations with more than one solution.

EXERCISE 7-3

1. Three times one number minus twice another equals 4. The sum of twice the first number plus three times the second is 7. Find the numbers.

2. If 5 times one number is divided by 3 times another, the result is 1. The sum of the numbers is 8. Find the numbers.

3. One-half the sum of two numbers is 6, and 3 times their difference is 6. Find the numbers.

4. Three times one number is equal to 4 times another, and half their sum is 7. Find the numbers.

5. Find two numbers such that 3 times their difference is 6, and the sum of 4 and the first number is 3 times the second.

6. If a certain number is added to the numerator and subtracted from the denominator of $\frac{5}{7}$, the result equals 3. The sum of half this number and a second one is 7. Find the numbers.

7. The rowing rate down a certain stream is 1 mph less than twice the upstream rowing rate. The rate upstream is 3 times the rate of the current. Find the rate of the current and the rate of rowing in still water. Let

$$x = \text{mph rowed in still water.}$$
$$y = \text{mph the current flows.}$$

Then

$$x + y = \text{mph rowed downstream.}$$
$$x - y = \text{mph rowed upstream.}$$

(1) $$x + y = 2(x - y) - 1.$$
(2) $$x - y = 3y.$$

The simultaneous solution of (1) and (2) yields: $x = 4$, $y = 1$ (Ans.).

8. The rate of rowing downstream is 2 mph less than 3 times the rate of the

current. The upstream rowing rate is $\frac{1}{3}$ the rate of the current. Find the rate of the current and the rate of rowing in still water.

9. A man can row downstream 5 miles in the same time it would take him to row 1 mile upstream. The rate of rowing in still water is 1 mph more than the rate of the current. Find the two last-mentioned quantities.

10. The rate of a boat in still water is 3 times the rate of the current and also 2 mph more than this rate. Find the two rates.

11. A plane can travel 550 mph with the wind, and its speed against the wind is 500 mph. Find its speed in still air and the velocity of the wind.

12. A plane goes twice as fast with the wind as against it. If the velocity of the wind were doubled, the speed of the plane when flying with the wind would be 100 mph more than 3 times its speed against the wind. Find the speed of the plane in still air and the velocity of the wind.

13. The sum of the digits of a 3-digit number is 6. The units' digit is twice the hundreds' digit. If the order of the digits is reversed, the new number is 99 more than the original one. Find the number. Let

$$h = \text{the hundreds' digit}$$
$$t = \text{the tens' digit}$$
$$u = \text{the units' digit.}$$

Then

$$100h + 10t + u = \text{the number.}$$

(3) $$h + t + u = 6.$$
(4) $$u = 2h.$$
(5) $$100u + 10t + h = 100h + 10t + u + 99.$$

Solving (3), (4), and (5) simultaneously, we get $h = 1$, $t = 3$, and $u = 2$, so that the number is 132 (Ans.).

14. The sum of the digits of a 2-digit number is 7. If the order of the digits is reversed, the resulting number is 2 more than twice the original number. Find the number.

15. The sum of the digits of a 3-digit number is 12. The tens' digit is 1 less, and the units' digit 1 more, than the hundreds' digit. Find the number.

16. The sum of the digits of a 3-digit number is 14. The units' digit is 1 more than twice the hundreds' digit and 1 less than twice the tens' digit. Find the number.

17. If the order of the digits of a certain 3-digit number is reversed, the new number exceeds the old one by 396. The tens' digit is 3 times the hundreds' digit, and the sum of the digits is 1 more than twice the tens' digit. Find the number.

18. The length of a rectangle in inches is 1 less than twice its width. If its length

is decreased by 1 inch and its width is increased by 3 inches, it becomes a square. Find its dimensions.

19. The length of a rectangle in inches is 2 less than twice its width. If its length is decreased by 2 inches and its width is increased by 3 inches, it becomes a square. Find its dimensions.

20. If the width of a rectangle is increased by 2 inches, its area is increased by 14 square inches. If its length is decreased by 2 inches, its area is decreased by 8 square inches. Find its dimensions.

21. If the length of a rectangle is decreased by 3 feet, and its width is increased by 2 feet, its area is increased by 2 square feet. If its length is decreased by 2 feet and its width is increased by 1 foot, its area is unchanged. Find its dimensions.

22. If the width of a rectangle is increased by 3 inches and its length is decreased by 4 inches, its area is unchanged and it becomes a square. Find its dimensions.

23. If $6,000 is invested, part at 5 percent and part at 6 percent, the total yearly interest is $340. Find the amount invested at each rate.

24. If $10,000 is invested, part at 5 percent and part at 6 percent, and if the total yearly interest is $540, find the amount invested at each rate.

25. If $8,000 is invested, part at 4 percent and part at 5 percent, and if the interest on the 4 percent investment is $50 more than the other, find the amount invested at each rate.

26. The interest received yearly on a 6 percent investment is twice as much as the interest on a 4 percent investment. If the total yearly interest is $360, find the amount of each investment.

27. If A works 3 days and B works 5 days, their combined pay is $180. If A works 5 days and B works 3 days, their combined pay is $204. Find the daily wage of each.

28. A man has $2 in dimes and nickels. If he has twice as many dimes and half as many nickels as he now has, he would have $2.50. How many of each has he?

29. A man has $3.50 in nickels, dimes, and quarters. If he had the same number of dimes but half as many nickels and twice as many quarters, he would have $4.50. If he traded his quarters for dimes and his dimes for quarters, he would have $4.10. How many coins of each kind does he have?

30. If 100 pounds of bananas of two grades, one selling for 15¢ per pound and the other for 16¢, bring $15.30, how many pounds of each grade are there?

31. One alloy is 5 percent pure silver and another 15 percent pure silver. How many pounds of each must be mixed to form 100 pounds of alloy of which 8 percent is pure silver?

32. A lady buys 10 pounds of grapes, of which part cost 75¢ for 2 pounds and the rest 75¢ for 3 pounds. If she paid $3.00 altogether, how many pounds of each kind did she buy?

33. How many pounds each of 80¢ and 95¢ coffee must be mixed to make 100 pounds of coffee worth 90¢ per pound?

34. If corn meal is worth 13¢ per pound and flour 14¢ per pound, how many pounds of each does one buy to get 50 pounds for $6.80?

chapter **8**

Matrix Algebra, Determinants, and Systems of Equations

8-1. INTRODUCTION

The general solution set of a system of two linear equations in two variables as involved in

$$f_1 = \{(x,y) \mid a_1x + b_1y = c_1\}$$

and

$$f_2 = \{(x,y) \mid a_2x + b_2y = c_2\}$$

has already been discussed in Sec. 7-3 and shown to be

$$f_1 \cap f_2 = \{(x,y)\} = \left\{ \left(\frac{b_2c_1 - b_1c_2}{a_1b_2 - a_2b_1}, \frac{a_1c_2 - a_2c_1}{a_1b_2 - a_2b_1} \right) \right\}, \qquad a_1b_2 - a_2b_1 \neq 0.$$

Although the above ordered pair provides a formula for the solution of the system, it is not convenient for memory purposes. If now a new symbol is introduced, namely, $\begin{vmatrix} r & s \\ t & v \end{vmatrix}$, where r, s, t, v represent real numbers, and if this symbol is defined as being equal to the number "$rv - st$," then the values of x and y in the solution set for $f_1 \cap f_2$ may be represented by writing

$$x = \frac{\begin{vmatrix} c_1 & b_1 \\ c_2 & b_2 \end{vmatrix}}{\begin{vmatrix} a_1 & b_1 \\ a_2 & b_2 \end{vmatrix}} = \frac{b_2c_1 - b_1c_2}{a_1b_2 - a_2b_1} \quad \text{and} \quad y = \frac{\begin{vmatrix} a_1 & c_1 \\ a_2 & c_2 \end{vmatrix}}{\begin{vmatrix} a_1 & b_1 \\ a_2 & b_2 \end{vmatrix}} = \frac{a_1c_2 - a_2c_1}{a_1b_2 - a_2b_1}.$$

These square arrays of numbers are fairly easy to form, convenient to remember, more easily memorized, and can be generalized to represent the solution set of a consistent system of n linear equations in n variables. The various sections in this chapter are devoted to such arrays of numbers, their properties, nomenclature, and application to the solution of systems of linear equations.

For example, in the system $3x - 5y = 7 \wedge 5x + 2y = 3$,

$$x = \frac{\begin{vmatrix} 7 & -5 \\ 3 & 2 \end{vmatrix}}{\begin{vmatrix} 3 & -5 \\ 5 & 2 \end{vmatrix}} = \frac{29}{31} \quad \text{and} \quad y = \frac{\begin{vmatrix} 3 & 7 \\ 5 & 3 \end{vmatrix}}{\begin{vmatrix} 3 & -5 \\ 5 & 2 \end{vmatrix}} = -\frac{26}{31},$$

and the solution set for the system is $\left\{ \left(\frac{29}{31}, -\frac{26}{31} \right) \right\}$. It will be pointed out that the new symbol used here is called a *second-order determinant* and that its number value is defined as has been indicated. It will also be shown that determinants are related to rectangular arrays of numbers called *matrices*. A basic and elementary introduction to these ideas will make up the major portion of this chapter. We will learn to manipulate both with matrices and with determinants. We will endeavor to point out the differences between them, and will learn the mathematical language that is introduced because of them.

8-2. MATRICES

A *matrix* is a set of mn numbers (usually referred to as *elements of the matrix*) arranged in a rectangular array of m rows and n columns, where the array is enclosed either in brackets, double vertical lines, or bold faced parentheses. A matrix with m rows and n columns is said to be of dimensionality $m \times n$ or of order $m \times n$, read "m by n." In general, matrices are denoted by capital letters such as A, B, C, ..., or by a typical element a_{ij} enclosed in parentheses, namely (a_{ij}). By agreement the subscripts i and j denote the row and column, respectively, in which the element a_{ij} is located in the matrix. Thus a_{21} is the element in the second row and first column, and is associated with the matrix (a_{ij}), where $i = 1, \ldots, m$ and $j = 1, \ldots, n$. The $m \times n$ matrix can be theoretically represented as

$$(1) \qquad A = (a_{ij}) = \begin{bmatrix} a_{11} & a_{12} & \cdots & a_{1n} \\ a_{21} & a_{22} & \cdots & a_{2n} \\ \vdots & \vdots & & \vdots \\ a_{m1} & a_{m2} & \cdots & a_{mn} \end{bmatrix}$$

$$\text{or } A = \begin{Vmatrix} a_{11} & a_{12} & \cdots & a_{1n} \\ a_{21} & a_{22} & \cdots & a_{2n} \\ \vdots & \vdots & & \vdots \\ a_{m1} & a_{m2} & \cdots & a_{mn} \end{Vmatrix} = \begin{pmatrix} a_{11} & a_{12} & \cdots & a_{1n} \\ a_{21} & a_{22} & \cdots & a_{2n} \\ \vdots & \vdots & & \vdots \\ a_{m1} & a_{m2} & \cdots & a_{mn} \end{pmatrix}.$$

For example, consider the 2×3 matrix

$$A = \begin{bmatrix} 1 & -3 & 4 \\ 0 & 5 & -2 \end{bmatrix}.$$

Its rows may themselves be considered as matrices and are $[1 \quad -3 \quad 4]$ and $[0 \quad 5 \quad -2]$ and accordingly its columns are

$$\begin{bmatrix} 1 \\ 0 \end{bmatrix}, \begin{bmatrix} -3 \\ 5 \end{bmatrix}, \text{ and } \begin{bmatrix} 4 \\ -2 \end{bmatrix}.$$

Matrix A is a "two by three" matrix. The element "-3" would be described as being in the first row and second column. Its theoretical symbolism would be a_{12} in accordance with notation in (1). When $m = n$, the matrix is called a *square matrix*, and is said to be of *order $n \times n$*, or simply of *order n*. For such a matrix the diagonal extending from the upper left-end corner to lower right-end corner is called its *principal* or *main diagonal*. Its elements are $a_{11}, a_{22}, \ldots, a_{nn}$.

Example. The matrix

$$\begin{bmatrix} 1 & 2 & -1 \\ 0 & 5 & 3 \\ 5 & 3 & -2 \end{bmatrix}$$

is a square matrix of order 3. The elements along the main diagonal are $1, 5$, and -2, and would be symbolized, in accordance with (1), as a_{11}, a_{22}, and a_{33} respectively. A square matrix with all elements on its principal diagonal equal to unity and all other elements zero is referred to as the *identity* or *unit matrix*, and is denoted by I. Thus

$$I = \begin{bmatrix} 1 & 0 & 0 & 0 \\ 0 & 1 & 0 & 0 \\ 0 & 0 & 1 & 0 \\ 0 & 0 & 0 & 1 \end{bmatrix}$$

is the identity matrix of order 4.

Two matrices A and B are said to be *equal* if, and only if, they are of the *same order* and if elements in *corresponding positions are equal*. Hence the equality of two $m \times n$ matrices is equivalent to a statement involving a system of mn equalities, one for each pair of corresponding elements.

Examples.

(a)   If $A = \begin{bmatrix} 1 & 7 \\ 6 & 4 \end{bmatrix}$ and $B = \begin{bmatrix} 6 & 7 \\ 1 & 4 \end{bmatrix}$,   then $A \neq B$.

(b)   If $A = \begin{bmatrix} 1 & 7 \\ 6 & 4 \end{bmatrix}$ and $B = \begin{bmatrix} 7-6 & 9-2 \\ 1 \cdot 6 & 2+2 \end{bmatrix}$,   then $A = B$.

(c)   If $A = B$, where $A = \begin{bmatrix} x+y & 2z+w \\ x-y & z-w \end{bmatrix}$ and $B = \begin{bmatrix} 3 & 5 \\ 1 & 4 \end{bmatrix}$

then $x + y = 3 \wedge x - y = 1 \wedge 2z + w = 5 \wedge z - w = 4$ is a system of 4 equations in the four unknowns x, y, z, and w. The solution set is found to be $\{(2,1,3,-1)\}$.

A matrix with m rows and 1 column is referred to as *column vector*; while a matrix with 1 row and n columns is referred to as a *row vector*. Column vectors are usually denoted by boldfaced, lowercase letters, whereas row vectors are usually denoted by primed, boldfaced, lowercase letters. A matrix with one row and one column is called a *scalar*, and is usually denoted by a lowercase letter which in turn is represented by the symbol for the element itself.

Examples.

$$\mathbf{a} = \begin{bmatrix} 3 \\ 4 \\ -1 \\ 2 \end{bmatrix} \quad \text{is a column vector,}$$

while

$$\mathbf{b}' = \begin{bmatrix} 2 & -3 & 7 & 5 & 1 \end{bmatrix} \quad \text{is a row vector}$$

and

$$c = [2] = 2 \quad \text{is a scalar.}$$

The *transpose* of a matrix A, denoted by A', or A^T, is the matrix obtained when the successive rows of A, in order, are written as its columns and its columns as its rows. If A is an $m \times n$ matrix, A' is an $n \times m$ matrix, and $a_{ji} = a_{ij}$.

Example.

$$\text{If } A = \begin{bmatrix} 3 & 6 & 2 \\ 2 & 1 & 0 \\ 5 & 9 & 7 \\ 1 & 0 & 6 \end{bmatrix}, \text{ then } A' = \begin{bmatrix} 3 & 2 & 5 & 1 \\ 6 & 1 & 9 & 0 \\ 2 & 0 & 7 & 6 \end{bmatrix}.$$

$$\text{If } \mathbf{a} = \begin{bmatrix} 3 \\ 4 \\ -1 \\ 2 \end{bmatrix} \text{ then } \mathbf{a}' = \begin{bmatrix} 3 & 4 & -1 & 2 \end{bmatrix}.$$

A matrix is defined as a single *mathematical entity*, which is subjected to algebraic operations guided by rules as described in what follows. These operations, indeed, must be defined, postulated, and be consistent in applications where matrices are effective.

8-3. MATRIX ADDITION AND SUBTRACTION

Let A and B be two matrices of the same order $m \times n$. The *sum* of $A = (a_{ij})$ and $B = (b_{ij})$, written as $A + B = (a_{ij}) + (b_{ij})$, is the matrix $C = (c_{ij})$ of order $m \times n$ such that the element

$$c_{ij} = a_{ij} + b_{ij},$$

where $i = 1, \ldots, m$ and $j = 1, \ldots, n$. That is, elements in corresponding positions for the two matrices A and B are added:

$$A + B = \begin{bmatrix} a_{11} & a_{12} & \cdots & a_{1n} \\ a_{21} & a_{22} & \cdots & a_{2n} \\ \vdots & \vdots & & \vdots \\ a_{m1} & a_{m2} & \cdots & a_{mn} \end{bmatrix} + \begin{bmatrix} b_{11} & b_{12} & \cdots & b_{1n} \\ b_{21} & b_{22} & \cdots & b_{2n} \\ \vdots & \vdots & & \vdots \\ b_{m1} & b_{m2} & \cdots & b_{mn} \end{bmatrix} = C$$

where

$$C = \begin{bmatrix} a_{11} + b_{11} & a_{12} + b_{12} & \cdots & a_{1n} + b_{1n} \\ a_{21} + b_{21} & a_{22} + b_{22} & \cdots & a_{2n} + b_{2n} \\ \vdots & \vdots & \vdots & \vdots \\ a_{m1} + b_{m1} & a_{m2} + b_{m2} & \cdots & a_{mn} + b_{mn} \end{bmatrix}.$$

Two matrices of different orders are defined as having no sum and cannot be combined under the matrix operation of addition.

Subtraction for like-ordered matrices is defined in a similar fashion. The matrix denoted by $-A$ has all its elements opposite in sign (additive inverses) to those of A.

Example. If

$$A = \begin{bmatrix} 1 & -2 & 4 \\ 0 & 3 & 5 \end{bmatrix} \quad \text{and} \quad B = \begin{bmatrix} 3 & 0 & -2 \\ 1 & -1 & 4 \end{bmatrix}$$

then

$$A + B = \begin{bmatrix} 1 & -2 & 4 \\ 0 & 3 & 5 \end{bmatrix} + \begin{bmatrix} 3 & 0 & -2 \\ 1 & -1 & 4 \end{bmatrix}$$

$$= \begin{bmatrix} 1+3 & -2+0 & 4+(-2) \\ 0+1 & 3+(-1) & 5+4 \end{bmatrix} = \begin{bmatrix} 4 & -2 & 2 \\ 1 & 2 & 9 \end{bmatrix},$$

$$B + A = \begin{bmatrix} 3 & 0 & -2 \\ 1 & -1 & 4 \end{bmatrix} + \begin{bmatrix} 1 & -2 & 4 \\ 0 & 3 & 5 \end{bmatrix} = \begin{bmatrix} 4 & -2 & 2 \\ 1 & 2 & 9 \end{bmatrix}.$$

What does this seem to imply when compared with $A + B$? _____

$$-A = \begin{bmatrix} -1 & 2 & -4 \\ 0 & -3 & -5 \end{bmatrix}, \quad -B = \begin{bmatrix} -3 & 0 & 2 \\ -1 & 1 & -4 \end{bmatrix}$$

$$A - B = A + (-B) = \begin{bmatrix} 1 & -2 & 4 \\ 0 & 3 & 5 \end{bmatrix} + \begin{bmatrix} -3 & 0 & 2 \\ -1 & 1 & -4 \end{bmatrix} = \begin{bmatrix} -2 & -2 & 6 \\ -1 & 4 & 1 \end{bmatrix}$$

$$B - A = B + (-A) = -(A - B) = \begin{bmatrix} 2 & 2 & -6 \\ 1 & -4 & -1 \end{bmatrix}.$$

What does this seem to imply? _____

An $m \times n$ matrix whose elements are all zero is called a *zero matrix* and is denoted by $0_{m \times n}$ or simply 0, if no ambiguity of usage with the real number zero occurs.

For matrices A, B, and C, all of the same order,

(a) $A + B = B + A$ Matrix addition of matrices is commutative

(b) $(A + B) + C = A + (B + C)$ Matrix addition of matrices is associative

(c) $A + 0 = 0 + A = A$ Matrix addition of the zero matrix to A leaves A unaltered

Example. If

$$A = \begin{bmatrix} 2 & 1 \\ 3 & 5 \end{bmatrix}, \quad B = \begin{bmatrix} -1 & 4 \\ 3 & 2 \end{bmatrix},$$

$$C = \begin{bmatrix} 2 & 1 \\ 4 & 0 \end{bmatrix}, \quad \text{and } 0_{2 \times 2} = 0 = \begin{bmatrix} 0 & 0 \\ 0 & 0 \end{bmatrix},$$

verify the (a), (b), (c) properties. This is left as an exercise. Properties (a), (b), (c) have not been proven for the general case, but are fairly well evident and as a consequence are also left as a student exercise.

8-4. SCALAR MULTIPLICATION

The product of a scalar k, as defined in Sec. 8-2 and a matrix A, written kA or Ak, is the matrix obtained by multiplying each element of A by k. Thus

$$kA = k \begin{bmatrix} a_{11} & a_{12} & \cdots & a_{1n} \\ a_{21} & a_{22} & \cdots & a_{2n} \\ \vdots & \vdots & & \vdots \\ a_{m1} & a_{m2} & \cdots & a_{mn} \end{bmatrix} = \begin{bmatrix} ka_{11} & ka_{12} & \cdots & ka_{1n} \\ ka_{21} & ka_{22} & \cdots & ka_{2n} \\ \vdots & \vdots & & \vdots \\ ka_{m1} & ka_{m2} & \cdots & ka_{mn} \end{bmatrix} = (ka_{ij}).$$

Example.

$$3 \begin{bmatrix} 1 & 2 & -3 \\ 0 & -1 & 4 \end{bmatrix} = \begin{bmatrix} 3 \cdot 1 & 3 \cdot 2 & 3(-3) \\ 3 \cdot 0 & 3(-1) & 3 \cdot 4 \end{bmatrix} = \begin{bmatrix} 3 & 6 & -9 \\ 0 & -3 & 12 \end{bmatrix}.$$

For any scalars k_1 and k_2 and matrices A and B of the same order, the following properties hold and can be proven for the general case.

(a) $(k_1 k_2)A = k_1(k_2 A) = A(k_1 k_2)$
(b) $k_1(A + B) = k_1 A + k_1 B = (A + B)k_1$
(c) $(k_1 + k_2)A = k_1 A + k_2 A = A(k_1 + k_2)$
(d) $1 \cdot A = A$ and $0 \cdot A = 0$
(e) $A + (-A) = -A + A = 0.$

These properties should be verified by the student by using specific matrices for A and B, and definite values for the scalars k_1 and k_2. For example, let

$$A = \begin{bmatrix} 2 & 1 & 3 \\ -4 & 0 & 2 \end{bmatrix}, \quad B = \begin{bmatrix} -3 & 2 & 1 \\ -5 & -1 & 2 \end{bmatrix}, \quad k_1 = 3, \, k_2 = 4,$$

and verify properties (a) to (e).

8-5. MATRIX MULTIPLICATION

If A is an $m \times p$ matrix and B is an $p \times n$ matrix, then the product $C = AB$ taken in that order is an $m \times n$ matrix, where each element c_{ij} of C is obtained by multiplying corresponding elements of the ith row of A by those of the jth column of B and then summing the results. Thus

$$
\begin{bmatrix}
a_{11} & a_{12} & \cdots & a_{1p} \\
a_{21} & a_{22} & \cdots & a_{2p} \\
\vdots & \vdots & & \vdots \\
\boxed{a_{i1} \quad a_{i2} \quad \cdots \quad a_{ip}} \\
\vdots & \vdots & & \vdots \\
a_{m1} & a_{m2} & \cdots & a_{mp}
\end{bmatrix}
\begin{bmatrix}
b_{11} & b_{12} & \cdots & \boxed{b_{1j}} & \cdots & b_{1n} \\
b_{21} & b_{22} & \cdots & \boxed{b_{2j}} & \cdots & b_{2n} \\
\vdots & \vdots & & \vdots & & \vdots \\
b_{p1} & b_{p2} & \cdots & \boxed{b_{pj}} & \cdots & b_{pn}
\end{bmatrix}
$$

$$
= \begin{bmatrix}
c_{11} & c_{12} & \cdots & & c_{1n} \\
c_{21} & c_{22} & \cdots & & c_{2n} \\
\vdots & \vdots & & \boxed{c_{ij}} & \vdots \\
\vdots & \vdots & & & \vdots \\
c_{m1} & c_{m2} & \cdots & & c_{mn}
\end{bmatrix}
$$

where $c_{ij} = a_{i1}b_{1j} + a_{i2}b_{2j} + \cdots + a_{ip}b_{pj}$, where $i = 1, 2, \ldots, m$ and $j = 1, 2, \ldots, n$. For the product AB to exist, *it is necessary for the number of rows in B to equal the number of columns in A.* Each row in A is multiplied, term by term, with those in each column in B, as is illustrated in the examples.

Example 1. Let

$$
A = \begin{bmatrix} 1 & 2 \\ 3 & 0 \end{bmatrix} \text{ a } 2 \times 2 \text{ matrix;} \quad B = \begin{bmatrix} 3 & 0 & 2 \\ 0 & 1 & 1 \end{bmatrix} \text{ a } 2 \times 3 \text{ matrix;}
$$

then

$$
C = AB = \begin{bmatrix} 1 & 2 \\ 3 & 0 \end{bmatrix} \begin{bmatrix} 3 & 0 & 2 \\ 0 & 1 & 1 \end{bmatrix}
$$

$$
= \begin{bmatrix} 1 \cdot 3 + 2 \cdot 0 & 1 \cdot 0 + 2 \cdot 1 & 1 \cdot 2 + 2 \cdot 1 \\ 3 \cdot 3 + 0 \cdot 0 & 3 \cdot 0 + 0 \cdot 1 & 3 \cdot 2 + 0 \cdot 1 \end{bmatrix}
$$

$$
= \begin{bmatrix} 3 & 2 & 4 \\ 9 & 0 & 6 \end{bmatrix} \text{ is a } 2 \times 3 \text{ matrix}
$$

Example 2.   Let

$$A = \begin{bmatrix} 1 & 2 \\ 3 & 5 \end{bmatrix}, \quad B = \begin{bmatrix} 1 & 1 \\ 0 & 2 \end{bmatrix}$$

then

$$AB = \begin{bmatrix} 1 & 2 \\ 3 & 5 \end{bmatrix} \begin{bmatrix} 1 & 1 \\ 0 & 2 \end{bmatrix} = \begin{bmatrix} 1 \cdot 1 + 2 \cdot 0 & 1 \cdot 1 + 2 \cdot 2 \\ 3 \cdot 1 + 5 \cdot 0 & 3 \cdot 1 + 5 \cdot 2 \end{bmatrix}$$

$$= \begin{bmatrix} 1 & 5 \\ 3 & 13 \end{bmatrix}$$

$$BA = \begin{bmatrix} 1 & 1 \\ 0 & 2 \end{bmatrix} \begin{bmatrix} 1 & 2 \\ 3 & 5 \end{bmatrix} = \begin{bmatrix} 1 \cdot 1 + 1 \cdot 3 & 1 \cdot 2 + 1 \cdot 5 \\ 0 \cdot 1 + 2 \cdot 3 & 0 \cdot 2 + 2 \cdot 5 \end{bmatrix}$$

$$= \begin{bmatrix} 4 & 7 \\ 6 & 10 \end{bmatrix}$$

Example 2 exhibits the fact than the commutative property for matrix multiplication does not necessarily hold for matrices. That is, the products AB and BA of two matrices A and B need not be equal. It is necessary therefore to distinguish between "premultiplication" of a matrix and "postmultiplication" of a matrix, or to speak of multiplying "on the left" or "on the right." If a matrix A is multiplied on the left by B (premultiplication), the product BA is obtained; if on the right (postmultiplication) by B, the product AB is obtained. It is also noted and emphasized that AB may exist and BA not, or it may be that neither product exists.

Example.   If

$$A = \begin{bmatrix} 1 & 4 \\ 3 & 2 \end{bmatrix} \text{ and } B = \begin{bmatrix} 3 & 1 \\ 2 & 4 \\ 5 & 1 \end{bmatrix},$$

then AB does not exist, but BA does. Why? _____

Example.   If

$$A = \begin{bmatrix} 1 & 4 \\ 3 & 2 \end{bmatrix} \text{ and } B = \begin{bmatrix} 3 & 1 & 2 \\ 2 & 0 & 3 \\ 1 & -1 & 4 \end{bmatrix},$$

then neither AB nor BA exist. Why? _____

A property related to real numbers say, a and b, which asserts that if $a \cdot b = 0$, then either a, or b, or both must be zero is not necessarily true for a matrix product. It is possible for a matrix product AB to be the zero matrix without either A or B or both being zero.

Example. Let

$$A = \begin{bmatrix} 2 & -1 \\ 10 & -5 \end{bmatrix} \text{ and } B = \begin{bmatrix} 1 & 3 \\ 2 & 6 \end{bmatrix},$$

then

$$
\begin{aligned}
AB &= \begin{bmatrix} 2 & -1 \\ 10 & -5 \end{bmatrix} \begin{bmatrix} 1 & 3 \\ 2 & 6 \end{bmatrix} \\
&= \begin{bmatrix} 2 \cdot 1 + (-1)2 & 2 \cdot 3 + (-1)6 \\ 10 \cdot 1 + (-5)2 & 10 \cdot 3 + (-5)6 \end{bmatrix} \\
&= \begin{bmatrix} 0 & 0 \\ 0 & 0 \end{bmatrix}
\end{aligned}
$$

It follows that, when dealing with matrices, if a matrix product $AB = 0$, a student should not jump to the immediate conclusion that either A or B or both are zero matrices. After all, one should realize that even though the word "product" is used with real numbers and also with matrices, the meaning is not the same. The word "product" is defined in each case and when used must be employed as defined.

Matrix multiplication does, however, satisfy the following properties, which are stated here without proof:

(a) $(AB)C = A(BC) = ABC$ (associative property)

(b) $A(B + C) = AB + AC$ (distributive property for premultiplication)

(c) $(A + B)C = AC + BC$ (distributive property for postmultiplication)

(d) $k(AB) = (kA)B = A(kB),$ where k is a scalar.

It is understood here that A, B, C are of the proper dimensions to make the statements meaningful.

Example. Let

$$A = \begin{bmatrix} 2 & 3 \\ 4 & 1 \end{bmatrix}, \quad B = \begin{bmatrix} -4 & 2 \\ 3 & 6 \end{bmatrix}, \quad C = \begin{bmatrix} 3 & 8 \\ 4 & 1 \end{bmatrix}, \quad k = 8.$$

Verify the statements (a) to (d) as applied to A, B, C.

Verification for property (a):

$$AB = \begin{bmatrix} 2 & 3 \\ 4 & 1 \end{bmatrix} \begin{bmatrix} -4 & 2 \\ 3 & 6 \end{bmatrix} = \begin{bmatrix} 1 & 22 \\ -13 & 14 \end{bmatrix}$$

(1) $(AB)C = \begin{bmatrix} 1 & 22 \\ -13 & 14 \end{bmatrix} \begin{bmatrix} 3 & 8 \\ 4 & 1 \end{bmatrix} = \begin{bmatrix} 91 & 30 \\ 17 & -90 \end{bmatrix}$

$$BC = \begin{bmatrix} -4 & 2 \\ 3 & 6 \end{bmatrix} \begin{bmatrix} 3 & 8 \\ 4 & 1 \end{bmatrix} = \begin{bmatrix} -4 & -30 \\ 33 & 30 \end{bmatrix}$$

(2) $A(BC) = \begin{bmatrix} 2 & 3 \\ 4 & 1 \end{bmatrix} \begin{bmatrix} -4 & -30 \\ 33 & 30 \end{bmatrix} = \begin{bmatrix} 91 & 30 \\ 17 & -90 \end{bmatrix}$

Compare (1) and (2) and it follows that for the given A, B, and C,

$$(AB)C = A(BC)$$

It is left as a student exercise to verify properties (b), (c), and (d).

In the special case where one of the matrix multipliers of AB is either a row or column vector, then the product is also a vector. A $1 \times p$ row vector premultiplying a $p \times n$ matrix results in a $1 \times n$ row vector as shown in Example 1.

Example 1.

$$[a_{11} \quad a_{12} \cdots a_{1p}] \begin{bmatrix} b_{11} & b_{12} & \cdots & b_{1n} \\ b_{21} & b_{22} & \cdots & b_{2n} \\ \vdots & \vdots & \cdots & \vdots \\ b_{p1} & b_{p2} & \cdots & b_{pn} \end{bmatrix} = [c_{11} \quad c_{12} \cdots c_{1n}],$$

is a $1 \times n$ row vector where

$$c_{11} = a_{11}b_{11} + a_{12}b_{12} + \cdots + a_{1p}b_{1p}$$
$$c_{12} = a_{11}b_{21} + a_{12}b_{22} + \cdots + a_{1p}b_{2p}$$
$$\vdots \qquad \vdots \qquad \vdots \qquad \qquad \vdots$$
$$c_{1n} = a_{11}b_{1n} + a_{12}b_{2n} + \cdots + a_{1p}b_{pn}$$

Example 2.

$$\begin{bmatrix} a_{11} & a_{12} & \cdots & a_{1p} \\ a_{21} & a_{22} & \cdots & a_{2p} \\ \vdots & \vdots & & \vdots \\ a_{m1} & a_{m2} & \cdots & a_{mp} \end{bmatrix} \begin{bmatrix} b_{11} \\ b_{21} \\ \vdots \\ b_{p1} \end{bmatrix} = \begin{bmatrix} c_{11} \\ c_{21} \\ \vdots \\ c_{m1} \end{bmatrix}$$

is a $n \times 1$ column vector where

$$c_{11} = a_{11}b_{11} + a_{12}b_{21} + \cdots + a_{1p}b_{p1}$$
$$c_{21} = a_{21}b_{11} + a_{22}b_{21} + \cdots + a_{2p}b_{p1}$$
$$\vdots \qquad \vdots \qquad \vdots \qquad \qquad \vdots$$
$$c_{m1} = a_{m1}b_{11} + a_{m2}b_{21} + \cdots + a_{mp}b_{p1}$$

Example 3. An illustration involving precise number values for elements follows.

$$[2 \quad -3 \quad 4] \begin{bmatrix} 1 & -3 \\ 5 & 0 \\ -2 & 4 \end{bmatrix} = [2 \cdot 1 + (-3)5 + 4(-2) \qquad 2(-3) + (-3)0 + 4 \cdot 4]$$

$$= [-21 \qquad 10]$$

$$\begin{bmatrix} 1 & -3 \\ 5 & 0 \\ -2 & 4 \end{bmatrix} \begin{bmatrix} 2 \\ -3 \end{bmatrix} = \begin{bmatrix} 1 \cdot 2 + (-3)(-3) \\ 5 \cdot 2 + 0(-3) \\ (-2)2 + 4(-3) \end{bmatrix}$$

$$= \begin{bmatrix} 11 \\ 10 \\ -16 \end{bmatrix}$$

8-6. MATRIX REPRESENTATION FOR A SYSTEM OF LINEAR EQUATIONS

A system of linear equations, such as

(1)
$$\begin{cases} x + y + z = 4 \\ \quad \wedge \\ x - y + 2z = 3 \\ \quad \wedge \\ 2x + y - z = 1 \end{cases}$$

is equivalent to the matrix equation

$$\begin{array}{ccc} C & X & = K \end{array}$$

(2)
$$\begin{bmatrix} 1 & 1 & 1 \\ 1 & -1 & 2 \\ 2 & 1 & -1 \end{bmatrix} \begin{bmatrix} x \\ y \\ z \end{bmatrix} = \begin{bmatrix} 4 \\ 3 \\ 1 \end{bmatrix}.$$

That is, any solution set for the system of equations (1) possesses a corresponding column vector solution to the matrix equation (2) $CX = K$, and vice versa. Here

$$C = \begin{bmatrix} 1 & 1 & 1 \\ 1 & -1 & 2 \\ 2 & 1 & -1 \end{bmatrix}, \quad X = \begin{bmatrix} x \\ y \\ z \end{bmatrix}, \quad K = \begin{bmatrix} 4 \\ 3 \\ 1 \end{bmatrix}.$$

The solution set for the system is $\{(x,y,z)\} = \left\{\left(\dfrac{5}{7}, \dfrac{10}{7}, \dfrac{13}{7}\right)\right\}$.

The column vector solution is

$$X = \begin{bmatrix} x \\ y \\ z \end{bmatrix} = \begin{bmatrix} \dfrac{5}{7} \\ \dfrac{10}{7} \\ \dfrac{13}{7} \end{bmatrix}$$

We shall now endeavor to establish matrix techniques for solving matrix equations of the type $CX = K$. At this stage, it is suggested as a student exercise to reexamine the simultaneous systems in Exercise 7-1, Probs 1–27, 49–54, and Exercise 7-2, Probs. 1–16, and rewrite each of these as matrix equations in the form $CX = K$. The number of problems that should be attempted is left to the instructor's discretion. The actual solutions for these systems of equations should be postponed until after the appropriate sections in this chapter have been studied. For the present, the student should become acquainted with the transformation of the linear simultaneous systems into their corresponding matrix forms. For example, Prob. 10, Exercise 7-1, can be transformed to

$$\begin{bmatrix} 2 & 6 \\ 3 & -5 \end{bmatrix}\begin{bmatrix} x \\ y \end{bmatrix} = \begin{bmatrix} -3 \\ 6 \end{bmatrix};$$

Prob. 49, Exercise 7-1, can be transformed to

$$\begin{bmatrix} a & b \\ b & -a \end{bmatrix}\begin{bmatrix} x \\ y \end{bmatrix} = \begin{bmatrix} ab \\ b^2 \end{bmatrix};$$

and Prob. 11, Exercise 7-2, can be transformed to

$$\begin{bmatrix} 1 & 2 & 0 & 0 \\ 0 & 1 & 0 & 2 \\ 0 & 0 & 2 & 1 \\ 1 & 0 & 2 & 0 \end{bmatrix}\begin{bmatrix} x \\ y \\ w \\ z \end{bmatrix} = \begin{bmatrix} 1 \\ 2 \\ 3 \\ 4 \end{bmatrix}.$$

8-7. DETERMINANTS

Related to every square matrix is a determinant, which by definition is a number associated with the square array of the elements making up the matrix. Since we have concentrated our attention on elements which are real numbers, the determinant associated with an n-ordered matrix is also a real number. If

$$A = \begin{bmatrix} a_{11} & a_{12} & \cdots & a_{1n} \\ a_{21} & a_{22} & \cdots & a_{2n} \\ \vdots & \vdots & & \vdots \\ a_{n1} & a_{n2} & \cdots & a_{nn} \end{bmatrix},$$

then the determinant is also described as being of the nth order and symbolized as

$$|A| = \det A = \begin{vmatrix} a_{11} & a_{12} & \cdots & a_{1n} \\ a_{21} & a_{22} & \cdots & a_{2n} \\ \vdots & \vdots & & \vdots \\ a_{n1} & a_{n2} & \cdots & a_{nn} \end{vmatrix},$$

and is equal to a real number. The evaluation techniques for obtaining this "real number" value is most important and will be discussed in what follows.

It is interesting to note that the concept of a determinant involves the *function idea*. If the domain D of the *determinant function* is made up of all $n \times n$ matrices with elements in the real number field, then the range R for this function is R_e. In accord with what is to follow, it will be observed that for each choice of an $n \times n$ matrix there will be a unique real number value associated with it. This real number value is called the *determinant*, the "value of the determinant" or the "expansion of the determinant." We now proceed to study appropriate rules for obtaining this "number value."

Definition. A determinant of the second order, denoted by the symbol

$$\begin{vmatrix} a_1 & b_1 \\ a_2 & b_2 \end{vmatrix},$$

where $a_1, a_2, b_1,$ and b_2 are real numbers, is defined to be the real number

$$a_1 b_2 - a_2 b_1.$$

That is,

$$\begin{vmatrix} a_1 & b_1 \\ a_2 & b_2 \end{vmatrix} = a_1 b_2 - a_2 b_1.$$

The numbers that appear in the square array of the determinant are called the *elements of the determinant*, and are said to be arranged in (horizontal) rows and in (vertical) columns.

Definition. A determinant of the third order, denoted by the symbol

$$\begin{vmatrix} a_1 & b_1 & c_1 \\ a_2 & b_2 & c_2 \\ a_3 & b_3 & c_3 \end{vmatrix},$$

where the elements are real numbers, is the real number obtained from the expansion*

$$a_1 \begin{vmatrix} b_2 & c_2 \\ b_3 & c_3 \end{vmatrix} - a_2 \begin{vmatrix} b_1 & c_1 \\ b_3 & c_3 \end{vmatrix} + a_3 \begin{vmatrix} b_1 & c_1 \\ b_2 & c_2 \end{vmatrix}$$

$$= a_1(b_2 c_3 - b_3 c_2) - a_2(b_1 c_3 - b_3 c_1) + a_3(b_1 c_2 - b_2 c_1)$$

$$= a_1 b_2 c_3 - a_1 b_3 c_2 - a_2 b_1 c_3 + a_2 b_3 c_1 + a_3 b_1 c_2 - a_3 b_2 c_1.$$

The symbol used to designate the determinant encloses its array of elements by vertical lines, in contrast to the use of brackets, boldfaced parentheses, or double vertical lines as used to denote the corresponding matrix.

The following schemes indicate convenient methods for the expansion of the second- and third-order determinants:

Second-order:

$$\begin{vmatrix} a_1 & b_1 \\ a_2 & b_2 \end{vmatrix}$$

Third-order:

The arrows indicate the elements that are taken together as factors to produce each of the resulting terms of the expansion. The sign of the product term is unchanged when the arrow containing the factors of the product term start in a downward path and are changed to their additive inverses when the arrows start in an upward path. Thus the product $a_2 b_3 c_1$ remains as is, but $a_2 b_1 c_3$ is changed to $-a_2 b_1 c_3$. By observing the

*It will be shown later that this is only one of six equivalent expansions.

diagram one can account for each of the six terms that make up the expansion of a third-order determinant.

An alternate method for evaluating a third-order determinant is to repeat its first two columns to the right as indicated in the following diagram:

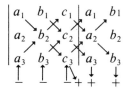

We now multiply together each three elements through which a line has been drawn. The obtained product should be left as is if the line through the elements starts downward, and a minus sign should be attached to each product where the line starts upward. The resulting expression will be the same as that given in the previous definition for the number value of the third order determinant.

The special methods for evaluating second- and third-order determinants apply only to these orders and should not be extended beyond. It is desirable and essential to introduce other methods which are theoretically more sound for evaluating determinants of orders higher than 3. Adequate procedures for such evaluation of higher- ordered determinants necessitates the introduction of the following material.

The *minor* of an element a_{ij} of a square matrix A of order n, denoted by M_{ij}, is the determinant of order $n - 1$ obtained by deleting the row and column in which the element is located. For example, consider a square matrix of order three, namely

$$\begin{bmatrix} a_{11} & a_{12} & a_{13} \\ a_{21} & a_{22} & a_{23} \\ a_{31} & a_{32} & a_{33} \end{bmatrix}.$$

Then

$$M_{11} = \begin{vmatrix} a_{11} & a_{12} & a_{13} \\ a_{21} & a_{22} & a_{23} \\ a_{31} & a_{32} & a_{33} \end{vmatrix} = \begin{vmatrix} a_{22} & a_{23} \\ a_{32} & a_{33} \end{vmatrix}$$

is the minor of a_{11},

$$M_{12} = \begin{vmatrix} a_{11} & a_{12} & a_{13} \\ a_{21} & a_{22} & a_{23} \\ a_{31} & a_{32} & a_{33} \end{vmatrix} = \begin{vmatrix} a_{21} & a_{23} \\ a_{31} & a_{33} \end{vmatrix}$$

is the minor of a_{12}, etc.

The *cofactor of an element* a_{ij} of a square matrix A of order n is denoted by C_{ij}, and is defined as being the signed minor

$$C_{ij} = (-1)^{i+j} M_{ij}, \qquad i = 1, 2, \ldots, n \quad \text{and } j = 1, 2, \ldots, n.$$

In the above example for the matrix of order three, the cofactor of the element a_{11} is

$$C_{11} = (-1)^{1+1} M_{11} = (+1) \begin{vmatrix} a_{22} & a_{23} \\ a_{32} & a_{33} \end{vmatrix},$$

and the cofactor of the element a_{12} is

$$C_{12} = (-1)^{1+2} M_{12} = (-1) \begin{vmatrix} a_{21} & a_{23} \\ a_{31} & a_{33} \end{vmatrix}.$$

Since the expression $(-1)^{i+j}$ is always $+1$ or -1, depending on the position of a_{ij}, the signs associated with the cofactors can be obtained from a checkerboard pattern alternating $+$'s (pluses) and $-$'s (minuses) in each row, where the odd-numbered rows start out with the $+$ signs while the even-numbered rows start out with $-$ signs. The checkerboard is herewith illustrated:

$$
\begin{array}{cccccl}
+ & - & + & - & \ldots & \text{1st row} \\
- & + & - & + & \ldots & \text{2nd row} \\
+ & - & + & \ominus & \ldots & \text{3rd row} \\
- & + & - & + & \ldots & \text{4th row}
\end{array}
$$

The circled sign $\ominus$ would be associated with the cofactor obtained for the element a_{34}.

Example.   If

$$A = \begin{bmatrix} 3 & 2 & -1 \\ 0 & 1 & 1 \\ 2 & -2 & 4 \end{bmatrix} = \begin{bmatrix} a_{11} & a_{12} & a_{13} \\ a_{21} & a_{22} & a_{23} \\ a_{31} & a_{32} & a_{33} \end{bmatrix},$$

the minor of the element $a_{32} = -2$ is represented by

$$M_{32} = \det \begin{bmatrix} 3 & -1 \\ 0 & 1 \end{bmatrix} = \begin{vmatrix} 3 & -1 \\ 0 & 1 \end{vmatrix} = 3,$$

and the corresponding cofactor of the element ($a_{32} = -2$) is represented
by

$$C_{32} = (-1)^{3+2}M_{32} = (-1) \det \begin{bmatrix} 3 & -1 \\ 0 & 1 \end{bmatrix}$$

$$= (-1)(3)$$

$$= -3.$$

If a matrix contains a single element, then its determinant is equal
to whatever this single element is. If A is a square matrix of order n,
where $n \geq 2$, then procedures for determining the value of its associated
determinants are necessary. The determination for such values may be
obtained by use of either the elements in the ith row or those of the jth
column in matrix A. The determinant value is given by

$$|A| = \det A = a_{i1}C_{i1} + a_{i2}C_{i2} + \ldots + a_{in}C_{in}, \qquad i = 1, 2, \ldots, n,$$

or

$$|A| = \det A = a_{1j}C_{1j} + a_{2j}C_{2j} + \cdots + a_{nj}C_{nj}, \qquad j = 1, 2, \ldots, n.$$

The value of det A is the same irrespective of whether row i or column j
had been chosen, and we use the descriptive phrase that det A has been
expanded about the ith row or the jth column, as the case might be.

Example 1.   The expansion of

$$\det \begin{bmatrix} 3 & 2 & -1 \\ 0 & 1 & 1 \\ 2 & -2 & 4 \end{bmatrix}$$

about the third row is

$$\begin{vmatrix} 3 & 2 & -1 \\ 0 & 1 & 1 \\ 2 & -2 & 4 \end{vmatrix} = 2(-1)^{3+1} \begin{vmatrix} 2 & -1 \\ 1 & 1 \end{vmatrix}$$

$$+ (-2)(-1)^{3+2} \begin{vmatrix} 3 & -1 \\ 0 & 1 \end{vmatrix} + 4(-1)^{3+3} \begin{vmatrix} 3 & 2 \\ 0 & 1 \end{vmatrix}$$

$$= 2[2 \cdot 1 - 1(-1)] - 2(-1)[3 \cdot 1 - 0(-1)]$$

$$+ 4[3 \cdot 1 - 0 \cdot 2]$$

$$= 6 + 6 + 12$$

$$= 24.$$

Example 2. The expansion of

$$\begin{vmatrix} 2 & 1 & -3 \\ 2 & 0 & 1 \\ 1 & 0 & 4 \end{vmatrix}$$

about the second column is

$$\begin{vmatrix} 2 & 1 & -3 \\ 2 & 0 & 1 \\ 1 & 0 & 4 \end{vmatrix} = 1(-1)^{1+2}\begin{vmatrix} 2 & 1 \\ 1 & 4 \end{vmatrix} + 0(-1)^{2+2}\begin{vmatrix} 2 & -3 \\ 1 & 4 \end{vmatrix} + 0(-1)^{3+2}\begin{vmatrix} 2 & -3 \\ 2 & 1 \end{vmatrix}$$

$$= (-1)[2\cdot4 - 1(1)] + 0 - 0$$

$$= -(8 - 1)$$

$$= -7.$$

It is left as a student exercise to expand the above determinant by choosing any of the other columns or any of the other rows, realizing that -7 is the value obtained accordingly by these other expansions. There should be six ways that this can be performed, since the determinant is of the third order. Why?

Examples 1 and 2 illustrate that a determinant is much easier to evaluate when there are zeros in a row or a column. Therefore it will be advantageous to establish some theorems where transformations can be performed upon determinants before expansions are carried out so as to obtain other determinants of equal value where as many zeros as possible have been conveniently created for its elements.

8-8. IMPORTANT THEOREMS ABOUT DETERMINANTS

To introduce theorems that will help us to create zeros in equal determinants, statements for same will follow with verifications illustrated through third-order determinants, even though these theorems are true in general for the nth order.

THEOREM 1: *Two determinants of the same order are equal if one is obtained from the other by interchanging the rows and columns.* Thus

$$\begin{vmatrix} a_1 & b_1 \\ a_2 & b_2 \end{vmatrix} = \begin{vmatrix} a_1 & a_2 \\ b_1 & b_2 \end{vmatrix} \quad \text{and} \quad \begin{vmatrix} a_1 & b_1 & c_1 \\ a_2 & b_2 & c_2 \\ a_3 & b_3 & c_3 \end{vmatrix} = \begin{vmatrix} a_1 & a_2 & a_3 \\ b_1 & b_2 & b_3 \\ c_1 & c_2 & c_3 \end{vmatrix}.$$

This can be proved by expanding the determinants and showing that the left-hand member equals the right-hand member.

THEOREM 2: *If two rows (or two columns) of a determinant are interchanged, then the sign of the determinant is changed.*
Thus

$$\begin{vmatrix} a_1 & b_1 \\ a_2 & b_2 \end{vmatrix} = - \begin{vmatrix} b_1 & a_1 \\ b_2 & a_2 \end{vmatrix} \quad \text{and} \quad \begin{vmatrix} a_1 & b_1 & c_1 \\ a_2 & b_2 & c_2 \\ a_3 & b_3 & c_3 \end{vmatrix} = - \begin{vmatrix} c_1 & b_1 & a_1 \\ c_2 & b_2 & a_2 \\ c_3 & b_3 & a_3 \end{vmatrix}.$$

This can be proved by expanding the determinants and showing that the left-hand member equals the right-hand member.

THEOREM 3: *If the corresponding elements of two rows (or two columns) are equal, then the value of the determinant is zero.*
Thus

$$\begin{vmatrix} a_1 & b_1 & a_1 \\ a_2 & b_2 & a_2 \\ a_3 & b_3 & a_3 \end{vmatrix} = 0.$$

The proof is left for the student.

THEOREM 4: *If each element of a row (or column) is multiplied by a constant k, then the value of the determinant is multiplied by k.*
Thus

$$\begin{vmatrix} ka_1 & kb_1 & kc_1 \\ a_2 & b_2 & c_2 \\ a_3 & b_3 & c_3 \end{vmatrix} = k \begin{vmatrix} a_1 & b_1 & c_1 \\ a_2 & b_2 & c_2 \\ a_3 & b_3 & c_3 \end{vmatrix}.$$

The proof is left for the student.

Consequently, Theorem 3 may be restated: *A determinant is zero in value if corresponding elements of two rows (two columns) are proportional.*

THEOREM 5: *If each element of a row (or column) is multiplied by a constant and then added to (or subtracted from) the corresponding element of another row (or column), the value of the determinant is unchanged.*
Thus

$$\begin{vmatrix} a_1 + ka_3 & b_1 + kb_3 & c_1 + kc_3 \\ a_2 & b_2 & c_2 \\ a_3 & b_3 & c_3 \end{vmatrix} = \begin{vmatrix} a_1 & b_1 & c_1 \\ a_2 & b_2 & c_2 \\ a_3 & b_3 & c_3 \end{vmatrix}.$$

This theorem can be proved by expanding the determinant by the altered row (or column) and expressing the expansion as the sum of two determinants, one of which is zero.

Example. Find a determinant equal to

$$\begin{vmatrix} -2 & 3 & 1 \\ 1 & 2 & 3 \\ 1 & 3 & 2 \end{vmatrix}$$

which possesses zeros in row 2 with the exception of the element in the first column. Expand the resulting determinant.

$$\begin{vmatrix} -2 & 3 & 1 \\ 1 & 2 & 3 \\ 1 & 3 & 2 \end{vmatrix} = \begin{vmatrix} -2 & 7 & 1 \\ 1 & 0 & 3 \\ 1 & 1 & 2 \end{vmatrix}$$ Multiply column 1 by -2 and add to column 2.

$$= \begin{vmatrix} -2 & 7 & 7 \\ 1 & 0 & 0 \\ 1 & 1 & -1 \end{vmatrix}$$ Multiply column 1 by -3 and add to column 3.

$$= (-1) \begin{vmatrix} 7 & 7 \\ 1 & -1 \end{vmatrix}$$

$$= (-1)(-7 \quad -7)$$

$$= 14.$$

The manner in which this is accomplished may be carried out in ways other than shown here. For example, start with row 1 and multiply its elements by -3 and add to the corresponding elements of row 2, etc. It is suggested that the student proceed from this point and accomplish the same value for the determinant.

8-9. THE INVERSE OF A SQUARE MATRIX—2 × 2 MATRIX

The identity matrix I has been defined as a square matrix with all of its elements on the principal diagonal equal to unity and all the others zero. The identity matrix performs in matrix algebra the same service that the number 1 carries out in arithmetic with numbers. If A is any square matrix of order n,

$$AI = IA = A.$$

If A is a square matrix, of order n, then the matrix B of order n is the *inverse* of A if and only if $A \cdot B = I$. The matrix B, when it exists, is denoted by A^{-1}, so that $AA^{-1} = I = A^{-1}A$. The inverse of a square matrix of order n does not always exist as will be observed in what follows.

The inverse of any 2×2 matrix can be computed in the following fashion when it exists:

Let

$$A = \begin{bmatrix} a_{11} & a_{12} \\ a_{21} & a_{22} \end{bmatrix} \quad \text{and } B = \begin{bmatrix} b_{11} & b_{12} \\ b_{21} & b_{22} \end{bmatrix}.$$

If B is the inverse of A, then $B = A^{-1}$ and

$$AB = A \cdot A^{-1} = A^{-1} \cdot A = I,$$

or

$$\begin{bmatrix} a_{11} & a_{12} \\ a_{21} & a_{22} \end{bmatrix} \begin{bmatrix} b_{11} & b_{12} \\ b_{21} & b_{22} \end{bmatrix} = \begin{bmatrix} 1 & 0 \\ 0 & 1 \end{bmatrix}.$$

Thus

$$\begin{bmatrix} a_{11}b_{11} + a_{12}b_{21} & a_{11}b_{12} + a_{12}b_{22} \\ a_{21}b_{11} + a_{22}b_{21} & a_{21}b_{12} + a_{22}b_{22} \end{bmatrix} = \begin{bmatrix} 1 & 0 \\ 0 & 1 \end{bmatrix}.$$

For two matrices to be equal, corresponding elements must be equal. As a consequence

$$\begin{cases} a_{11}b_{11} + a_{12}b_{21} = 1 \\ \quad \wedge \\ a_{21}b_{11} + a_{22}b_{21} = 0 \end{cases} \qquad \begin{cases} a_{11}b_{12} + a_{12}b_{22} = 0 \\ \quad \wedge \\ a_{21}b_{12} + a_{22}b_{22} = 1. \end{cases}$$

The solution set for the left-hand system of linear equations is (see Sec. 8-1.)

$$|A| = \begin{vmatrix} a_{11} & a_{12} \\ a_{21} & a_{22} \end{vmatrix} = a_{11}a_{22} - a_{21}a_{12}$$

$$b_{11} = \frac{\begin{vmatrix} 1 & a_{12} \\ 0 & a_{22} \end{vmatrix}}{|A|} = \frac{a_{22}}{|A|}$$

$$b_{21} = \frac{\begin{vmatrix} a_{11} & 1 \\ a_{21} & 0 \end{vmatrix}}{|A|} = \frac{-a_{21}}{|A|},$$

and for the right-hand system is

$$b_{12} = \frac{\begin{vmatrix} 0 & a_{12} \\ 1 & a_{22} \end{vmatrix}}{|A|} = \frac{-a_{12}}{|A|}$$

$$b_{22} = \frac{\begin{vmatrix} a_{11} & 0 \\ a_{21} & 1 \end{vmatrix}}{|A|} = \frac{a_{11}}{|A|}.$$

Therefore the inverse of any 2×2 matrix, if it exists, is

$$A^{-1} = \begin{bmatrix} \dfrac{a_{22}}{|A|} & \dfrac{-a_{12}}{|A|} \\ \dfrac{-a_{21}}{|A|} & \dfrac{a_{11}}{|A|} \end{bmatrix} = \frac{1}{|A|} \begin{bmatrix} a_{22} & -a_{12} \\ -a_{21} & a_{11} \end{bmatrix}.$$

The inverse matrix A^{-1} clearly exists if and only is $|A| \neq 0$. The student should multiply $A \cdot A^{-1}$ and $A^{-1}A$ to verify that the product is indeed I.

Example. The inverse of $A = \begin{bmatrix} 2 & 1 \\ 3 & 4 \end{bmatrix}$ is computed as follows:

$$|A| = \begin{vmatrix} 2 & 1 \\ 3 & 4 \end{vmatrix} = 2(4) - 3(1) = 5 \quad (|A| \neq 0).$$

Thus A has the inverse

$$A^{-1} = \begin{bmatrix} \dfrac{4}{5} & -\dfrac{1}{5} \\ -\dfrac{3}{5} & \dfrac{2}{5} \end{bmatrix}.$$

Note that

$$AA^{-1} = \begin{bmatrix} 2 & 1 \\ 3 & 4 \end{bmatrix} \begin{bmatrix} \dfrac{4}{5} & -\dfrac{1}{5} \\ -\dfrac{3}{5} & \dfrac{2}{5} \end{bmatrix} = \begin{bmatrix} 2\left(\dfrac{4}{5}\right) + 1\left(-\dfrac{3}{5}\right) & 2\left(-\dfrac{1}{5}\right) + 1\left(\dfrac{2}{5}\right) \\ 3\left(\dfrac{4}{5}\right) + 4\left(-\dfrac{3}{5}\right) & 3\left(-\dfrac{1}{5}\right) + 4\left(\dfrac{2}{5}\right) \end{bmatrix}$$

$$= \begin{bmatrix} 1 & 0 \\ 0 & 1 \end{bmatrix}.$$

It can be verified that $A^{-1}A = I$ which is left as an exercise. The manner in which the inverse of a 2×2 matrix is formed should be memorized by observing its construction. If

$$A = \begin{bmatrix} a & c \\ b & d \end{bmatrix}$$

it should be noted that its inverse is

$$\frac{1}{ad - bc} \begin{bmatrix} d & -c \\ -b & a \end{bmatrix}.$$

In it you will observe that the elements in the principal diagonal have been interchanged from those of their original position; that the elements in the secondary diagonal are the additive inverses for their original values; that this inverse matrix possesses the scalar factor $\dfrac{1}{ad - bc} = \dfrac{1}{\det A} = \dfrac{1}{|A|}$. Thus the inverse for

$$A = \begin{bmatrix} 2 & -5 \\ 3 & 6 \end{bmatrix}$$

would be

$$A^{-1} = \frac{1}{27} \begin{bmatrix} 6 & 5 \\ -3 & 2 \end{bmatrix}.$$

A check of AA^{-1} will verify that A^{-1} is the correct inverse.

8-10. THE INVERSE OF A 3 X 3 MATRIX

There are various methods for finding the inverse of a square matrix. Consider first the following definitions:

(a) A square matrix A is said to be singular if $\det A = |A| = 0$ and nonsingular if $\det A = |A| \neq 0$.

(b) If $A = (a_{ij})$ is a square matrix of order n, the cofactor matrix of A, denoted by "cof A" or by C is the square matrix of order n whose entry in the ith row and jth column is C_{ij}, the cofactor of a_{ij} in A.

(c) The adjoint matrix of A, denoted by "adj A" is the transpose of the matrix C consisting of the cofactors of each element a_{ij} in A. The following examples should be studied carefully for procedure.

Example.   If

$$A = \begin{bmatrix} 2 & 3 & 0 \\ 0 & 2 & -1 \\ 1 & 0 & 2 \end{bmatrix}$$

then

$$C = \text{cof } A = \begin{bmatrix} +\begin{vmatrix} 2 & -1 \\ 0 & 2 \end{vmatrix} & -\begin{vmatrix} 0 & -1 \\ 1 & 2 \end{vmatrix} & +\begin{vmatrix} 0 & 2 \\ 1 & 0 \end{vmatrix} \\ -\begin{vmatrix} 3 & 0 \\ 0 & 2 \end{vmatrix} & +\begin{vmatrix} 2 & 0 \\ 1 & 2 \end{vmatrix} & -\begin{vmatrix} 2 & 3 \\ 1 & 0 \end{vmatrix} \\ +\begin{vmatrix} 3 & 0 \\ 2 & -1 \end{vmatrix} & -\begin{vmatrix} 2 & 0 \\ 0 & -1 \end{vmatrix} & +\begin{vmatrix} 2 & 3 \\ 0 & 2 \end{vmatrix} \end{bmatrix}$$

$$= \begin{bmatrix} 4 & -1 & -2 \\ -6 & 4 & 3 \\ -3 & 2 & 4 \end{bmatrix}.$$

Hint: Compare with symbolic form

$$\begin{bmatrix} C_{11} & C_{12} & C_{13} \\ C_{21} & C_{22} & C_{23} \\ C_{31} & C_{32} & C_{33} \end{bmatrix}.$$

$$\text{adj } A = \text{adj } \begin{bmatrix} 4 & -1 & -2 \\ -6 & 4 & 3 \\ -3 & 2 & 4 \end{bmatrix} = \begin{bmatrix} 4 & -6 & -3 \\ -1 & 4 & 2 \\ -2 & 3 & 4 \end{bmatrix}.$$

Hint: Compare with symbolic form

$$\begin{bmatrix} C_{11} & C_{21} & C_{31} \\ C_{12} & C_{22} & C_{32} \\ C_{13} & C_{23} & C_{33} \end{bmatrix}.$$

We now use the very important following theorem:

THEOREM: *If A is a square matrix of order n, an inverse matrix A^{-1} exists, if and only if A is nonsingular, and A^{-1} is given by*

$$A^{-1} = \frac{1}{|A|} \, (adj\ A).$$

Continuing the solution for our example where

$$A = \begin{bmatrix} 2 & 3 & 0 \\ 0 & 2 & -1 \\ 1 & 0 & 2 \end{bmatrix}$$

then

$$|A| = 2 \begin{vmatrix} 2 & -1 \\ 0 & 2 \end{vmatrix} + 3 \left(- \begin{vmatrix} 0 & -1 \\ 1 & 2 \end{vmatrix} \right) + 0 \begin{vmatrix} 0 & 2 \\ 1 & 0 \end{vmatrix}$$

$$= 2(4) + 3(-1)$$

$$= 5$$

and

$$\mathrm{adj}\ A = \begin{bmatrix} 4 & -6 & -3 \\ -1 & 4 & 2 \\ -2 & 3 & 4 \end{bmatrix}$$

as shown previously.

Thus

$$A^{-1} = \frac{1}{5} \begin{bmatrix} 4 & -6 & -3 \\ -1 & 4 & 2 \\ -2 & 3 & 4 \end{bmatrix} = \begin{bmatrix} \frac{4}{5} & -\frac{6}{5} & -\frac{3}{5} \\ -\frac{1}{5} & \frac{4}{5} & \frac{2}{5} \\ -\frac{2}{5} & \frac{3}{5} & \frac{4}{5} \end{bmatrix}.$$

Note that

$$A A^{-1} = \begin{bmatrix} 2 & 3 & 0 \\ 0 & 2 & -1 \\ 1 & 0 & 2 \end{bmatrix} \begin{bmatrix} \frac{4}{5} & -\frac{6}{5} & -\frac{3}{5} \\ -\frac{1}{5} & \frac{4}{5} & \frac{2}{5} \\ -\frac{2}{5} & \frac{3}{5} & \frac{4}{5} \end{bmatrix}$$

$$\text{or } AA^{-1} = \begin{bmatrix} \dfrac{8}{5} - \dfrac{3}{5} & -\dfrac{12}{5} + \dfrac{12}{5} & -\dfrac{6}{5} + \dfrac{6}{5} \\[2mm] -\dfrac{2}{5} + \dfrac{2}{5} & \dfrac{8}{5} - \dfrac{3}{5} & \dfrac{4}{5} - \dfrac{4}{5} \\[2mm] \dfrac{4}{5} - \dfrac{4}{5} & -\dfrac{6}{5} + \dfrac{6}{5} & -\dfrac{3}{5} + \dfrac{8}{5} \end{bmatrix}$$

$$= \begin{bmatrix} 1 & 0 & 0 \\ 0 & 1 & 0 \\ 0 & 0 & 1 \end{bmatrix}.$$

8-11. SOLUTION OF A SYSTEM OF LINEAR EQUATIONS BY MATRIX PROCEDURES

A system of linear equations may be solved by algebraic procedures as already discussed in previous chapters. However, the solution of a system of equations gains in difficulty by use of algebraic methods when the number of equations in the system increases. Matrix algebra provides a unified and systematic method for solving a system of linear equations. The systematic steps by matrix methods are such that they can be conveniently programmed for electronic computers to speed the calculations.

The method of solving a system of linear equations can best be illustrated by an example. The procedure is illustrated for a system of 2 linear equations involving 2 unknowns, although the procedure is applicable to a system of n linear equations involving n unknowns. The difficulty that arises at all times is the finding of inverses to given square matrices.

Example 1. Given

$$f = \{(x, y) \mid x + y = 6\}$$

and

$$g = \{(x,y) \mid x + 3y = 16\},$$

find $f \cap g$. The two simultaneous equations can be expressed in matrix form as

$$\begin{bmatrix} 1 & 1 \\ 1 & 3 \end{bmatrix} \begin{bmatrix} x \\ y \end{bmatrix} = \begin{bmatrix} 6 \\ 16 \end{bmatrix},$$

or

$$AX = B.$$

The matrix A is the matrix of coefficients of the unknowns x and y; the matrix X is the matrix of the unknowns; and the matrix B is the matrix of the right-hand sides of the given system.

If the matrix equation $AX = B$ is premultiplied on both sides by A^{-1}, there results

$$A^{-1}(AX) = A^{-1}B$$
$$(A^{-1}A)X = A^{-1}B$$
$$IX = A^{-1}B$$
$$X = A^{-1}B.$$

The technique for solving a system of linear equations now becomes the problem of finding the inverse of the coefficient matrix A. The value $|A|$ is computed first, as follows

$$|A| = \begin{vmatrix} 1 & 1 \\ 1 & 3 \end{vmatrix} = (1)(3) - (1)(1) = 2.$$

Since $|A| \neq 0$, A is nonsingular and has an inverse and

$$A^{-1} = \frac{1}{2}\begin{bmatrix} 3 & -1 \\ -1 & 1 \end{bmatrix} = \begin{bmatrix} \frac{3}{2} & -\frac{1}{2} \\ -\frac{1}{2} & \frac{1}{2} \end{bmatrix}.$$

Hint: Use method suggested in Sec. 8-9. The solution of the system is thus given by

$$\begin{bmatrix} \frac{3}{2} & -\frac{1}{2} \\ -\frac{1}{2} & \frac{1}{2} \end{bmatrix}\begin{bmatrix} 1 & 1 \\ 1 & 3 \end{bmatrix}\begin{bmatrix} x \\ y \end{bmatrix} = \begin{bmatrix} \frac{3}{2} & -\frac{1}{2} \\ -\frac{1}{2} & \frac{1}{2} \end{bmatrix}\begin{bmatrix} 6 \\ 16 \end{bmatrix}$$

$$X = \begin{bmatrix} \frac{3}{2} & -\frac{1}{2} \\ -\frac{1}{2} & \frac{1}{2} \end{bmatrix}\begin{bmatrix} 6 \\ 16 \end{bmatrix}$$

or

$$\begin{bmatrix} x \\ y \end{bmatrix} = \begin{bmatrix} \left(\frac{3}{2}\right)(6) + \left(-\frac{1}{2}\right)(16) \\ \left(-\frac{1}{2}\right)(6) + \left(\frac{1}{2}\right)(16) \end{bmatrix}$$

$$= \begin{bmatrix} 1 \\ 5 \end{bmatrix}.$$

Therefore $x = 1$ and $y = 5$, and $f \cap g = \{(1,5)\}$.

Example 2. By use of the information obtained in the example of Sec. 8-10, obtain the solution set $f \cap g \cap h$ if

$$f = \{(x,y,z) \mid 2x + 3y = 8\}$$
$$g = \{(x,y,z) \mid 2y - z = 1\}$$
$$h = \{(x,y,z) \mid x + 2z = 7\}.$$

The problem here is to solve

$$\begin{bmatrix} 2 & 3 & 0 \\ 0 & 2 & -1 \\ 1 & 0 & 2 \end{bmatrix} \begin{bmatrix} x \\ y \\ z \end{bmatrix} = \begin{bmatrix} 8 \\ 1 \\ 7 \end{bmatrix}.$$

Proceed and finish the matrix manipulation by using the information of Sec. 8-10.

8-12. SOLUTION OF SYSTEMS OF EQUATIONS BY DIRECT USE OF DETERMINANTS

The value of any unknown in a system of equations may be represented directly without using matrices. This is illustrated in Examples 1 and 2.

Example 1. Solve the system

$$2x - 3 = y$$
$$\wedge$$
$$x + 1 = 3y.$$

Solution. First, arrange the equations thus:

$$2x - y = 3$$
$$\wedge$$
$$x - 3y = -1.$$

Then

$$x = \frac{\begin{vmatrix} 3 & -1 \\ -1 & -3 \end{vmatrix}}{\begin{vmatrix} 2 & -1 \\ 1 & -3 \end{vmatrix}} = \frac{-10}{-5} = 2,$$

and

$$y = \frac{\begin{vmatrix} 2 & 3 \\ 1 & -1 \end{vmatrix}}{\begin{vmatrix} 2 & -1 \\ 1 & -3 \end{vmatrix}} = \frac{-5}{-5} = 1.$$

The solution set is $\{(2,1)\}$.

It will be noted that the determinant in each denominator is composed of the coefficients of x and y arranged in the same order in which they occur in the equations. The determinant in each numerator is the same except that the numbers to the right of the equality signs replace the coefficients of the letter whose value is sought.

Example 2. Solve the system

$$3x - 2y - z = 3$$
$$\wedge$$
$$2x + 3y + z = 1$$
$$\wedge$$
$$x - y - 2z = -2.$$

Solution.

$$x = \frac{\begin{vmatrix} 3 & -2 & -1 \\ 1 & 3 & 1 \\ -2 & -1 & -2 \end{vmatrix}}{\begin{vmatrix} 3 & -2 & -1 \\ 2 & 3 & 1 \\ 1 & -1 & -2 \end{vmatrix}} = \frac{-18 + 4 + 1 - 6 + 3 - 4}{-18 - 2 + 2 + 3 + 3 - 8} = \frac{-20}{-20} = 1.$$

$$y = \frac{\begin{vmatrix} 3 & 3 & -1 \\ 2 & 1 & 1 \\ 1 & -2 & -2 \end{vmatrix}}{\begin{vmatrix} 3 & -2 & -1 \\ 2 & 3 & 1 \\ 1 & -1 & -2 \end{vmatrix}} = \frac{-6 + 3 + 4 + 1 + 6 + 12}{-20 \text{ (evaluated above)}} = \frac{20}{-20} = -1.$$

$$z = \dfrac{\begin{vmatrix} 3 & -2 & 3 \\ 2 & 3 & 1 \\ 1 & -1 & -2 \end{vmatrix}}{\begin{vmatrix} 3 & -2 & -1 \\ 2 & 3 & 1 \\ 1 & -1 & -2 \end{vmatrix}} = \dfrac{-18 - 2 - 6 - 9 + 3 - 8}{-20} = \dfrac{-40}{-20} = 2.$$

Ans. $(x = 1, y = -1, z = 2)$ or the solution set is $\{(1, -1, 2)\}$.

Note that the denominator in each case contains the coefficients arranged in their normal order.

The only difference between the numerator and the denominator in each fraction is that, in the numerator, the constants on the right-hand sides of the equations replace the coefficients of the letter whose value is sought. Applying this method to the general system:

$$ax + by + cz = k$$
$$dx + ey + fz = l$$
$$gx + hy + mz = n,$$

it follows that

$$x = \frac{N_x}{D}$$

$$y = \frac{N_y}{D}$$

$$z = \frac{N_z}{D};$$

where

$$N_x = \begin{vmatrix} k & b & c \\ l & e & f \\ n & h & m \end{vmatrix},$$

$$N_y = \begin{vmatrix} a & k & c \\ d & l & f \\ g & n & m \end{vmatrix},$$

$$N_z = \begin{vmatrix} a & b & k \\ d & e & l \\ g & h & n \end{vmatrix},$$

$$D = \begin{vmatrix} a & b & c \\ d & e & f \\ g & h & m \end{vmatrix}.$$

It should be noted that if $D = 0$, then the system may be inconsistent or may need further study, as was discussed in Sec. 7-4.

EXERCISE 8-1

1–27. Solve Probs. 1–27 of Exercise 7-1 by use of determinants.

28–36. Solve Probs. 1–9 of Exercise 7-2 by use of determinants.

GENERAL REVIEW EXERCISE OF MATRICES

Perform the indicated operations in Probs. 1–5.

1. (a) $\begin{bmatrix} 2 & 3 & 5 \\ 1 & -1 & 0 \\ 2 & 1 & 1 \\ 3 & 3 & 3 \end{bmatrix} + \begin{bmatrix} 1 & 0 & 0 \\ 0 & 1 & 0 \\ 1 & 1 & 1 \\ 1 & 1 & 0 \end{bmatrix}$

   (b) $\begin{bmatrix} 1 & 2 & -3 & 4 \\ 0 & -5 & 1 & -1 \end{bmatrix} + \begin{bmatrix} 3 & -5 & 6 & -1 \\ 2 & 0 & -2 & -3 \end{bmatrix}$

2. (a) $\begin{bmatrix} 2 & 3 & 5 & 3 \\ 1 & -2 & -3 & 2 \\ 6 & 5 & 4 & 1 \end{bmatrix} \cdot \begin{bmatrix} 1 & 0 \\ 0 & 1 \\ 1 & 1 \\ 0 & 0 \end{bmatrix}$

   (b) $5 \begin{bmatrix} 2 & 4 \\ -3 & 1 \end{bmatrix} - 2 \begin{bmatrix} 1 & 7 \\ 2 & -3 \\ 0 & -1 \end{bmatrix} - \begin{bmatrix} 2 & -1 & 0 \\ 3 & 1 & 4 \end{bmatrix}$

3. $\left\{ \begin{bmatrix} 2 & 0 & 1 \\ 3 & 2 & 1 \\ -1 & 5 & 2 \end{bmatrix} + \begin{bmatrix} -1 & 0 & 1 \\ 1 & 0 & 1 \\ 2 & 1 & 1 \end{bmatrix} \right\} \cdot \begin{bmatrix} 2 & 2 & 2 \\ 1 & 1 & 1 \\ 3 & 1 & 1 \end{bmatrix}$

4. $\begin{bmatrix} -1 & 0 & 1 & 2 \\ 2 & 1 & 3 & 4 \\ 5 & 1 & -1 & 0 \\ 2 & 1 & 3 & 1 \end{bmatrix} \begin{bmatrix} 1 & 0 & 0 & 0 \\ 0 & 1 & 0 & 0 \\ 0 & 0 & .1 & 0 \\ 0 & 0 & 0 & 1 \end{bmatrix}$

5. (a) $\begin{bmatrix} 3 & 2 & 1 & 5 \end{bmatrix} \begin{bmatrix} 0 \\ 1 \\ 2 \\ 4 \end{bmatrix}$,   (b) $\begin{bmatrix} 2 & 1 \end{bmatrix} \begin{bmatrix} 1 & -2 & 0 \\ 4 & 5 & -3 \end{bmatrix}$

6. If A, B, and C are 2×2 matrices, show that

$$A(B + C) = AB + AC.$$

7. (a) Let $A = \begin{bmatrix} 3 & 1 \\ 6 & 2 \end{bmatrix}$ and $B = \begin{bmatrix} -1 & -1 \\ 3 & 3 \end{bmatrix}$. Show that $AB = 0$ even

though neither A nor B is zero.

(b) Let $A = \begin{bmatrix} 1 & 2 & 0 \\ 3 & -1 & 4 \end{bmatrix}$. Find $A'A$, AA'.

8. Evaluate:

(a) $\begin{vmatrix} 0 & -3 & 1 \\ 5 & 3 & 0 \\ 3 & -5 & -6 \end{vmatrix}$ (b) $\begin{vmatrix} 3 & -2 & 5 & 2 \\ -2 & -1 & 4 & 0 \\ 1 & 2 & -3 & -5 \\ 3 & 5 & 2 & 0 \end{vmatrix}$

9. Produce an equal determinant for the given ones where the starred elements have been replaced by zeros. Evaluate this equal determinant.

(a) $\begin{vmatrix} 2 & 3 & -1 \\ 4 & 5^* & 0 \\ 2 & 10 & 3 \end{vmatrix}$ (b) $\begin{vmatrix} 3 & 1 & 4 \\ 5 & -3^* & 2 \\ 3 & 4^* & 1 \end{vmatrix}$

(c) $\begin{vmatrix} 3^* & 1 & 4 & 2 \\ 0 & -2 & 5 & 3 \\ -6^* & 4 & 2 & 1 \\ 1 & 5 & 3 & 2^* \end{vmatrix}$

10. Given

$$A = \begin{bmatrix} 1 & -2 \\ 3 & 4 \end{bmatrix}, \quad B = \begin{bmatrix} 3 & 1 \\ 2 & 6 \end{bmatrix}, \text{ and } I = \begin{bmatrix} 1 & 0 \\ 0 & 1 \end{bmatrix}.$$

(a) Show that $AI = A$.
(b) Show that $IA = A$.
(c) Show that $BI = B$.
(d) Show that $IB = B$.

11. Find the inverse of each matrix A, if the inverse exists. Check by use of $AA^{-1} = I$ and $A^{-1}A = I$.

(a)

$$A = \begin{bmatrix} 3 & 5 \\ 5 & 3 \end{bmatrix}$$

(b)

$$A = \begin{bmatrix} -4 & 2 \\ -1 & 1 \end{bmatrix}$$

(c)

$$A = \begin{bmatrix} 4 & 5 \\ 9 & 7 \end{bmatrix}$$

(d)

$$A = \begin{bmatrix} 1 & -6 \\ 2 & 3 \end{bmatrix}$$

(e)

$$A = \begin{bmatrix} 1 & -2 & 3 \\ 4 & 5 & -6 \\ 7 & 8 & 9 \end{bmatrix}$$

(f)

$$A = \begin{bmatrix} 3 & 5 & -1 \\ 2 & -7 & 8 \\ 4 & 1 & 6 \end{bmatrix}$$

12. Solve by matrix procedures:

(a) $\begin{cases} -3y + z = 5 \\ \quad \wedge \\ 5x + 3z = 1 \\ \quad \wedge \\ 3x - 5y = -6 \end{cases}$

(b) $\begin{cases} 2A + B - C = 3 \\ \quad \wedge \\ A - 3B + 2C = -2 \\ \quad \wedge \\ 3A + B - 3C = -1 \end{cases}$

(c) $\begin{cases} \dfrac{3}{x} - \dfrac{2}{y} + \dfrac{1}{z} = 2 \\ \quad \wedge \\ -\dfrac{2}{x} + \dfrac{1}{y} - \dfrac{4}{z} = 0 \\ \quad \wedge \\ \dfrac{3}{x} - \dfrac{4}{z} = 0 \end{cases}$

(d) $\begin{cases} ax + by = c \\ \quad \wedge \\ 2bx - ay = w, \end{cases}$ for x and y; for a and b.

13. Verify that "the transpose" of a product of two matrices of appropriate dimensions is equal to the product of their transposes in reverse order. Use the matrices

$$A = \begin{bmatrix} 4 & 1 \\ 2 & -3 \\ -1 & 4 \end{bmatrix}, \quad B = \begin{bmatrix} 4 & -5 \\ -6 & 3 \end{bmatrix}$$ and show that $(AB)' = B'A'$.

14. A square matrix in which $a_{ij} = a_{ji}$ is referred to as being symmetric. It follows that if an inverse exists, then its transpose has the same inverse. Find A^{-1}, if

$$A = \begin{bmatrix} 1 & 2 & 3 \\ 2 & 3 & 4 \\ 3 & 4 & 5 \end{bmatrix}.$$

15. Verify that

$$[x \quad y] \begin{bmatrix} a & b \\ b & c \end{bmatrix} \begin{bmatrix} x \\ y \end{bmatrix} + [e \quad f] \begin{bmatrix} x \\ y \end{bmatrix} + g[1]$$

is the matrix made up of the single element

$$ax^2 + 2bxy + cy^2 + ex + fy + g.$$

16. Solve 12(a), (b), (c) directly by use of determinants.

17. A system such as

$$3x - 2y + 4z = 0$$
$$\wedge$$
$$2x + y - z = 0$$
$$\wedge$$
$$3x - 4y + z = 0$$

is called *homogeneous*. Note that all members on the right-hand side are zero. The solution to such a system is the trivial one, namely, $x = 0$, $y = 0$, $z = 0$, or has infinitely many 3-tuples "(x,y,z)" that satisfy it. The situation depends upon the determinant of the coefficients of x, y, z. If the determinant so formed is nonzero, the only answer to the system is the trivial one. Otherwise a further study of the system is essential, and an infinite number of 3-tuples satisfy it. What is the situation for the homogeneous system given by

$$2x - y + z = 0$$
$$\wedge$$
$$3x + y - z = 0$$
$$\wedge$$
$$7x - y + z = 0.$$

Hint: Here $D = 0$. Use two of the equations of the system and solve for two of the unknowns in terms of the third one. Check the results obtained in the three equations. What do your answers mean?

chapter 9

Exponents and Radicals

9-1. THE LAWS OF EXPONENTS

As we have already seen, the symbol a^m, when m is a positive integer, means "the base a taken m times as a factor." Thus $2^3 = 2 \cdot 2 \cdot 2 = 8$. This process of raising to powers is called *involution*.

We shall now examine the laws concerning operations with positive integral exponents.

Perhaps even more useful than knowledge of the laws themselves is the realization of how very easily these working rules can be discovered at first hand by anyone who understands the meaning of the symbol a^m. There is not a better place to apply the arithmetic tests which are so useful in algebra. For example, which is correct: $a^m a^n = a^{m+n}$, or $a^m a^n = a^{mn}$? Try it with small numbers, say $a = 2$, $m = 2$, $n = 3$. Then, $a^m a^n = 2^2 2^3 = (2 \cdot 2)(2 \cdot 2 \cdot 2) = 2 \cdot 2 \cdot 2 \cdot 2 \cdot 2 = 2^5$. Evidently the exponents here are *added*, and not multiplied. This suggests that the correct law is: $a^m a^n = a^{m+n}$.

Once the simplicity of the testing-by-arithmetic method is grasped, the student will be self-reliant when his memory fails. But he can save time by learning the five all-sufficient laws below, which, when supplemented by certain definitions, will be shown to hold *even when the exponents are not positive integers*. It is helpful to learn them in groups of 2, 2, and 1, called respectively the *repeated base*, the *repeated exponent*, and the *single base* cases. Easy extensions of the laws are indicated by the illustrative examples.

Repeated Base Cases

$a \in R_e$; $m, n \in N$, where N represents the set of natural numbers

Law 1.

$$a^m a^n = a^{m+n}.$$

Examples. $2^3 2^4 = 2^7$; $3^4 3^2 3 = 3^{4+2+1} = 3^7$.

Law 2.

$$\frac{a^m}{a^n} = a^{m-n}, m > n.$$

Example.

$$\frac{2^7}{2^3} = 2^{7-3} = 2^4.$$

Thus if the same number or letter appears as a *base* in each of two exponential numbers which are multiplied or divided, *this same base* appears in the result.*

Repeated Exponent Cases

Law 3.

$$a^m b^m = (ab)^m.$$

Examples. $\qquad 3^3 5^3 = (3 \cdot 5)^3 = (15)^3$;

$$2^2 3^2 5^2 a^2 = (2 \cdot 3 \cdot 5a)^2 = (30a)^2.$$

Law 4.

$$\frac{a^m}{b^m} = \left(\frac{a}{b}\right)^m, (b \neq 0)$$

Examples.

$$\frac{8^2}{2^2} = \left(\frac{8}{2}\right)^2 = 4^2;$$

$$\frac{(3a)^m b^m}{a^m} = \left(\frac{3ab}{a}\right)^m = (3b)^m, a \neq 0.$$

That is, if the same number or letter appears as an *exponent* in each of two exponential numbers which are multiplied or divided, *this same exponent* appears in the result.

*An apparent exception to this statement appears in the example: $\dfrac{a^m}{a^m} = 1$. However, 1 can be written in the form a^0 by definition of a^0 (Sec. 9-5). Note that Law 2 gives: $\dfrac{a^m}{a^m} = a^{m-m} = a^0$ (or 1).

Single Base Case

Law 5.

$$(a^m)^n = a^{mn}.$$

Examples. $(4^3)^2 = 4^{3 \cdot 2} = 4^6$; $(2a^2b^3c^4)^3 = 2^3a^6b^9c^{12}$.

Sometimes it is convenient to use the laws in reverse order, or as read from right to left. The memorization in the form given, however, is simpler and more likely to prevent certain common errors.

Question. Can $2^5 3^2$ be simplified by use of a law of exponents?

Ans. No, since neither the base nor the exponent is repeated.

While the definitions given later (Sec. 9.5) enable us to say that the above five laws are true for *all* values of the exponents, whether positive, negative, zero, or fractional, the proofs below apply only when the exponents involved are positive integers, and when $m > n$ in Law 2.

Proof of Law 1:

$$a^m a^n = \overbrace{a \cdot a \cdots a}^{m \text{ factors}} \overbrace{a \cdot a \cdots a}^{n \text{ factors}}$$

$$= \overbrace{a \cdot a \cdots a}^{m + n \text{ factors}}$$

$$= a^{m+n}$$

Proof of Law 2 (assuming that $m > n$):

$$\frac{a^m}{a^n} = \frac{\overbrace{a \cdot a \cdots a}^{m \text{ factors}}}{\underbrace{a \cdot a \cdots a}_{n \text{ factors}}}$$

$$= \overbrace{a \cdot a \cdots a}^{m - n \text{ factors}}$$

$$= a^{m-n}$$

Proof of Law 3:

$$a^m b^m = \overbrace{a \cdot a \cdots a}^{m \text{ factors}} \cdot \overbrace{b \cdot b \cdots b}^{m \text{ factors}}$$

$$= \overbrace{(ab) \cdot (ab) \cdots (ab)}^{m \text{ factors}}$$

$$= (ab)^m$$

Proof of Law 4:

$$\frac{a^m}{b^m} = \overbrace{\frac{a \cdot a \cdots a}{b \cdot b \cdots b}}^{m \text{ factors}} = \overbrace{\left(\frac{a}{b}\right)\left(\frac{a}{b}\right)\cdots\left(\frac{a}{b}\right)}^{m \text{ factors}}$$

$$\underbrace{\phantom{\frac{a \cdot a \cdots a}{b \cdot b \cdots b}}}_{m \text{ factors}}$$

$$= \left(\frac{a}{b}\right)^m$$

Proof of Law 5:

$$(a^m)^n = \overbrace{a^m \cdot a^m \cdots a^m}^{n \text{ factors}}$$
$$= a^{m+m+\cdots+m\,(n \text{ terms})}$$
$$= a^{mn} \qquad \text{(by Law 1)}$$

9-2. POWERS OF A NEGATIVE NUMBER

A *power of x* is a number of the form x^n, where n is an integer. It is an even power when n is even and an odd power when n is odd.

Since $(-3)^n$, for example, has n negative factors, it is positive or negative according as n is even or odd. More generally:

For negative numbers, even powers are positive and odd powers are negative. Thus

$$(-2)^2 = (-2)(-2) = 4$$
$$(-2)^3 = (-2)(-2)(-2) = -8.$$

EXERCISE 9-1 (ORAL)

Apply and specify what laws of exponents you used to simplify the following exercises.

1. x^2x^3*.	2. a^5a^2.	3. a^4a^3.	4. x^7x.
5. x^6x^4.	6. xx^2x^3.	7. x^4x^2x.	8. x^5xx^4.
9. a^5a^2a.	10. $x^{10}x^2x^4$.	11. $(2^2)^3$.	12. $(a^2)^2$.
13. $(a^3)^2$.	14. $(x^4)^2$.	15. $(x^5)^3$.	16. $(x^2)^a$.
17. $(x^a)^3$.	18. $(x^2y)^2$.	19. $(x^2y^2)^3$.	20. $(x^5y^2)^4$.
21. $(xy^2)^3$.	22. $(x^ay^b)^2$.	23. $(x^2y^3)^{3a}$.	24. $(x^2y^{3b})^c$.
25. a^3b^3.	26. $a^xb^{2x}c^{3x}$.	27. $(x^2y^3)^6$.	28. $(x^4y^2)^4$.
29. 2^4a^4.	30. 2^5x^5.	31. $(-a)^3$.	32. $(-2a)^4$.
33. $(-.1a)^2$.	34. $(-.2x)^3$.	35. $(-abc)^3$.	36. $(-xy^2z^3)^4$.

*Ans. to 1. $x^2x^3 = x^5$; Law 1—repeated bases.

37. $\dfrac{x^3}{x^2}$.

38. $\dfrac{a^5}{a^2}$.

39. $\dfrac{x^5}{x^3}$.

40. $\dfrac{x^{10}}{x^5}$.

41. $\dfrac{a^3 x^5}{ax^3}$.

42. $\dfrac{x^4 y^2}{x^2 y}$.

43. $\dfrac{x^5 y^6}{x^3 y^4}$.

44. $\dfrac{x^2}{y^2}$.

45. $\left(\dfrac{-x^2}{y}\right)^2$.

46. $\left(\dfrac{-x^4}{y^4}\right)^3$.

47. $\left(\dfrac{-x^3}{y^2}\right)^4$.

48. $\left(\dfrac{x^5 y^4}{x^3 y}\right)^5$.

9-3. RADICALS, ROOTS, AND PRINCIPAL ROOTS

The radical $\sqrt[r]{a}$, read "the principal rth root of a," is a number whose rth power is a. That is, $(\sqrt[r]{a})^r = a$. Thus,

$$(\sqrt[3]{8})^3 = 8;\ (\sqrt[4]{10})^4 = 10;\ (\sqrt[5]{-17})^5 = -17.$$

The symbol $\sqrt{}$ is called the *radical sign*; the quantity below it, or a in the case of $\sqrt{a}$, is the *radicand*; and the integer r is the *index* of the root.

If the index is 2, it is customarily omitted, and the symbol $\sqrt{a}$ is read "the principal square root of a." In other roots such as $\sqrt[3]{a}$, or "the principal cube root of a," the index must be written.

There are *two* numbers whose squares are a given positive number. For instance, $(+2)^2 = 4$ and also $(-2)^2 = 4$. Thus 4 has two square roots. However, the symbol $\sqrt{4}$ stands *only* for $+2$, which is called the *principal* square root of 4. The root -2 is designated as $-\sqrt{4}$.

By more advanced methods it can be shown that any number has 3 cube roots, 4 fourth roots, 5 fifth roots, etc. The symbol $\sqrt[r]{a}$, however, represents *only one* of the r rth roots of a—namely, the one which is called the *principal rth root of a*. When a is positive this root is positive; when a is negative and r is odd, it is negative. Thus, $\sqrt{9} = 3$; $\sqrt[3]{8} = 2$; $\sqrt[4]{16} = 2$; and $\sqrt[3]{-8} = -2$, since $(-2)^3 = -8$.

In Chapter 10 we shall consider the case in which a is negative and r is even.

9-4. RATIONAL AND IRRATIONAL NUMBERS

From the definition in Sec. 9-3, the number $\sqrt{2}$ must be a positive number such that $(\sqrt{2})^2 = 2$. But what is it exactly? It is more than 1.4 and less than 1.5, since $(1.4)^2 = 1.96$ and $(1.5)^2 = 2.25$. That is, $\sqrt{2}$ is between 1.4 and 1.5, or $1.4 < \sqrt{2} < 1.5$. Similarly we can show that $1.4142 < \sqrt{2} < 1.4143$. If $\sqrt{2}$ were *exactly* equal to, say, the decimal number 1.4142, it would then equal $\dfrac{14142}{10000}$ or $\dfrac{7071}{5000}$, and hence it would be the quotient of two integers. It can be proved* that $\sqrt{2}$ cannot be such a quotient. The same is true of $\sqrt[3]{4}$, $\sqrt[4]{6}$, and in general the *rth root of a number which is not a perfect rth power*. Such roots are called *surds*, and are included in the large group of *irrational numbers*

An irrational number is one which cannot be expressed exactly as the quotient of two integers.

Examples. All surds, such as $\sqrt{2}$ and $\sqrt[3]{5}$, and many other numbers such as π, the ratio of the circumference to the diameter of a circle.

A rational number is one which can be expressed as the quotient of two integers.

Examples.

$$\frac{2}{3}, \frac{9}{5}, \sqrt{\frac{9}{4}} \left(\text{or } \frac{3}{2} \right), 1.41 \left(\text{or } \frac{141}{100} \right), 3 \left(\text{or } \frac{3}{1} \right).$$

As suggested by the alternate forms of 3 and 1.41 in parentheses above, all integers and all decimal numbers are rational. It follows that irrational numbers cannot be expressed exactly in decimal form. Most of the numbers in various tables, such as lists of square and cube roots (Table 1 in this text) are merely *decimal approximations*, or numbers as close to the actual roots as possible with the given number of decimal places.

Irrational numbers are connected in an interesting manner with incommensurable quantities in geometry. Consider, for example, the length OP in Fig. 9-1. It may be computed by use of the famous Pythagorean theorem, which states that in a right triangle the square of the hypotenuse is equal to the sum of the squares of the sides. Since the sides of the right

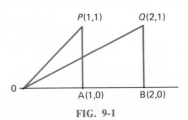

P(1,1)   Q(2,1)

0

A(1,0)   B(2,0)

FIG. 9-1

*Assume that $\sqrt{2} = \frac{p}{q}$, where p and q are integers and the fraction $\frac{p}{q}$ is reduced to lowest terms. Then p and q have no factors in common, and q cannot be 1, since $\sqrt{2}$ is not an integer. Squaring both sides of the equation, we have: $2 = \frac{p^2}{q^2} = \frac{pp}{qq}$, which is impossible since there are no common factors in p and q to be canceled out. Hence our assumption is impossible. Similarly we can prove that $\sqrt[3]{4}$, $\sqrt[4]{7}$, etc., cannot be expressed as quotients of integers.

triangle OAP are 1 and 1, the hypotenuse OP is equal to $\sqrt{1^2 + 1^2} = \sqrt{1 + 1} = \sqrt{2}$. Geometrically, if OA and OP had a common unit of measure which would go into OP exactly m times, say, and into OA exactly n times, then $\dfrac{OP}{OA} = \dfrac{m}{n}$. But we know this to be impossible, since $\dfrac{OP}{OA} = \sqrt{2}$, and $\sqrt{2}$ cannot be expressed as the quotient of two integers. Hence OP and OA have no common unit of measure and are said to be *incommensurable*. Similarly, since OQ is $\sqrt{5}$ units long, it is incommensurable with the unit length BQ.

EXERCISE 9-2

1. Give the two square roots of the following numbers, naming the principal root first: (a), 1; (b), 4; (c), $\dfrac{1}{4}$; (d), $\dfrac{4}{9}$; (c), $\dfrac{25}{4}$; (f), x^2; $x > 0$; $x < 0$.

2. In each case below state whether the radical is rational or irrational. If it is rational, find its exact value; otherwise give its approximate value as found in Table 1.
   (a), $\sqrt{9}$; (b), $\sqrt{10}$; (c), $\sqrt[3]{8}$; (d), $\sqrt[3]{-27}$; (c), $\sqrt[3]{9}$; (f), $\sqrt{12}$; (g), $\sqrt{16}$; (h), $\sqrt[3]{-1}$; (i), $\sqrt[3]{1}$; (j), $\sqrt[3]{-7}$; (k), $\sqrt[3]{-8}$; (l), $\sqrt{8}$.

3. Find the exact lengths of the diagonals of the rectangles whose dimensions in inches are as follows:
   (a), 1×2; (b), 2×3; (c), 3×4; (d), 3×7; (e), 5×12; (f), 4×6; (g), 8×15.

4. In which cases in Prob. 3 are the lengths of the diagonals rational?

5. The following equated values are usually given: $\sqrt{2} = 1.41$, $\sqrt{3} = 1.73$, $\pi = 3.14$. It then follows that $\sqrt{2} + \sqrt{3} = \pi$, since $1.41 + 1.73 = 3.14$. What is incorrect in our reasoning?

9-5. NEGATIVE, ZERO, AND FRACTIONAL EXPONENTS

It is desirable that the five laws stated in Sec. 9-1 shall be true even when the exponents are not positive integers. It can be so arranged by use of the following definitions.

Definition 1.
$$a^0 = 1. \quad (a \neq 0.)$$

By Law 1, $a^0 a^m = a^{0+m} = a^m$. Also, by the definition, $a^0 a^m = 1 \cdot a^m = a^m$. Or again, by division, $\dfrac{a^m}{a^m} = 1$; while by Law 2 and the definition, $\dfrac{a^m}{a^m} = a^{m-m} = a^0 = 1$. In other words, the laws remain valid when the exponent zero is involved, given this definition.

Definition 2.

$$a^{-k} = \frac{1}{a^k}.$$

Consider first a numerical example. By Law 2, $\dfrac{2^2}{2^5} = 2^{2-5} = 2^{-3}$.

This is correct when 2^{-3} is defined as $\dfrac{1}{2^3}$, since

$$\frac{2^2}{2^5} = \frac{2 \cdot 2}{2 \cdot 2 \cdot 2 \cdot 2 \cdot 2} = \frac{1}{2 \cdot 2 \cdot 2} = \frac{1}{2^3}.$$

In general, when $n > m$, $\dfrac{a^m}{a^n} = a^{m-n} = a^{-(n-m)}$, and by this definition,

$$a^{-(n-m)} = \frac{1}{a^{n-m}}.$$

Two convenient rules are consequences of Definition 2.

(1)
$$\left(\frac{a}{b}\right)^{-m} = \left(\frac{b}{a}\right)^m.$$

For

$$\left(\frac{a}{b}\right)^{-m} = \frac{1}{\left(\dfrac{a}{b}\right)^m} = \frac{1}{\dfrac{a^m}{b^m}} = \frac{b^m}{a^m} = \left(\frac{b}{a}\right)^m.$$

(2)   *If the term a^{-m} is a factor of the denominator of a fraction, it may be changed to a^m and written as a factor of the numerator; if it is a factor of the numerator, it may be changed to a^m and written as a factor of the denominator.*

Examples.

$$\frac{3^{-2}4}{5} = \frac{4}{3^2 \cdot 5} = \frac{4}{45};$$

$$\frac{a}{b^{-3}(c + d)} = \frac{ab^3}{c + d};$$

$$\frac{a}{b(c + d)^{-2}} = \frac{a(c + d)^2}{b}.$$

Note, however, that in the case: $\dfrac{a^{-1} - b^{-1}}{a^{-1} + b^{-1}}$, the terms with negative exponents are *not* factors of the numerator or denominator. In such cases the simplification must be made by replacing a^{-1} by $\dfrac{1}{a}$, b^{-1} by $\dfrac{1}{b}$, etc., and then simplifying the complex fraction. Or, more directly,

$$\frac{a^{-1} - b^{-1}}{a^{-1} + b^{-1}} = \frac{(a^{-1} - b^{-1})\, ab}{(a^{-1} + b^{-1})\, ab} = \frac{b - a}{b + a}.$$

Definition 3.

$$a^{1/r} = \sqrt[r]{a}.$$

By Law 5, $(a^{1/r})^r = a^{(1/r)r} = a^1 = a$. Also by the definition, $(a^{1/r})^r = (\sqrt[r]{a})^r = a$. For the special case $r = 3$, for example, $a^{1/3} a^{1/3} a^{1/3} = a^{1/3 + 1/3 + 1/3}$ (by Law 1) $= a^1 = a$, while $\sqrt[3]{a}\, \sqrt[3]{a}\, \sqrt[3]{a} = (\sqrt[3]{a})^3 = a$.

Definition 4.

$$a^{p/q} = (\sqrt[q]{a})^p = \sqrt[q]{a^p}.*$$

For, by Law 5 and Definition 3, $a^{p/q} = (a^{1/q})^p = (\sqrt[q]{a})^p$, and also $a^{p/q} = (a^p)^{1/q} = \sqrt[q]{a^p}$.

Thus, $8^{2/3} = (\sqrt[3]{8})^2 = 2^2 = 4$, and also $8^{2/3} = \sqrt[3]{8^2} = \sqrt[3]{64} = 4$. Here the final result is more easily calculated from the first form of Definition 4. This should be used for $a^{p/q}$ when a is a perfect qth power.

Again, $7^{2/3} = (\sqrt[3]{7})^2$, and also $7^{2/3} = \sqrt[3]{7^2} = \sqrt[3]{49}$. In this case the second definition of $a^{p/q}$ is preferable, since 7 is not a perfect cube.

Note. The reason for the use of the adjectives "rational" and "integral" as applied to letters is suggested in Secs. 9-4 and 9-5. Just as $\sqrt{2}$ is not rational, and 2^{-1}, or $\dfrac{1}{2}$, is not integral, so by definition $\sqrt{x}$ *is not rational in* x, *and* x^{-1}, *or* $\dfrac{1}{x}$, *is not integral in* x.

EXERCISE 9-3

Evaluate each of the following.

1. $4^{1/2}$.
2. $8^{1/3}$.
3. $9^{3/2}$.
4. $4^{3/2}$.

5. $(16)^{3/4}$.
6. $(25)^{3/2}$.
7. $-(36)^{1/2}$.
8. $(-64)^{2/3}$.

9. $(-125)^{2/3}$.
10. $(27)^{2/3}$.
11. $-(81)^{2/4}$.
12. $-(64)^{2/3}$.

13. $(-8)^{2/3}$.
14. $-8^{2/3}$.
15. $-(125)^{2/3}$.
16. $(81)^{1/4}$.

17. $8^{4/3}$.
18. $(32)^{3/5}$.
19. $(-32)^{3/5}$.
20. $(-32)^{3/5}$.

21. $-(32)^{3/5}$.
22. $(243)^{2/5}$.
23. $(-243)^{2/5}$.
24. $(-243)^{3/5}$.

25. $2^0 \cdot 3^{-1}$.
26. $2^2 \cdot 3^0$.
27. $4^{1/2} \cdot 2^{-1}$.
28. $8^{-1/3} \cdot 2^0$.

*The fraction $\dfrac{p}{q}$ must be reduced to lowest terms. Note that $(-1)^{2/4}$, or $\sqrt[4]{(-1)^2}$ ($= \sqrt[4]{1} = 1$) is not the same as $(-1)^{1/2} (= \sqrt{-1})$.

29. $9^{1/2}(-3)^0$.   30. $27^{-1/3}\left(\dfrac{2}{3}\right)^0$.   31. $5^0.8^{-2/3}$.   32. $2^{-2}.4^{3/2}$.

33. $9^{-1/2}.8^{-2/3}$.   34. $2^{-2}.9^{1/2}$.   35. $2^{-3}.9^{3/2}$.   36. $(-3)^{-3}$.

37. $\left(-\dfrac{32}{243}\right)^{-3/5}$.   38. $\left(\dfrac{4}{9}\right)^{-1/2}$.

39. $(-27)^{-4/3}$.   40. $-(5b)^0 + (-5b)^0$.

41. $\dfrac{1}{3}(3a)^0$.   42. $(-0.027)^{1/3}$.

43. $-\left(\dfrac{1}{4}\right)^{-2}$.   44. -5^{-1}.

45. $\left(-\dfrac{2}{3}\right)^{-3}$.   46. $-(-3)^{-1}$.

47. $[2 \cdot 4^0 + (16)^{-3/4}]^{-1}$.

Change each of the following to expressions in which the exponents are positive, and in which the operations indicated in Laws 1 to 5 have been carried out completely.

48. $\dfrac{2x^0}{y \cdot 2}$.   49. $\dfrac{3x^{-3}}{2x^0}$.   50. $\dfrac{4^0 x^{-1}}{3y^{-2}}$.   51. $\dfrac{2x^{-3}y^0}{3^0 y^{-2}}$.

52. $\dfrac{5^0 x^{-1}}{3y^{-2}}$.   53. $\dfrac{6x^{-2}}{2^0 y^{-1}}$.   54. $\dfrac{2^{-1}x^0}{3^0 y^{-3}}$.   55. $\dfrac{3^{-2}x^{-1}}{2^0 y^{-2}}$.

56. $\dfrac{7^0 x^{-2}}{2^{-1}y^{-2}}$.   57. $\dfrac{5x^{-1}y^2}{2^0 xy^{-2}}$.   58. $\dfrac{4^{-1}x^0 y}{2^0 x^{-1}y^{-1}}$.   59. $\dfrac{2^{-1}2x^0}{3^0 x^{-1}y}$.

60. $\dfrac{(2x^0 y^2)^2}{(3^0 x^2 y^{-1})^3}$.   61. $\dfrac{(5x^{-2}y^2)^2}{(3x^2 y^{-2})^2}$.   62. $\dfrac{(4^0 x^2 y^{-3})^4}{(200xy)^0}$.

63. $\dfrac{(3^{-1}x^{-2}y^0)^2}{2xy}$.   64. $\dfrac{(2^{-1}x^3 y^0)^3}{2x^2 y^{-2}}$.   65. $\dfrac{(3^0 x^{-1}y^2)^{-1}}{2x^2 y^{-3}}$.

66. $\dfrac{(2x^0 y^{-2})^{-2}}{3x^{-1}y}$.   67. $\dfrac{(5x^{-2}y)^3}{3x^2 y^{-1}}$.   68. $\dfrac{(4^0 x^{-3}y^{-1})^{-2}}{2xy^2}$.

69. $\dfrac{(3^{-2}x^{-1}y^0)^{-3}}{2x^2 y}$.   70. $\dfrac{(7^0 a^{-1}b^0)^{-2}}{2^{-1}a^2 b^{-1}}$.   71. $\dfrac{(8^0 a^{-2}b)^{-3}}{3^{-1}a^2 b^4}$.

72. $(x - y)^2(x + y)^{-1}$.   73. $(a + b)^{-3}(a - b)$.

74. $(2x - y)^{-1}(x + 2y)$.   75. $(3x + y)^3(x + y)^{-2}$.

76. $(2x - 3y)^{-2}(x + y)^0$.   77. $(5x - y)^0(x - y)^{-1}$.

78. $(x - y)^{1/2}(x - y)^{-1/2}$.   79. $(x + y)^{1/2}(x + y)^{-1/2}$.

80. $(a^2 - x^2)^{1/2}(a^2 - x^2)^{-1/2}$.   81. $(2x^2 + a^2)^{-1/2}(2x^2 + a^2)^{1/2}$.

82. $(a^2 + x^2)^{1/4}(a^2 + x^2)^{-1/2}$.   83. $(x^2 - a^2)^{1/2}(x^2 - a^2)^{-1/4}$.

Express each of the following as a complex fraction and simplify to a simple fraction in lowest terms.

84. $\dfrac{2}{a^{-2} + b^{-2}}$. *Solution.* $\dfrac{2}{\dfrac{1}{a^2} + \dfrac{1}{b^2}} = \dfrac{2a^2b^2}{b^2 + a^2}$.

85. $\dfrac{ab^{-2} + a^{-2}b}{a^{-1} + b^{-1}}$.

86. $(x^{-2} - y^{-2})^{-1}$.

87. $\dfrac{a(a + b)^{-1} - b(a - b)^{-1}}{a^{-1} - b^{-1}}$.

88. $\dfrac{(a^2 + x^2)^{-2} + x^{-2}}{(a^2 + x^2)^2 + x^2}$.

89. Select appropriate multipliers for each of the problems 85, 87, and 88 and simplify without first expressing each as a complex fraction.

Reduce the following to fractions whose numerators have no fractional exponents.

90. $\dfrac{(a - x)^{1/2} + (a - x)^{-1/2}}{a - x}$. *Solution.* Multiply both numerator and denominator by $(a - x)^{1/2}$.

$$\dfrac{(a - x)^{1/2} + (a - x)^{-1/2}}{a - x} \cdot \dfrac{(a - x)^{1/2}}{(a - x)^{1/2}} = \dfrac{(a - x)^1 + (a - x)^0}{(a - x)^{3/2}}$$

$$= \dfrac{a - x + 1}{(a - x)^{3/2}}.$$

91. $\dfrac{(a^2 - x^2)^{1/2} + (a^2 - x^2)^{-1/2}}{a^2 - x^2}$.

92. $\dfrac{(a^2 + x^2)^{1/2} + (a^2 + x^2)^{-1/2}}{(a^2 + x^2)^{1/2}}$.

93. $\dfrac{(a^2 - x^2)^{1/2} - (a^2 - x^2)^{-1/2}}{(a^2 - x^2)^{1/2}}$.

94. $\dfrac{(a^2 + x^2)^{1/2} - (a^2 + x^2)^{-1/2}}{a^2 + x^2}$.

95. $\dfrac{(a^2 - x^2)^{1/2} + x^2(a^2 - x^2)^{-1/2}}{(a^2 - x^2)^{1/2}}$.

96. $\dfrac{(a^2 + x^2)^{1/2} - x^2(a^2 + x^2)^{-1/2}}{(a^2 + x^2)^{3/2}}$.

Reduce the following to fractions whose denominators have no fractional exponents.

97. $\dfrac{(a^2 - x^2)^{1/2}}{(a^2 - x^2)^{-1/2} - a^2(a^2 - x^2)^{-1/2}}$.

98. $\dfrac{(a^2 + x^2)^{1/2}}{(a^2 + x^2)^{1/2} - a^2(a^2 + x^2)^{-1/2}}$.

99. $\dfrac{a^2 - x^2}{x^2(a^2 - x^2)^{-1/2} - (a^2 - x^2)^{-1/2}}$.

100. $\dfrac{a^2 + x^2}{x^2(a^2 + x^2)^{-1/2} - (a^2 + x^2)^{1/2}}$.

101. $\dfrac{a^2 - x^2}{a^2(a^2 - x^2)^{-1/2} + (a^2 - x^2)^{1/2}}$.

102. $\dfrac{(a^2 + x^2)^{3/2}}{a^2(a^2 + x^2)^{-1/2} - (a^2 + x^2)^{1/2}}$.

9-6. LAWS CONCERNING RADICALS

Operations with radicals may be performed by changing them to exponential form and then applying the laws of exponents.

Example 1. $\dfrac{\sqrt{8}}{\sqrt{2}} = \dfrac{8^{1/2}}{2^{1/2}} = \left(\dfrac{8}{2}\right)^{1/2} = 4^{1/2} = \sqrt{4} = 2.$

Example 2. $\sqrt[3]{\sqrt{2}} = (2^{1/2})^{1/3} = 2^{1/6} = \sqrt[6]{2}.$

However, while this method should be held in reserve in case of doubt, it is more efficient to learn directly the more frequently used rules involving radicals. The student may prove each rule by changing the radicals to exponential form.

The laws as stated below are valid when all letters stand for positive integers. (Otherwise some exceptions are necessary.)

Law 1.
$$\sqrt[r]{a^{kr}} = a^k.$$

Examples. $\sqrt[3]{2^{12}} = \sqrt[3]{2^{4\cdot3}} = 2^4; \; \sqrt[5]{3^{10}} = 3^2.$

Law 2.
$$\sqrt[r]{ab} = \sqrt[r]{a}\,\sqrt[r]{b}.$$

From this rule we see that *a factor of the radicand which is a perfect rth power may be taken from the radicand if its rth root is written outside the radical sign.* When all such factors have been removed the radical is said to be *reduced to lowest terms.*

Example 1.
$$\sqrt{8} = \sqrt{4\cdot2} = \sqrt{4}\,\sqrt{2} = 2\sqrt{2}.$$

Example 2.
$$\sqrt[3]{32a^4b^6} = \sqrt[3]{2^3a^3b^6(4a)} = 2ab^2\sqrt[3]{4a}.$$

Example 3.
$$\sqrt{4a^2 + 16b^2} = \sqrt{4(a^2 + 4b^2)} = 2\sqrt{a^2 + 4b^2}.$$

(Why not $\sqrt{4a^2 + 16b^2} = \sqrt{4a^2} + \sqrt{16b^2} = 2a + 4b?$)

This common error should be carefully noted and avoided.*

Law 3.
$$\frac{\sqrt[r]{a}}{\sqrt[r]{b}} = \sqrt[r]{\frac{a}{b}}.$$

---

*Historically, the symbol $\sqrt{}$ is a union of two symbols: $\sqrt{}$ (take the root of) and the vinculum $\overline{}$ (treat as a single number.) Thus,

$$\sqrt{64} + 36 = \sqrt{64} + 36 \neq \sqrt{64} + \sqrt{36} \neq 14,$$

but $\sqrt{64 + 36}$ is equal to $\sqrt{100} = 10.$

Example 1.

$$\frac{\sqrt[3]{16a^7}}{\sqrt[3]{2a}} = \sqrt[3]{\frac{16a^7}{2a}} = \sqrt[3]{8a^6} = 2a^2.$$

Example 2.

$$\frac{\sqrt{8} + 3\sqrt{20}}{2\sqrt{2}} = \frac{\sqrt{8}}{2\sqrt{2}} + \frac{3\sqrt{20}}{2\sqrt{2}} = \frac{1}{2}\sqrt{\frac{8}{2}} + \frac{3}{2}\sqrt{\frac{20}{2}}$$

$$= \frac{1}{2}\sqrt{4} + \frac{3\sqrt{10}}{2} = 1 + \frac{3\sqrt{10}}{2}.$$

Law 4.

$$\sqrt[m]{\sqrt[n]{a}} = \sqrt[n]{\sqrt[m]{a}} = \sqrt[mn]{a}.$$

Examples. $\sqrt[3]{\sqrt{2}} = \sqrt[6]{2}$; $\sqrt[3]{\sqrt{8}} = \sqrt{\sqrt[3]{8}} = \sqrt{2}.$

9-7. ADDITION AND SUBTRACTION OF RADICALS

Radicals are of the same *order* if the indices of the roots are equal. Thus cube roots are all of the same order, having the index 3.

Radicals of the same order whose radicands are equal are called *like* radicals. *Only like radicals can be combined by addition and subtraction.* To determine whether two radicals are like radicals, the radicands should first be reduced to lowest terms, as in the examples below.

Example 1. $\sqrt{12} + \sqrt{27} = 2\sqrt{3} + 3\sqrt{3} = 5\sqrt{3}.$

Example 2. $\sqrt[3]{54a} - \sqrt[3]{16a} = 3\sqrt[3]{2a} - 2\sqrt[3]{2a} = \sqrt[3]{2a}.$

The sums or differences of unlike radicals may either be left uncombined or else may be approximated in decimal form.

For example, $\sqrt{3} + \sqrt{2}$ cannot be further simplified in exact form, but $\sqrt{3} + \sqrt{2} = 1.732 + 1.414 = 3.146$ (nearly). Note that $\sqrt{3} + \sqrt{2}$ *is not* $\sqrt{5}$, since $\sqrt{5} = 2.236$ (nearly).

9-8. MULTIPLICATION OF RADICALS

By the use of Law 2, the product of two radicals of the same order can be found directly. The law can be extended to handle cases where the multiplicand or multiplier or both are indicated sums of radicals.

The following illustrative examples show the direct use of Law 2:

Example 1.   Find the product of $\sqrt{28}$ and $\sqrt{\frac{3}{7}}.$

Solution. $\sqrt{28} \cdot \sqrt{\frac{3}{7}} = \sqrt{(28)\left(\frac{3}{7}\right)} = \sqrt{12} = 2\sqrt{3}.$

Example 2.   Find the product of $\sqrt{5} + 3\sqrt{2}$ and $2\sqrt{5} - 4\sqrt{2}$.
Solution.

$$\sqrt{5} + 3\sqrt{2}$$
$$\underline{2\sqrt{5} - 4\sqrt{2}}$$
$$2 \cdot 5 + 6\sqrt{10}$$
$$\underline{\qquad - 4\sqrt{10} - 12 \cdot 2}$$
$$10 + 2\sqrt{10} - 24 = -14 + 2\sqrt{10}$$

Thus

$$(\sqrt{5} + 3\sqrt{2})(2\sqrt{5} - 4\sqrt{2}) = -14 + 2\sqrt{10}.$$

EXERCISE 9-4

Reduce the radicands to lowest terms.

1. $\sqrt{9}$.
2. $\sqrt{16}$.
3. $\sqrt{36}$.
4. $\sqrt[3]{8}$.

5. $\sqrt[3]{27}$.
6. $\sqrt[3]{125}$.
7. $\sqrt{12}$.
8. $\sqrt{20}$.

9. $\sqrt{28}$.
10. $\sqrt{32}$.
11. $\sqrt{18}$.
12. $\sqrt{27}$.

13. $\sqrt{45}$.
14. $\sqrt{54}$.
15. $\sqrt{63}$.
16. $\sqrt{72}$.

17. $\sqrt{90}$.
18. $\sqrt[3]{-81}$.
19. $-\sqrt[3]{128}$.
20. $-\sqrt[3]{-135}$.

21. $\sqrt{96}$.
22. $\sqrt{128x^3}$.
23. $\sqrt{125x^2}$.
24. $\sqrt{50x^3}$.

25. $\sqrt{75x^2}$.
26. $\sqrt{150x}$.
27. $\sqrt{175x^4}$.
28. $\sqrt{200x^5}$.

29. $\sqrt{250x}$.
30. $\sqrt{108x^4}$.
31. $\sqrt{72x^6}$.
32. $\sqrt{180x^{13}}$.

33. $\sqrt{216x^{16}}$.
34. $\sqrt{98x^3}$.
35. $\sqrt{147x}$.
36. $\sqrt{245x^7}$.

37. $\sqrt[3]{16x^4}$.
38. $\sqrt[3]{24x^3}$.
39. $\sqrt[3]{32x^4}$.
40. $\sqrt[3]{40x^5}$.

41. $\sqrt[3]{48x^2}$.
42. $\sqrt[3]{56y^3}$.
43. $\sqrt[3]{72y^7}$.
44. $\sqrt[3]{54b^6}$.

45. $\sqrt[3]{80a^3}$.
46. $\sqrt[3]{81y^4}$.
47. $\sqrt[3]{108y^7}$.
48. $\sqrt[3]{250x^5}$.

49. $\sqrt[3]{375y^9}$.
50. $\sqrt[4]{32x^{11}}$.
51. $\sqrt[4]{48y^7}$.
52. $\sqrt[3]{32x^6}$.

53. $\sqrt[3]{64x^4}$.
54. $\sqrt[3]{96x^6}$.
55. $(\sqrt{8})(\sqrt{12})$.

Solution for Prob. 55: $\sqrt{8}\sqrt{12} = (2\sqrt{2})(2\sqrt{3}) = 4\sqrt{6}$.

56. $\sqrt{3}\sqrt{27}$.
57. $\sqrt{8}\sqrt{20}$.
58. $\sqrt{5}\sqrt{20}$.
59. $\sqrt{18}\sqrt{27}$.

60. $\sqrt{7}\sqrt{63}$.
61. $\sqrt[3]{8}\sqrt[3]{16}$.
62. $\sqrt[3]{5}\sqrt[3]{200}$.
63. $\sqrt[3]{16}\sqrt[3]{54}$.

64. $\sqrt[3]{9}\sqrt[3]{24}$.
65. $\sqrt[3]{16}\sqrt[3]{32}$.
66. $\sqrt[3]{25}\sqrt[3]{40}$.

67. $\dfrac{\sqrt[3]{250}}{\sqrt[3]{2}} = \sqrt[3]{\dfrac{250}{2}} = \sqrt[3]{125} = 5$.
68. $\dfrac{\sqrt{98}}{\sqrt{2}}$.
69. $\dfrac{\sqrt{48x^2}}{\sqrt{3}}$.

70. $\dfrac{\sqrt{96x^3}}{\sqrt{6}}$.

71. $\dfrac{\sqrt[3]{81x^4}}{\sqrt[3]{3}}$.

72. $\dfrac{\sqrt[3]{108x^5}}{\sqrt[3]{4}}$.

73. $\sqrt{4 - 8x^2} = \sqrt{4(1 - 2x^2)} = 2\sqrt{1 - 2x^2}$.

74. $\sqrt{4 + 12x^2}$.

75. $\sqrt{9 - 18y^2}$.

76. $\sqrt{9 + 27x^2}$.

77. $\sqrt{4 - 16x^2}$.

78. $\sqrt{16 - 4a^2}$.

79. $\sqrt{25 + 100x^2}$.

80. $\sqrt{4a^2 - 36x^2}$.

81. $\sqrt{9x^2 + 36y^2}$.

82. $\sqrt{25y^2 + 100x^2}$.

83. $\sqrt{\dfrac{1}{2} + \dfrac{1}{2}}$.

84. $\sqrt{\dfrac{4}{x^2} - \dfrac{4}{y^2}}$.

85. $\sqrt[3]{\sqrt{8}} = \sqrt{\sqrt[3]{8}} = \sqrt{2}$.

86. $\sqrt[3]{\sqrt{27}}$.

87. $\sqrt{\sqrt[3]{16}}$.

88. $\sqrt[3]{\sqrt{64}}$.

89. $\sqrt{\sqrt[3]{64}}$.

90. $\sqrt[3]{\sqrt{32}}$.

91. $\sqrt{\sqrt[3]{36}}$.

92. $\sqrt[3]{\sqrt{125}}$.

Combine the following radicals as indicated.

93. $\sqrt{27} - \sqrt{12}$.

94. $\sqrt{75} - \sqrt{12}$.

95. $\sqrt{32} - \sqrt{18}$.

96. $\sqrt{50} - 2\sqrt{8}$.

97. $\sqrt{75} + 2\sqrt{12}$.

98. $\sqrt{27a^3} + \sqrt{12ab^2}$

99. $(1 - \sqrt{8}) + (2 + \sqrt{18})$.

100. $\sqrt{12x^3y} - \sqrt{27xy^3}$.

101. $(1 + \sqrt{8}) - (2 + \sqrt{18})$.

102. $\sqrt{98} + \sqrt{72}$.

103. $(5 - \sqrt{50}) - (4 - \sqrt{32})$.

104. $\sqrt{125x} - \sqrt{45x}$.

105. $(4 - \sqrt{75}) - (2 - \sqrt{108})$.

106. $2(\sqrt{3} + 1) - 3\sqrt{3}$.

107. $\sqrt{5}(1 - \sqrt{2}) + \sqrt{2}(\sqrt{5} - 1)$.

108. $\sqrt{3}(1 - \sqrt{5x}) + \sqrt{5}(\sqrt{3x} - 1)$.

109. $\sqrt{7}(\sqrt{2} - 1) + \sqrt{2}(1 - \sqrt{7})$.

110. $2\sqrt{8} \cdot 3\sqrt{6}$.

111. $(2\sqrt{6} - 3\sqrt{3})(3\sqrt{6} + 4\sqrt{3})$.

112. $(-4 - 2\sqrt{7})(-4 + 2\sqrt{7})$.

113. $(\sqrt{2x} + \sqrt{50})^2$.

114. $(3\sqrt{7} - 2)(3\sqrt{7} + 2)$.

115. $(3 - 2\sqrt{3})^2 - 2(3 - 2\sqrt{3}) - 2$.

116. $(1 + \sqrt{2} - \sqrt{3})(1 - \sqrt{2} + \sqrt{3})$.

117. $(3 + 5\sqrt{2})(2\sqrt{5} - 3\sqrt{8} + \sqrt{6})$.

Criticise the errors made in the following.

118. $\dfrac{\overset{1}{\cancel{2}} + \sqrt{7}}{\underset{1}{\cancel{2}}} \overset{?}{=} 1 + \sqrt{7}.$

119. $\dfrac{\overset{1}{\cancel{a+b}} + \sqrt{a^2 - b^2}}{\underset{1}{\cancel{a+b}}} \overset{?}{=} 1 + \sqrt{a^2 - b^2}.$

120. $\dfrac{c - d \pm \sqrt{c^2 - 4cd + 4d^2}}{2c} \overset{?}{=} \dfrac{c - d \pm c - 2d}{2c}.$

Simplify the following.

121. $x = \dfrac{-(6b - a) \pm \sqrt{36b^2 + 12ab + a^2}}{6b}.$

122. $x = \dfrac{-4 \pm \sqrt{32}}{4}.$ 123. $x = \dfrac{ac \pm \sqrt{a^2m + a^2p}}{4a}.$

9-9.   RATIONALIZING DENOMINATORS

It is possible and often desirable to move all radicals appearing in a simple fraction into the numerator. This operation is called *rationalizing the denominator*.

For comments on the illustrative examples below, see the paragraph that follows them.

Example 1.

$$\sqrt[3]{\dfrac{3}{2}} = \sqrt[3]{\dfrac{3 \cdot 2^2}{2 \cdot 2^2}} = \sqrt[3]{\dfrac{12}{2^3}} = \dfrac{\sqrt[3]{12}}{2}.$$

Example 2.

$$\sqrt[4]{\dfrac{a^5}{bc^2d^7}} = \sqrt[4]{\dfrac{a^5(b^3c^2d)}{bc^2d^7(b^3c^2d)}} = \sqrt[4]{\dfrac{a^5b^3c^2d}{b^4c^4d^8}} = \dfrac{a\sqrt[4]{ab^3c^2d}}{bcd^2}.$$

Example 3.

$$\dfrac{1}{\sqrt{2a}} = \dfrac{1}{\sqrt{2a}} \cdot \dfrac{\sqrt{2a}}{\sqrt{2a}} = \dfrac{\sqrt{2a}}{2a}.$$

Example 4.

$$\dfrac{1}{\sqrt[3]{2a}} = \dfrac{1}{\sqrt[3]{2a}} \cdot \dfrac{\sqrt[3]{(2a)^2}}{\sqrt[3]{(2a)^2}} = \dfrac{\sqrt[3]{4a^2}}{2a}.$$

Example 5.

$$\frac{\sqrt{3}+1}{\sqrt{3}-1} = \frac{(\sqrt{3}+1)(\sqrt{3}+1)}{(\sqrt{3}-1)(\sqrt{3}+1)} = \frac{3+2\sqrt{3}+1}{(\sqrt{3})^2-(1)^2}$$

$$= \frac{4+2\sqrt{3}}{2} = \frac{\overset{1}{\cancel{2}}(2+\sqrt{3})}{\underset{1}{\cancel{2}}} = 2+\sqrt{3}.$$

Example 6.

$$\frac{\sqrt[3]{3}+1}{\sqrt[3]{3}-1} = \frac{(\sqrt[3]{3}+1)}{(\sqrt[3]{3}-1)} \frac{(\sqrt[3]{9}+\sqrt[3]{3}+1)}{(\sqrt[3]{9}+\sqrt[3]{3}+1)}$$

$$= \frac{\sqrt[3]{27}+2\sqrt[3]{9}+2\sqrt[3]{3}+1}{(\sqrt[3]{3})^3-(1)^3}$$

$$= \frac{4+2\sqrt[3]{9}+2\sqrt[3]{3}}{2}$$

$$= 2+\sqrt[3]{9}+\sqrt[3]{3}$$

Example 7.

$$x^{2/3}y^{-1}z^{-3/2} = \frac{x^{2/3}}{yz^{3/2}} = \frac{x^{2/3}z^{1/2}}{yz^2} = \frac{x^{4/6}z^{3/6}}{yz^2} = \frac{\sqrt[6]{x^4z^3}}{yz^2}.$$

These illustrations show some of the commonly used methods. In each of Examples 1 and 2 the numerator and denominator of the radicand are multiplied by a factor which makes the denominator a perfect rth power, so that it can be taken from under the radical sign. In Examples 3 and 4, where the radicals appear first in the denominators only, the multipliers must themselves be radicals. Example 5 makes use of the fact that $(a - b)(a + b) = a^2 - b^2$. Example 6 makes use of the fact that $(a - b)(a^2 + ab + b^2) = a^3 - b^3$. Example 7 shows how the laws of exponents can be used to rationalize an expression which involves fractional exponents for some of its divisors in a denominator.

An important advantage of the process of rationalizing the denominator appears in numerical cases, where it shortens the work of getting decimal approximations to the values of surds.

Example. Evaluate $\dfrac{1}{\sqrt{2}}$ to four decimal places.

Long solution.

$$\frac{1}{\sqrt{2}} = \frac{1}{1.4142} = .7071 \text{ (by long division).}$$

Short solution.

$$\frac{1}{\sqrt{2}} = \frac{\sqrt{2}}{2} = \frac{1.4142}{2} = .7071.$$

While the rationalization of denominators is useful at times, the student should not get the impression that the resulting form is necessarily the "better" one. For example, $\sqrt{\dfrac{a}{b}}$ is shorter than $\dfrac{\sqrt{ab}}{b}$ and just as good for many purposes. Certainly $\dfrac{10}{\sqrt{543}}$ is preferable to $\dfrac{10\sqrt{543}}{543}$ when one is preparing to square this fraction.

EXERCISE 9-5

Rationalize the denominators. Approximate in decimal form the values of the numerical fractions by use of Table 1.

1. $\sqrt{\dfrac{1}{2}}$.

2. $\sqrt{\dfrac{1}{3}}$.

3. $\sqrt{\dfrac{3}{2}}$.

4. $\sqrt{\dfrac{3}{4}}$.

5. $\sqrt{\dfrac{2}{5}}$.

6. $\sqrt{\dfrac{3}{5}}$.

7. $\sqrt{\dfrac{4}{5}}$.

8. $\sqrt{\dfrac{5}{6}}$.

9. $\sqrt{\dfrac{3}{8}}$.

10. $\sqrt{\dfrac{5}{8}}$.

11. $\sqrt{1 + \dfrac{1}{2}}$.

12. $\sqrt{2 - \dfrac{1}{3}}$.

13. $\sqrt{3 - \dfrac{1}{5}}$.

14. $\sqrt{4 + \dfrac{3}{5}}$.

15. $\sqrt{3 - \dfrac{3}{5}}$.

16. $\sqrt{5 - \dfrac{2x}{3y}}$.

17. $\sqrt{3 + \dfrac{2x^0}{5y^{-1}}}$.

18. $\sqrt{1 - \dfrac{3x^{-2}}{5y^2}}$.

19. $\sqrt[3]{\dfrac{1}{2}}$.

20. $\sqrt[3]{\dfrac{1}{3}}$.

21. $\sqrt[3]{\dfrac{2}{3}}$.

22. $\sqrt[3]{\dfrac{3}{4}}$.

23. $\sqrt{1 + \dfrac{1}{x}}$.

24. $\sqrt{2 - \dfrac{3}{x}}$.

25. $\sqrt{x + \dfrac{1}{x}}$.

26. $\sqrt{x - \dfrac{2}{x}}$.

27. $\sqrt{x - \dfrac{1}{x}}$.

28. $\sqrt{3x - \dfrac{1}{x}}$.

29. $\sqrt{\dfrac{3}{x} - x}$.

30. $\sqrt{\dfrac{2}{x} + x}$.

31. $\sqrt{\dfrac{1}{x} - x^2}$.

32. $\sqrt{x - \dfrac{2}{x^3}}$.

33. $\sqrt{x^2 + \dfrac{1}{x^3}}$.

Change to radical form and rationalize the denominator.

34. $x^{1/2}y^0z^{-3/2}$.   35. $x^0y^{3/2}z^{-1/2}$.   36. $(3^{-1/2}x^{-3/2}y^0)(x^{3/2}y^{1/2})$.

37. $\dfrac{3x^{1/2}y^0}{z^{3/2}}$.   38. $\dfrac{2x^{-1/2}y^{3/2}z^0}{3x}$.   39. $\dfrac{4^0x^{-1/2}y}{3xy^{1/2}}$.   40. $\dfrac{5^{1/2}x^0y^{-3/2}}{3x^{-3/2}y}$.

Rationalize the denominators and simplify.

41. $\dfrac{1+\sqrt{2}}{\sqrt{2}}$.   42. $\dfrac{1-\sqrt{3}}{\sqrt{3}}$.   43. $\dfrac{2+\sqrt{5}}{\sqrt{5}}$.

44. $\dfrac{3-\sqrt{2}}{\sqrt{2}}$.   45. $\dfrac{5-\sqrt{3}}{\sqrt{3}}$.   46. $\dfrac{\sqrt{3}-\sqrt{2}}{\sqrt{3}+\sqrt{2}}$.

47. $\dfrac{\sqrt{3}+\sqrt{2}}{\sqrt{3}-\sqrt{2}}$.   48. $\dfrac{2}{1+\sqrt{3}}$.   49. $\dfrac{3}{1-\sqrt{2}}$.

50. $\dfrac{\sqrt{2}}{\sqrt{2}-1}$.   51. $\dfrac{\sqrt{3}}{\sqrt{3}+1}$.   52. $\dfrac{5}{\sqrt{3}-1}$.

53. $\dfrac{1}{\sqrt{3x}}$.   54. $\dfrac{3}{\sqrt{3ab}}$.   55. $\dfrac{2}{\sqrt{a+b}}$.

56. $\dfrac{2}{\sqrt{a}+\sqrt{b}}$.   57. $\dfrac{1}{\sqrt[3]{3x^2}}$.   58. $\dfrac{1}{\sqrt[4]{8x}}$.

59. $\dfrac{5}{\sqrt[3]{5x}}$.   60. $\sqrt{\dfrac{2xy^0}{z}}$.   61. $\sqrt[3]{\dfrac{x^{-3}y^4z^0}{xy^{-3}}}$.

62. $\dfrac{\sqrt{x}+\sqrt{y}}{\sqrt{x}-\sqrt{y}}$.   63. $\dfrac{\sqrt{x}-\sqrt{y}}{\sqrt{x}-y}$.   64. $\dfrac{\sqrt{ab^3}+\sqrt{a^3b}}{\sqrt{ab^3}-\sqrt{a^3b}}$.

65. $\dfrac{\sqrt{3x}+1}{\sqrt{3x}+1}$.   66. $\dfrac{\sqrt{8a}}{2}+\sqrt{\dfrac{a}{2}}$.   67. $\dfrac{\sqrt{a+b}}{\sqrt{a^2-b^2}}$.

68. $\dfrac{5\sqrt{6}+2}{3\sqrt{2}+6}$.   69. $\dfrac{3\sqrt{2}-\sqrt{3}}{2\sqrt{3}-\sqrt{2}}$.   70. $\dfrac{2\sqrt{5}-3\sqrt{2}}{3\sqrt{5}+2\sqrt{2}}$.

71–84.   Rationalize the numerators in Probs. 41–47 and 61–67.

Simplify the following expressions, leaving the denominators rationalized.

85. $\left(\sqrt{\dfrac{2}{3}}\right)^3$ *Solution 1.* $\left(\sqrt{\dfrac{2}{3}}\right)^3 = \left(\sqrt{\dfrac{2}{3}}\right)^2\left(\sqrt{\dfrac{2}{3}}\right) = \dfrac{2}{3}\cdot\dfrac{\sqrt{6}}{3} = \dfrac{2\sqrt{6}}{9}$.

Solution 2. $\left(\sqrt{\dfrac{2}{3}}\right)^3 = \left[\left(\dfrac{2}{3}\right)^{1/2}\right]^3 = \left(\dfrac{2}{3}\right)^{3/2} = \dfrac{2^{3/2}}{3^{3/2}}$

$= \dfrac{2^{3/2}\cdot3^{1/2}}{3^2} = \dfrac{2\cdot2^{1/2}\cdot3^{1/2}}{9} = \dfrac{2\sqrt{6}}{9}$.

86. $\left(\sqrt{\dfrac{1}{2}}\right)^3$.   87. $\left(\sqrt{\dfrac{1}{5}}\right)^3$.   88. $\left(\sqrt{\dfrac{3}{2}}\right)^3$.   89. $\left(\sqrt[3]{\dfrac{1}{2}}\right)^4$.

90. $\left(\sqrt[3]{\dfrac{2}{3}}\right)^4$.   91. $\left(\sqrt[3]{\dfrac{3}{2}}\right)^4$.   92. $\left(\sqrt[3]{\dfrac{3}{5}}\right)^4$.   93. $\sqrt{\left(\dfrac{2}{3}\right)^3}$.

94. $\sqrt{\left(\dfrac{1}{2}\right)^3}$.   95. $\sqrt{\left(\dfrac{1}{3}\right)^5}$.   96. $\sqrt{\left(\dfrac{2}{5}\right)^3}$.   97. $\sqrt{\left(\dfrac{3}{2}\right)^3}$.

98. $\sqrt[3]{\left(\dfrac{1}{2}\right)^4}$.   99. $\sqrt[3]{\left(\dfrac{2}{3}\right)^4}$.   100. $\sqrt[3]{\left(\dfrac{2}{5}\right)^4}$.   101. $\sqrt[3]{\left(\dfrac{3}{2}\right)^4}$.

Rationalize the denominator in Probs. 102 through 105.

102. $\dfrac{\sqrt[3]{3} - 1}{\sqrt[3]{3} + 1}$.

103. $\dfrac{x}{\sqrt[3]{x} - \sqrt[3]{y}}$.

104. $\dfrac{a - b}{2a - \sqrt[3]{b}}$.

105. $\dfrac{a - \sqrt[3]{b}}{2a + \sqrt[3]{b}}$.

106. Show that $\dfrac{\left(\dfrac{1}{3}\right)y^{-1/3} + \left(\dfrac{1}{3}\right)y^{1/3}x^{-2/3}}{x^{2/3}}$ reduces to

   $\dfrac{4}{3x^{4/3}y^{1/3}}$, if $x^{2/3} + y^{2/3} = 4$.

107. Show that $\dfrac{\dfrac{1}{2} + \dfrac{1}{2}y^{1/2}x^{-1/2}}{x}$ reduces to $\dfrac{1}{x^{3/2}}$ if $x^{1/2} + y^{1/2} = 2$.

9-10. CHANGING THE ORDER OF RADICALS

When the index of a radical is replaced by a smaller integer the order is said to be *reduced*. This is possible in the radical $\sqrt[r]{a^m}$ when m and r have a common factor larger than 1. The details may be carried through by changing to exponential form.

   Example 1. $\sqrt[4]{4} = \sqrt[4]{2^2} = 2^{2/4} = 2^{1/2} = \sqrt{2}$.

   Example 2. $\sqrt[10]{a^6} = a^{6/10} = a^{3/5} = \sqrt[5]{a^3}$.

It is possible always to equalize the orders of two radicals—a fact sometimes used for comparison purposes.

   Example. Which is larger, $\sqrt{2}$ or $\sqrt[3]{3}$?

Solution.

$$\sqrt{2} = 2^{1/2} = 2^{3/6} = \sqrt[6]{2^3} = \sqrt[6]{8}.$$
$$\sqrt[3]{3} = 3^{1/3} = 3^{2/6} = \sqrt[6]{3^2} = \sqrt[6]{9}.$$

Hence

$$\sqrt[3]{3} > \sqrt{2}.$$

When the orders of two radicals are equalized their product or quotient may be found as a single radical, as illustrated below.

Example 1. $\sqrt{2} \sqrt[3]{3} = 2^{3/6}3^{2/6} = (2^3 3^2)^{1/6} = \sqrt[6]{2^3 3^2} = \sqrt[6]{72}.$

Example 2.

$$\frac{\sqrt{5}}{\sqrt[4]{2}} = \frac{5^{1/2}}{2^{1/4}} = \frac{5^{2/4}}{2^{1/4}} = \sqrt[4]{\frac{5^2}{2}} = \frac{\sqrt[4]{5^2 2^3}}{2} = \frac{\sqrt[4]{200}}{2}.$$

9-11. STEPS IN SIMPLIFYING A RADICAL

When the following steps are taken, a radical is said *by definition* to be in *simplest form*. The order of steps as indicated is satisfactory, though not necessary.

1. The radicand is made a simple fraction.
2. Negative and zero exponents are removed by use of the proper definitions.
3. The radicand is reduced to lowest terms.
4. The order is reduced as much as possible.
5. The denominator is rationalized.

In all cases involving radicals the student should keep in mind two fundamental principles:

1. Operations may be verified in cases of doubt by changing the radicals to exponential form.
2. When the processes are long and involved the practical procedure may be to use the decimal approximations for various surds.

EXERCISE 9-6

Change the orders of the following radicals as directed.

1. $\sqrt{3}$ to the 4th order.   2. $\sqrt{2}$ to the 6th order.

3. $\sqrt[3]{2}$ to the 6th order.   4. $\sqrt[3]{3}$ to the 6th order.

5. $\sqrt[4]{25}$ to the 2nd order.   6. $\sqrt[6]{8}$ to the 2nd order.

7. $\sqrt[5]{2}$ to the 10th order.   8. $\sqrt[10]{32}$ to the 2nd order.

9. $\sqrt[9]{27}$ to the 3rd order.   10. $\sqrt[6]{36}$ to the 2nd order.

Find the larger quantity in each pair.

11. $\sqrt{3}, \ \sqrt[3]{5}.$ 12. $\sqrt{5}, \ \sqrt[3]{11}.$ 13. $\sqrt[3]{2}, \ \sqrt[4]{3}.$

14. $\sqrt[3]{2}, \ \sqrt[6]{5}.$ 15. $\sqrt[4]{2}, \ \sqrt[6]{3}.$

Reduce the radicals in each problem below to the same order, and then perform the indicated operations.

16. $\sqrt{2} \ \sqrt[3]{2}.$ 17. $\sqrt{3} \ \sqrt[3]{3}.$ 18. $\sqrt[3]{2} \ \sqrt{3}.$ 19. $\sqrt[4]{2} \ \sqrt{2}.$

20. $\sqrt[6]{9} \ \sqrt[3]{2}.$ 21. $\sqrt{3} \ \sqrt[6]{8}.$ 22. $\dfrac{\sqrt[6]{8}}{\sqrt{2}}.$ 23. $\dfrac{\sqrt[4]{2}}{\sqrt{2}}.$

24. $\dfrac{\sqrt[3]{2}}{\sqrt[6]{9}}.$ 25. $\dfrac{\sqrt[10]{4}}{\sqrt[5]{2}}.$ 26. $\dfrac{\sqrt[6]{9}}{\sqrt[3]{3}}.$ 27. $\dfrac{\sqrt{3}}{\sqrt[6]{9}}.$

28. $\dfrac{\sqrt[3]{x}}{\sqrt{x}}.$ 29. $\dfrac{\sqrt[3]{x^2}}{\sqrt{x}}.$ 30. $\dfrac{\sqrt{x}}{\sqrt[3]{x}}.$ 31. $\dfrac{\sqrt{x^3}}{\sqrt[3]{x^4}}.$

Express in simplest form.

32. $\sqrt{x^2 - \dfrac{x^4}{4}}.$ 33. $\sqrt[4]{\dfrac{a^6}{9}}.$ 34. $\sqrt[3]{\dfrac{x^4 y^0}{4a}}.$

35. $\sqrt[5]{1 - \dfrac{x^5}{y^5}}.$ 36. $\sqrt[3]{\dfrac{3x^0 y}{2x^{-1} y^{-2}}}.$ 37. $\sqrt[4]{\dfrac{2x^0 y^{-1} z^{-2}}{27 y^2 z}}.$

GENERAL REVIEW EXERCISE OF EXPONENTS AND RADICALS

1. $(y^{1/3} - a^{-1})(y^{1/3} + a^{-1}).$

2. $(a^{1/2} + b^{-1/2})(a^{1/2} - b^{-1/2}).$

3. $(y^{2/3} - z^{1/3} y^{1/3} + z^{2/3})(y^{1/3} + z^{1/3}).$

4. $(3x^{1/2} - 2)(2x^{1/2} + 3 - x^{-1/2}).$

5. $(3^{-1} - 2^{-1})(3^{-1} + 2^{-1}).$

6. $[(x + y)^{1/3} + (y - x)^{1/3}][(x + y)^{2/3}$
$- (x + y)^{1/3}(y - x)^{1/3} + (y - x)^{2/3}].$

Divide:

7. $a^{1/2} - b^{1/2}$ by $a^{1/4} + b^{1/4}.$

8. $a^{1/3} - b^{1/3}$ by $a^{1/9} - b^{1/9}.$

9. $a^{-1} - b^{-1}$ by $a^{-1/3} - b^{-1/3}.$

Classify Probs. 10–30 as true or false. Wherever a statement is false, change the expression on the right-hand side to make the given statement correct.

10. $4^2 \cdot 4^3 = 4^6$.

11. $(3a^2)^3 = 3a^6$.

12. $(27)^{-1/3} = \dfrac{1}{3}$.

13. $-27^{2/3} = 9$.

14. $(-27)^{2/3} = 9$.

15. $(x - y)^2 = x^2 - y^2$.

16. $4^{-2} = -16$.

17. $a^{-1} + b^{-1} = \dfrac{1}{a} + \dfrac{1}{b}$.

18. $a^3 + 27 = (a + 3)(a^2 + 3a + 9)$.

19. $a^3 - 27 = (a + 3)(a^2 - 3a + 27)$.

20. $(x^{-1} + y^{-1})^2 = x^{-2} + y^{-2}$.

21. $\left(\dfrac{x^3}{3}\right)^2 = \dfrac{x^6}{3}$.

22. $[(x + y)^{1/3}]^{1/2} = (x + y)^{1/6} = x^{1/6} + y^{1/6}$.

23. $\dfrac{1}{-5^{-2}} = (-5)^2 = 25$.

24. $52^0 = 1$.

25. $x^3 + 8 = (x + 2)(x + 2)(x + 2)$.

26. $(-3x^2)^4 = -3^4 x^8 = 81x^8$.

27. $a^6 \div a^2 = a^3$.

28. $3(a^2)^3 = (3a^2)^3$.

29. $3(1 + 3^5) = 1 + 3^6$.

30. $\dfrac{1}{2^{-1} + b} = \dfrac{2}{1 + b}$.

Simplify Probs. 31–47.

31. $\left(\dfrac{1}{3}\right)^{-2}$.

32. $(x^0 + y^0)^{-2}; xy \neq 0$.

33. $4(x + y)^{-1}$.

34. $2^{-3} + 3^{-1}$.

35. $\dfrac{1}{2^{-3} + 3^{-1}}$.

36. $\dfrac{2^{-3}}{3^{-1}}$.

37. $\dfrac{x}{y^{-2}}$.

38. $\dfrac{x}{3y^{-1}}$.

39. $\left(\dfrac{1}{9}\right)^{-1/2}$.

40. $\dfrac{x^{-2} + y^{-2}}{x^{-4} - y^{-4}}$.

41. $\dfrac{(x - y)^{-1}}{x^{-1} - y^{-1}}$.

42. $3^{-2} \cdot 2^2 \left(\dfrac{2}{3}\right)^{-2}$.

43. $[(-27)^{-2/3}]^{-2}$.

44. $\dfrac{2^{-1} - 3^{-1}}{5^{-1}}$.

45. If $6^2 = a$ and $6^7 = b$, then $6^9 =$ _____.

46. If $3^{6n} = 27^4$, then $n =$ _____.

47. If $4^{2x+1} = 64^3$, then $x =$ _____.

Simplify and combine like terms in Probs. 48–58.

48. $3\sqrt{2} + 6\sqrt{8} - 4\sqrt{32} - 2\sqrt{16}$.

49. $3\sqrt[3]{16} - 2\sqrt[3]{54} + \sqrt[3]{250} - \dfrac{1}{4}\sqrt[3]{128}$.

50. $y\sqrt{x} - \sqrt{x^2y} + 3y\sqrt{x}$.

51. $.09\sqrt{50} + .04\sqrt{18} - .02\sqrt{72}$.

52. $3\sqrt{2a} + 2\sqrt{8a^2} - \sqrt{98a^3} + 3a\sqrt{\dfrac{a}{2}}$.

53. $2\sqrt[3]{c^3d^2} + 3\sqrt[3]{\dfrac{1}{d}} - \sqrt[3]{64d^5}$.

54. $\sqrt{4x - 4y} + 3\sqrt{9x - 9y} + \sqrt{x - y}$.

55. $\sqrt{5a^2 - 10a + 5} - 3\sqrt{5a^2 + 20a + 20}$.

56. $\sqrt{y + 2} - \sqrt{(y + 2)^3}$.

57. $\sqrt{\dfrac{a}{b}} - \sqrt{\dfrac{b}{a}}.$

58. $\sqrt[6]{a} + \sqrt[6]{\dfrac{a}{32}}.$

Perform the indicated operations in Probs. 59–68.

59. $(2\sqrt{3})(4\sqrt{12}).$

60. $(-2\sqrt{3})^3.$

61. $(3\sqrt{10})(-5\sqrt{20}).$

62. $(\sqrt{6} - \sqrt{2} + 1)(\sqrt{6} + \sqrt{2} + 1).$

63. $(2\sqrt{3} + 3\sqrt{2} - 1)^2.$

64. $(2\sqrt{3} + \sqrt{6} + 2)(2\sqrt{3} - \sqrt{6} - 2).$

65. $(3\sqrt{x} - y)(x - 2\sqrt{y}).$

66. $(3 - 3\sqrt{x})^2.$

67. $\sqrt{a + \sqrt{b}}\sqrt{a + \sqrt{b}}.$

68. $\sqrt{a + \sqrt{b}}\sqrt{a - \sqrt{b}}.$

Perform the indicated division and leave all answers with rationalized denominators in Probs. 69–76.

69. $\dfrac{\sqrt{2}}{3\sqrt{8}}.$

70. $\dfrac{8\sqrt[3]{16}}{4\sqrt[3]{2}}.$

71. $3\sqrt{15} \div 4\sqrt{60}.$

72. $\sqrt[5]{x^4} \div \sqrt[4]{x}.$

73. $3\sqrt{200} \div \sqrt{\dfrac{1}{2}}.$

74. $(\sqrt{56} - 3\sqrt{6}) \div 3\sqrt{2}.$

75. $\dfrac{3\sqrt{20} + 5\sqrt{30} + 2\sqrt{40}}{3\sqrt{10}}.$

76. $4\sqrt[3]{6} \div (-\sqrt[3]{4}).$

Express each of Probs. 77–80 with rational denominator, then find its decimal value to the nearest hundredth using Table 1, page 403.

77. $\dfrac{5\sqrt{12}}{3\sqrt{7}}.$

78. $\dfrac{-2\sqrt{3}}{2\sqrt{6}}.$

79. $\dfrac{7}{3\sqrt{2}}.$

80. $\dfrac{8\sqrt{5}}{16\sqrt{10}}.$

Express the quotients with rational denominators in Probs. 81–85.

81. $\dfrac{3\sqrt{2} + \sqrt{5}}{3\sqrt{2} - \sqrt{5}}.$

82. $\dfrac{2\sqrt{5} - 1}{2\sqrt{5} + 1}.$

83. $\dfrac{3\sqrt{2} + \sqrt{3}}{3\sqrt{2} + 4\sqrt{3}}.$

84. $(2\sqrt{6} - \sqrt{2}) \div (3\sqrt{6} + \sqrt{2}).$

85. $(\sqrt{a} + \sqrt{b}) \div (\sqrt{a} - \sqrt{b}).$

Simplify each term and then reduce to a single fraction in Probs. 86–88.

86. $\dfrac{3}{2 - \sqrt{5}} + \dfrac{1}{2 + \sqrt{5}} - 3\sqrt{20}.$

87. $\dfrac{1}{\sqrt{5} - \sqrt{7}} + \dfrac{1}{\sqrt{5} + \sqrt{7}} - 2\sqrt{5}.$

88. $\dfrac{1}{2\sqrt{11} + \sqrt{7}} - \dfrac{1}{2\sqrt{11} - \sqrt{7}} - 5\sqrt{7}.$

89. The formula for the volume of a sphere is $V = \dfrac{4}{3}\pi r^3$. Solve for r and then find r in simplest radical form if $V = 88$ cubic inches. (Use $\pi = \dfrac{22}{7}$.)

90. If $K = \dfrac{1}{2}mv^2$, compute v to the nearest hundredth if $K = 80$ and $m = 3$.

91. If $x^2 + y^2 = z^2$, compute y if $x = 5, z = 13$.

92. If $x = 27$, evaluate $3x^{-2/3} + x^{-1/3} - (5x^{-1/3})^0$.

93. Solve $\sqrt{\dfrac{S}{\pi}} = r$ for S. Compute r if $S = 81\pi$.

94. Solve $\sqrt{\dfrac{A}{\pi h}} = r$ for A. Compute r if $A = 22\pi, h = \dfrac{11}{16}$.

95. Write each of the following in simplest form.

   (a) $3x\sqrt{72x^2}$.

   (b) $5\sqrt[3]{-90x^5}$.

   (c) $\dfrac{6x}{\sqrt{18}}$.

96. Rationalize the denominators in the following.

   (a) $\dfrac{3}{2 - 3\sqrt{2} + \sqrt{3}}$.

   (b) $\dfrac{2 + \sqrt{5}}{3 - \sqrt{2} - 3\sqrt{5}}$.

   (c) $\dfrac{5x}{x\sqrt{y} - 2y + x}$.

Solution for (a):

$$\frac{3}{2 - 3\sqrt{2} + \sqrt{3}} = \frac{3}{[(2 - 3\sqrt{2}) + \sqrt{3}]} \cdot \frac{[(2 - 3\sqrt{2}) - \sqrt{3}]}{[(2 - 3\sqrt{2}) - \sqrt{3}]}$$

$$= \frac{6 - 9\sqrt{2} - 3\sqrt{3}}{(2 - 3\sqrt{2})^2 - 3}$$

$$= \frac{6 - 9\sqrt{2} - 3\sqrt{3}}{19 - 12\sqrt{2}}$$

$$= \frac{(6 - 9\sqrt{2} - 3\sqrt{3})(19 + 12\sqrt{2})}{(19 - 12\sqrt{2})(19 + 12\sqrt{2})}$$

$$= \frac{(6 - 9\sqrt{2} - 3\sqrt{3})(19 + 12\sqrt{2})}{73}$$

$$= \text{etc.}$$

chapter 10

The Number System

10-1. IMAGINARY NUMBERS

In the discussions where the set of real numbers has been involved, it was observed that some real numbers are not rational, but irrational such as $\sqrt{2}$, $\sqrt{5}$, $\sqrt[3]{7}$, and $\sqrt[3]{-2}$. When dealing with the set of rational numbers under the operations of addition, subtraction, multiplication, division, and raising to powers, the resulting numbers were also rational. However, this is not true when we introduce the idea of extracting roots of rational numbers. For example, $\sqrt{3}$ is not a rational number. In order to solve the equation $x^2 = 3$ for x, it became necessary to include the irrational numbers $\sqrt{3}$ and $-\sqrt{3}$ in the number system. Consequently the set of rational numbers had to be extended to be a more inclusive set of real numbers. This extension to the rational numbers had two purposes in mind, namely:

(a) to help the rational number system answer number situations where it was being used in the operation of extracting roots, and to increase the effectiveness so as

(b) to establish a one-to-one correspondence between the real numbers and the points on the real number line.

However, even with the inclusion of the set of irrational numbers such as $\sqrt{3}$, π, etc, the set of real numbers, as we have intuitively accepted its existence throughout this text, was still not completely adequate to answer all number situations. The extraction of square (or even) roots of real numbers presented a most serious challenge to the already accepted real number system. There is no real number whose square is a negative real number. In particular, there is no real number x such that $x^2 = -1$. In order to obtain a number system that would enjoy complete freedom in being able to answer all number situations, a new type of number had to be identified with the property that its square is -1. This number is assigned the symbolic representative, $\sqrt{-1}$. By agreement and definition, the number $\sqrt{-1}$ is designated by the letter i, and defined as $(\sqrt{-1})^2 =$ $\sqrt{-1} \cdot \sqrt{-1} = i^2 = -1$. It is called the *imaginary unit* of this newly extended number system which in turn is referred to as the *complex number system*. The other square root of -1 is $-\sqrt{-1}$, or $-i$.

Among the rules for operations with radicals (Sec. 9-6) is the property that $\sqrt{ab} = \sqrt{a} \sqrt{b}$ for all cases where a and b are ≥ 0. In order to follow a pattern in conformity with this property, we define for $a \geq 0$, $\sqrt{-a} = \sqrt{(-1)a} = \sqrt{-1} \sqrt{a} = i\sqrt{a}$. That is,

(1) $$\sqrt{-a} = i\sqrt{a}, a \geq 0.$$

The number represented by the symbol $\sqrt{-a}$ is referred to as the principal square root of $-a$.

Examples.

$$\sqrt{-4} = i\sqrt{4} = 2i$$
$$\sqrt{-7} = i\sqrt{7}$$
$$-\sqrt{-9} = -i\sqrt{9} = -3i.$$

The $\sqrt[4]{-16}$ cannot be either $+2$ or -2 since $(-2)^4 = (+2)^4 = 16$. In general, it can be shown that all even roots of negative numbers are imaginary, or expressible by use of the imaginary unit i. One fourth root of -16, $(\sqrt[4]{-16})$, is $2i$. There are still other fourth roots for $\sqrt[4]{-16}$ which can be expressed in terms of i but we shall not consider them here.

Definition. An imaginary number is one that can be written in the standard form $a + bi$, where a and b are real and $b \neq 0$.

The *real number a* is called the *real part* of "$a + bi$"; and the *real number b* is called the imaginary part of "$a + bi$." *Two imaginary numbers are said to be equal if, and only if, their real parts are equal and their imaginary parts are equal.* The set of complex numbers is the union of the set of real numbers with the set of imaginary numbers.

Examples.

$$i, -\frac{3i}{2}, \quad 4 + 5i, \quad 6 - i, \quad \sqrt{-4}, \sqrt[6]{-2}.$$

Imaginary numbers should be expressed in terms of i before they are used in algebraic operations. For instance, it is false that $\sqrt{-3} \sqrt{-3} = \sqrt{(-3)(-3)} = \sqrt{9} = 3$, since from the definition of the square root, $(\sqrt{-3})^2 = -3$. But if we write $\sqrt{-3}$ as $i\sqrt{3}$, then

$$(\sqrt{-3})^2 = i^2(\sqrt{3})^2 = (-1)(3) = -3.$$

10-2. POWERS OF i

Any power of i is equal to one of the four numbers i, -1, $-i$, and 1. This conclusion is reached as follows:

$$i^1 = i.$$
$$i^2 = -1 \text{ (by definition)}.$$
$$i^3 = i^2 i = (-1)i = -i.$$
$$i^4 = i^3 i = (-i)i = -i^2 = 1.$$

$$i^5 = i^4 i = 1 \cdot i = i.$$
$$i^6 = i^4 i^2 = 1(-1) = -1.$$
$$i^7 = i^4 i^3 = 1(-i) = -i.$$
$$i^8 = i^4 i^4 = 1 \cdot 1 = 1.$$
$$i^9 = i^8 i = 1 \cdot i = i, \text{ etc.}$$

Note that $i^5 = i^1, i^6 = i^2, i^7 = i^3, i^8 = i^4, i^9 = i^1$, etc.

Rule for Finding the Value of any Power of i. Divide by 4 the exponent m of i^m, where m is a nonnegative integer. The remainder will be either 0, 1, 2, or 3. The corresponding values of the power are $i^0 = 1$, $i^1 = i$, $i^2 = -1$, and $i^3 = -i$. This follows from the fact that i^4 is another way of writing 1, and when either an integral multiple of 4 is added or subtracted from the exponent m, it indicates division or multiplication by unity.

Examples.

$$i^{20} = 1, i^{25} = i^1, i^{30} = i^2 = -1, i^{27} = i^3 = -i.$$

10-3. OPERATIONS WITH COMPLEX NUMBERS

The results of performing the operations of addition, subtraction, multiplication, and division upon complex numbers produces a complex number in the standard form $a + bi$ as indicated in the following definitions. It is assumed throughout this text that we are acquainted with the real number system and its properties. In the following, $a, b, c, d \in R_e$.

1. Addition

$$(a + bi) + (c + di) = (a + c) + (b + d)i$$

2. Subtraction

$$(a + bi) - (c + di) = (a + bi) + (-c - di) = (a - c) + (b - d)i$$

Examples.

$$\begin{aligned}(2 + 3i) + (4 - 5i) &= (2 + 4) + (3i - 5i) \\ &= 6 - 2i \\ &= 6 + (-2)i\end{aligned}$$

$$\begin{aligned}(3 - 7i) - (4 - 9i) &= (3 - 7i) + (-4 + 9i) \\ &= (3 - 4) + (-7i + 9i) \\ &= -1 + 2i\end{aligned}$$

It is now possible to establish the following properties of the set of complex numbers, with respect to the operations of addition and subtraction.

(a) Closure

$(a + bi) + (c + di)$ is a complex number (by definition)
$(a + bi) - (c + di)$ is a complex number (by definition)

Closure means that when we add or subtract two complex numbers, we always get a complex number.

(b) Commutative Law for Addition

$$(a + bi) + (c + di) = (c + di) + (a + bi)$$

The result of adding one complex number to another is the same irrespective of the order in which addition is performed.

(c) Associative Law for Addition

$$[(a + bi) + (c + di)] + (e + fi)$$
$$= (a + bi) + [(c + di) + (e + fi)]$$
$$= (a + bi) + (c + di) + (e + fi)$$

The result of adding three complex numbers can be performed in any order and the sum will be the same complex number.

(d) Identity for Addition

There is exactly one complex number zero $(0 = 0 + 0 \cdot i)$ such that $(a + bi) + 0 = a + bi$ for any $a + bi$. This means that when zero is added to any complex number, the complex number is reproduced.

(e) Inverse for Addition

For each $a + bi$, there is exactly one complex number, $-(a + bi) = (-a - bi)$, called its additive inverse, which possesses the property indicated by

$$(a + bi) + [-(a + bi)] = 0.$$

Also,

$$-(a + bi) = -a + (-b)i = -a - bi.$$

3. Multiplication for Complex Numbers

The product of two complex numbers is defined to be the resulting complex number obtained by applying laws such as were applied to algebraic expressions in Chapter 2, with $i^2 = -1$. These laws were the distributive, associative, and commutative laws for polynomials. Thus, carrying out the algebra as though we are working with algebraic expressions, we obtain

$$
\begin{aligned}
(a + bi)(c + di) &= (a + bi)c + (a + bi)di \\
&= (ac + bci) + (adi + bdi^2) \\
&= (ac + bci) + [adi + bd(-1)] \\
&= (ac + bci) + (adi - bd) \\
&= (ac - bd) + (bc + ad)i
\end{aligned}
$$

Note that $(a + bi)(a - bi) = a^2 - b^2i^2$
$$= a^2 + b^2$$

rather than $a^2 - b^2$.

Example.

$$(3 + 2i)(4 - i) = 12 + 8i - 3i - 2i^2$$
$$= 12 + 5i - 2(-1)$$
$$= 14 + 5i.$$

Example.

$$(4 + \sqrt{-3})(3 - \sqrt{-4}) = (4 + 3i)(3 - 2i)$$
$$= 12 + 9i - 8i - 6i^2$$
$$= 12 + 9i - 8i - 6(-1)$$
$$= 12 + 9i - 8i + 6$$
$$= 18 + i.$$

4. Division

The quotient of two complex numbers is defined so that division retains its meaning as the inverse operation of multiplication. Hence

$$\frac{a + bi}{c + di} = (a + bi) \div (c + di)$$

$$= (a + bi)\frac{1}{c + di} \qquad \text{provided } (c + di) \neq 0.$$

In order to perform the operation of division, the term *conjugate of a complex number* is introduced. The conjugate of $a + bi$ is defined to be $a - bi$; the conjugate of $a - bi$ is defined to be $a + bi$. Recall that $(a + bi)(a - bi) = a^2 + b^2$. It is now possible to show that the reciprocal (or multiplicative inverse) of $(a + bi) \neq 0$, namely $\dfrac{1}{a + bi}$, is the complex number obtained by multiplying the numerator and denominator of $\dfrac{1}{a + bi}$ by the conjugate of $a + bi$, namely, $a - bi$. Hence

$$\frac{1}{a + bi} = \left(\frac{1}{a + bi}\right)\left(\frac{a - bi}{a - bi}\right)$$

$$= \frac{a - bi}{a^2 + b^2}$$

$$= \frac{a}{a^2 + b^2} + \left(\frac{-b}{a^2 + b^2}\right)i$$

$$= \frac{a}{a^2 + b^2} - \frac{b}{a^2 + b^2}i.$$

We verify this by what follows:

$$(a + bi)\left[\frac{a}{a^2 + b^2} + \frac{-bi}{a^2 + b^2}\right] = \frac{a^2 + abi}{a^2 + b^2} + \frac{-ab - b^2i}{a^2 + b^2}i$$

$$= \frac{a^2 + abi}{a^2 + b^2} + \frac{-abi - b^2i^2}{a^2 + b^2}$$

$$= \frac{a^2 + abi - abi - b^2i^2}{a^2 + b^2}$$

$$= \frac{a^2 - b^2(-1)}{a^2 + b^2}$$

$$= \frac{a^2 + b^2}{a^2 + b^2}$$

$$= 1,$$

which confirms the property possessed by a nonzero complex number and its multiplicative inverse.

Example.

Express $\dfrac{1}{1 + 2i}$ in the $(a + bi)$ form.

Solution:

$$\frac{1}{1 + 2i} = \left(\frac{1}{1 + 2i}\right)\left(\frac{1 - 2i}{1 - 2i}\right)$$

$$= \frac{1 - 2i}{1 - 4i^2}$$

$$= \frac{1 - 2i}{1 + 4}$$

$$= \frac{1 - 2i}{5}$$

$$= \frac{1}{5} + \left(-\frac{2}{5}\right)i$$

$$= \frac{1}{5} - \frac{2}{5}i.$$

Example. Divide

$$\frac{2 - \sqrt{-1}}{1 + \sqrt{-9}}$$

Solution:

$$\frac{2 - \sqrt{-1}}{1 + \sqrt{-9}} = \frac{2 - i}{1 + 3i}$$

$$= \left(\frac{2 - i}{1 + 3i}\right)\left(\frac{1 - 3i}{1 - 3i}\right)$$

$$= \frac{-1 - 7i}{1 - 9i^2}$$

$$= \frac{-1 - 7i}{1 + 9}$$

$$\frac{2 - \sqrt{-1}}{1 + \sqrt{-9}} = -\frac{1}{10} + \left(-\frac{7}{10}\right)i$$

$$= -\frac{1}{10} - \frac{7}{10} i.$$

The following properties can be established for the multiplication of two complex numbers:

(a) Closure: $(a + bi)(c + di)$ is a complex number.

(b) Commutative Law: $(a + bi)(c + di) = (c + di)(a + bi)$

(c) Associative Law: $[(a + bi)(c + di)](e + fi)$
$$= (a + bi)[(c + di)(e + fi)]$$

(d) Identity. For any complex number $a + bi$, there is exactly one complex number $1 = 1 + 0i$ such that

$$(a + bi)(1) = a + bi$$

(e) Inverse: For each $a + bi \neq 0$, there is exactly one complex number $\dfrac{1}{a + bi}$, called the *reciprocal* (or *multiplicative inverse*) of $a + bi$, such that

$$(a + bi)\frac{1}{a + bi} = 1;$$

where $\dfrac{1}{a + bi}$ is equal to

$$\frac{a}{a^2 + b^2} + \left(\frac{-b}{a^2 + b^2}\right)i$$

as was shown in the preceding example.

(f) Distributive Law:

$$(a + bi)[(c + di) + (e + fi)] = (a + bi)(c + di) + (a + bi)(e + fi).$$

It is suggested that the student analyze the statements in these laws as applied to multiplication with complex numbers, and then try to express in storylike fashion what they mean.

EXERCISE 10-1

Reduce each of the following expressions to the standard form $a + bi$:

1. $\sqrt{-25}$. *Ans.: 5i.*   2. $\sqrt{-17}$. *Ans.: $i\sqrt{17}$.*

3. $\sqrt{-4x^2}$. *Ans.: 2ix.*   4. $\sqrt{-36}$.

5. $\sqrt{-7}$.   6. $\sqrt{-9}$.   7. $\sqrt{-49}$.

8. $\sqrt{-47}$.   9. $\sqrt{-64}$.   10. $\sqrt{-19}$.

11. $\sqrt{-144}$.   12. $-\sqrt{-4}$.   13. $-\sqrt{-9}$.

14.. $-\sqrt{-11}$.

15. $-\sqrt{-25}$.

16. $\sqrt{-9a^2}$.

17. $\sqrt{-16x^2}$.

18. $-\sqrt{-25y^4}$.

19. $\sqrt{-17x^4}$.

20. $-\sqrt{-5x^2}$.

21. $-\sqrt{-23a^2}$.

22. i^{10}.

23. i^{11}.

24. i^{14}.

25. i^{26}.

26. i^{29}.

27. $(1 + i)^2$.

28. $(1 - i)^2$.

29. $(2 + i)^2$.

30. $(2 - i)^2$.

31. $(1 - 2i)^2$.

32. $(3 + 2i)(3 - 2i)$.

33. $(5 + 4i)(5 - 4i)$.

34. $(2 + 3i)(3 - i)$.

35. $(4 + i)(4 - 3i)$.

36. $(6 + 5i)(6 - 5i)$.

37. $i(3 + 4i)$.

38. $3i(3 - i)$.

39. $2(3 - i)^2$.

40. $\dfrac{3}{2 + i}$.

41. $\dfrac{2}{3 - i}$.

42. $\dfrac{3}{4 + i}$.

43. $\dfrac{2}{3 + 2i}$.

44. $\dfrac{5}{3 - 2i}$.

45. $\dfrac{1 + i}{1 - i}$.

46. $\dfrac{1 - i}{1 + i}$.

47. $\dfrac{2 + 3i}{3 - i}$.

48. $\dfrac{2 - 3i}{3 + i}$.

49. $\dfrac{3 + 2i}{2 + i}$.

50. $\dfrac{3 - 4i}{4 + 3i}$.

51. $\dfrac{4 + 3i}{3 - 4i}$.

52. $\dfrac{3}{2i}$.

53. $\dfrac{-2}{3i}$.

54. $\dfrac{-1}{i}$.

55. $\dfrac{3}{5i^7}$.

56. $\dfrac{-7}{3i^5}$.

57. $\dfrac{10}{3i^3}$.

58. $\dfrac{6}{2i^9}$.

59. $\dfrac{5}{3i^{11}}$.

60. $\sqrt{-5}\,\sqrt{-5}$.

61. $\sqrt{-3}\,\sqrt{-12}$.

62. $\sqrt{-4}(5 + \sqrt{-25})$.

63. $\sqrt{-4} + \sqrt{-16}$.

64. $\sqrt{-3} + 2\sqrt{-12}$.

65. $\sqrt{-2}\,\sqrt{-3}\,\sqrt{-5}$.

66. $\dfrac{\sqrt{-10}}{\sqrt{-5}}$.

67. $\dfrac{\sqrt{-10}}{\sqrt{5}}$.

68. $\dfrac{5}{2 + \sqrt{-9}}$.

69. $\dfrac{\sqrt{4} + \sqrt{-4}}{3\sqrt{-16}}$.

70. $\dfrac{2\sqrt{-9}}{\sqrt{9} + \sqrt{-9}}$.

71. $\dfrac{\sqrt{4} - \sqrt{-4}}{\sqrt{-4}}$.

Determine the real numbers x and y for which the following equations are true.

72. $x + yi = 1 + 3i$.

73. $2x + 3yi = 9i$.

74. $(x + i)^2 = y$.

75. $(x + 2y + 2) + (2x + y)i = 0$.

76. $(3x - y) + (2x + y - 1)i = 2 + 2i$.

77. $(3x - y + 4) + (x + 3y - 2)i = 7 + 9i$.

78. Show that

(a) $\left(\dfrac{-1 + i\sqrt{3}}{2}\right) \cdot \left(\dfrac{-1 - i\sqrt{3}}{2}\right) = 1$.

(b) $\left(\dfrac{-1 + i\sqrt{3}}{2}\right)^3 = 1$.

(c) $\left(\dfrac{-1 - i\sqrt{3}}{2}\right)^3 = 1$.

(d) $\left(\dfrac{-1 + i\sqrt{3}}{2}\right)^2 = \dfrac{-1 - i\sqrt{3}}{2}$.

(e) $\left(\dfrac{-1 - i\sqrt{3}}{2}\right)^2 = \dfrac{-1 + i\sqrt{3}}{3}$.

(f) Show that if $x = \dfrac{-1 + i\sqrt{3}}{2}$, then $x^2 + x + 1$ is equal to zero.

Does it seem reasonable to say that the cube roots of unity are 1, $\dfrac{-1 + i\sqrt{3}}{2}$,

and $\dfrac{-1 - i\sqrt{3}}{2}$?   Hint: $x^3 = 1$ implies $(x - 1)(x^2 + x + 1) = 0$.

10-4. GEOMETRIC REPRESENTATION OF IMAGINARY NUMBERS

A complex number $a + bi$, where a and b are real, may be represented graphically by interpreting "the real part a" as a directed distance along a horizontal axis, called the axis of reals, and by interpreting the "imaginary part b" as the directed distance along a vertical axis, called the axis of imaginaries. The axis of imaginaries contains all numbers, such as i, $-2i$, $i\sqrt{7}$, which have the form $a + bi$, where $a = 0$ and $b \neq 0$. Such numbers are conventionally called pure imaginary numbers. The general number $a + bi$, where a and b are real, is represented by a point whose coordinates would be (a, b) if the axes of reals and imaginaries are respectively chosen as the x and y axes of the rectangular coordinate plane. Thus the point representing the number $1 - 2i$ has the rectangular coordinates $(1, -2)$ and this ordered pair could have been used as a representation of the complex number.

The numbers represented in their totality by all of the points on the plane are called *complex numbers*. The plane containing them is known as the *complex plane*.

For example, the complex numbers i, $2i$, $-3i$, $-\frac{3}{2}$, $\sqrt{2}$, π, $-3 + i$, $3 + i$, $1 + i$, and $-1 - 2i$ are represented in Fig. 10-1.

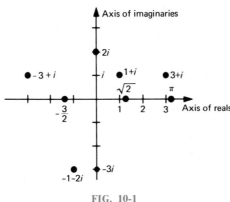

FIG. 10-1

EXERCISE 10-2

Plot each of the following points in a complex plane.

1. $2 + i$.
2. $-i^2$.
3. $i^2 + 1$.
4. $3(1 - 2i)$.
5. $1 - 5i$.
6. $-3 - 2i$.
7. $(2i + 3)(2i)$.
8. -3.
9. $-3 + 2i$.
10. $-4i$.

10-5. CLASSIFICATIONS OF NUMBERS

The following diagram is helpful.

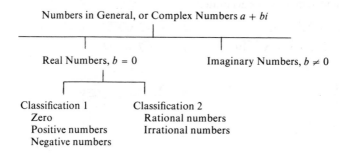

In this diagram Classification 1 divides the real numbers, represented by points on the axis of reals, into three groups corresponding with: (1), the point 0 (zero); (2), points to the right of 0; and (3), points to the left of 0.

Classification 2 is simply another grouping of real numbers. Here algebra and reason have stepped beyond geometry, since the points representing rational and irrational numbers are mixed together too thickly in any segment of the axis of reals to be separated visually, though we may find sample points representing each of the two types.

10-6. NUMBERS AS ROOTS OF EQUATIONS

It is interesting that the requirements for roots of rational integral equations in one unknown, which appear in the solutions of very simple problems, have called into use all the types of numbers thus far discussed. The following table illustrates the point.

	Equation	Root or roots	Type of Number Represented by the root
(1)	$x = 0.$	0	A type by itself
(2)	$x - 3 = 0.$	3	Positive integer
(3)	$x + 2 = 0.$	-2	Negative integer
(4)	$2x - 1 = 0.$	$\dfrac{1}{2}$	Positive fraction
(5)	$3x + 5 = 0.$	$-\dfrac{5}{3}$	Negative fraction
(6)*	$x^2 - 2 = 0.$	$\pm\sqrt{2}$	Irrational numbers
(7)*	$x^2 + 2 = 0.$	$\pm i\sqrt{2}$	Pure imaginary numbers
(8)*	$x^2 + x + 2 = 0.$	$\dfrac{-1 \pm i\sqrt{7}}{2}$	Imaginary numbers

*The solutions of these equations are discussed in Chapter 11.

EXERCISE 10-3

Indicate whether each of the following is true or false. If false, correct the right side to make same accurate.

1. $(\sqrt{-3})^2 = 3.$

2. $\sqrt{-5}\,\sqrt{-3} = \sqrt{+15}.$

3. $\sqrt{2}\,\sqrt{-5} = \sqrt{-10}.$

4. $\sqrt{-7} = -7i.$

5. $i^{63} = i.$

6. $i^{72} = 1.$

7. $\dfrac{1}{i} = -i.$

8. $\dfrac{\sqrt{-10}}{\sqrt{2}} = \sqrt{-5}.$

9. $\dfrac{\sqrt{-10}}{\sqrt{-2}} = \sqrt{5}.$

10. $3 + 2i$ is the conjugate of the complex number $-3 - 2i$.

11. $(2 - 5i)(2 + 5i)$ is a pure imaginary number.

Perform the indicated operations in the following:

12. $8\sqrt{-9} + 5\sqrt{-25}$.

13. $6\sqrt{-4x^2} - 2\sqrt{-9x^2}$.

14. $\dfrac{6}{2\sqrt{-2}}$.

15. $(-2\sqrt{-6})^3$.

16. $(-2\sqrt{5} + 3i)(-\sqrt{5} - \sqrt{-9})$.

17. Simplify $(2 + i)^3 - 2(2 + i)^2 + 3(2 + i)$.

18. Simplify i^{105}, $\dfrac{1}{i^{10}}$, i^{74}, i^{-12}, i^{-3}, $\dfrac{1}{i^{-23}}$.

19. Rationalize the denominator in each term and express the result in the form "$a + bi$:"

$$\frac{3}{2 + 3\sqrt{-4}} + \frac{2}{3 - 2\sqrt{-9}}.$$

20. If $x = 2 - 3i$, what is the value in the form "$a + bi$" for the expression $\dfrac{3 + x}{2 - x}$?

21. (a) Is $x^2 + y^2 = x^2 - i^2y^2 = (x - yi)(x + yi)$?

(b) Factor $x^2 + 4y^2$ where the coefficients in the factors are permitted to contain i.

chapter **11**

Quadratic Equations

11-1. THE QUADRATIC EQUATION

This chapter pays special attention to the solution of a most important type of equation, namely the quadratic or second-degree equation in the variable or unknown x. The solution set and various properties concerning this type of equation will be explored as fully as possible in the sections which follow.

In many scientific applications involving mathematical techniques, the solution set of a quadratic equation and its various properties dictate that we have as much know-how of this important type of equation as our maturity at this stage permits.

11-2. THE QUADRATIC EQUATION IN STANDARD FORM

The standardized form for the quadratic equation in the variable x is conveniently represented as

$$ax^2 + bx + c = 0 \wedge a \neq 0.$$

The coefficients a, b, c do not involve the x, and may be described as follows:

  a = collected coefficient of all terms involving the square of the variable x

  b = collected coefficient of all terms involving the first power of the variable x

  c = constant term and is the algebraic sum of all the terms that do not involve the x

It is understood that when a, b and c are read in the equation $ax^2 + bx + c = 0$, all terms have been algebraically grouped, collected, placed on one side of the equation and equated equal to zero.

If a, b, c are chosen from the real numbers, the quadratic equation is usually referred to as a *real quadratic equation*. This type of choice of coefficients does not restrict the possibility for x to involve $i = \sqrt{-1}$ in the solution set for $ax^2 + bx + c = 0$. Examples of quadratic equations are as follows:

$2x^2 - 3x + 1 = 0$ is a quadratic equation in x, where a, b, c respectively correspond to 2, -3, and 1.

$3y^2 - 2ay + by^2 + c = 0$ is a quadratic equation in y where a, b, c respectively correspond to $3 + b$, $-2a$, c. In this example, the collected coefficient for the square of y is $3 + b$.

In the algebraic statement $5x^2 - 7x + 3 = 2x^2 + 3x - 4$, the standard form after regrouping of terms becomes $3x^2 - 10x + 7 = 0$, a quadratic equation in x, where a, b, c correspond respectively to 3, -10, and 7.

For the algebraic statement $(2x + 3)^2 = x\left(x + \dfrac{1}{2}\right)$ the standard form after carrying out indicated operations and regrouping terms becomes

$$3x^2 + \frac{23}{2}x + 9 = 0.$$

A comparison of this equation with $ax^2 + bx + c = 0$ indicates that a, b, c correspond to $3, \dfrac{23}{2}$, and 9, respectively. However, if each of the sides of this equation is multiplied by 2, the equivalent equation

$$6x^2 + 23x + 18 = 0$$

is obtained where a, b, c now correspond to 6, 23, and 18 respectively. The solution set of both $3x^2 + \dfrac{23}{2} x + 9 = 0$ and $6x^2 + 23x + 18 = 0$ are the same, but since the coefficients in the latter equation are integers, it is more convenient to obtain the solution set from this equation rather than one involving fractional coefficients.

11-3. THE SOLUTION OF A QUADRATIC EQUATION

In general, when finding the solution set of a quadratic equation, the assumption is made that the replacement set for the variable x is understood to be the set of complex numbers, symbolized as C, and its solution set may be represented as

$$f = \{x \in C \mid ax^2 + bx + c = 0 \wedge a \neq 0\}.$$

The solution set of an equation consists of those numbers or expressions which satisfy it when substituted for the unknown (in this case, x). Thus for the quadratic equation involved in the descriptive set notation

(1) $$f = \{x \mid x^2 + 4x - 5 = 0\},$$

the solution set when spelled out is $f = \{-5, 1\}$. Direct substitution of -5 and 1 into the given equation shows that both of these elements are solutions of $x^2 + 4x - 5 = 0$.

The solution set for

(2) $g = \{x \mid x^2 + 4x - 1 = 0\}$ is $g = \{-2 + \sqrt{5}, -2 - \sqrt{5}\}$.

The check of these roots is left as an exercise.

Again, the quadratic equation

(3) $$x^2 + 4x + 4 = 0$$

is satisfied by $x = -2$; but in this case there is no second root different from the first one. For reasons to be discussed later -2 is said to be a double root of (3). The solution set would be represented as $\{-2\}$, and some other means would be employed to point out that -2 is a double root if it was essential to be aware of this fact.

Finally,

(4) $h = \{x \mid x^2 + 4x + 8 = 0\} = \{-2 + 2i, -2 - 2i\},$

where i is the imaginary unit. If $x = -2 + 2i$, then $x^2 + 4x + 8 = (-2 + 2i)^2 + 4(-2 + 2i) + 8 = 4 - 8i + 4i^2 - 8 + 8i + 8 = 0$. Similarly, $x = -2 - 2i$ satisfies (4).

The solutions of equations (1)–(4) represent four different kinds of solution sets for quadratic equations—rational and unequal roots, irrational roots, rational and equal roots, and imaginary roots. In Sec. 11-9 a geometric interpretation of the various types of solution sets will be discussed. As may be suspected here, and will be proved later, *every quadratic equation has two roots, though in some cases they are equal.*

EXERCISE 11-1

Write each of the equations in Probs. 1–23 in standard form. Comparing it with: $ax^2 + bx + c = 0$, find the values which correspond to a, b, and c in each case. Prove that each of the numbers listed is a solution (or root).

1. $3x^2 - 2x = 1; \left\{1, -\dfrac{1}{3}\right\}.$

Solution: $3x^2 - 2x - 1 = 0$

$3x^2 + (-2)x + (-1) = 0; \quad a = 3, b = -2, \text{ and } c = -1;$

$3 \cdot 1^2 - 2 \cdot 1 = 1:$

$3\left(-\dfrac{1}{3}\right)^2 - 2\left(-\dfrac{1}{3}\right) = 1.$

2. $4x = 1 + 4x^2; \left\{\dfrac{1}{2}\right\}.$

3. $6 = 2x^2 + x; \left\{-2, \dfrac{3}{2}\right\}.$

4. $1 = 3x^2 + 2x; \left\{-1, \dfrac{1}{3}\right\}.$

5. $-3x = 2x^2 + 1; \left\{-1, -\dfrac{1}{2}\right\}.$

6. $3 = x^2 + 2x; \{1, -3\}.$

7. $6 = 5x + 4x^2; \left\{-2, \dfrac{3}{4}\right\}.$

8. $3 = x + 2x^2; \left\{1, -\dfrac{3}{2}\right\}.$

9. $3x = -2 - x^2; \{-1, -2\}.$

10. $5x = 2x^2 + 2; \left\{2, \dfrac{1}{2}\right\}.$

11. $4x = 3 - 4x^2; \left\{\dfrac{1}{2}, -\dfrac{3}{2}\right\}.$

12. $8x = -3 - 4x^2; \left\{-\dfrac{1}{2}, -\dfrac{3}{2}\right\}.$

13. $2x = x^2; \{0, 2\}.$

14. $x^2 = 3x; \{0, 3\}.$

15. $2x^2 = 3x; \left\{0, \dfrac{3}{2}\right\}.$

16. $2x = -3x^2; \left\{0, -\dfrac{2}{3}\right\}.$

17. $3x = -2x^2; \left\{0, -\dfrac{3}{2}\right\}.$

18. $d^2 = x^2; \{d, -d\}.$

19. $4x^2 = 9e^4; \left\{\dfrac{3e^2}{2}, -\dfrac{3e^2}{2}\right\}.$

20. $x^2 - (r + s)x + rs = 0; \{r, s\}.$

21. $4d^2x^2 = e^2; \left\{\dfrac{e}{2d}, \dfrac{-e}{2d}\right\}.$

22. $x^2 + (r - s)x - rs = 0; \{-r, s\}.$

23. $a^2x^2 = 16b^2; \left\{\dfrac{4b}{a}, \dfrac{-4b}{a}\right\}.$

Write each of the equations in Probs. 24–30 in standard form and find the expressions which correspond to a, b, and c.

24. $Ax^2 + x - Bx = C + x^2 - 4.$

   Answer:
   $(A - 1)x^2 + (1 + B)x + (4 - C) = 0;$
   $a = A - 1; \quad b = 1 - B; \quad c = 4 - C.$

25. $3x^2 + 4x + 2 = Ax^2 + Bx + C.$ 26. $2x^2 - Ax + 4 = Cx^2 + Bx - A$

27. $3x^2 + Bx - x = Ax^2 - Cx + 1.$ 28. $Ax^2 + B + Cx = Bx^2 - Ax + C.$

29. $Ax^2 + B = Cx^2 + Dx.$ 30. $ex^2 + 2Bx = 4 - x + Ax.$

11-4. THE SOLUTION OF QUADRATIC EQUATIONS BY FACTORING

A special case of the quadratic equation $ax^2 + bx + c = 0$ occurs when $b = 0$. The general quadratic equation takes the form

$$ax^2 + c = 0 \wedge a \neq 0,$$

and for convenience is referred to as a pure quadratic equation in x.

Since $a \neq 0$, division of both members of $ax^2 + c = 0 \wedge a \neq 0$ by a results in

$$x^2 + \frac{c}{a} = 0$$

or

$$x^2 - \left(-\frac{c}{a}\right) = 0.$$

Treating this as a difference of two squares it follows that

$$\left(x + \sqrt{-\frac{c}{a}}\right)\left(x - \sqrt{-\frac{c}{a}}\right) = 0.$$

Thus

$$x = \sqrt{-\frac{c}{a}} \quad \text{or} \quad x = -\sqrt{-\frac{c}{a}}.$$

Hence the solution set of every pure quadratic equation

$$ax^2 + c = 0 \wedge a \neq 0 \text{ is } \left\{\sqrt{-\frac{c}{a}}, \ -\sqrt{-\frac{c}{a}}\right\}.$$

$\sqrt{-\frac{c}{a}}$ designates a real number if either c or a (but not both) is a negative number, and an imaginary number if either both a and c represent positive numbers or both represent negative numbers.

Example 1. If $f = \{x \mid 4x^2 - 9 = 0\}$, $x^2 = \frac{9}{4}$, and the solution set is $\left\{\frac{3}{2}, -\frac{3}{2}\right\}$.

Example 2. If $f = \{x \mid 2x^2 - 3 = 0\}$, $x^2 = \frac{3}{2}$, and the solution set is $\left\{\frac{\sqrt{6}}{2}, -\frac{\sqrt{6}}{2}\right\}$.

Example 3. If $f = \{x \mid 4x^2 + 5 = 0\}$, $x^2 = -\frac{5}{4}$, and the solution set is $\left\{-\frac{i\sqrt{5}}{2}, \frac{i\sqrt{5}}{2}\right\}$.

[*Hint:* Represent $4x^2 + 5$ as $4x^2 - 5i^2 = (2x)^2 - (\sqrt{5}i)^2$ and factor.]

Example 4. Find the solution set for $f = \left\{x \mid \frac{3}{5x^2 - 1} = \frac{2}{1 + 4x^2}\right\}$.

Solution.

Multiply both members of the equation by $(5x^2 - 1)(1 + 4x^2)$. The new equation becomes $3 + 12x^2 = 10x^2 - 2$, or $2x^2 = -5$. Hence, $x^2 = -\dfrac{5}{2}$, and the solution set is

$$\left\{ \frac{i\sqrt{10}}{2}, -\frac{i\sqrt{10}}{2} \right\}.$$

Another special case occurs when $c = 0$. The general quadratic equation takes the form

$$ax^2 + bx = 0 \wedge a \neq 0.$$

Here there is a factor x contained in the left-hand member of the equation. Thus

$$x(ax + b) = 0.$$

Recalling the important property of real or complex numbers—namely, that if the product AB of two real or complex numbers A and B is zero, then at least one of these numbers A or B is zero. Hence, for the equation $ax^2 + bx = 0$,

$$x = 0 \vee ax + b = 0.$$

The solution set is therefore $\left\{ 0, -\dfrac{b}{a} \right\}$.

Example.   Solve by factoring: $f = \{x \mid 3x^2 + x = 0\}$.

Solution.

$$3x^2 + x = 0$$
$$x(3x + 1) = 0$$
$$x = 0 \vee 3x + 1 = 0$$
$$3x = -1$$
$$x = -\frac{1}{3}$$

The solution set is $\left\{ 0, -\dfrac{1}{3} \right\}$.

Direct substitution of 0 and $-\dfrac{1}{3}$ into the given equation shows that both roots are solutions of $3x^2 + x = 0$.

When the left-hand member of $ax^2 + bx + c = 0$ possesses factors that can be found readily, the equation can be conveniently solved by the method illustrated below.

Example 1.   Obtain the roots in the solution set of

$$f = \{x \mid x^2 + 4x - 5 = 0\}.$$

Solution.   Factor the left member of the equation $x^2 + 4x - 5 = 0$. Thus

(1) $(x - 1)(x + 5) = 0$.

This equation is satisfied by $x = 1$, since $(1 - 1)(1 + 5) = 0 \cdot 6 = 0$; and also by $x = -5$, since $(-5 - 1)(-5 + 5) = (-6)(0) = 0$.   Hence $\{1, -5\}$ is the solution set.   The root $x = 1$ is found by considering the factor $x - 1$ equal to zero.   When this occurs, $x = 1$.   Either $x - 1$ is zero or, if it is not, then $x - 1$ has a nonzero multiplicative inverse $\dfrac{1}{x - 1}$. When we multiply both sides of equation (1) by this multiplicative inverse we obtain $(x + 5) = 0$.   Thus $x + 5 = 0$ gives $x = -5$.   Note that when $x - 1$ is set equal to zero, the factor $(x + 5)$ equals 6, and when $x + 5$ is set equal to zero, the factor $(x - 1)$ is equal to -6.

Example 2.   Solve

$$4x^2 + 12x + 9 = 0.$$

Solution.   Noting that the left-hand member is a perfect square, we have

(2) $(2x + 3)^2 = 0$,   or $(2x + 3)(2x + 3) = 0$.

Each factor, in turn placed equal to zero, yields $x = -\dfrac{3}{2}$. This explains the algebraic basis for calling $-\dfrac{3}{2}$ a repeated or double root.   The geometric reason will appear later.

Caution.   *The solution of a quadratic equation by factoring the left-hand member is correct in principle only when the right-hand member is zero.* For example, as a test will show, the roots of the quadratic

(3) $(x - 2)(x - 3) = 12$

are not found by setting $x - 2$ or $x - 3$ equal to 12.   The correct roots of (3), which are 6 and -1, are found by putting equation (3) in standardized form, $ax^2 + bx + c = 0$.

Example 3.   Solve

$$f = \left\{ x \,\middle|\, \frac{7}{4} - \frac{6}{2x - 1} = \frac{2x - 3}{2x + 3} \right\}.$$

Solution.   After clearing fractions by multiplying through by the L.C.D. $4(2x - 1)(2x + 3)$, there results

(4) $7(2x - 1)(2x + 3) - 24(2x + 3) = 4(2x - 3)(2x - 1)$,

which simplifies, after the indicated operations are performed, to

(5) $4x^2 + 4x - 35 = 0$.

The factors of the left-hand member of (5) are $2x + 7$ and $2x - 5$, so that the solution set is $\left\{-\dfrac{7}{5}, \dfrac{5}{2}\right\}$. Each of these values for x will be found to satisfy the original equation. [Note: $(2x - 1)(2x + 3) \neq 0$.]

EXERCISE 11-2

Find the solution set in Probs. 1–70 and represent it so that x is precisely given. Checks should be included where multiplication by algebraic expressions involving x are involved.

1. $2x^2 - 8 = 0$.
2. $3x^2 - 12 = 0$.
3. $5x^2 - 20 = 0$.
4. $2x^2 - 18 = 0$.
5. $2x^2 - 98 = 0$.
6. $4x^2 - 100 = 0$.
7. $3x^2 + 27 = 0$.
8. $2x^2 + 8 = 0$.
9. $3x^2 + 12 = 0$.
10. $2x^2 + 18 = 0$.
11. $2x^2 + 98 = 0$.
12. $4x^2 + 100 = 0$.
13. $2x^2 - 36 = 0$.
14. $3x^2 - 36 = 0$.
15. $2x^2 - 100 = 0$.
16. $2a^2x^2 - 64 = 0$.
17. $2b^2x^2 - 24 = 0$.
18. $a^2x^2 - 96c^2 = 0$.
19. $2x^2 + 36a^2 = 0$.
20. $3x^2 + 36b^2 = 0$.
21. $a^2x^2 + 100b^2 = 0$.
22. $2x^2 + 64b^2 = 0$.
23. $2x^2 + 48c^2 = 0$.
24. $a^2x^2 + 96b^2 = 0$.
25. $ax^2 + 25b = 0$.
26. $ax^2 + 100c = 0$.
27. $20b = -ax^2$.
28. $(x - 2)(x + 3) = 6$.
29. $(x + 2)(x - 3) = 6$.
30. $x(x + 5) = 14$.
31. $(x - 1)(x - 2) = 6$.
32. $(x + 1)(x - 2) = 4$.
33. $x(x - 3) = 10$.
34. $2x^2 + x - 1 = 0$.
35. $3x^2 + 2x - 1 = 0$.
36. $3x^2 - 2x - 1 = 0$.
37. $4x^2 - 3x - 1 = 0$.
38. $4x^2 - 4x + 1 = 0$.
39. $9x^2 + 6x + 1 = 0$.
40. $4x^2 + 12bx + 9b^2 = 0$.
41. $x^2 - 8ax + 16a^2 = 0$.
42. $9x^2 + 30x + 25 = 0$.
43. $6x^2 - x = 0$.
44. $9x^2 - 3x = 0$.
45. $8x^2 + 10x = 0$.
46. $10x^2 + ax = 0$.
47. $ax^2 + bx = 0$.
48. $cx^2 - dx = 0$.
49. $6x^2 + x = 2$.
50. $8x^2 + 10x = 3$.
51. $10x^2 - 13x = 3$.
52. $10x^2 - x = 2$.
53. $15x^2 + x = 2$.
54. $x = 2 - 15x^2$.
55. $11x = 6 + 3x^2$.
56. $9x = -2 - 10x^2$.
57. $9x = 2 + 10x^2$.
58. $23x = -6 - 21x^2$.
59. $23x = 6 + 21x^2$.
60. $25x = -6 - 14x^2$.
61. $\dfrac{2x}{5 - x} = \dfrac{15}{2} - \dfrac{2x - 10}{x}$.

62. $\dfrac{5}{2x^2 - 3} = \dfrac{7}{1 - 2x^2}$.

63. $\dfrac{15}{x + 5} + \dfrac{12}{x + 10} = 1$.

64. $(2x - 3)(2x + 3) = 7x^2 - 4$.

65. $\dfrac{x + 5}{x - 2} + \dfrac{5x - 2}{x - 8} = 0$.

(*Hint:* Here $x \neq 2$ or $x \neq 8$. If ultimate equation does not result in these values for x, no check is necessary unless arithmetic errors have been made.)

66. $\dfrac{1}{4x^2 + 5} + \dfrac{1}{4x^2 - 5} = \dfrac{3}{16x^4 - 25}$.

67. $\dfrac{x + 1}{x - 2} + \dfrac{2}{5(2 - x)} = -\dfrac{1 - x}{x + 2}$.

68. $10x^2 = 7x$.

69. $\dfrac{5}{x} = \dfrac{11}{x^2}$.

70. $8x^2 - 3x = 0$.

11-5. SOLVING QUADRATIC EQUATIONS BY COMPLETING THE SQUARE

The algebraic methods of solving quadratics thus far discussed, while short and efficient, cannot always be conveniently applied. The method called "completing the square" has the advantage that it will obtain solution sets for all types of quadratic equations, besides giving practice in an operation which is useful elsewhere in mathematics. The aim of this method is to produce from the given quadratic equation a perfect square trinomial which is equal to a constant; that is $(x + k)^2 = l$.

The equation $(x + k)^2 = l$ is equivalent to the equation

$$(x + k)^2 - l = 0,$$

whose left-hand member can now be factored.

Thus

$$(x + k - \sqrt{l})(x + k + \sqrt{l}) = 0$$

and $x = -k + \sqrt{l}$ or $x = -k - \sqrt{l}$.

To illustrate, consider the equation

(1) $$3x^2 - 2x - 2 = 0.$$

Step 1. Divide both members by 3 (if in the quadratic equation $ax^2 + bx + c = 0$, $a \neq 0$, it is convenient to divide by a first):

(2) $$x^2 - \dfrac{2x}{3} - \dfrac{2}{3} = 0.$$

Step 2.   Form a new equation in which the constant term is on one side of the equation (say the right-hand side):

(3) $$x^2 - \frac{2x}{3} = \frac{2}{3}.$$

Step 3.   Add to both sides the number that will make the left member a perfect square. Note that in the perfect square

$$(x - a)^2 = x^2 - 2ax + a^2,$$

the third term, or a^2, is $\left[\left(\frac{1}{2}\right)(-2a)\right]^2$. Hence add to both members of the equation the square of *one-half the coefficient of x*, or in this case $\left[\left(\frac{1}{2}\right)\left(-\frac{2}{3}\right)\right]^2$, yielding

(4) $$x^2 - \frac{2x}{3} + \left(-\frac{1}{3}\right)^2 = \frac{2}{3} + \left(-\frac{1}{3}\right)^2 = \frac{2}{3} + \frac{1}{9}$$

or

(5) $$\left(x - \frac{1}{3}\right)^2 = \frac{7}{9},$$

which is equivalent to

$$\left[\left(x - \frac{1}{3} - \frac{\sqrt{7}}{3}\right)\right]\left[\left(x - \frac{1}{3}\right) + \frac{\sqrt{7}}{3}\right] = 0$$

Note that the number added to complete the square is *always positive*, and that the middle sign of the left member of (5) is the same as the sign before the term of first degree in (4).

Step 4.   Solve for $x - \frac{1}{3}$ by using in turn the factors

$$\left[\left(x - \frac{1}{3}\right) - \frac{\sqrt{7}}{3}\right] = 0 \text{ and } \left[\left(x - \frac{1}{3}\right) + \frac{\sqrt{7}}{3}\right] = 0$$

(6) $$x - \frac{1}{3} = + \sqrt{\frac{7}{9}} = +\frac{\sqrt{7}}{3} \quad \text{or} \quad x - \frac{1}{3} = -\sqrt{\frac{7}{9}} = -\frac{\sqrt{7}}{3}.$$

Step 5.   Add $\frac{1}{3}$ to both sides of the equations in (6) and equation (7) follows.

(7) $$x = \frac{1}{3} + \frac{\sqrt{7}}{3} \quad \text{or} \quad x = \frac{1}{3} - \frac{\sqrt{7}}{3}.$$

Equation (7)* is another way of stating that the solution set to the equation $3x^2 - 2x - 2 = 0$ is

(8) $$\left\{\frac{1 + \sqrt{7}}{3}, \frac{1 - \sqrt{7}}{3}\right\}.$$

Note that the various steps yield equivalent equations, and that the two equations in (6), (7), and (8) are equivalent to the one equation (5). In other words, each of the two values of x shown in (8) satisfies (1), as the student may verify.

If, at the stage in the solution represented by equation (5), the right side is negative, the roots will be imaginary. For example, given

(9) $$x^2 + 2x + 4 = 0,$$

then

(10) $$x^2 + 2x + 1 = -4 + 1;$$

(11) $$(x + 1)^2 = -3;$$

or

$$(x + 1)^2 + 3 = 0;$$

or

$$[(x + 1)^2 - (\sqrt{-3})^2] = 0;$$

or

$$[(x + 1)^2 - i^2(\sqrt{3})^2] = 0;$$

or

$$[(x + 1) + i\sqrt{3}][(x + 1) - i\sqrt{3}] = 0.$$

(12) $x + 1 = +\sqrt{-3}$ or $x + 1 = -\sqrt{-3}$
         $x + 1 = +i\sqrt{3}$ or $x + 1 = -i\sqrt{3}$

(13) $x = -1 + i\sqrt{3}$ or $x = -1 - i\sqrt{3}.$

Here the solution set is $\{-1 + i\sqrt{3}, -1 - i\sqrt{3}\}$.

11-6.   THE SUM AND PRODUCT OF THE ROOTS

To obtain a result which will prove useful for checking purposes, note that

(1) $$ax^2 + bx + c = 0 \wedge a \neq 0$$

---

*Equation (7) can also be stated as $x = \frac{1}{3} \pm \frac{\sqrt{7}}{3}$, which is a popular form. For clarity, it is preferable to separate the answers.

is equivalent to

(2)
$$x^2 + \frac{bx}{a} + \frac{c}{a} = 0,$$

which is obtained from (1) by dividing the coefficients by a. Now

(3)
$$x^2 - (r + s)x + rs = 0$$

is satisfied by $x = r$ and by $x = s$, as may be verified by trial. Hence if the general equation (1) is also satisfied by the roots r and s, it follows, by comparison of (3) with (2), that

(4)
$$r + s = -\frac{b}{a},$$

and

(5)
$$rs = \frac{c}{a}.$$

In words, *the sum of the roots of* (1) *is* $-\dfrac{b}{a}$, *and their product is* $\dfrac{c}{a}$.

This result may be used in checking the roots found in the solution of any quadratic. The check is often shorter than that obtained by substitution of the roots in the original equation, particularly when the roots are irrational or imaginary.

Example 1. By use of the sum and product formulas, show that $\dfrac{1 + \sqrt{11}}{2}$ and $\dfrac{1 - \sqrt{11}}{2}$ are roots of the equation,

$$2x^2 - 2x - 5 = 0.$$

Solution.
$$-\frac{b}{a} = -\frac{(-2)}{2} = 1,$$

and
$$\frac{1 + \sqrt{11}}{2} + \frac{1 - \sqrt{11}}{2} = 1.$$

Also,
$$\frac{c}{a} = -\frac{5}{2},$$

and
$$\left(\frac{1 + \sqrt{11}}{2}\right)\left(\frac{1 - \sqrt{11}}{2}\right) = \frac{1^2 - \sqrt{11}^2}{4} = -\frac{10}{4} = -\frac{5}{2}.$$

Example 2. Show that $r = \dfrac{-3 + i\sqrt{31}}{4}$ and $s = \dfrac{-3 - i\sqrt{31}}{4}$

are roots of the equation, $2x^2 + 3x + 5 = 0$.

Solution. Here $a = 2, b = 3, c = 5$.

$$r + s = -\frac{6}{4} = -\frac{3}{2} = -\frac{b}{a}.$$

Also,

$$rs = \left(-\frac{3}{4}\right)^2 - \left(\frac{i\sqrt{31}}{4}\right)^2 = \frac{9}{16} - \frac{-31}{16} = \frac{40}{16} = \frac{5}{2} = \frac{c}{a}.$$

EXERCISE 11-3

Find the solution set of the equations in Probs. 1–33 by the method of completing the square, and check by use of the sum and product formulas.

1. $x^2 - 6x + 8 = 0$.
2. $x^2 + 5x + 6 = 0$.
3. $x^2 + 2x - 8 = 0$.
4. $x^2 - 3x - 10 = 0$.
5. $x^2 - 2x - 8 = 0$.
6. $x^2 + 3x - 10 = 0$.
7. $6x^2 - 7x - 3 = 0$.
8. $6x^2 + x - 2 = 0$.
9. $6x^2 + 7x - 3 = 0$.
10. $6x^2 - x - 2 = 0$.
11. $12x^2 + 7x - 12 = 0$.
12. $8x^2 - 6x - 9 = 0$.
13. $3x^2 - 2x - 2 = 0$.
14. $5x^2 + 3x - 3 = 0$.
15. $5x^2 - 5x - 7 = 0$.
16. $3x^2 + 4x = 5$.
17. $2x^2 + 6x = 5$.
18. $8x^2 + 4x = 3$.
19. $7x^2 = 14x - 3$.
20. $9x^2 = 6x - 5$.
21. $5x^2 = -3x - 4$.
22. $3x^2 = -5x - 4$.
23. $4x^2 = -6x - 3$.
24. $10x^2 = -3x - 2$.
25. $3x = x^2 + 7$.
26. $2x = 5 + x^2$.
27. $3x = x^2 + 6$.
28. $4x = x^2 + 6$.
29. $6x = x^2 + 2$.
30. $8x = x^2 + 3$.
31. $(x + 1)(x - 2) = 3$.
32. $(x - 2)(x + 3) = -7$.
33. $(x + 3)(x - 4) = 1$.

34–43. Check by direct substitution the answers found in Probs. 1–10.

Solve Probs. 44–45 and check the answers by direct substitution.

44. $\dfrac{x + 3}{x - 1} - \dfrac{3 - 2x}{2x + 2} = \dfrac{7}{2}$.

45. $2(y - 1) - \dfrac{5(y + 1) - 5}{y + 2} = 3(1 - y) - \dfrac{5 + 2(y + 3)}{3}$.

*11-7. THE QUADRATIC FORMULA

When we solve the general quadratic equation

(1) $$ax^2 + bx + c = 0 \wedge a \neq 0$$

by completing the square, the various equivalent equations obtained in the successive steps are as follows:

Divide each side by a:

(2) $$x^2 + \frac{bx}{a} + \frac{c}{a} = 0$$

Add $-\dfrac{c}{a}$ to both members:

(3) $$x^2 + \frac{bx}{a} = -\frac{c}{a}$$

Complete the square:

(4) $$x^2 + \frac{bx}{a} + \left(\frac{b}{2a}\right)^2 = -\frac{c}{a} + \left(\frac{b}{2a}\right)^2$$

Factor the left-hand member and simplify the right-hand member:

(5) $$\left[x + \left(\frac{b}{2a}\right)\right]^2 = \frac{b^2 - 4ac}{4a^2}$$

which is equivalent to

$$\left[x + \left(\frac{b}{2a}\right)\right]^2 - \frac{b^2 - 4ac}{4a^2} = 0$$

Take the square root of each member (remember there are two square roots).

(6) $$\left[x + \frac{b}{2a} + \frac{\sqrt{b^2 - 4ac}}{2a}\right]\left[x + \frac{b}{2a} - \frac{\sqrt{b^2 - 4ac}}{2a}\right] = 0.$$

Place respective factors in turn equal to zero.

(7) $$x + \frac{b}{2a} = +\frac{\sqrt{b^2 - 4ac}}{2a} \vee x + \frac{b}{2a} = -\frac{\sqrt{b^2 - 4ac}}{2a}$$

Solve for x:

(8) $$x = \frac{-b + \sqrt{b^2 - 4ac}}{2a} \vee x = \frac{-b - \sqrt{b^2 - 4ac}}{2a}.$$

Since a, b, and c were chosen completely arbitrarily, except $a \neq 0$,

---

*It is understood that a, b, c can be any complex numbers, even though we shall be using this equation mainly when $a, b, c \in R_e$.

the solution set*

$$\left\{ x = \frac{-b + \sqrt{b^2 - 4ac}}{2a}, \quad x = \frac{-b - \sqrt{b^2 - 4ac}}{2a} \right\}$$

can be used as the quadratic formula for the solution of $ax^2 + bx + c = 0$. The infinitely many quadratic equations are here solved collectively once and for all. They are seen to have two roots apiece, though these roots are equal when the quantity under the radical sign is zero. To get the roots of a specific quadratic it is necessary only to identify the coefficients a, b, and c, and then to substitute their values in (8). If the equation is quadratic in some letter or quantity other than x, this letter or quantity should replace x in (8).

Example. Solve the quadratic equation

(9) $3x^2 - 2x - 4 = 0$.

Solution. Here $a = 3$, $b = -2$, and $c = -4$. Substituting these values in (8), we have

$$x = \frac{-(-2) + \sqrt{(-2)^2 - 4(3)(-4)}}{2 \cdot 3}$$

$$= \frac{2 + \sqrt{52}}{6}$$

$$= \frac{2 + 2\sqrt{13}}{6}$$

$$= \frac{1 + \sqrt{13}}{3}$$

$$\vee$$

$$x = \frac{-(-2) - \sqrt{(-2)^2 - 4(3)(-4)}}{2 \cdot 3}$$

$$= \frac{2 - \sqrt{52}}{6}$$

$$= \frac{2 - 2\sqrt{13}}{6}$$

$$= \frac{1 - \sqrt{13}}{3}$$

The solution set is $\left\{ \dfrac{2 + 2\sqrt{13}}{6}, \dfrac{2 - 2\sqrt{13}}{6} \right\} = \left\{ \dfrac{1 + \sqrt{13}}{3}, \dfrac{1 - \sqrt{13}}{3} \right\}$.

*May also be represented as

$$\left\{ x = \frac{-b \pm \sqrt{b^2 - 4ac}}{2a} \right\}.$$

After getting $x = \dfrac{2 + 2\sqrt{13}}{6} \vee x = \dfrac{2 - 2\sqrt{13}}{6}$, the careless stu-

dent is likely to write $x = \dfrac{4\sqrt{13}}{6}$ or $x = \dfrac{0\sqrt{13}}{6}$. Why are these results incorrect? _____

Note that if (9) were solved by carrying out all the steps necessary for completing the square, the correct simplified root would have been obtained at once. This is one reason why some who work in the field of applied mathematics prefer the square-completing procedure to that of the formula. The latter method, on the other hand, is shorter for some problems, especially where literal coefficients are involved; and it also gives other useful information about quadratics, as we shall see.

11-8. THE DISCRIMINANT OF A QUADRATIC EQUATION

The roots of the quadratic equation

(1) $$ax^2 + bx + c = 0 \wedge a \neq 0,$$

as given in the quadratic formula, may be written

(2) $$r = \frac{-b + \sqrt{b^2 - 4ac}}{2a}; \quad s = \frac{-b - \sqrt{b^2 - 4ac}}{2a}.$$

The radicand $b^2 - 4ac$ in (2), designated by D, is called the *discriminant* of the quadratic equation (1).

For example, the discriminant of

(3) $$2x^2 - 3x - 4 = 0,$$

for which $a = 2, b = -3$, and $c = -4$ is $(-3)^2 - 4(2)(-4) = 9 + 32 = 41$. Hence, the roots of (3) will involve the radical $\sqrt{41}$, and will be irrational.

The discriminant D is of particular significance and interest when the coefficients a, b, and c are real numbers. In such cases, the following conclusions can be drawn:

Premise about D	Then the roots of (1) are
(a) $D > 0$ and a perfect square of a rational number	Real, unequal, and rational, if a, b, c are also rational
(b) $D > 0$ and not a perfect square of a rational number	Real, unequal, and irrational
(c) $D = 0$	Real, equal, and rational, if a, b, c are also rational
(d) $D < 0$	Imaginary

These results have immediate and practical application as an aid to the solution of real quadratic equations. When for a particular equation

D is negative or not a perfect square of a rational number, it is useless to waste time on the factoring method of solution, since the roots are imaginary or irrational.

Question. Can $3x^2 - 4x - 5$ be conveniently factored?

Ans. Since $D = (-4)^2 - 4 \cdot 3(-5) = 16 + 60 = 76$ (not a perfect square), the answer, if we bar factors with irrational coefficients,* is "No." Hence, the quadratic $3x^2 - 4x - 5 = 0$ should be solved by completing the square or by use of the quadratic formula. If the latter method is used the test-value $D = 76$ already found can be used in writing down

at once the solution:

$$x = \frac{4 + \sqrt{76}}{6} = \frac{2 + \sqrt{19}}{3} \text{ or } x = \frac{4 - \sqrt{76}}{6} = \frac{2 - \sqrt{19}}{3}.$$

EXERCISE 11-4

In each of Probs. 1–45, determine the nature of the roots by use of the discriminant. Then solve the equation by factoring if D is a perfect square of a rational number, otherwise by use of the quadratic formula. (Note that zero is a perfect square.)

1. $2x^2 - 3x + 5 = 0.$ 2. $3x^2 + 5x - 2 = 0.$
3. $4x^2 - 4x + 1 = 0.$ 4. $5x^2 + 2x - 3 = 0.$
5. $x^2 - 3x + 2 = 0.$ 6. $x^2 - 6x - 9 = 0.$
7. $x^2 + x - 3 = 0.$ 8. $x^2 + 3x - 1 = 0.$
9. $x^2 - 3x + 1 = 0.$ 10. $x^2 - 2x + 2 = 0.$
11. $x^2 - x + 3 = 0.$ 12. $9x^2 - 30x + 25 = 0.$
13. $x^2 + x + 1 = 0.$ 14. $2x^2 - 5x + 1 = 0.$
15. $3x^2 + x - 3 = 0.$ 16. $4x^2 + x - 1 = 0.$
17. $x^2 - 10x + 1 = 0.$ 18. $10y^2 - y + 1 = 0.$
19. $3x^2 - 5x + 1 = 0.$ 20. $3x^2 - 7x + 2 = 0.$
21. $4y^2 - 5y + 1 = 0.$ 22. $7x^2 - 8x + 1 = 0.$
23. $9x^2 - 3x + 2 = 0,$ 24. $6y^2 - 5y + 1 = 0.$
25. $5x^2 - 6x + 1 = 0.$ 26. $8x^2 - 7x - 1 = 0.$
27. $3y^2 - 9y + 2 = 0.$ 28. $5x^2 - 4x - 1 = 0.$
29. $10x^2 - 3x - 1 = 0.$ 30. $3y^2 - 9y + 2 = 0.$
31. $7x^2 - 3x - 2 = 0.$ 32. $12x^2 - 8x + 1 = 0.$

*Note that $3x^2 - 4x - 5 = 3\left(x - \frac{2}{3} - \frac{\sqrt{19}}{3}\right)\left(x - \frac{2}{3} + \frac{\sqrt{19}}{3}\right)$, as we discover *after* solving the equation.

33. $8y^2 - 12y + 1 = 0.$ 34. $11x^2 - 12x + 1 = 0.$

35. $15x^2 - 10x + 1 = 0.$ 36. $12y^2 - 10y + 2 = 0.$

37. $ax^2 - bx - c = 0.$ 38. $bx^2 + cx + a = 0.$

39. $a^2y^2 + b^2y + c^2 = 0.$ 40. $ax^2 + 2bx + 3c = 0.$

41. $3ax^2 + 2bx + c = 0.$ 42. $2ay^2 - by - 2c = 0.$

43. $(x - 1)(x - 2) = 3.$ 44. $(x - 1)(x + 2) = 2.$

45. $y(y + 4) = 5.$

46. Solve $s = v_0 t - \dfrac{1}{2}gt^2$ for t; for v_0.

47. Solve $s = \dfrac{n}{2}[2a + (n - 1)d]$ for n.

48. Solve $x^2 + y^2 + 4x + 2y - 1 = 0$ for y.

49. Solve $g = \dfrac{R}{R^2 + x^2}$ for R; for x.

50. Solve $c = \dfrac{b(3kd - 2c)}{3(2kd - c)}$ for c.

11-9. THE GRAPHICAL SOLUTION OF A QUADRATIC EQUATION

Four types of results for quadratic equations are illustrated by the roots of the quadratic equations (1)–(4) which were discussed in Sec. 11-3. If the zero on the right-hand side of each of these equations is replaced by y, the quadratic function

$$f = \{(x,y) \mid y = f(x) = ax^2 + bx + c\}$$

Equation	D	Nature of Roots	Roots	Graph
(1) $y = x^2 + 4x - 5$	$16 + 20 = 36$	Real, unequal and rational	1 -5	Crosses x-axis at ordered pairs $(-5,0)$ and $(1,0)$
(2) $y = x^2 + 4x - 1$	$16 + 4 = 20$	Real, unequal, and irrational	$-2 + \sqrt{5}$ $-2 - \sqrt{5}$	Crosses x-axis at ordered pairs $(-2 + \sqrt{5},0)$ and $(-2 - \sqrt{5},0)$
(3) $y = x^2 + 4x + 4$	$16 - 16 = 0$	Real, equal, and rational	-2 -2	Tangent to x-axis at ordered pair $(-2,0)$
(4) $y = x^2 + 4x + 8$	$16 - 32 = -16$	Imaginary	$-2 + 2i$ $-2 - 2i$	Does not touch x-axis

is obtained. The four functions are

(1) $\qquad f_1 = \{(x,y) \mid y = f_1(x) = x^2 + 4x - 5\}$

(2) $\qquad f_2 = \{(x,y) \mid y = f_2(x) = x^2 + 4x - 1\}$

(3) $\qquad f_3 = \{(x,y) \mid y = f_3(x) = x^2 + 4x + 4\}$ and

(4) $\qquad f_4 = \{(x,y) \mid y = f_4(x) = x^2 + 4x + 8\}$

The four graphs are shown in Fig. 11-1. The curves are all members of the *family of curves*

(5) $\qquad f = \{(x,y) \mid y = x^2 + 4x + c\}.$

Each value assigned to c yields a special curve, as indicated in the figure.

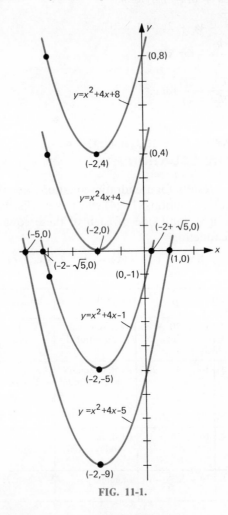

FIG. 11-1.

The graph of (1) crosses the x-axis at the points represented by the distinct ordered pairs $(1,0)$ and $(-5,0)$. Another way of saying this is that the x-intercepts of the graph are 1 and -5. These numbers are the roots of the equation

$$(6) \qquad x^2 + 4x - 5 = 0.$$

For evidently at $x = 1$ and $x = -5$ the curve (1) crosses the x-axis, so that for these values of x, $y = 0$ and hence (6) is satisfied.

Similarly, the graph of (2) crosses the x-axis in two distinct points; but in this case their abscissas or x-values are irrational, namely, $-2 + \sqrt{5}$ and $-2 - \sqrt{5}$. These numbers are the roots of the quadratic equation

$$(7) \qquad x^2 + 4x - 1 = 0.$$

In the graph of (3) the curve has in effect been lifted upward until the two intercept points have coincided at the single point represented by the ordered pair $(-2,0)$. Hence the equation

$$(8) \qquad x^2 + 4x + 4 = 0$$

may be said still to have two roots (-2 and -2) which are identical. The graph of (3) is said to be *tangent* to the x-axis at $(-2,0)$.

Finally, since the graph of (4) does not intersect the x-axis, there are no positive or negative values of x for which $y = 0$, and hence there are no real roots of

$$(9) \qquad x^2 + 4x + 8 = 0.$$

In summary, *if the roots of the quadratic equation*

$$(10) \qquad ax^2 + bx + c = 0 \wedge a \neq 0,$$

where $a, b, c \in R_e$, *and if the roots are real, they may be found as accurately as the precision of the drawing allows from the graph of the corresponding equation*

$$(11) \qquad y = ax^2 + bx + c.$$

Incidentally, the graph of (11), where $a \neq 0$, will always be a *parabola*, a very important curve entering into life and mathematics in many ways. Different sets of values for a, b, and c give different parabolas; but all of them are shaped in general like those shown in Fig. 11-1. They open upward as in that figure where a is positive, and downward when a is negative. The formula for the abscissa (or x-value) of the vertex of each parabola represented by (11) is

$$(12) \qquad x = -\frac{b}{2a}.$$

Example. Sketch the parabola

(13) $y = -2x^2 + 4x - 1.$

Solution. Using (12) and (13), we find that the coordinates of the vertex are: $x = -\dfrac{4}{-4} = 1; y = -2(1^2) + 4 \cdot 1 - 1 = 1.$ The curve opens downward, since the coefficient of x^2 is negative. The ordered pair $(0, -1)$, representing the point at which the curve crosses the y-axis are easily found by setting $x = 0$.

Since the vertex, the direction of the axes, and one ordered pair for the curve are known, the parabola can be sketched as shown in Fig. 11-2. For greater accuracy, more ordered pairs whose coordinates

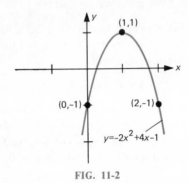

FIG. 11-2

satisfy (13) should be found. From the graph the values of the two roots of

(14) $-2x^2 + 4x - 1 = 0$

may be estimated as approximately $x = 0.3$ and $x = 1.7$. Actually they are $x = \dfrac{2 + \sqrt{2}}{2}$ and $x = \dfrac{2 - \sqrt{2}}{2}$, or very nearly as estimated.

The graphical solution of a quadratic equation is interesting not only because it gives geometric meaning to the different types of roots encountered, but also because it illustrates a very general method of getting approximations to the real roots of an equation in one variable. This method is very reliable as a last resort if no shorter way can be found. In the case of quadratic equations, however, the algebraic methods are more efficient, precise and practical.

EXERCISE 11-5

Graph the left-hand members of Eqs. 1–15, Exercise 11-3. From the graphs, estimate to one decimal place the values of the real roots, and compare with the precise values found algebraically.

11-10.   QUADRATIC EQUATIONS WITH GIVEN ROOTS

THEOREM 1:   *If* r *is a root of the equation*

(1) $ax^2 + bx + c = 0,$

then $x - r$ *is a factor of the left-hand member of (1).*

Proof.   To say that r is a root of (1) means that

(2) $ar^2 + br + c = 0.$

From (1) and (2),

$$(ax^2 + bx + c) - (ar^2 + br + c) = a(x^2 - r^2) + b(x - r),$$

or, since

$$ar^2 + br + c = 0,$$
$$ax^2 + bx + c = a(x - r)(x + r) + b(x - r)$$
$$= (x - r)(ax + ar + b).$$

Example.   The quadratic equation $2x^2 + 5x - 3 = 0$ has the root $x = \dfrac{1}{2}$, and, therefore, by the theorem, $x - \dfrac{1}{2}$ must be a factor of $2x^2 + 5x - 3$. Actually, $2x^2 + 5x - 3 = 2\left(x - \dfrac{1}{2}\right)(x + 3)$.

From Theorem 1 there follows, as a corollary,

THEOREM 2:   *All quadratic equations whose roots are* r *and* s, *must take the form*

(3) $a(x - r)(x - s) = 0,$

where a can be any constant except zero.

Example 1.   Find a quadratic equation with integral coefficients whose roots are $\dfrac{3}{2}$ and $-\dfrac{2}{3}$.

Solution.   The equation must have the form

$$a\left(x - \frac{3}{2}\right)\left[x - \left(-\frac{2}{3}\right)\right] = 0,$$

$$a\left(x - \frac{3}{2}\right)\left(x + \frac{2}{3}\right) = 0.$$

Letting $a = 6$ to clear fractions, we have

$$6x^2 - 5x - 6 = 0 \qquad (Ans.)$$

Example 2.   Find a quadratic equation with integral coefficients whose roots are $\dfrac{2 + i\sqrt{3}}{2}$ and $\dfrac{2 - i\sqrt{3}}{2}$.

Solution. The equation must have the form

$$a\left[x - \frac{2 + i\sqrt{3}}{2}\right]\left[x - \frac{2 - i\sqrt{3}}{2}\right] = 0,$$

or, when $a = 4$,

$$(2x - 2 - i\sqrt{3})(2x - 2 + i\sqrt{3}) = 0,$$

or

$$(2x - 2)^2 - (i\sqrt{3})^2 = 0,$$

or

$$4x^2 - 8x + 7 = 0.$$

EXERCISE 11-6

Find equations with integral coefficients whose roots are the numbers below.

1. 1, 2.

2. 3, −1.

3. −1, −3.

4. 0,2

5. 0, −4.

6. $\frac{1}{2}, \frac{3}{4}$.

7. $\frac{2}{3}, -\frac{1}{2}$.

8. $0, \frac{2}{5}$.

9. $1, -\frac{3}{5}$.

10.* $2 \pm \sqrt{3}$.

11. $3 \pm \sqrt{2}$.

12. $1 \pm \frac{\sqrt{3}}{2}$.

13. $\frac{1 \pm \sqrt{3}}{2}$.

14. $\pm i$.

15. $1 \pm i$.

16. $2 \pm 3i$.

17. $2 \pm i\sqrt{3}$. 18. $1 \pm \frac{i}{2}$.

*This means the roots are $2 + \sqrt{3}$ and $2 - \sqrt{3}$.

11-11. STATED PROBLEMS LEADING TO QUADRATIC EQUATIONS

The solution of many stated problems calls for the use of quadratic equations. If two different numbers satisfy the conditions of the problem, they will be the roots of the quadratic equation obtained. If only one number meets the required condition, either this number will appear as a double root or else the second root must be rejected as meaningless. Finally, if the conditions as stated are inconsistent, this fact will appear algebraically in the form of imaginary solutions to the quadratic.

Example 1. Find two consecutive numbers whose product is 56.
Solution. Let x = the smaller number (algebraically).

Then

$$x + 1 = \text{the other number.}$$
$$x(x + 1) = 56.$$

Solving, we have

$$x = 7 \qquad \text{or} \qquad x = -8$$
$$x + 1 = 8 \qquad \text{or} \qquad x + 1 = -7$$

Hence the numbers are 7 and 8; and -8 and -7. Here *both* roots of the quadratic meet the required condition.

Example 2. A building lot has an area of 56 square rods. Its length is one rod greater than its width. Find its dimensions.

Solution. Here the quadratic obtained is the same as that for Example 1; but the root $x = -8$ must be rejected as meaningless in this case.

Example 3. The area in square feet of a certain square is 4 units less than its perimeter in feet. Find the length of its side.

Solution. Let $x = $ number of feet in the length of a side

Then

$$x^2 = \text{number of square feet in the area}$$

and

$$4x = \text{number of feet in the perimeter}$$
$$x^2 = 4x - 4.$$
$$x = 2 \qquad (Ans.)$$

The solution set is $\{2\}$. Here $x = 2$ is a repeated root, and this solution, stated in words when x is replaced by 2 in

$$x = \text{number of feet in the length of a side,}$$

reads

"2 equals the number of feet in the length of the side."

Example 4. The area in square feet of a certain square is 5 units less than its perimeter in feet. Find the length of its side.

Solution. Stating the conditions as in Example 3, we have

$$x^2 = 4x - 5.$$

The quadratic formula yields

$$x = \frac{4 + 2i}{2} = 2 + i \lor x = \frac{4 - 2i}{2} = 2 - i$$

and hence the conditions are not met by any square in our kind of physical space, where real numbers are the only type involved when discussing squares and their areas.

EXERCISE 11-7

1. Find two numbers whose difference is 3 and whose product is 40.

2. The base of a ladder 20 feet long which leans against a barn is x feet from the barn. The top of the ladder is $x + 4$ feet above the ground. Find x.

3. A rectangular lot is $\frac{3}{4}$ as wide as it is long. The length of its diagonal is 250 feet. Find its dimensions.

4. A lot is 70 feet longer than it is wide. The length of its diagonal is 130 feet. Find its dimensions.

5. Find two numbers whose sum is 20 and whose product is 99.

6. The length of a rectangle is 3 inches longer than its width. If its length is increased by 2 inches and its width is increased by 3 inches, its area will be doubled. Find its dimensions.

7. The length of a rectangle is twice its width. If its width is increased by 1 inch and its length by 3 inches, its area will be doubled. Find its dimensions.

8. The diagonal of a square is 2 feet longer than its side. Solve for the length of its side (a), by use of a linear equation only; (b), by use of a quadratic equation.

9. The diagonal of a rectangle is 2 inches longer than its length and 9 inches longer than its width. Find its dimensions.

10. The area of a certain square, in square feet, is (a), 5 units more than, (b) equal to, and (c) 5 units less than, its perimeter in feet. Which of these conditions, if any, are possible, and what are the dimensions in these cases?

11. The length of a rectangle is 1 inch more than its width, and its area in square inches is equal to its perimeter in inches. Find its perimeter if the conditions are consistent.

12. The length of a rectangle is 1 inch more than its width, and its area in square inches is one-half of its perimeter in inches. Find its perimeter if the conditions are consistent.

13. One root of the quadratic, $2x^2 - bx - 1 = 0$, is 1. Find the other root.

14. One root of $3x^2 + 2x + c = 0$ is -1. Find the other root.

15. One root of $ax^2 - 4x + 3 = 0$ is 2. Find the other root.

16. The sum of the roots of the equation $2x^2 - hx + 2k = 0$ is 4, and their product is -3. What must be the values of h and k?

17. Find the value of b if the roots of the equation $3x^2 + bx + 2 = 0$ are equal.

chapter 12

Special Equations in One Unknown

12-1. INTRODUCTION

In Chapter 6 a function was defined as a special type of relation such that no two ordered pairs in the relation have the same first element. We reemphasize this fact by repeating that a function is a set of ordered pairs, and consists of three parts—a set of elements called the *domain*, a set of elements called the *range*, and a rule that assigns to each element in the domain a *unique element* in the range. The domain consists of that set formed by taking all the first elements of the ordered pairs, and the range consists of that set formed by taking all the second elements. The lower-case letters $f, g, h, \ldots$, are usually employed to denote functions. For example,

$$(1) \qquad f = \{(x, y) \mid y = f(x) = ax + b\}$$

is a linear function whose defining condition or equation or rule of correspondence is given by

$$y = ax + b \qquad \text{or} \qquad f(x) = ax + b.$$

The domain for f is either specified or is understood to be the largest subset of real numbers that can be chosen for which $y, f(x)$, or the value of the function, is real.

A quadratic function is a function of the form

$$(2) \qquad f = \{(x, y) \mid y = f(x) = ax^2 + bx + c \wedge a \neq 0\}.$$

Here the rule is $f(x) = ax^2 + bx + c$, with the understanding that the domain of this f satisfies the requirements as stated under (1) for a linear function.

Thus far, linear equations of the form $ax + b = 0$ and quadratic equations of the form $ax^2 + bx + c = 0$ have been solved both alge-braically and graphically. The graphical method for approximating the real roots of linear and quadratic equations has been introduced, which consists of drawing the graph of associated functions in an $R_e \times R_e$ space (Cartesian coordinate system) and then approximating as nearly as the accuracy of the graph allows, the x-intercept points and their correspond-ing ordered pairs. The first elements of these ordered pairs will be the real roots of the given equation. The graphical procedure should be used as a last resort when algebraic methods fail to expose the real roots of an algebraic equation in a single variable x.

This chapter stresses special procedures above and beyond those used for equations in one variable or unknown in the preceding chapters. The methods introduced are particularly concerned with equations where the solution set can be found by algebraic means. Linear and quadratic equations which belong to this category have been studied in Chapters 5 and 11. Certain of the procedures used therein will be expanded upon and employed to help solve equations of higher degrees.

12-2. SOLVING EQUATIONS BY FACTORING

The method employed for solving a quadratic equation by factoring the left-hand member when the right-hand member is zero carries over directly to equations of higher degree. This method is particularly successful when all factors found are linear or quadratic.

Example 1. Solve the equation

(1) $$x^5 - x = 0.$$

Solution. When the left-hand member is factored,

$$\begin{aligned}
x^5 - x &= x(x^4 - 1) \\
&= x(x^2 + 1)(x^2 - 1) \\
&= x(x^2 + 1)(x + 1)(x - 1) \\
&= x(x + i)(x - i)(x + 1)(x - 1) = 0.
\end{aligned}$$

The roots obtained by setting each of these factors separately equal to zero are 0, i, $-i$, 1, and -1. Since $i^5 = i$ (Sec. 10-2), it follows that $i^5 - i = i - i = 0$. The student may check each of the other four roots. The solution set is $\{0, 1, -1, i, -i\}$.

Example 2. Solve the equation

(2) $$x^3 = 1, \qquad \text{or} \qquad x^3 - 1 = 0.$$

Solution. Factoring the left-hand member,

$$x^3 - 1 = (x - 1)(x^2 + x + 1) = 0.$$

When $x - 1 = 0$, $x = 1$; when $x^2 + x + 1 = 0$, $x = \dfrac{-1 + i\sqrt{3}}{2}$ and

$x = \dfrac{-1 - i\sqrt{3}}{2}$. Hence the roots of (2), or the three cube roots of unity,

are 1, $\dfrac{-1 + i\sqrt{3}}{2}$, and $\dfrac{-1 - i\sqrt{3}}{2}$. The solution set is

$$\left\{ 1, \ \frac{-1 + i\sqrt{3}}{2}, \ \frac{-1 - i\sqrt{3}}{2} \right\}.$$

In the last example one might easily overlook the two imaginary roots; but he will not do so if he remembers the following simple and important result, proved in more advanced courses:

THEOREM 1: *Every rational integral equation of the nth degree has exactly n roots, not necessarily all different.*

For example, the hundredth-degree equation,

(3) $$x(x - 1)^{99} = 0,$$

has exactly 100 roots, including the single root zero and the *multiple* or *repeated* root 1, which is of *multiplicity* 99.

It should be noted that the cube roots of unity have some interesting properties that will be proposed in Exercise 12-1.

12-3. EQUATIONS WITH GIVEN ROOTS

As a corollary of the factoring method, and also an extension of the method of Sec. 11-10 as applied to quadratic equations, it is possible to create an equation in one unknown which will possess any preassigned roots.

Example 1. Obtain an equation whose roots are 0, 1, 2, and -3.

Solution. $a(x - 0)(x - 1)(x - 2)[x - (-3)] = 0$, where a can be any nonzero constant. Then by letting $a = 1$ and performing the indicated multiplication, the result, $x^4 - 7x^2 + 6x = 0$, is obtained. Another answer is $2x^4 - 14x^2 + 12x = 0$, where $a = 2$. An infinite number of such equations can be obtained by giving different values to a. However, all the equations which can be formed are equivalent equations (have the same roots).

Example 2. Write an integral rational equation with integral coefficients whose roots are $1 + i$, $1 - i$, $\dfrac{2 + \sqrt{3}}{3}$, and $\dfrac{2 - \sqrt{3}}{3}$ (four numbers).

Solution. An equation with the desired roots, unsimplified, is

$$a[x - (1 + i)][x - (1 - i)]\left[x - \frac{2 + \sqrt{3}}{3}\right]\left[x - \frac{2 - \sqrt{3}}{3}\right] = 0.$$

This, however, is not an answer, since the problem calls for an equation with integral coefficients. Hence we must let $a = 9$ (or 18, or 27, etc.) to clear fractions. With $a = 9$, we obtain

$$(x - 1 - i)(x - 1 + i)(3x - 2 - \sqrt{3})(3x - 2 + \sqrt{3})$$
$$= [(x - 1)^2 - i^2][(3x - 2)^2 - (\sqrt{3})^2]$$
$$= (x^2 - 2x + 2)(9x^2 - 12x + 1) = 0,$$

or

$$9x^4 - 30x^3 + 43x^2 - 26x + 2 = 0. \qquad (Ans.)$$

If $a = 18$ has been chosen, the equation obtained would have coefficients with the common factor 2. When all common integral factors of the coefficients different from $+1$ or -1 are divided out, the equation is said to be *reduced to simplest form*, as is the answer above.

EXERCISE 12-1

Solve by the factoring method.

1. $x^3 = -1$.
2. $x^4 = 1$.
3. $x^4 + 2x^2 + 1 = 0$.
4. $x^5 - 2x^3 + x = 0$.
5. $x^3 + x^2 - 6x = 0$.
6. $x^4 - x^3 - 6x^2 = 0$.
7. $x^4 - x^3 - x + 1 = 0$.
8. $x^4 - x^3 + x^2 - x = 0$.
9. $2x^3 - 4x^2 + 3x - 6 = 0$.
10. $x^5 - 2x^4 = x - 2$.
11. $x^4 - 4 = 0$.
12. $x^5 + x^3 + x = 0$.

Find rational integral equations, with integral coefficients, lowest degree, and reduced to simplest form, whose roots are the given set of numbers in Probs. 13–28.

13. $1, 2, 3$.
14. $1, -2, -3$.
15. $0, 1, -2$.
16. $0, 2, -3$.
17. $1, -1, i, -i$.
18. $0, 1 + \sqrt{2}, 1 - \sqrt{2}$.
19. $0, 1 + i\sqrt{2}, 1 - i\sqrt{2}$.
20. $1, 2 + 3i, 2 - 3i$.
21. $\frac{1}{2}, 1 + \frac{i}{2}, 1 - \frac{i}{2}$.
22. $1 + \sqrt{2}, 1 - \sqrt{2},$

$$1 + \frac{\sqrt{3}}{2}, 1 - \frac{\sqrt{3}}{2}.$$

23. $0, 1, -\dfrac{1}{2}, \dfrac{2}{3}.$ 24. $1, 1, 2, 2.$

25. $i, i, -i, -i.$ 26. $0, 0, 0.$

27. $-1, -1, -1.$ 28. $0, 0, 1, 1.$

29. Solve $x^3 = 1$ and designate the results for x as x_1, x_2, and x_3. If x_2 and x_3 are the roots containing the unit $i = \sqrt{-1}$, show that

    (a) $(x_2)^2 = x_3.$ (b) $(x_3)^2 = x_2.$ (c) $1 + x_2 + (x_2)^2 = 0.$

    (d) $1 + x_3 + (x_3)^2 = 0.$ (e) $x_2 x_3 = 1.$

    (f) $(x_1)^3 = (x_2)^3 = (x_3).^3$ (g) $x_2 x_3 = x_1.$ (h) $(x_2)^4 = x_2.$

State your conclusions as exhibited in (a) through (h) in words. [*Hint:* (e) says "that the product of the imaginary roots of unity is 1."]

12-4. EQUATIONS IN QUADRATIC FORM

It has already been shown that equations of the form

$$ax^2 + bx + c = 0, \qquad a \neq 0,$$

can be solved algebraically by three methods, namely, factoring, completing the square, or the quadratic formula. There are many other equations which are not quadratic, but which may be expressed in a quadratic form and then solved by quadratic methods. For example, consider the quadratic equation in the variable u: $u^2 - 5u + 6 = 0$. When u is replaced by the expression $(x^2 - 1)$ the resulting equation is $(x^2 - 1)^2 - 5(x^2 - 1) + 6 = 0$. This equation is certainly not quadratic in x; however, it is quadratic in $x^2 - 1$. For this reason, it is said to be a quadratic equation for the expression $x^2 - 1$.

Example 1. Find the solution set of the equation

$$x^4 - 7x^2 - 8 = 0.$$

Solution. This equation is of the 4th degree in x but by means of substituting $u = x^2$, it can be expressed as the quadratic equation

$$u^2 - 7u - 8 = 0.$$

Factoring,

$$(u - 8)(u + 1) = 0$$
$$u - 8 = 0 \qquad \text{or} \qquad u + 1 = 0$$
$$u = 8 \qquad \vee \qquad u = -1$$

When $u = 8$, $x^2 = 8$ and $x = 2\sqrt{2}$ or $x = -2\sqrt{2}$.
When $u = -1$, $x^2 = -1$ and $x = i$ or $x = -i$.

    Therefore, the solution set is $\{2\sqrt{2}, -2\sqrt{2}, i, -i\}$.

Actually it should not be necessary to make the substitution $u = x^2$. It should be apparent that the equation $x^4 - 7x^2 - 8 = 0$ can be written in the form

$$(x^2)^2 - 7(x^2) - 8 = 0,$$

which is a quadratic equation in x^2. The solution by factoring then follows as

$$(x^2 - 8)(x^2 + 1) = 0$$
$$x^2 - 8 = 0 \vee x^2 + 1 = 0,$$

from which the solution set is that given previously.

Example 2. Solve for x:

$$\frac{2x^2 + 3}{x} - \frac{5x}{2x^2 + 3} = 4.$$

Solution. By means of the substitution $u = \dfrac{2x^2 + 3}{x}$, the equation

can be written $u - \dfrac{5}{u} = 4$.

Clearly $u \neq 0$, since this value would make the denominator of the fraction equal to zero. Clearing of fractions produces the equation

$$u^2 - 4u - 5 = 0$$

from which

$$(u - 5)(u + 1) = 0$$

and

$$u = 5 \vee u = -1.$$

When $u = 5$,

$$\frac{2x^2 + 3}{x} = 5 \quad \text{and} \quad 2x^2 - 5x + 3 = 0.$$

Thus

$$x = \frac{3}{2} \quad \text{and} \quad x = 1.$$

When $u = -1$,

$$\frac{2x^2 + 3}{x} = -1 \quad \text{and} \quad 2x^2 + x + 3 = 0.$$

Here

$$x = \frac{-1 + i\sqrt{23}}{4} \quad \text{and} \quad x = \frac{-1 - i\sqrt{23}}{4}$$

by use of the quadratic formula.

The roots obtained should be checked in the original equation, since multiplication by u was involved in an intermediate step. By doing so, it will be found that the solution set is $\left\{\dfrac{3}{2}, 1, \dfrac{-1 + i\sqrt{23}}{4}, \dfrac{-1 - i\sqrt{23}}{4}\right\}$.

Example 3. Solve for x:

$$\frac{x + 2}{x - 2} + \frac{x - 2}{x + 2} = 3$$

Solution:

The form of the equation dictates immediately that $x \neq 2$, nor $x \neq -2$. We now clear of fractions by multiplying both members of the equation by $(x - 2)(x + 2)$. The student should always be careful when multiplication is performed upon an equation by a factor, or factors (particularly if a factor contains the variable x), since extra roots may be introduced into the newly formed equation that do not satisfy the original equation. Roots introduced in this fashion are called *extraneous roots*. The equation becomes

$$(x + 2)^2 + (x - 2)^2 = 3(x + 2)(x - 2)$$
$$x^2 + 4x + 4 + x^2 - 4x + 4 = 3x^2 - 12$$
$$x^2 = 20$$
$$x = 2\sqrt{5} \lor x = -2\sqrt{5}$$

The student should now check each root in the original equation. Are both of these roots solutions of the original equation? If they are, then $x = 2\sqrt{5} \lor x = -2\sqrt{5}$, giving the solution set $\{2\sqrt{5}, -2\sqrt{5}\}$.

EXERCISE 12-2

Solve the equations in Probs. 1–25 by quadratic procedures.

1. $2x^4 - x^2 - 6 = 0$.
2. $2x^4 + x^2 - 6 = 0$.
3. $6x^4 + x^2 - 1 = 0$.
4. $6x^4 - x^2 - 1 = 0$.
5. $2x^4 - x^2 - 1 = 0$.
6. $2x^4 + x^2 - 1 = 0$.
7. $x^6 + 7x^3 - 8 = 0$.
8. $x^6 - 7x^3 - 8 = 0$.
9. $x^6 + 26x^3 - 27 = 0$.
10. $x^6 - 26x^3 - 27 = 0$.
11. $8x^6 - 63x^3 - 8 = 0$.
12. $8x^6 + 63x^3 - 8 = 0$.
13. $x^6 - 28x^3 + 27 = 0$.
14. $8x^6 - 19x^3 - 27 = 0$.
15. $8x^6 + 19x^3 - 27 = 0$.
16. $2(x^2 + x)^2 - 5(x^2 + x) + 3 = 0$.
17. $2(x^2 - x)^2 - (x^2 - x) - 3 = 0$.
18. $(x^2 - x - 1)^2 - 2x^2 + 2x + 2 = 0$.

19. $(x^2 + x - 1)^2 - 3(x^2 + x - 1) + 2 = 0.$

20. $(x^2 + x + 1)^2 - x^2 - x - 3 = 0.$

21. $(2x^2 - x)^2 + 2x^2 - x - 2 = 0.$

22. $(x^2 + x + 1) + \dfrac{2}{x^2 + x + 1} = 3.$

23. $\dfrac{2(x^2 + 1)}{x} + \dfrac{2x}{x^2 + 1} = 5.$

24. $\dfrac{2(x^2 - 1)}{x} - \dfrac{2x}{x^2 - 1} = 3.$

25. $2(x^2 - x) - \dfrac{3}{x^2 - x} + 1 = 0.$

12-5. EQUATIONS INVOLVING RADICALS

When the unknown appears in one radicand, or in several, the processes necessary to eliminate the radicals may lead to rational integral equations of the types already considered.

Example 1. Solve the equation

(1) $$\sqrt{2x + 3} + \sqrt{x + 1} = 1$$

Solution. Here the student often makes the error of lifting off the radicals with the mistaken impression that he is thus squaring both sides. But this is a serious error, since $(a + b) = a^2 + 2ab + b^2$, and hence $(\sqrt{2x + 3} + \sqrt{x + 1})^2 = (\sqrt{2x + 3})^2 + 2\sqrt{2x + 3}\sqrt{x + 1} + (\sqrt{x + 1})^2$. Thus the radical $2\sqrt{(2x + 3)(x + 1)}$ still remains. To get a simpler radicand, however, it is better first to rewrite (1) thus

(2) $$\sqrt{2x + 3} = 1 - \sqrt{x + 1}.$$

When its members are squared, (2) becomes

(3) $2x + 3 = 1^2 - 2\sqrt{x + 1} + (\sqrt{x + 1})^2 = 1 - 2\sqrt{x + 1} + x + 1.$

Simplifying and carrying out appropriate steps, an equation is obtained where the one remaining radical is by itself in the left-hand member. Thus

(4) $$2\sqrt{x + 1} = -x - 1.$$

A second squaring yields

(5) $$4(x + 1) = x^2 + 2x + 1,$$

or

(6) $$x^2 - 2x - 3 = 0,$$

from which $x = 3$ or $x - 1.$

But the problem is not completed. For when both members of the equations in steps (3) and (5) are squared, we were actually multiplying both sides of the involved equations by algebraic expressions in x, and hence extraneous roots may have been introduced. Checking $x = 3$ in the left-hand member of the original equation (1),

$$\sqrt{2 \cdot 3 + 3} + \sqrt{3 + 1} = \sqrt{9} + \sqrt{4} = 3 + 2 = 5 \neq 1.$$

It follows that $x = 3$ is extraneous and must be rejected. But, for $x = -1$,

$$\sqrt{2(-1) + 3} + \sqrt{-1 + 1} = 1 + 0 = 1.$$

Thus $x = -1$ satisfies (1) and is its only root. The solution set is $\{-1\}$.

Example 2. Solve

(7) $$\sqrt{x} = -1.$$

Solution. Squaring both sides results in $x = 1$. But this root must be rejected since $\sqrt{1} \neq -1$. Hence (7) has no root. The solution here is the empty set $\emptyset$.

We observe that (7) is not a rational integral equation in x. As noted previously, it can be proved that every rational integral equation of the nth degree has n roots, but other types of equations depend upon conditions surrounding the equation before the number of roots it possesses can be determined.

EXERCISE 12-3

Solve the equations involving radicals in Probs. 1–18. (Remember, your problem is not solved until checks for all x's are made in the original equation.)

1. $\sqrt{2x - 3} = 5.$

2. $\sqrt{x + 5} = 5.$

3. $\sqrt{4 - x} = 2.$

4. $\sqrt{5x - 1} - \sqrt{x - 1} = 2.$

5. $\sqrt{x + 1} - \sqrt{x - 3} = 2.$

6. $\sqrt{1 - 3x} - \sqrt{3 + 2x} = 1.$

7. $\sqrt{x + 2} + \sqrt{3 - x} = 1.$

8. $\sqrt{x + 2} + \sqrt{2x + 5} = 1.$

9. $\sqrt{2x + 3} - \sqrt{4x - 1} = 1.$

10. $\sqrt[3]{x + 1} = 1.$

11. $\sqrt[3]{x^2 - 1} = 2.$

12. $\sqrt{x + \sqrt{x - 1}} = 1.$

13. $\sqrt{x + \sqrt{x + 2}} = 2.$

14. $\sqrt{3x - \sqrt{x^2 + 3}} = 1.$

15. $\sqrt{3x} + \sqrt{x + 1} = \sqrt{8x + 1}.$

16. $\sqrt{x + 1} + \sqrt{x + 2} = \sqrt{2x + 3}.$

17. $\sqrt{x + a} + \sqrt{x + b} = \sqrt{2x + a + b}.$

18. $\sqrt{x - 1} + \sqrt{x + 3} = \sqrt{2x + 2}.$

12-6. REMAINDER THEOREM

In this and the following articles a few theorems and rules are given which are found to be of great assistance in solving equations of a higher degree than the second. For supplementary material covering this work a student is referred to the chapter on Theory of Equations usually included in modern algebra texts.

Let $P(x)$ be a polynomial and let r be any fixed complex number. If $P(x)$ is divided by a divisor of the form $(x - r)$, until a constant remainder R is obtained, it will be equal to $P(r)$.*

Proof. Let

(1) $$P(x) = (x - r)\,Q(x) + R,$$

where $Q(x)$ is the Quotient and R is the constant remainder obtained when $P(x)$ is divided by $x - r$. The defining condition (1) becomes an identity and is true for all values of x; in particular it is true for $x = r$ (r can be any fixed complex number; for example 2, $\sqrt{3}$, $3 - i$, 1, etc.). Then

(2) $$P(r) = (r - r)\,Q(r) + R = 0 \cdot Q(r) + R = R.$$

Example.

Divide $2x^3 - 3x^2 + x - 1$ by $x - 1$.

$$
\begin{array}{r}
2x^2 - x \\
\hline
x - 1\,\overline{\smash{\big)}\,2x^3 - 3x^2 + x - 1} \\
\underline{2x^3 - 2x^2 } \\
-x^2 + x - 1 \\
\underline{-x^2 + x } \\
- 1
\end{array}
$$

Thus

$$\frac{2x^3 - 3x^2 + x - 1}{x - 1} = 2x^2 - x + \frac{-1}{x - 1}$$

$$= 2x^2 - x - \frac{1}{x - 1}$$

or

$$2x^3 - 3x^2 + x - 1 = (x - 1)(2x^2 - x) - 1.$$

In this example $x - r$ is $x - 1$, so that $r = 1$; the remainder, denoted by R, is -1. Here according to the theorem, if 1 is substituted for

---

*A *polynomial* in x, as used here, means an integral and rational function of x, with integral coefficients, such as $3x^3 - 2x^4 + x^2 - 4x + 3$. (See Sec. 2-8.) For brevity, it is often designated as $f(x)$. Thus $f(x) = 2x^4 + 3x - 1$ means that $f(x)$ here stands for the particular polynomial, $2x^4 + 3x - 1$.

x in the polynomial $2x^3 - 3x^2 + x - 1$, the value of the polynomial will be -1. To check this, we note that

$$2(1)^3 - 3(1)^2 + (1) - 1 = 2 - 3 + 1 - 1 = -1.$$

12-7. SYNTHETIC DIVISION

If a given polynomial $P(x)$ is divided by a linear polynomial of the form $x - r$, the procedure may be carried out by an algorithm process called *long division*. Since this is often lengthy, a shorter *algorithm method* called *synthetic division* has been devised.

As an illustration, consider the division of $x^4 + 3x^2 + x - 1$ by $x - 1$:

$$
\begin{array}{r}
x^3 + x^2 + 4x + 5 \\
x - 1 \overline{\smash{\big)}\, x^4 \qquad\quad + 3x^2 + \quad x - 1} \\
\underline{x^4 - x^3} \qquad\qquad\qquad\quad \\
x^3 + 3x^2 + \quad x - 1 \\
\underline{x^3 - \quad x^2} \qquad\qquad\quad \\
4x^2 + \quad x - 1 \\
\underline{4x^2 - 4x} \qquad\quad \\
5x - 1 \\
\underline{5x - 5} \\
4
\end{array}
$$

It should be noted that both polynomials are arranged in descending powers of x, and that an open space was left for the missing power of x whose coefficient was zero $(0 \cdot x^3)$.

If $P(x)$ is the dividend polynomial, and $Q(x)$ the quotient polynomial, the coefficients of the terms of $P(x)$ are $1, 0, 3, 1, -1$ and those of $Q(x)$ are $1, 1, 4, 5$. The constant remainder R is 4. Thus

$$\frac{x^4 + 3x^2 + x - 1}{x - 1} = x^3 + x^2 + 4x + 5 + \frac{4}{x - 1},$$

or

$$x^4 + 3x^2 + x - 1 = (x - 1)(x^3 + x^2 + 4x + 5) + 4$$

Thus

$$P(x) = (x - 2)\, Q(x) + R,$$

where

$$P(x) = x^4 + 3x^2 + x - 1, \quad Q(x) = x^3 + x^2 + 4x + 5, \quad R = 4.$$

It should be noted that when the algorithm division process is being performed, the x and its various powers as involved in $P(x)$, $Q(x)$, and R are assumed to be indeterminates. By this we mean that we do not associate any number values with the x's but treat same as place-holders with the properties that $x^0 = 1$, and $x^m \cdot x^n = x^{m+n}$, where m and n are positive integers.

Rewriting the division problem, but this time retaining only the coefficients involved in $P(x)$, $x - 1$, $Q(x)$ and R, we obtain the pattern

$$
\begin{array}{r}
\quad\quad 1 \quad\quad 1 \quad\ 4 \quad\ 5 \\
1 - 1 \overline{)\ 1 \quad\quad 0 \quad\ 3 \quad\ 1 \quad -1} \\
(1) \quad -1 \\
\hline
1 \quad (3) \quad 1 \quad -1 \\
(1) \quad -1 \\
\hline
4 \quad (1) \quad -1 \\
(4) \quad -4 \\
\hline
5 \ (-1) \\
(5) \quad -5 \\
\hline
4
\end{array}
$$

Notice that in the preceding pattern the numbers in parentheses are repetitions of the numbers directly above them. If we omit these repetitions, this algorithm process of division for the problem may be condensed into the following form.

$$
\begin{array}{r}
\quad\quad\ 1 \quad\ 1 \quad\ 4 \quad\ 5 \\
1 \quad -1 \overline{)\ 1 \quad\ 0 \quad\ 3 \quad\ 1 \quad -1} \\
-1 \quad -1 \quad -4 \quad -5 \\
\hline
1 \quad\ 1 \quad\ 4 \quad\ 5 \ \boxed{\ 4}
\end{array}
$$

With the exception of the last term (the remainder 4) the bottom row in this form is identical to its top row and therefore the top row may be omitted for convenience. The first coefficient 1 of the divisor $(x - 1)$ is not specially needed for the subtractions involved and thus may also be omitted. The subtractions themselves may be changed to additions by changing the second coefficient "-1" in the divisor $x - 1$ to its additive inverse "$+1$" as is indicated in the final diagrammatic scheme. The division of

$$x^4 + 3x^2 + x - 1 \text{ by } x - 1$$

is now condensed into the diagrammatic scheme called *synthetic division*:

$$
\begin{array}{r}
\underline{1} | \quad 1 \quad 0 \quad 3 \quad 1 \quad -1 \\
1 \quad 1 \quad 4 \quad\ \ 5 \\
\hline
1 \quad 1 \quad 4 \quad 5 \ \boxed{\ 4}
\end{array}
$$

A step-by-step procedure for this algorithm operation called synthetic division is now illustrated.

Example 1. Divide $3x^3 - 5x - 4x^2 + 7$ by $x - 2$.

Step 1. Arrange the terms of the dividend in descending powers of x and copy the coefficients of these terms in order, supplying zeros for every missing power of the variable in appropriate positions when necessary. Place the additive inverse 2 (the value of r associated with $x - r$) in the position of a divisor. The diagram becomes

$$\underline{2} \quad 3 \quad -4 \quad -5 \quad 7$$

Step 2. Draw a line two spaces below the coefficients and copy the first number ($+3$ in this example) below this line. Multiply this number by r ($+2$ in this example), write the product under the second coefficient, and add. Multiply this new sum by r, and continue in this manner until the last column has been totaled.

$$
\begin{array}{r|rrrr}
2 & 3 & -4 & -5 & 7 \\
 & & 6 & 4 & -2 \\
\hline
 & 3 & 2 & -1 & 5
\end{array}
$$

Step 3. The first three numbers in the third row are the coefficients of the quotient Q and the last number ($+5$ in this example) represents the constant remainder R. Since the dividend is a polynominal of degree 3, and the divisor is a first-degree polynomial, the degree of the quotient polynomial is 2. The complete quotient and remainder for our example, is

$$3(x^2) + 2(x) - 1 \quad \text{and a remainder of } +5$$

or

$$Q(x) = 3x^2 + 2x - 1 \quad \text{and constant remainder } R = 5.$$

Thus,

$$\frac{3x^3 - 4x - 5x + 7}{x - 2} = 3x^2 + 2x - 1 + \frac{5}{x - 2}.$$

The constant remainder R is of utmost importance in the resulting division because it is the value of the *polynomial dividend* when 2 is substituted for x. In our example, $P(x) = 3x^3 - 4x^2 - 5x + 7$, and $P(2) = 3(2)^3 - 4(2)^2 - 5(2) + 7 = 5$ which agrees with the remainder previously found.

Example 2. Find $P(1)$, (a) by synthetic division, (b) by direct substitution, if

$$P(x) = 2x^3 - 3x^2 + x - 1.$$

Solution. (a)

$$
\begin{array}{r|rrrr}
1 & 2 & -3 & 1 & -1 \\
 & & 2 & -1 & 0 \\
\hline
 & 2 & -1 & 0 & -1
\end{array}
$$

Therefore $P(1) = -1$

(b) By direct substitution, $P(1) = 2(1)^3 - 3(1)^2 + 1 - 1 = -1$

Example 3. Divide $2x^5 - 2x^3 + 1$ by $x + 3$.

Solution.

$$
\begin{array}{r|rrrrrr}
-3 & 2 & 0 & -2 & 0 & 0 & 1 \\
& & -6 & 18 & -48 & 144 & -432 \\
\hline
& 2 & -6 & 16 & -48 & 144 & \underline{|-431}
\end{array}
$$

Therefore

$$\frac{2x^5 - 2x^3 + 1}{x + 3} = 2x^4 - 6x^3 + 16x^2 - 48x + 144 - \frac{431}{x + 3}$$

Note here that $x - r = x - (-3)$, so that $r = -3$, and that zeros have been placed for all missing terms in appropriate positions for the expression $2x^5 - 2x^3 + 1$. Here again the constant remainder -431 is the value of $2x^5 - 2x^3 + 1$ when x is replaced by -3.

12-8. THE FACTOR THEOREM

The factor theorem which is closely related to the remainder theorem is usually stated as follows:

Let $P(x)$ represent a polynomial, and let r be any complex number. *Then $(x - r)$ is a factor of $P(x)$ if and only if $P(r) = 0$.*

The factor theorem is an "if and only if" theorem, and as a consequence the following two statements must be proven:

(a) If $(x - r)$ is a factor of $P(x)$, then $P(r) = 0$.

(b) If $P(r) = 0$, then $(x - r)$ is a factor of $P(x)$.

Proof. (a) Assume that $x - r$ is a factor of $P(x)$. If it is, then a division algorithm process exists which produces a polynomial $Q(x)$ such that

(1) $$P(x) = (x - r)\,Q(x).$$

It is noted again for emphasis that while this $Q(x)$ is obtained, x and its various powers are considered as indeterminates. After the established identity (1) is produced, we can now drop the role for x being an indeterminate and assign any number values we please to the x. Thus if $x = r$,

$$
\begin{aligned}
P(r) &= (r - r)\,Q(r) \\
&= 0 \cdot Q(r) \\
&= 0
\end{aligned}
$$

(b) Assume that $P(r) = 0$. Then by the remainder theorem,

$$P(x) = (x - r) \cdot Q(x) + R$$

Since $R = P(r)$,

$$P(x) = (x - r) \cdot Q(x) + P(r)$$
$$= (x - r) \cdot Q(x) + 0$$
$$= (x - r) \cdot Q(x)$$

Here $P(x)$ is shown to be the product of two polynomials in x and each is thus a factor of $P(x)$. Therefore $x - r$ is a factor of $P(x)$.

Example.   State whether $x - 2$ is a factor of

$$P(x) = 2x^3 - 3x^2 + 5x - 14.$$

Solution.

$$\begin{array}{r|rrrr} 2 & 2 & -3 & 5 & -14 \\ & & 4 & 2 & 14 \\ \hline & 2 & 1 & 7 & 0 \end{array}$$

Therefore $P(2) = 0$, and $x - 2$ is a factor of $P(x)$.

EXERCISE 12-4

Divide, using synthetic division.

1. $(3x^3 - 2x^2 + 4x - 5) \div (x - 1)$.
2. $(5x^4 + 3x^3 - x^2 - x - 2) \div (x + 1)$.
3. $(2x^4 - 7x^3 + 8x^2 - 7x + 6) \div (x - 2)$.
4. $(3x^4 + 6x^3 - 2x^2 - 3x + 2) \div (x + 2)$.
5. $(4x^3 + 12x^2 - 3x - 9) \div (x + 3)$.
6. $(x^5 - 5x^4 - x + 5) \div (x - 5)$.
7. $(3x^4 - 12x^3 - 8x + 32) \div (x - 4)$.
8. $(2x^4 - 12x^3 - 3x + 18) \div (x - 6)$.
9. $(3x^3 - 5x^2 + 2x + 4) \div (x - 3)$.
10. $(5x^3 + 4x^2 - 3) \div (x - 2)$.
11. $(3x^4 - 2x^2 + 5) \div (x - 1)$.
12. $(4x^5 - 3x^3 + 2x^2 - 5) \div (x + 1)$.
13. $(7x^3 - 6x^2 + 5x) \div (x + 4)$.
14. $(3x^4 - 6x^3 - 2x^2 + 4x) \div (x - 2)$.

By use of the factor theorem determine whether or not the expression on the left is a factor of the polynomial on the right.

15. $x + 2; x^4 + 2x^3 - x - 2$.
16. $x - 1; x^4 + 2x^3 - x - 2$.
17. $x + 1; 3x^4 + x^3 + x^2 + 4x + 1$.

18. $x + 3; 2x^4 + 6x^3 - x - 3.$

19. $x + 2; 3x^3 + x^2 - 10x.$

20. $x - 3; 5x^4 - 3x^3 + x - 2.$

21. $x + 4; x^3 - 3x^2 + 2x - 8.$

12-9. THEOREM ON RATIONAL ROOTS

If an equation

$$a_0x^n + a_1x^{n-1} + a_2x^{n-2} + \cdots + a_{n-1}x + a_n = 0,$$

with integral coefficients, has a rational root $\dfrac{p}{q}$, where $\dfrac{p}{q}$ is reduced to lowest terms, then p is an integral divisor of a_n, and q is an integral divisor of a_0.

Example. If the equation

$$3x^3 - 4x^2 + 5x + 2 = 0$$

has a rational root, it must be one of the following numbers:

$$\pm \frac{2}{3}, \quad \pm \frac{2}{1}, \quad \pm \frac{1}{3}, \quad \pm \frac{1}{1}.$$

Corollary. Any rational root of an equation

$$x^n + b_1x^{n-1} + b_2x^{n-2} + \cdots + b_{n-1}x + b_n = 0,$$

with integral coefficients, is an integral divisor of b_n.

Example. If the equation

$$x^3 - 3x^2 + 4x + 12 = 0$$

has a rational root, it will be one of the following numbers:

$$\pm 1, \quad \pm 2, \quad \pm 3, \quad \pm 4, \quad \pm 6, \quad \pm 12.$$

12-10. UPPER AND LOWER LIMITS OF ROOTS

The possible rational roots are checked by synthetic division to determine whether or not they are actual roots. If, when any positive number is tested, the sums beneath the line are all positive, or zero, it can be proved* that there is no root larger than the number being tested. This number is therefore an upper limit of the roots.

Similarly if, when a negative number is tested, the sums are alternately plus and minus throughout the line, it can be shown that there is no

---

*The proof is not difficult. The student is challenged to try it in Prob. 23 of Exercise 12-5. See also Prob. 24.

root less than the number being tested. That number is therefore a lower limit.

Example. Test the number 2 as a possible root of

$$3x^3 - 4x^2 + 5x + 2 = 0.$$

$$
\begin{array}{r|rrrr}
2 & 3 & -4 & 5 & 2 \\
  &   & 6 & 4 & 18 \\
\hline
  & 3 & 2 & 9 & 20
\end{array}
$$

The signs are all plus in the lower line, and hence the roots of this equation are all less than 2.

Test -1 as a possible root.

$$
\begin{array}{r|rrrr}
-1 & 3 & -4 & 5 & 2 \\
   &   & -3 & 7 & -12 \\
\hline
   & 3 & -7 & 12 & -10
\end{array}
$$

The signs in the lower line are alternately plus and minus, and hence the roots of the equation are greater than -1.

By this means some of the "possible roots" may be eliminated without testing them by synthetic division.

12-11. DEPRESSED EQUATIONS

Consider the equation

(1) $$(x^2 - 3x + 2)(x - 3) = 0.$$

Any value of x that makes $x - 3 = 0$, or any value of x that makes $x^2 - 3x + 2 = 0$, is a root of (1). The statements, $x - 3 = 0$, and $x^2 - 3x + 2 = 0$ are called *depressed equations* with relation to equation (1). The depressed equation is found by synthetic division.

Example 1. Solve

$$x^3 - 6x^2 + 11x - 6 = 0.$$

Solution.

$$
\begin{array}{r|rrrr}
3 & 1 & -6 & 11 & -6 \\
  &   & 3 & -9 & 6 \\
\hline
  & 1 & -3 & 2 & 0
\end{array}
$$

Here the remainder is zero. Use the numbers below the line as coefficients and reduce the degree of the expression by one. The depressed equation, then, is $x^2 - 3x + 2 = 0$. Since any root of the depressed equation is also a root of the original equation, we solve the depressed equation for the remaining roots.

$$x^2 - 3x + 2 = 0,$$

or

$$(x - 2)(x - 1) = 0.$$
$$x - 2 = 0 \text{ or } x - 1 = 0$$
$$x = 2 \quad \vee \quad x = 1.$$

The solution set for the original equation is

$$\{1, 2, 3\}$$

Example 2. Find the roots of the equation

$$4x^3 + 8x^2 - 3x - 6 = 0.$$

Solution. The possible rational roots are

$$\pm 1, \quad \pm 2, \quad \pm 3, \quad \pm 6, \quad \pm \frac{1}{2}, \quad \pm \frac{3}{2}, \quad \pm \frac{1}{4}, \quad \pm \frac{3}{4}.$$

Testing -3,

$$
\begin{array}{r|rrrr}
-3 & 4 & 8 & -3 & -6 \\
   &   & -12 & 12 & -27 \\
\hline
   & 4 & -4 & 9 & -33
\end{array}
$$

Thus -3 is not a root, and this test shows that all roots are greater than -3, since the sums below the line alternate in sign. Next,

$$
\begin{array}{r|rrrr}
-2 & 4 & 8 & -3 & -6 \\
   &   & -8 & 0 & 6 \\
\hline
   & 4 & 0 & -3 & 0
\end{array}
$$

This test shows that -2 is a root, since the remainder is zero. The depressed equation is $4x^2 + 0x - 3 = 0$. Upon solving the latter, there results $x^2 = \frac{3}{4}$, and $x = \pm \frac{\sqrt{3}}{4} = \pm \frac{1}{2} \sqrt{3}$. Thus the roots are -2, $\frac{\sqrt{3}}{2}$, and $-\frac{\sqrt{3}}{2}$, and the solution set is $\left\{ -2, \frac{\sqrt{3}}{2}, -\frac{\sqrt{3}}{2} \right\}$.

EXERCISE 12-5

By use of the preceding theory, determine what numbers could possibly be roots of the equations in Probs. 1–22, and then test them. If the final depressed equation is quadratic, find all the roots, and the corresponding solution set.

1. $x^3 - 3x^2 - x + 3 = 0.$
2. $x^3 - 3x + 2 = 0.$
3. $x^3 + 2x - 3 = 0.$
4. $x^4 - 2x^3 + 1 = 0.$
5. $x^4 - 3x^2 + 2 = 0.$
6. $2x^5 + 3x^4 - 3x^2 + 2 = 0.$
7. $2x^3 - x^2 - 2x + 1 = 0.$
8. $6x^3 + 19x^2 + 15x + 2 = 0.$
9. $x^4 + 3x^3 - 3x^2 - 12x - 4 = 0.$

10. $6x^3 + 19x^2 + x - 6 = 0.$

11. $x^4 - 2x^3 - 6x^2 + 6x + 9 = 0.$

12. $8x^4 - 4x^3 - 14x^2 + 5x + 5 = 0.$

13. $6x^4 + 3x^3 - 11x^2 - 4x + 4 = 0.$

14. $2x^4 + 5x^2 + 2 = 0.$

15. $3x^4 + 2x^3 + 13x^2 + 8x + 4 = 0.$

16. $x^3 + x - 2 = 0.$

17. $3x^4 + 2x^3 - 49x^2 - 32x + 16 = 0.$

18. $x^5 + 3x^3 - x^2 - 3 = 0.$

19. $x^5 - 4x^3 - 8x^2 + 32 = 0.$

20. $4x^4 - 12x^3 - 25x^2 + 27x + 36 = 0.$

21. $x^4 + 8x^3 - 12x^2 - 24x + 27 = 0.$

22. $x^4 + 3x^3 + x^2 - 2 = 0.$

23. Prove the statement beginning "... it can be proved" in the first paragraph of Sec. 12-10.

24. Prove the statement beginning "... it can be shown" in the second paragraph of Sec. 12-10.

chapter 13

Simultaneous Equations

13-1. QUADRATIC EQUATIONS IN TWO VARIABLES

In Chapter 7 we studied systems of equations and learned how to obtain their solution sets by using both graphic and algebraic methods. Although those discussions were mainly restricted to linear systems, the same or equivalent definitions for a system involving more complicated equations and its solution set apply in general. In this chapter we use corresponding techniques for systems involving quadratic equations in two variables.

The general quadratic equation in two variables, x and y, possesses the standard form

$$(1) \qquad Ax^2 + Bxy + Cy^2 + Dx + Ey + F = 0,$$

where A, B, C, D, E, and F are real constants and at least one of the constants A, B, and C is different from zero.

The second-degree terms in x and y are Ax^2, Bxy and Cy^2.

The first-degree, or linear, terms in x and y are Dx and Ey.

The constant term F is said to be of degree zero in x and y.

Since the degree of a polynomial equation is determined by choosing the highest degree involved among its terms, the general quadratic equation in x and y is an equation of the second degree.

The solution set, or simply the solution, of equation (1) is the set of all ordered pairs determined by

$$(2) \qquad f = \{(x,y) \in R_e \times R_e \mid Ax^2 + Bxy + Cy^2 + Dx + Ey + F = 0\}.$$

In general, a quadratic equation in two variables has infinitely many solutions. Each ordered pair (x,y) must satisfy (2) in order to be a solution of equation (1).

Examples of quadratic equations in two variables are

(a) $x^2 + y^2 = 4$
(b) $xy = 1$
(c) $y^2 - 4x + 2y + 5 = 0.$

Note that $(-2,0)$ is a solution of $x^2 + y^2 = 4$; $\left(2, \dfrac{1}{2}\right)$ is a solution of $xy = 1$; and $(+1, -1)$ is a solution of $y^2 - 4x + 2y + 5 = 0$. Can you find other solutions? _____

Our primary concern will be with the solution of systems of equations in two variables where one equation is linear and the other quadratic, and also several special cases where both equations of the simultaneous system are quadratic.

13-2. GRAPHIC SOLUTION

The graphical method, which was employed to solve systems of linear equations, can also be applied to any system of equations that involve at most not more than two variables. We sketch the graphs of the separately involved equations on one and the same set of coordinate axes and then by inspection approximate the coordinates of the points of intersection, if they exist. Each of these points corresponds to an ordered pair of real numbers which is a solution of the system in an $R_e \times R_e$ space.

13-3. TYPICAL LOCI

The graphs of $Ax^2 + Bxy + Cy^2 + Dx + Ey + F = 0$ are called *conic sections*, or *conics*. By methods employed in analytic geometry, it can be shown that this equation is associated with the geometric intersection of a plane and a right circular cone having two nappes, as illustrated in Fig. 13-1. The different types of such intersections are shown in

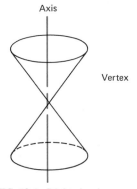

FIG. 13-1. Right circular cone.

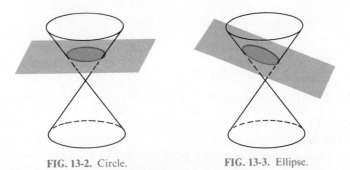

FIG. 13-2. Circle.   **FIG. 13-3.** Ellipse.

Figs. 13-2 through 13-8. The last three cases, Figs. 13-6, 13-7, and 13-8, are referred to as *degenerate forms* of a conic. Still another possibility is when the quadratic equation in two variables produces the empty set. For example, there is no ordered pair (x, y) that satisfies the equation

$$x^2 + y^2 = -4,$$

since the sum of two squares of real numbers cannot be negative.

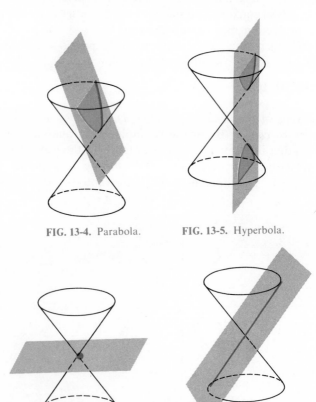

FIG. 13-4. Parabola.   **FIG. 13-5.** Hyperbola.

FIG. 13-6. Point.   **FIG. 13-7.** Straight line.

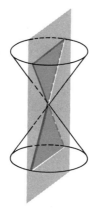

FIG. 13-8. Two intersecting straight lines.

If the locus or graph exists, it is always one of the following:

(a)   an ellipse (Fig. 13-9), including the circle as a special case

(b)   a parabola (Fig. 13-10)

(c)   a hyperbola (Fig. 13-11)

(d)   two straight lines which may or may not coincide (Fig. 13-12)

or

(e)   a single point.

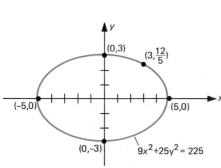

FIG. 13-9. Ellipse.

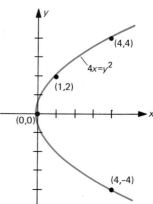

FIG. 13-10. Parabola.

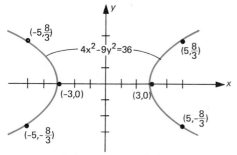

FIG. 13-11. Hyperbola.

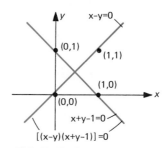

FIG. 13-12. Two straight lines.

For purposes of this chapter we may note that if the general appearance of each of the three curves in (a), (b), (c), or (d) is memorized one can sketch them from a few well-selected points upon their graph.

Example. Sketch the curve represented by

(2) $$f = \{(x, y) \mid 9x^2 + 25y^2 = 225\}.$$

Solution. Solving $9x^2 + 25y^2 = 225$ for y, we have

(3) $$y = +\frac{3}{5}\sqrt{25 - x^2} \quad \text{or} \quad y = -\frac{3}{5}\sqrt{25 - x^2}.$$

Assigning to x the values 0, 3, -3, 5, and -5, we find from (3) that the corresponding values of y are $+3$, -3, $+\dfrac{12}{5}$, $-\dfrac{12}{5}$, 0.

These points are on the ellipse of Fig. 13-9. Note that if x exceeds 5 numerically, y is imaginary. This means that the curve does not extend to the right of the line $x = 5$, nor to the left of the line $x = -5$.

EXERCISE 13-1

The graphs of the equations in Probs. 1 and 2 below are ellipses; in 3 and 4, parabolas; in 5 and 6, hyperbolas. Find at least 6 points on each, and sketch the curve.

1. $x^2 + y^2 = 25$ (a circle).   2. $4x^2 + 9y^2 = 36$.

3. $y = 2x^2 + x - 4$.   4. $y^2 - 4y - x + 3 = 0$.

5. $x^2 - y^2 = 9$.   6. $9y^2 - 4x^2 = 36$.

Draw the graphs indicated for Probs. 7–15. They are straight lines.

7. $(x - y)(x + y - 1) = 0$.   8. $(3x - 4y - 6)(4x + 3y - 6) = 0$.

9. $(x - y)^2 = 1$.   10. $(x - y - 2)^2 = 0$.

11. $x^2 - 4 = 0$.   12. $y^2 = 0$.

13. $y^2 = 4$.   14. $(2x + 3y + 6)^2 = 0$.

15. $y^2 - x^2 = 0$.

Graph the equations in Probs. 16-24.

16. $9x^2 + 4y^2 = 36$.   17. $9x^3 - 4y^2 = 36$.   18. $9x^2 - 4y^2 = 0$.

19. $x^2 + y^2 = 9$.   20. $x^2 - y^2 = 9$.

21. $x^2 - y^2 = 0$.   22. $(x - y)^2 = 0$.

23. $x^2 + y^2 = 0$.   24. $(x - 2)^2 + (y + 1)^2 = 0$.

13-4.   LINEAR AND QUADRATIC EQUATIONS—ALGEBRAIC SOLUTION BY SUBSTITUTION

Suppose, for example, we seek the dimensions of a rectangle whose diagonal is 10 inches long and whose perimeter is 28 inches.

Designating the two unknowns, the measures of length and width in

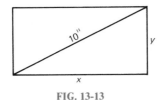

FIG. 13-13

inches, by x and y respectively, we have, from Fig. 13-13 and the Pythagorean relation,

(1) $$x^2 + y^2 = 10^2.$$

Also, since half of the perimeter is 14,

(2) $$x + y = 14.$$

Solving (2) for y, we have

(3) $$y = 14 - x.$$

Substitution of the value of y from (3) in (1) yields

(4) $$x^2 + (14 - x)^2 = 100.$$

The solutions of (4) are $x = 6$ or $x = 8$. Substituting in (2), or, better yet, in (3), we obtain the solution set $\{(6,8), (8,6)\}$. Both of these ordered pairs satisfy (1) and (2); but since algebraic solutions must be examined in the light of the demands of the problem, and since by agreement x stands for the measure of length, the first pair of values must be rejected. The required rectangle is 8 inches long and 6 inches wide.

To solve a linear and quadratic pair, then, we proceed as follows, as illustrated by the example above.

1. Solve the linear equation for one letter in terms of the other.
2. Substitute the obtained literal value of the first letter in the second-degree equation.
3. Solve the resulting quadratic equation in the second letter.
4. Substitute each of the two quadratic roots now found in the *linear* equation to find the corresponding value of the first letter.

Consider next the graphical interpretation of the above problem. The circle (1) and the line (2) intersect at the points (8,6) and (6,8), (Fig. 13-14). It should be noted that there are *two* points on the circle and only

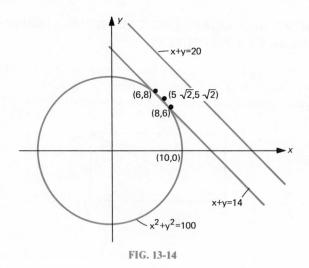

FIG. 13-14

one on the line for which $x = 8$. This suggests the reason for the emphasis upon substitution of the found value in the *linear* instead of the quadratic equation.

Suppose, in this problem, that the perimeter were increased to $20\sqrt{2}$ inches, with the diagonal length unchanged. The algebraic solution of the two equations

(5) $$x^2 + y^2 = 100$$

and

(6) $$x + y = 10\sqrt{2}$$

yields the one ordered pair $(5\sqrt{2}, 5\sqrt{2})$. Geometrically, this means that the line (6) touches the circle (5) at the single point $(5\sqrt{2}, 5\sqrt{2})$ (Fig. 13-14). Finally, with an assumed perimeter of 40, the algebraic solution leads to the empty set, as might be suspected from the fact that the line, $x + y = 20$, in Fig. 13-14, does not cross the circle.

In general, the physical impossibility of a pair of simultaneous conditions is indicated *algebraically* whenever i appears in the solution of the equation for the stated conditions, as well as by inconsistent equations; and it is shown *graphically* by the nonintersection of the loci of these equations. This result applies not only to linear and quadratic pairs, but also to simultaneous equations of many types and degrees in two unknowns.

13-5. THE NUMBER OF SOLUTION PAIRS

An inspection of the sample second degree curves shown in Figs. 13-9 through 13-12 indicates that a straight line cannot cross one of them in more than two points, and also that two of them cannot intersect in more than four points. The corresponding algebraic results may be stated as follows:

     A.*   *There are at most two distinct pairs of real numbers which satisfy simultaneously a linear and quadratic equation in two unknowns.*

     B.*   *There are at most four distinct pairs of real numbers which satisfy simultaneously two quadratic equations in two unknowns.*

EXERCISE 13-2†

     Obtain the solution set for the systems of equations in Probs. 1–16 graphically, estimating the coordinates of the points of intersection in case they intersect. Then check by solving algebraically.

1. $x^2 + y^2 = 25$ 2. $x^2 + y^2 = 25$ 3. $x^2 + y^2 = 25$

         $\wedge$ $\wedge$ $\wedge$

     $3x - 4y = 0.$ $x + y = 5.$ $x - y = 0.$

4. $x^2 + y^2 = 25$ 5. $x^2 + y^2 = 25$ 6. $x^2 + y^2 = 25$

         $\wedge$ $\wedge$ $\wedge$

     $3y - 2x = 1.$ $3x - 4y = 25.$ $y = 6.$

7. $x^2 - y^2 = 16$ 8. $x^2 - y^2 = 16$ 9. $x^2 - y^2 = 16$

         $\wedge$ $\wedge$ $\wedge$

     $3x - 5y = 0.$ $y - 3 = 0.$ $x + y = 4.$

10. $x^2 - y^2 = 16$ 11. $x^2 - y^2 = 16$ 12. $x^2 - y = 0$

         $\wedge$ $\wedge$ $\wedge$

     $2x - 3y = 1.$ $x = 3.$ $3y - 4x = 4.$

13. $x^2 - y = 0$ 14. $x^2 - y = 0$ 15. $x - y^2 = 0$

         $\wedge$ $\wedge$ $\wedge$

     $2x - y = 1.$ $2x - y = 2.$ $x + y = 2.$

16. $x - y^2 = 0$

         $\wedge$

     $4 - x = 0.$

     By algebraic methods, obtain the solution set in Probs. 17–22.

17. $x^2 + xy + y^2 = 3$ 18. $x^2 + 4y^2 = 2$

               $\wedge$ $\wedge$

        $x + y = 2.$ $x + 2y = 0.$

     *It is assumed here that the equations are *independent*. That is, we bar pairs, such as $x + y - 1 = 0$ and $(x + y - 1)(x - y) = 0$, whose graphs have a straight line in common, or such as $x^2 + y^2 = 1$ and $2x^2 + 2y^2 = 2$, whose graphs are identical.

     †Each of these problem exercises are special cases of $g = \{(x,y)\,|\,Ax^2 + Bxy + Cy^2 + Dx + Ey + F = 0\}$ and $f = \{(x,y)\,|\,ax + by = c\}$, where we are asking for the solution set $f \cap g$.

19. $4y^2 + xy + x + 2y - 1 = 0$ 20. $x^2 - xy - y^2 = 1$

              $\wedge$ $\wedge$

          $x - 4y = 4.$ $x + y = 1.$

21. $xy = ab$ 22. $2x - y = a + 2b$

          $\wedge$ $\wedge$

   $2x + y = 2a + b.$ $xy + ab = 0.$

23. Find the dimensions of a rectangular field whose area is 20 square rods and whose perimeter is 24 rods.

24. Find the dimensions of a rectangle whose perimeter is 34 inches and whose diagonal is 13 inches.

13-6. SIMULTANEOUS QUADRATICS IN GENERAL

The algebraic solution of simultaneous quadratic equations in two variables is in the general case long and tedious, involving the solution of a fourth-degree equation. We shall consider, in the next two sections, two special but important cases.

13-7. ALGEBRAIC SOLUTION OF SIMULTANEOUS EQUATIONS IN LINEAR FORM

If no more than two of the five quantities, x^2, y^2, xy, x, and y appear altogether in two simultaneous quadratics, the method for *linear* equations may be applied at once to get these two unknowns. After the latter are found, the values of x and y follow at once. Each of the following seven pairings is of interest here: x^2 and y^2; x^2 and xy; y^2 and xy; x^2 and y; y^2 and x; xy and x; xy and y.

For certain special cases it is possible to eliminate one of the variables by "the addition-and-subtraction method," which is similar to that used for linear systems. Each equation of the system is multiplied by an appropriate constant and the resulting equations are then added algebraically with the objective of eliminating one of the variables. Values for the remaining variable are then found from the newly formed equation. Each of these values is then substituted into either of the original equations to find the other associated member of the solution (x,y). All such ordered pairs (x,y) which satisfy each of the equations in the original system constitutes the solution set of the system.

Example 1. Obtain the solution set $f \cap g$ of the system involved in

$$f = \{(x,y) \mid 2x^2 + 3y^2 = 5\}$$
$$g = \{(x,y) \mid 7x^2 - 4y^2 = 3\}$$

Solution. Suppose we choose to eliminate y^2. Multiply the first equation by 4 and the second by 3. Then the equivalent system

$$\begin{cases} 8x^2 + 12y^2 = 20 \\ \wedge \\ 21x^2 - 12y^2 = 9 \end{cases}$$

is obtained. Adding we obtain

$$29x^2 = 29$$
$$x^2 = 1$$
$$x = 1 \quad \text{or} \quad x = -1.$$

Any solution of the system then, is also a solution of

$$\begin{cases} 2x^2 + 3y^2 = 5 \\ \wedge \\ x = 1 \end{cases} \quad \text{or} \quad \begin{cases} 2x^2 + 3y^2 = 5 \\ \wedge \\ x = -1 \end{cases}$$

By substitution,

$$y = 1 \qquad y = -1 \qquad\qquad y = 1 \qquad y = -1$$
$$\text{or} \qquad\qquad\qquad \text{or}$$
$$x = 1 \qquad x = 1 \qquad\qquad x = -1 \qquad x = -1$$

Thus the solution set is the set

$$f \cap g = \{(1,1), (1,-1), (-1,1), (-1,-1)\}.$$

Note that the solution is not complete until the values have been paired properly.

Example 2. Obtain the solution set for the system

(3) $$f = \{(x,y) \mid 2x^2 - 3xy = 1\}$$

(4) $$g = \{(x,y) \mid 3x^2 + xy = 7\}.$$

Solution. Treating the equations in (3) and (4) as linear in the unknowns x^2 and xy, we find that $x^2 = 2$ and $xy = 1$. Hence $x = \sqrt{2}$ or $x = -\sqrt{2}$. Since $y = \dfrac{1}{x}$, $y = \dfrac{1}{\sqrt{2}}$, or $y = -\dfrac{1}{\sqrt{2}}$, $\left(\text{or } y = \dfrac{\sqrt{2}}{2} \text{ or } y = -\dfrac{\sqrt{2}}{2}\right)$. Thus the solutions are $\left(\sqrt{2}, \dfrac{\sqrt{2}}{2}\right)$ and $\left(-\sqrt{2}, -\dfrac{\sqrt{2}}{2}\right)$, and the solution set is $f \cap g = \left\{\left(\sqrt{2}, \dfrac{\sqrt{2}}{2}\right), \left(-\sqrt{2}, -\dfrac{\sqrt{2}}{2}\right)\right\}$.

Example 3. Solve simultaneously:

(5) $$f = \{(x,y) \mid x^2 + 2y = 4\}$$

(6) $$g = \{(x,y) \mid 2x^2 - y = -12\}.$$

Solution. The involved equations are linear in x^2 and y. Solving, we obtain $x^2 = -4$, $y = 4$; so that the final solutions are $(2i, 4)$ and $(-2i, 4)$. The imaginary values for x indicate that the curves do not intersect. This is seen in Fig. 13-15 to be the case. Hence the solution set

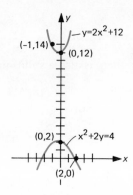

FIG. 13-15

$f \cap g = \phi$ in an $R_e \times R_e$ space, but is $\{(-2i, 4), (2i, 4)\}$ in an $C \times C$ space, where C = the complex number system.

Example 4. Figure 13-16 shows the graphical solution for the simultaneous system

$$x^2 + y^2 = 13$$
$$\wedge$$
$$x^2 - y^2 = 5.$$

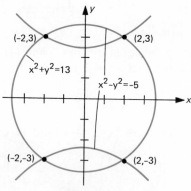

FIG. 13-16

What does the graphical representation tell you about the solution set? _____

Confirm your conclusion by solving same algebraically.

EXERCISE 13-3

Obtain the solution set in Probs. 1–16 by algebraic methods. In Probs. 1–6, solve graphically also.

1. $x^2 + y^2 = 25$
   $\wedge$
   $x^2 - y^2 = 4.$

2. $x^2 + y^2 = 25$
   $\wedge$
   $2x^2 + 3y^2 = 50.$

3. $x^2 + y^2 = 1$
   $\wedge$
   $x^2 - y^2 = 4.$

4. $x^2 + y^2 = 4$
   $\wedge$
   $4x^2 + 9y^2 = 36.$

5. $2x - 3y^2 = 1$
   $\wedge$
   $3x + 2y^2 = 8.$

6. $4x^2 - y = 3$
   $\wedge$
   $3x^2 - 1 - 2y = 0.$

7. $2x^2 + xy = 6$
   $\wedge$
   $x^2 + 2xy = 0.$

8. $3xy + y^2 = 1$
   $\wedge$
   $4xy + y^2 = 2.$

9. $4x^2 + 3y = 5$
   $\wedge$
   $3y - 8x^2 + 4 = 0.$

10. $3y^2 + 2x - 1 = 0$
    $\wedge$
    $2y^2 - 3x + 8 = 0.$

11. $3(xy - x) = 1$
    $\wedge$
    $3x(y + 2) = 7.$

12. $y(2x - 3) = 3$
    $\wedge$
    $2y - xy + 1 = 0.$

13. $x^2 = 4xy - 3$
    $\wedge$
    $2xy = 3x^2 + 4.$

14. $y^2 = 3xy - 5$
    $\wedge$
    $6xy + 2 + y^2 = 0.$

15. $2x^2 + 4y^2 = 3a$
    $\wedge$
    $3x^2 - 8y^2 = -a.$

16. $2x^2 + 3xy = 2a + 3b$
    $\wedge$
    $3x^2 - 2xy = 3a - 2b.$

13-8. ALGEBRAIC SOLUTIONS WHEN EQUATIONS ARE REDUCIBLE TO SIMPLER FORMS

When quadratic equations in two unknowns are written with the right members zero, the simultaneous solution of a pair of them is much simplified if the left member of at least one of the equations is or can be factored.

Example 1. Solve simultaneously:

(1) $(3x - 2y - 1)(x + y + 1) = 0,$

(2) $x^2 + y^2 - 25 = 0.$

Solution. Since any pair of values satisfying

(3) $3x - 2y - 1 = 0,$

or

(4) $x + y + 1 = 0,$

will also satisfy (1), it follows that any common solution of (3) and (2) or of (4) and (2) will be one of the desired solutions of (1) and (2). Hence the problem reduces to the solution of two linear-and quadratic pairs: (3)–(2) and (4)–(2). The solutions of (3) and (2) are $(3, 4)$ and $\left(-\dfrac{33}{13}, -\dfrac{56}{13}\right)$; those of (4) and (2) are $(-4, 3)$ and $(3, -4)$. The loci of (1) and (2) are shown in Fig. 13-17.

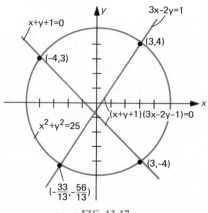

FIG. 13-17

Example 2. Solve simultaneously:

(5) $(2x - 3y - 4)(x + y - 2) = 0,$

(6) $(3x - y + 1)(2x - y - 3) = 0.$

Solution. Equation (5) is satisfied by the coordinates of any point on either one of the lines

(7) $2x - 3y - 4 = 0,$

or

(8) $x + y - 2 = 0.$

Similarly, (6) is satisfied by solutions of either

(9) $3x - y + 1 = 0,$

or

(10) $2x - y - 3 = 0.$

Hence the problem reduces to the simultaneous solution of the following four pairs of linear equations: (7)–(9), (7)–(10), (8)–(9), and (8)–(10). We must be sure that each pair comprises a factor from (5) and also a factor from (6). The rest of the solution is left to the student.

Evidently the method of Example 1 could have been used if the left member of either (5) or (6) had been left in the unfactored form. Here the process is shortened.

Example 3. Solve simultaneously:

(11) $x^2 - xy = 3,$

(12) $4y^2 - 3xy = -2.$

Solution. This system does not come directly under the types illustrated in Examples 1 and 2. However, it can be reduced to such a type by first producing an equation from the given pair in which the constant term is zero. This new equation is then used to form a system which may be solved in the same manner as the above examples.

Both members of (11) and (12) are multiplied respectively by 2 and 3, resulting in the equations:

(13) $2x^2 - 2xy = 6,$

(14) $12y^2 - 9xy = -6.$

Adding corresponding members of (13) and (14), we obtain

(15) $2x^2 - 11xy + 12y^2 = 0.$

Since all common solutions of (11) and (12) must also satisfy (15), a new system can be established in which (15) is used as one of the equations, with either (11) or (12) as the other. The simpler of the two—in this case, (11)—should be given preference.

The left-hand member of (15) has the factors $2x - 3y$ and $x - 4y$, so that the new system becomes

(16) $x^2 - xy = 3,$

(17) $(2x - 3y)(x - 4y) = 0.$

This system presents no new difficulty, and by the method of Example 1 the solution set is found to be $\left\{(3,2), (-3, -2), \left(2, \tfrac{1}{2}\right), \left(-2, -\tfrac{1}{2}\right)\right\}.$

EXERCISE 13-4

Solve algebraically and obtain the solution set in Probs. 1–10. In Probs. 1–6, solve graphically also.

1. $x^2 + y^2 = 25$ 2. $x^2 - 4y = 0$
            $\wedge$ $\wedge$
   $(x - 3)(x + y + 1) = 0.$ $(x - y)(2x + 4y + 1) = 0.$

3. $x^2 - y^2 = 16$ 4. $x^2 - y^2 = 16$
            $\wedge$ $\wedge$
   $(3x - 5y)(y - 3) = 0.$ $(x - y - 2)(x - 2y + 1) = 0.$

5. $x^2 + y^2 = 25$ 6. $x^2 - y^2 = 16$
            $\wedge$ $\wedge$
   $(x - y)(x + y) = 0.$ $(x - y - 1)(x + y - 1) = 0.$

7. $x^2 + xy + 2y^2 = 1$ 8. $2x^2 + 2xy - y^2 = 2$
            $\wedge$ $\wedge$
   $(x - y)(x + y) = 0.$ $(2x - y)(x + y - 3) = 0.$

9. $3x^2 - xy - y^2 = 1$ 10. $x^2 - 2xy + 4y^2 = 1$
            $\wedge$ $\wedge$
   $(x + y - 2)(2x - y - 1) = 0.$ $(x - 2y)(x + 4y - 3) = 0.$

Factor both left members in Probs. 11–14, and then solve graphically. State the solution set in each case.

11. $2x^2 + xy - y^2 = 0$ 12. $6x^2 - 7xy - 3y^2 = 0$
            $\wedge$ $\wedge$
       $x^2 - 4y^2 = 0.$ $(2x - y)^2 - 4 = 0.$

13. $(x + y - 1)^2 - 9 = 0$ 14. $2x^2 + 5xy - 3y^2 = 0$
            $\wedge$ $\wedge$
     $(2x + y)^2 - 4 = 0.$ $(x + y)^2 - 1 = 0.$

Solve by the method of illustrative Example 3 and state the solution set in each of Probs. 15–18.

15. $x^2 - 3y^2 = -2$ 16. $3x^2 + xy = 5$
            $\wedge$ $\wedge$
     $xy + 2y^2 = 3.$ $x^2 + y^2 = 5.$

17. $2x^2 - 13xy + 2y^2 = -9$ 18. $2y^2 + 3xy - 4 = 0$
            $\wedge$ $\wedge$
     $x^2 + 3xy + y^2 - 5 = 0.$ $3x^2 + 2xy - 2 = 0.$

REVIEW EXERCISE—SIMULTANEOUS EQUATIONS

Draw the graph of each of the equations in Probs. 1–6.

1. $\{(x,y) \mid x^2 = 4y\}.$
2. $\{(x,y) \mid x^2 + y^2 = 4\}.$

3. $\{(x,y) \mid x^2 + 9y^2 = 4\}$.

4. $\{(x,y) \mid y^2 = 3x - 2\}$.

5. $\{(x,y) \mid xy = 6\}$.

6. $\{(x,y) \mid x^2 - xy - 6y^2 = 0\}$.

Determine by inspection the character of the graph of each of the equations in Probs. 7–11.

7. $x^2 + y^2 = 9$.   8. $x^2 - y^2 = 4$.   9. $x^2 = 4y$.

10. $xy = -8$.   11. $10y^2 + x^2 = 90$.

Solve each of the systems of equations in Probs. 12-21. Be careful to associate the x and y correctly in the ordered pairs constituting the solution set. Consider solutions only in an $R_e \times R_e$ space.

12. $x - y = 6$
      $\wedge$
      $x^2 + y^2 = 26$.

13. $x + y = 7$
      $\wedge$
      $x^2 - y^2 = 21$.

14. $x - 2y = -2$
      $\wedge$
      $xy + 3x = 10$.

15. $xy - 3x^2 = -30$
      $\wedge$
      $x + 4y = 1$.

16. $3y^2 + x^2 = 40$
      $\wedge$
      $\sqrt{3x} - y = 0$.

17. $x^2 + xy = 8$
      $\wedge$
      $3x^2 - xy = 56$.

18. $3xy + 2y^2 = 0$
      $\wedge$
      $5xy - 3y^2 = -57$.

19. $25x^2 + 4y^2 = 100$
      $\wedge$
      $x^2 + y^2 = 4$.

20. $\dfrac{1}{x^2} - \dfrac{1}{y^2} = 12$
      $\wedge$
      $\dfrac{1}{x} - \dfrac{1}{y} = -3$.

21. $\pi w^2 - \pi v^2 = 9\pi$
      $\wedge$
      $w - v = 3$.

22. The sum of two numbers is 5, the difference of their squares is -5, what are the numbers?

23. A rectangle has a perimeter of 44 feet and an area of 120 square feet. What are its dimensions?

24. Find two numbers whose sum multiplied by their difference is 44 and whose sum divided by their difference equals 11.

25. A rear wheel of a tricycle makes 110 more revolutions than the front wheel in going 1 mile, but if the circumference of each is increased by 4 feet, a rear wheel will make 66 more revolutions than the front wheel. Find the circumference of each wheel.

chapter 14

Absolute Values and Inequalities

14-1. INTRODUCTION

In the preceding chapters we have studied equations in which statements equating two algebraic expressions are made. However, it is possible to study situations wherein two expressions are not equal to one another, but one of them is either greater than or less than the other. The problem now is to find the conditions under which such defining conditions make mathematical sense. The procedures and techniques for doing this in many ways parallel those used in solving equations.

14-2. DEFINITIONS, ORDER POSTULATES, AND THEOREMS

The *order relation* between two real numbers is indicated either by the symbol "=" which of course implies equality, or by the symbol "<" which means "is less than," and the symbol ">" which means "is greater than." The concept of "is less than" between two real numbers has already been introduced in Sec. 2-5. To recall the meaning of this phrase, it is repeated here so that it can be used in the manner to be described.

A real number a "is less than" a real number b, written as $a < b$, if there exists a positive real number p such that $a + p = b$.

Accordingly, when we say that the real number a "is greater than" the real number b (symbolized $a > b$), it implies that b "is less than" a. In other words,

If a and b are real numbers, then $a > b$ if and only if $b < a$.

For example, $2 < 5$ because $2 + 3 = 5$, and $5 > 2$ because $2 < 5$.

A mathematical defining condition which involves any of the symbols, namely, $>, <, \geq, \leq$, called *order relations*, is an inequality. Two inequalities such as $a < b$ and $c < d$ are called *inequalities of the same order* or possessing the same sense, while the inequalities $a < b$ and $c > d$ are called *inequalities of opposite order* or possessing opposite sense.

Since all numbers to the right of zero on the real-number line are positive numbers, it follows that when one writes "$a > 0$" it is another way of saying "a is greater than zero," or that "a is a positive number." Similarly, "$a < 0$" is another way of saying "a is less than zero," or that "a is a negative number." Zero itself is neither positive nor negative, but may be referred to as a neutral number in R_e.

The basic properties dealing with the order relations are as follows.

If $a, b, c \in R_e$, then:

1. *For any two real numbers a and b exactly one and only one of the following is true (trichotomy property)*

$$a < b \quad or \quad a = b \quad or \quad a > b$$

2. *If $a < b$ and $b < c$, then $a < c$ (transitive property)*

3. *If $a < b$, then $a + c < b + c$ (addition of the same number to both sides of inequality does not change the sense of the inequality.)*

4. *If $a < b$ and $c > 0$, then $ac < bc$ (multiplication by a positive number does not change the sense of the inequality.)*

5. *If $a < b$ and $c < 0$, then $ac > bc$ (multiplication by a negative number changes the sense of the inequality.)*

6. *If $a > 0$ and $b > 0$, then $a + b > 0$ (the sum of two positive numbers is a positive number.)*

7. *If $a > 0$ and $b > 0$ then $ab > 0$ (the product of two positive numbers is a positive number.)*

Example. Use the definition of $a < b$ to illustrate the proof of 3:

If $a < b$, then $a + c < b + c$.

Proof. If $a < b$, then by definition $a + p = b$, from which it follows that $b + c = (a + p) + c = (a + c) + p$, where p is a positive number. Thus $(a + c) + p = b + c$, where p is a positive number, implies that $a + c < b + c$ in accord with the definition of "$<$."

Many theorems are logical consequences of the definition of order and the order properties. Some of these theorems are given herewith without proof.

THEOREM 1:   *If $a < b$ and $c < d$, then $a + c < b + d$.*

THEOREM 2:   *If $ab > 0$, then either both $a > 0$ and $b > 0$ or both $a < 0$ and $b < 0$.*

THEOREM 3:   *If $a < b$, then $-a > -b$.*

THEOREM 4:   *If a is a real number and $a < 0$, then $-a > 0$.*

Example.

(a) If $2 < 5$, then $2 + 4 < 5 + 4$ or $6 < 9$.

(b) If $2 < 5$, then $2(3) < 5(3)$ or $6 < 15$

$$2\left(\frac{1}{2}\right) < 5\left(\frac{1}{2}\right) \text{ or } 1 < \frac{5}{2}.$$

However, if $2 < 5$, then $2(-3) > 5(-3)$ or $-6 > -15$

$$2\left(-\frac{1}{2}\right) > 5\left(-\frac{1}{2}\right) \text{ or } -1 > -\frac{5}{2}$$

(c) If $2 < 5$ and $3 < 6$, then $2 + 3 < 5 + 6$ or $5 < 11$

(d) If $2 < 5$, then $-2 > -5$

(e) If $a = -2$, then since $a < 0$, $-a > 0$; or since $-2 < 0$, then $-(-2) > 0$, which is equivalent to saying $2 > 0$. This is so since every real number possesses a *unique* additive inverse. As a consequence, it follows that $-(-2)$ and 2 must represent the same additive inverse for -2. What does this actually imply? What is the additive inverse for $-[-(-a)]$?_____

14-3. INEQUALITIES ON THE NUMBER LINE; INTERVAL NOTATION

The graphical representation of the real number line is often an assist in dealing with the solution of inequalities. For example, the set $\{x \in R_e \,|\, x > 2\}$ is shown graphically in Fig. 14-1.

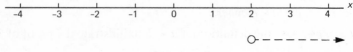

FIG. 14-1

The open circle below the number 2 indicates that 2 is excluded from the solution set; the solution set is indicated by the half-line starting at 2 and includes all number values greater than 2 as shown by the directed arrowhead of the lower line in Fig. 14-1.

The set $\{x \in R_e \,|\, x \leq 1\}$ is graphed as shown in Fig. 14-2.

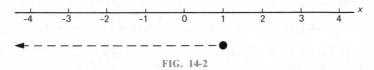

FIG. 14-2

The shaded-in circle on the lower line in Figure 14-2 below the number 1 indicates that 1 is to be included in the solution set, as well as all other real numbers to the left of 1, since x is less than or equal to 1.

The symbolic statement $x \leq a$ as pointed out in Sec. 2-5 means that either "x may be less than a or that x may equal a" and the statement $x \geq a$ means that either "x may be greater than a or that x may equal a."

Intersections and unions of inequalities can be conveniently handled by graphical methods. Since $a < b$ whenever $a < c$ and $c < b$ by use of the transitive-order property, the corresponding symbolic statements $a < x$ and $x < b$ may be expressed as the continued inequality $a < x < b$, which is read "x is between a and b."

In terms of set-notation symbolism, intersections and unions of inequalities as related to the real-number line may be represented as follows.

(1) $\{x \mid a < x\} \cap \{x \mid x < b\} = \{x \mid a < x \wedge x < b\} = \{x \mid a < x < b\}$

(2) $\{x \mid x > a\} \cap \{x \mid x > b\} = \{x \mid x > a\}$ if $a > b$

(3) $\{x \mid x < a\} \cap \{x \mid x < b\} = \{x \mid x < a\}$ if $a < b$

(4) $\{x \mid x < a\} \cup \{x \mid x > b\} = \{x \mid x < a \vee x > b\}$

The set-notation symbolism used in (1) to (4) is replaced by special set notation called "interval notation" which is associated *only* with the set of real numbers and the real-number line. When using this interval notation one must not confuse it with the "parentheses" as used in the concept of ordered pairs. The context and environment in which notation is used will dictate its meaning in any mathematical situation. The symbol $[a,b]$ where $a < b$, and $a, b \in R_e$ means an interval graphed on the real-number line which includes the end points a and b and all the other real numbers between a and b. This notation provides an alternative symbolism for the writing of the continued inequality $a \leq x \leq b$. When an end point is not included in the interval being designated, say b, we write $a \leq x < b$ or $[a,b)$.

Consequently,

$[a,b] = \{x \in R_e: x \in [a,b]\} \leftrightarrow a \leq x \leq b$

(Closed interval from a to b)

$[a,b) = \{x \in R_e: x \in [a,b)\} \leftrightarrow a \leq x < b$

(Half-open interval from a to b including a but excluding b)

$(a,b] = \{x \in R_e: x \in (a,b]\} \leftrightarrow a < x \leq b$

(Half-open interval from a to b including b but excluding a)

$(a,b) = \{x \in R_e: x \in (a,b)\} \leftrightarrow a < x < b$

(Open interval from a to b excluding both a and b)

The symbols $+\infty$ ("plus infinity"), $-\infty$ ("minus infinity") are not numbers but special symbols used to assist in describing certain features of interval notation. They are employed in the following manner.

The set $[0, +\infty)$ defines the set of all nonnegative real numbers, while $(-\infty, 0)$ defines the set of all negative real numbers. The set

$(-\infty, +\infty)$ symbolizes the set of all real numbers on the real-number line which is described as extending from $-\infty$ to $+\infty$. It is noted that $(-\infty, +\infty) = (-\infty, 0] \cup [0, +\infty)$. When $a = b$, the interval

$$[a,b] = [a,a] = \{a\}$$

corresponds to the singleton real number a on the real-number line. We note that $[a,b] \cup [b,b] = [a,b]$ and when $a = b$,

$$(a,b] = [a,b) = (a,b) = \phi.$$

Example 1.   Illustrate $\{x \mid -1 < x < 2\} = (-1,2)$ graphically.

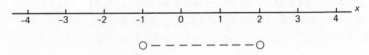

Example 2.   Illustrate $\{x \mid x < -1 \lor x \geq 2\} = (-\infty, -1) \cup [2, +\infty)$ graphically.

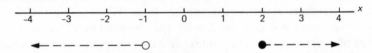

Example 3.   Since interval notation is a form of set notation, the operations of union and intersection may be used with real-number intervals. For example, we can replace a single interval $[2,7] \cap [-3,2]$ and $(-7,3) \cup [2,6)$. After examining either graphically or otherwise, it is possible to show that

$$[2,7] \cap [-3,2] = [2,2] = \{2\}$$

and

$$(-7,3) \cup [2,6) = (-7,6).$$

EXERCISE 14-1

1.   Which of the following statements are true?

(a) $-7 > 0.$ (b) $-7 > -9.$ (c) $\dfrac{3}{4} > \dfrac{2}{3}.$

(d) $-8 < -4.$ (e) $\dfrac{1}{3} < .3333.$ (f) $\pi > \dfrac{22}{7}.$

(g) $\sqrt{2} < 1.4142.$ (h) $\dfrac{1 - \sqrt{3}}{2} > -0.35.$

2. Insert the appropriate order symbol selected from $=$, $>$, $<$ which should be placed between each of the following pairs of numbers.

(a) $2, 3$.   (b) $0, 7$.   (c) $-0, -3$.
(d) $-6, 2$.   (e) $\sqrt{3}, 1.73$.   (f) $-\sqrt{11}, -\sqrt{15}$.

3. By use of interval notation, find the set defined by each of the following and represent same graphically.

(a) $[4,8] \cup [6,22]$.   (b) $[0,3) \cup [-7,1]$.   (c) $[-6,10) \cap (-16,2]$.
(d) $[6,9] \cap (2,7]$.   (e) $(-\infty,3) \cup (-1,4]$. (f) $[-7,3) \cup [-2,-2]$.
(g) $(-2,3) \cup [3,7) \cup [5,5]$.   (h) $(1,4) \cap [3,3]$.

4. Discuss the validity of each of the following statements.

(a) $[-5,2] \subset (-5,7)$.   (b) $3 \in [0,3]$.   (c) $-5 \in [0,+\infty)$.
(d) $(-\infty,0) \subset (-\infty,+\infty)$. (e) $[3,3] \subset [1,5]$.   (f) $3 \subset [1,5]$.
(g) $3 \in [1,5]$.

5. Rewrite the following by use of interval notation.

(a) $3 < x < 7$.   (b) $-3 \leq x \leq 8$.   (c) $-4 \leq x < -1$.
(d) $0 < x < 7$.   (e) $-1 \leq x < .6$.   (f) $-\infty < x < -2$.
(g) $\dfrac{1}{5} \leq x < +\infty$.

6. Show by a counterexample that the following are false. Let x, y, z, w, u, $v \in R_e$.

(a) If $x^2 > y^2$, then $x > y$. (*Hint:* Counterexample—let $x^2 = 25$, $y^2 = 9$. Use $x = -5, y = 3$.)
(b) If $x > y \wedge z > w$, then $zx > yw$.
(c) If $x + y > u + v$, then $x > u \wedge y > v$.
(d) If $x > y$, then $\dfrac{1}{x} > \dfrac{1}{y}$.
(e) If $x > y \wedge z > w$, then $x - z > y - w$. (*Hint:* Let $x = 2, y = 1$, $z = 3, w = 0$.)

7. Graph each of the following sets on the real-number line. Assume in all cases that $x \in R_e$.

(a) $\{x \mid -2 < x < 4\}$.
(b) $\{x \mid 0 < x \leq 5\}$.
(c) $\{x \mid x \in [-5,2) \vee x \in [-1,4)\}$.
(d) $\{x \mid x \in [0, +\infty) \vee x \in (-\infty,0]\}$.

14-4. SOLUTIONS OF INEQUALITIES

The solution set of an inequality is the set of replacement values for the variable (say x) which makes the inequality a true mathematical statement. *Two inequalities are said to be equivalent if and only if they possess the same solution set.* As is the case when solving equations, the given inequality leads to a sequence of equivalent ones from which eventually an inequality results whose solution set is either evident or is readily obtained. The various order properties and related theorems for inequalities provide the basic techniques for finding other equivalent inequalities from an initial one. To solve an inequality becomes similar to that of solving an equation with the important exception that multiplication (or division) by a negative number causes the order or sense of the inequality to change.

Inequalities are classified as being either *absolute, conditional*, or *impossible inequalities*. When an inequality is true for all real-number values of the variable (say x) it is called an *absolute inequality*; when it is true only for some real-number values of the variable but not for others, it is called a *conditional inequality*; and when it is not true for any real-number value of the variable it is called an *impossible inequality* (solution set is the null set ϕ).

Examples.

(a) $x + 1 > x$ is an absolute inequality, since its solution set is the set of all real numbers $R_e = (-\infty, +\infty)$.

(b) $x + 1 < 3$ is a conditional inequality, since its solution set is $\{x \mid x < 2\} = (-\infty, 2)$.

(c) $x - 2 > x$ which implies that $-2 > 0$ results in an impossible inequality. The solution set is the empty set ϕ.

14-5. LINEAR INEQUALITIES—ALGEBRAIC PROCEDURES

To obtain the *solution set* for a *linear inequality* by an *algebraic method*, the steps taken are essentially those used for solving a corresponding linear equation:

Step 1. Equal appropriate expressions are either added or subtracted to each member of the given inequality, so as to produce an equivalent inequality where the terms involving the variable are contained in the left-hand member and the constant terms are in the right-hand member.

Step 2. Combine all like terms in each member.

Step 3. Divide both members, of the resulting inequality obtained in Step 2, by the collected coefficient of the variable which is being considered as the unknown.

Example. Find the solution set of $\{x \in R_e \mid 3x + 1 < x - 5\}$.

Solution. $3x + 1 < x - 5$

By adding $-x$ (or equivalently subtracting x) to both members,

$$3x - x + 1 < -5$$

results as an equivalent inequality. Thus

$$2x + 1 < -5$$

By adding -1 to both members of this newly formed inequality

$$2x < -5 - 1$$

or

$$2x < -6$$

follows. After dividing both members by 2,

$$x < -3.$$

Hence the solution set is $\{x \mid x < -3\} = (-\infty, -3)$.

Example. Find the solution set of

$$\{x \mid 2 - x \leq 6 + 3x\}.$$

Solution.

$$
\begin{aligned}
2 - x &\leq 6 + 3x \\
2 - x - 3x &\leq 6 && \text{Adding } -3x \text{ to both members} \\
2 - 4x &\leq 6 \\
-4x &\leq -2 + 6 && \text{Adding } -2 \text{ to both members} \\
-4x &\leq 4 \\
x &\geq -1 && \text{Dividing both members by } -4
\end{aligned}
$$

Thus the solution set is $\{x \mid x \geq -1\} = [-1, +\infty)$.

The student should bear in mind that if the collected coefficient of the variable considered as the unknown is negative, the sense of the involved inequality must be reversed when both members are divided by this coefficient.

Example. $\dfrac{x}{x + 1} > 2$.

Solution. Since the inequality has the variable x involved in the denominator, $x + 1 \neq 0$. Thus $x \neq -1$. Here we consider the two cases, namely: where $x + 1 > 0$ and where $x + 1 < 0$. The solution set then becomes the union of the respective solution sets for these two cases.

Case 1. Suppose $x + 1 > 0$; then $x > -1$. Since $x + 1 > 0$, multiplication of both members by $x + 1$ does not change the order. Thus

$$x > 2x + 2 \land x > -1$$

or

$$-x > 2 \quad \land \quad x > -1$$

or

$$x < -2 \quad \land \quad x > -1$$

which is inconsistent, since x cannot be less than -2 and at the same time be greater than -1. Solution set for Case 1 is

$$\{x \mid x > -1 \land x < -2\} = \phi.$$

Case 2. Suppose $x + 1 < 0$; then $x < -1$. Since $x + 1 < 0$, multiplication of both members by $x + 1$ does change the order. Thus

$$x < 2x + 2 \land x < -1$$

or

$$-x < 2 \quad \land \quad x < -1$$

or

$$x > -2 \quad \land \quad x < -1.$$

The solution set for Case 2 is

$$\{x \mid x < -1 \land x > -2\} = \{x \mid -2 < x < -1\} = (-2,-1).$$

The union of the respective solution sets for the two cases is

$$\{x \mid -2 < x < -1\} \cup \phi = \{x \mid -2 < x < -1\} = (-2,-1).$$

Alternate solution. An alternate procedure involves a technique discussed in Sec. 14-6. Since $(x + 1)^2$ is positive for all real values of $x \neq -1$, $\dfrac{x}{x + 1} > 2$ becomes $x(x + 1) > 2(x + 1)^2$ upon multiplication by $(x + 1)^2$. From this equivalent inequality follows

$$x^2 + x > 2x^2 + 4x + 2$$

or

$$x^2 + 3x + 2 < 0$$

or

$$(x + 2)(x + 1) < 0,$$

which is readily solvable by the procedure explained in Sec. 14-6. We leave the problem here for the student to confirm the interval solution set $(-2,-1)$ after he has become acquainted with the methods used in the illustrative examples of Sec. 14-6.

EXERCISE 14-2

Assume that the domain for the variable x in the inequality is always $R_e = (-\infty, +\infty)$ unless otherwise specified. Obtain the solution set for Probs. 1–8. In each case represent the result in the interval notation where convenient.

1. $3x + 5 > 12$.

2. $6 > x + 3$.

3. $4 \le x + 1$.

4. $2x - 5 \ge 3x + 7$.

5. $\dfrac{3x - 1}{x} > -1$.

6. $\dfrac{2x}{x - 4} < 5$.

7. $(3x - 1)^2 + x > 9x^2 - 2$.

8. $\dfrac{2}{x - 1} + 3 > -2$.

9. Solve by finding the solution set for $5x \ge -3 + 2x$ if the domain of the variable x is $\{-3, -2, -1, 0, 1\}$.

10. Solve by finding the solution set for $7 + x > 3$ if the domain of the variable x is the set of integers.

11. Obtain the solution set for $\{x \in I^+ \mid 3x - 5 \le 2x - (3 - 4x)\}$.   Here I^+ = set of positive integers.

12. Obtain the solution set for $\left\{ x \in R_e \left| \dfrac{2x - 1}{3x} + \dfrac{2}{x} \ge 4 \right. \right\}$.

14-6. NONLINEAR INEQUALITIES

To obtain the solution set for nonlinear inequalities, use is made of the following theorems. Let $a, b \in R_e$. Then

1.   If $ab > 0$, then both $a > 0$ and $b > 0$, or both $a < 0$ and $b < 0$.

2.   If $ab < 0$, then either $a < 0$ and $b > 0$; or $a > 0$ and $b < 0$.

Example 1.   Find the solution set of $2x^2 < 2 - 3x$.

Solution.

$$2x^2 < 2 - 3x$$

becomes

$$2x^2 + 3x - 2 < 0$$

after adding $-2 + 3x$ to both members. Thus

$$(2x - 1)(x + 2) < 0.$$

The following cases occur:

   Case 1. $2x - 1 > 0$ and $x + 2 < 0$

   Case 2. $2x - 1 < 0$ and $x + 2 > 0$.

In set notation, the solution set is

$$\{x \mid 2x - 1 > 0 \wedge x + 2 < 0\} \cup \{x \mid 2x - 1 < 0 \wedge x + 2 > 0\}.$$

Case 1.   If $2x - 1 > 0$, then $x > \dfrac{1}{2}$

$$\wedge$$

If $x + 2 < 0$, then $x < -2$.

Case 2.   If $2x - 1 < 0$, then $x < \dfrac{1}{2}$

$$\wedge$$

If $x + 2 > 0$, then $x > -2$.

Continuation of Case 1.

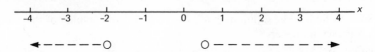

x cannot be greater than $\dfrac{1}{2}$ and less than -2 at the same time and

$$\{x \mid 2x - 1 > 0\} \cap \{x \mid x + 2 < 0\} = \phi.$$

Continuation of Case 2.

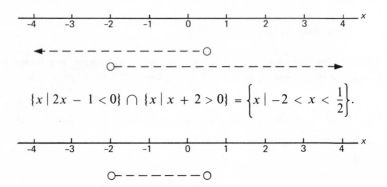

$$\{x \mid 2x - 1 < 0\} \cap \{x \mid x + 2 > 0\} = \left\{x \mid -2 < x < \dfrac{1}{2}\right\}.$$

Thus the solution set is

$$\left\{x \mid -2 < x < \dfrac{1}{2}\right\} \cup \phi = \left\{x \mid -2 < x < \dfrac{1}{2}\right\} = \left(-2, \dfrac{1}{2}\right).$$

Example 2.   Find the solution set of $(x + 1)(x + 2) > 0$.

Solution.   The following cases occur:

Case 1. $x + 1 > 0$ and $x + 2 > 0$

Case 2. $x + 1 < 0$ and $x + 2 < 0$.

The solution set will be, in set notation,

$$\{x \mid x + 1 > 0 \land x + 2 > 0\} \cup \{x \mid x + 1 < 0 \land x + 2 < 0\}.$$

Case 1. If $x + 1 > 0, x > -1$
If $x + 2 > 0, x > -2.$

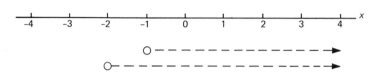

Then

$$\{x \mid x + 1 > 0 \land x + 2 > 0\} = \{x \mid x > -1\} = (-1, +\infty).$$

Case 2. If $x + 1 < 0, x < -1$
If $x + 2 < 0, x < -2.$

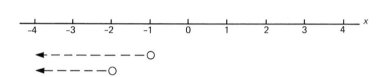

Then

$$\{x \mid x + 1 < 0 \land x + 2 < 0\} = \{x \mid x < -2\} = (-\infty, -2).$$

Thus the solution set is $\{x \mid x > -1\} \cup \{x \mid x < -2\}$ or in interval notation may be represented as $(-\infty, -2) \cup (-1, +\infty)$. The solution set could
also be stated as $x < -2$ *or* $x > -1.$

Example 3. Find the solution set for $\dfrac{x}{2x - 1} > 3.$

Solution. Here $2x - 1 \neq 0$ or $x \neq \dfrac{1}{2}$. Since $(2x - 1)^2$ is positive
for all $x \in R$, it follows that

$$x(2x - 1) > 3(2x - 1)^2$$

or

$$x(2x - 1) - 3(2x - 1)^2 > 0.$$

Thus

$$(2x - 1)[x - 3(2x - 1)] > 0$$

or

$$(2x - 1)(3 - 5x) > 0$$

Case 1. $2x - 1 > 0 \land 3 - 5x > 0$

or

$$x > \frac{1}{2} \land x < \frac{3}{5}$$

Solution set in interval notation is $\left(\frac{1}{2}, \frac{3}{5}\right)$.

Case 2. $2x - 1 < 0 \land 3 - 5x < 0$

or

$$x < \frac{1}{2} \land x > \frac{3}{5}$$

which is impossible. Thus the solution set for this case is ϕ. The solution set of $\dfrac{x}{2x - 1} > 3$ is given by

$$\left\{ x \mid \frac{1}{2} < x < \frac{3}{5} \right\} = \left(\frac{1}{2}, \frac{3}{5}\right).$$

EXERCISE 14-3

Obtain the solution set for Probs. 1 to 10. Wherever possible use the real number line to help verify the results obtained by algebraic methods. State the solution set by use of interval notation where convenient.

1. $\{x \in R_e \mid x^2 - 2x - 3 < 0\}$.

2. $\{x \in R_e \mid \dfrac{2x - 1}{3x} \geq -4\}$. (*Hint:*   Multiply both sides by $3x^2 > 0$.)

3. $\{x \in R_e \mid x^2 - 16 > 0\}$.

4. $\{x \in R_e \mid x^2 + 25 > 0\}$.

5. $\{x \in R_e \mid x^2 + 36 < 0\}$.

6. $\{x \in R_e \mid x^2 + 9 \geq 0\}$.

7. $\{x \in R_e \mid \dfrac{x - 3}{x + 2} > 0\}$.

8. $\{x \in R_e \mid (3x + 1)(2x - 1) < 0\}$.

9. $\{x \in R_e \mid (3x - 1)(2x + 1) < 0\}$.

10. $\{x \in R_e \mid (3x - 1)(1 - 2x) < 0\}$.

If $A = \{0,1,2,3,4,5\}$, obtain the solution set for Probs. 11–15.

11. $\{x \in A \mid 3x < 4\}$.

12. $\{x \in A \mid x^2 - 2x - 3 < 0\}$.

13. $\{x \in A \mid x(x - 2) \le 3(x - 2)\}$.

14. $\left\{ x \in A \mid \dfrac{3}{x - 2} < \dfrac{x}{x + 3} \right\}$.

15. $\left\{ x \in A \mid \dfrac{x}{2} - 5 + \dfrac{3x - 1}{3} > 0 \right\}$.

In Probs. 16–21 indicate whether the conditions specified are consistent or otherwise. If consistent replace by a simpler defining condition.

16. $(-1 < x \le 3) \wedge \left(\dfrac{1}{2} \le x < 1 \right)$.

17. $(-2 < x < -1) \wedge (0 < x < +\infty)$.

18. $x \ge 1 \wedge x < -3$.

19. (a) $[2,5] \cup [4,6)$.

   (b) $[2,5] \cap [4,6)$.

20. $\left(-\dfrac{1}{3} \le x \le \dfrac{1}{2} \right) \vee \left(-3 \le x \le -\dfrac{1}{4} \right)$.

21. $\left(-\dfrac{1}{3} \le x \le \dfrac{1}{2} \right) \wedge \left(-3 \le x \le -\dfrac{1}{4} \right)$.

In Probs. 22–25, find all the values of x for which the given expression is a real number.

22. $\sqrt{4x - 2}$. (*Hint:* $4x - 2 \ge 0$.)

23. $\sqrt{x^2 - 5x + 4}$.

24. $\sqrt{16 - x^2}$.

25. $\sqrt{x^2 + 2x + 1}$.

14-7. SOLVING INEQUALITIES BY GRAPHICAL METHODS

The real-number line has been used in the preceding sections to ver-ify solution sets for inequalities that were also solved by algebraic procedures. Variations of the graphical approach for solving inequalities where two variables play an important role will now be studied.

The graph of the linear equation $y = ax + b$ divides the xy-plane into three distinct regions, namely (see Fig. 14-3)

(a) $y = ax + b$
(b) $y < ax + b$
(c) $y > ax + b.$

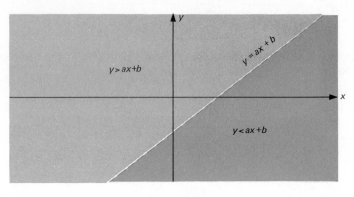

FIG. 14-3

The straight line is the graph of $y = ax + b$. The region on one side of the line $y = ax + b$ represents all points satisfying $\{(x, y) \mid y > ax + b\}$, while the region on the other side of the line represents all points satisfying $\{(x, y) \mid y < ax + b\}$.

To graph an inequality of the form $y < ax + b$ or $y > ax + b$, first graph the equality $y = ax + b$ and then from it obtain the desired region.

To select the desired region, it is only necessary to select any arbitrary ordered pair (r, s) and upon substituting r for x and s for y, make a comparison between the resulting values obtained from y and $ax + b$. This means that we compare the value s with $ar + b$. It will either show that $s = ar + b$, or $s > ar + b$, or $s < ar + b$. If $s > ar + b$, then all points on the same side of the line $y = ax + b$ as (r, s) was will maintain the same sense of the inequality. If $s < ar + b$, then accordingly all points on the same side of the line as the (r, s) will retain this sense of the equality. If the (r, s) chosen makes $s = ar + b$, then the (r, s) is on the line and some other ordered pair should be chosen to distinguish "> and < regions" for the graphical representation of y versus $ax + b$. For example, if $(2, -1)$ is used to check the situation for the line $3x - 2y = 7$, then upon replacing x and y respectively by 2 and -1, the inequality $8 > 7$ is obtained. This indicates that all points on the same side of the line

$3x - 2y = 7, \left(y = \dfrac{3x - 7}{2}\right)$ as $(2, -1)$ will retain the sense of $3x - 2y > 7$ $\left(\text{or } y < \dfrac{3x - 7}{2}\right)$.

Example. Find the solution set of $y \le 2x - 4$ by graphical methods.

Solution. First graph the equation $y = 2x - 4$. We graph a solid line to indicate that the points of this line are included in the solution set. Had the statement been $y < 2x - 4$, the procedure would be exactly the same except that a dotted or broken line would indicate that $y = 2x - 4$ is the boundary of the region of points in the solution *and* that no points of the solution are on this line. The region indicated in Fig. 14-4 represents

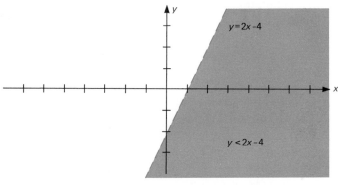

FIG. 14-4

the points $\{(x,y) \mid y \le 2x - 4\}$, since upon substituting the ordered pair $(6, -1)$ for y and $2x - 4$, the inequality $-1 < 8$ results. The solution set is represented by the line and the shaded region and is described by the set

$$\{(x,y) \mid y \le 2x - 4\}.$$

Example. By graphical procedures find the solution set for the quadratic inequality $x^2 - 5x < -6$. Write the result in interval notation.

Solution. If 6 is added to both members of the inequality the equivalent inequality $x^2 - 5x + 6 < 0$ is produced. If the left-hand member of the inequality is now set equal to y [or $f(x)$], the defining condition of a quadratic function is obtained, namely

$$f = \{(x,y) \mid y = f(x) = x^2 - 5x + 6\}.$$

The object now is to seek the values of x by graphical means which will show where $y < 0$. The graph of f is shown in Fig. 14-5. It is a parabola and crosses the x-axis at the points whose abscissas are 2 and 3, respectively. Obviously the graph lies below the x-axis ($y < 0$) for all values of x greater than 2 and less than 3. Hence the solution set is

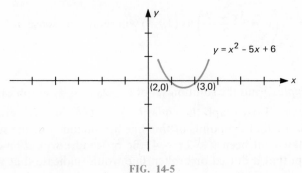

FIG. 14-5

$$\{x \mid 2 < x < 3\} = (2,3)$$

by use of interval notation.

In summary, the procedure for obtaining the solution set of an inequality by use of a graphical method is:

Step 1. Add the appropriate expression to each member of the given inequality so as to obtain an equivalent one in which the right member is zero.

Step 2. The right member of the resulting inequality is now set equal to y.

Step 3. Sketch the graph of the function created by the defining condition given through the equation obtained in Step 2.

Step 4. The solution set consists of *the set of values of x for which the graph is above the x-axis if the expression obtained in Step 1 is greater than zero;* or *the set of values of x for which the graph is below the x-axis if the expression in Step 1 is less than zero.*

EXERCISE 14-4

Consider the sets (assume $a \neq 0$):

$$S_1 = \{(x,y) \mid y = ax + b\}$$
$$S_2 = \{(x,y) \mid y > ax + b\}$$
$$S_3 = \{(x,y) \mid y < ax + b\}$$
$$S_4 = \{(x,y) \mid y = ax^2 + bx + c\}$$
$$S_5 = \{(x,y) \mid y > ax^2 + bx + c\}$$
$$S_6 = \{(x,y) \mid y < ax^2 + bx + c\}$$

Graph each of the sets $S_1, S_2, S_3, \ldots, S_6$ if $(x,y) \in R_e \times R_e$ and the values for a, b, c are designated as they appear in the accompanying table. In each of the Probs. 1–4, place S_1, S_2, S_3 accurately in the same graphical representation. Do likewise for S_4, S_5, S_6 in Probs. 5–8.

	a	b	Defining Condition for S_1	Defining Condition for S_2	Defining Condition for S_3
1.	1	2	$y = x + 2$	$y > x + 2$	$y < x + 2$
2.	1	-2			
3.	3	0			
4.	-2	-3			

	a	b	c	Defining Condition for S_4	Defining Condition for S_5	Defining Condition for S_6
5.	1	-3	-2	$y = x^2 - 3x - 2$	$y > x^2 - 3x - 2$	$y < x^2 - 3x - 2$
6.	1	3	2			
7.	3	2	-1			
8.	3	2	1			

9. Graph each of the following sets where $(x,y) \in R_e \times R_e$.

   · (a) $\{(x,y) \mid x + y > 3\}$.   (b) $\left\{(x,y) \mid y < \dfrac{2x - 1}{3}\right\}$.

   (c) $\{(x,y) \mid x < -2\}$.   (d) $\{(x,y) \mid y < 0\}$.

   (e) $\{(x,y) \mid y > -4\}$.

10. Graph each of the following sets where $(x,y) \in R_e \times R_e$.

   (a) $\{(x,y) \mid y > x^2\}$.   (b) $\{(x,y) \mid y < x^2\}$.

   (c) $\{(x,y) \mid y < -x^2\}$.   (d) $\{(x,y) \mid y \leq x^2\}$.

   (e) $\{(x,y) \mid y \leq -x^2\}$.

11. Solve by graphical procedures.

   (a) $\left\{x \in R_e \mid \dfrac{2x - 1}{x} > 3\right\}$.   *Hint:* First multiply by x^2 and obtain $2x^2 - x > 3x^2$. Then put $y = x^2 + x$. Sketch the set $\{(x,y) \mid y = x^2 + x\}$ etc.

   (b) $\left\{x \in R_e \mid \dfrac{x}{2x - 1} > 3\right\}$

   (c) $\{x \in R_e \mid 3x(x - 1) > 4\}$

   (d) $\left\{x \in R_e \mid \dfrac{2x}{x - 1} + \dfrac{3}{2} \leq -2\right\}$

14-8 ABSOLUTE-VALUE EQUATIONS AND INEQUALITIES

As previously pointed out in Sec. 2-5, the absolute value of $x \in R_e$ is denoted by

$$|x| = x \text{ if } x > 0$$
$$|x| = -x \text{ if } x < 0$$
$$|x| = 0 \text{ if } x = 0.$$

Therefore, we repeat for emphasis that the absolute value of a positive number or zero is equal to the number itself. The absolute value of a negative number is its additive inverse. For example, $|5| = 5$, $|-3| = 3$, $|7 - 11| = |-4| = -(-4) = 4$. The absolute value of a number is either positive or zero; in other words, it is a nonnegative number.

Graphically, the absolute value of a number x is its undirected distance (which is always a nonnegative number) from 0 on the real number line. In general, $|a - b|$ may be regarded as the undirected distance between a and b.

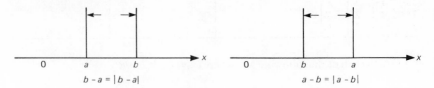

If $P(x)$ is a polynomial in the variable x such as $ax + b$ or $ax^2 + bx + c$ where $x \in R_e$ and k is a nonnegative real number, then the solution set of $|P(x)| = k$ is the union of the solution sets of $P(x) = k$ and $-P(x) = k$.

Example 1. Find the solution set of the absolute value equation

$$|2x + 1| = 3.$$

Solution: Case 1. Suppose $2x + 1 \geq 0$, then $|2x + 1| = 2x + 1$ and the original equation can be written as

$$2x + 1 = 3 \wedge x \geq -\frac{1}{2}$$

which has the solution $x = 1$. Hence the solution set for Case 1 is

$$\left\{x \mid x \geq -\frac{1}{2}\right\} \cap \{x \mid x = 1\} = \{x \mid x = 1\}.$$

Case 2. Suppose $2x + 1 < 0$, then $|2x + 1| = -(2x + 1)$ and the original equation takes the form

$$-(2x + 1) = 3 \wedge x < -\frac{1}{2}$$

which has the solution $x = -2$. Hence the solution set for Case 2 is

$$\left\{x \mid x < -\frac{1}{2}\right\} \cap \{x \mid x = -2\} = \{x \mid x = -2\}.$$

Therefore the solution set is

$$\{x \mid x = 1\} \cup \{x \mid x = -2\} = \{1, -2\}.$$

Example 2. Solve $|x - 2| < 4$.

Solution: Case 1. Suppose $x - 2 \geq 0$, then $|x - 2| = x - 2$ and the inequality becomes $x - 2 < 4 \wedge x \geq 2$ or $x < 6 \wedge x \geq 2$. The solution set for Case 1 is

$$\{x \mid x \geq 2\} \cap \{x \mid x < 6\} = \{x \mid 2 \leq x < 6\}.$$

Case 2. Suppose $x - 2 < 0$, then $|x - 2| = -(x - 2)$ and the inequality becomes $-(x - 2) < 4 \wedge x < 2$ or $x > -2 \wedge x < 2$. The solution set for Case 2 is

$$\{x \mid x < 2\} \cap \{x \mid x > -2\} = \{x \mid -2 < x < 2\}.$$

Therefore the solution set is

$$\{x \mid 2 \leq x < 6\} \cup \{x \mid -2 < x < 2\} = \{x \mid -2 < x < 6\}.$$

A graphical representation of the various solution sets by use of the real-number line will aid the student in his search for the solution set of the *original absolute-value inequality*. Thus the solution set for Case 1, where $x \geq 2 \wedge x < 6$, is shown in the sequence of graphical representations in Figs. 14-6 and 14-7.

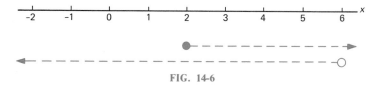

FIG. 14-6

The intersection of these two sets, namely $2 \leq x < 6$ is

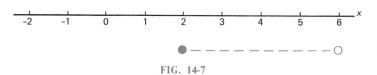

FIG. 14-7

For Case 2, where $x < 2 \wedge x > -2$ the solution set is shown in the sequence of graphical representations in Figs. 14-8 and 14-9.

FIG. 14-8

The intersection of these two sets, namely, $-2 < x < 2$, is

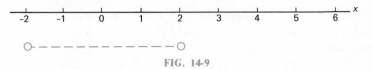

FIG. 14-9

The solution set for the original absolute value inequality $-2 < x < 6$ now follows as the union of the sets found in Cases 1 and 2 and is herewith represented graphically in Fig. 14-10.

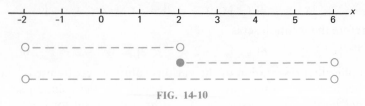

FIG. 14-10

14-9.   GRAPHS OF ABSOLUTE-VALUE FUNCTIONS AND RELATIONS

In order to graph an absolute-value function or relation, it is necessary to set up the different cases which arise when the definition of absolute value is interpreted and then to treat these situations separately.

Example. Graph $f = \{(x,y) \mid y = \mid x - 1 \mid \}$.

Solution: Case 1. Suppose $x - 1 \geq 0$, then $\mid x - 1 \mid = x - 1$ and the equation can be written

$$y = x - 1 \wedge x \geq 1.$$

Case 2. Suppose $x - 1 < 0$, then $\mid x - 1 \mid = -(x - 1)$ and the equation can be written

$$y = -(x - 1)$$

FIG. 14-11

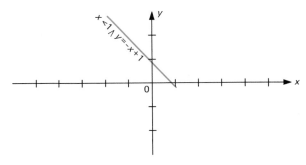

FIG. 14-12

or

$$y = -x + 1 \wedge x \leq 1.$$

The graph of the function f is a union of the two graphs for Cases 1 and 2 on the same set of axes. The graph of $\{(x,y) \mid y = x - 1 \wedge x \geq 1\}$ is represented in Fig. 14-11, while the graph for $\{(x,y) \mid y = 1 - x \wedge x < 1\}$ is represented in Fig. 14-12 and the graph of $f = \{(x,y) \mid y = |x - 1|\}$ is shown in Fig. 14-13.

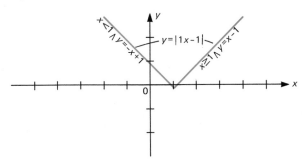

FIG. 14-13

Example. Graph the relation given by $f = \{(x,y) \mid |x| + |y| = 2\}$.

Solution. There are four cases to be considered in this example.

Case 1. Suppose $x \geq 0$ and $y \geq 0$. Then the equation can be written as

$$x + y = 2 \wedge x \geq 0 \wedge y \geq 0$$

which is the graph of the line $x + y = 2$ in the first quadrant as shown in Fig. 14-14.

Case 2. Suppose $x \leq 0$ and $y > 0$. Then the equation can be written

$$-x + y = 2 \wedge x \leq 0 \wedge y > 0,$$

which is the graph of the line $-x + y = 2$ in the second quadrant as shown in Fig. 14-15.

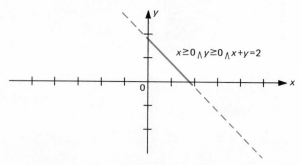

FIG. 14-14

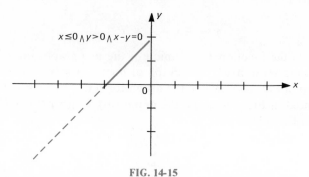

FIG. 14-15

Case 3. Suppose $x < 0$ and $y < 0$. Then the equation can be written

$$-x - y = 2 \wedge x < 0 \wedge y < 0,$$

which is the graph of the line $-x - y = 2$ in the third quadrant. The open circled points would be excluded. Its graphical representation is shown in Fig. 14-16.

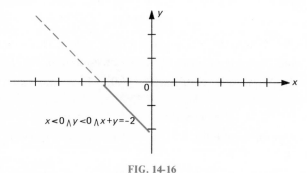

FIG. 14-16

Case 4. Suppose $x \geq 0$ and $y < 0$. Then the equation can be written

$$x - y = 2 \wedge x \geq 0 \wedge y < 0,$$

which is the graph of the line $x - y = 2$ in the fourth quadrant with the open circled point lacking as shown in Fig. 14-17.

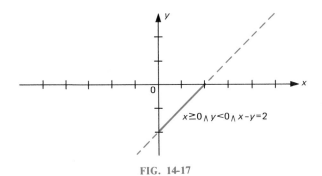

FIG. 14-17

Combining all four cases, the graph of f is as shown in Fig. 14-18.

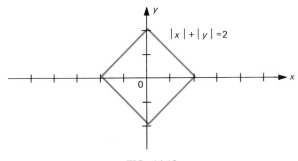

FIG. 14-18

The student should be able to explain why f is a relation and not a function, but may be considered as a union of four distinct functions.

EXERCISE 14-5

If $x \in R_e$, find the solution set in Probs. 1–9.

1. $|5x + 1| = 3.$

2. $|2x - 1| = 4x + 3.$

3. $|3x + 1| = -1$

4. $|x - 2| < 3.$

5. $\left|\dfrac{3 - x}{2 + x}\right| < 2.$ (*Hint:* $-2 < \dfrac{3 - x}{2 + x} < 2$ which resolves itself into

$\dfrac{3 - x}{2 + x} > -2 \wedge \dfrac{3 - x}{2 + x} < 2$, etc.)

6. $|3x + 2| > 5$

7. $|6 - 2x| \geq 7.$

8. $\left|\dfrac{6 - 5x}{3 + x}\right| \leq \dfrac{1}{2}.$

9. $\left| \dfrac{x + 2}{2x - 3} \right| < 4.$

Graph the equations in Probs. 10–15 where $(x, y) \in R_e \times R_e$.

10. $A = \{(x, y) \mid |x| + y = 1\}$
11. $A = \{(x, y) \mid |x| + |y| = 1\}$
12. $A = \{(x, y) \mid y = |x - 3|\}$
13. $A = \{(x, y) \mid y = 3 - |x|\}$
14. $A = \{(x, y) \mid x + |x| = y\}$
15. $A = \{(x, y) \mid |x| - |y| = 1\}$

14-10.   SIMULTANEOUS LINEAR INEQUALITIES IN TWO VARIABLES

A set of two or more inequalities arising from the forms $ax + by + c > 0$ or $ax + by + c < 0$ where $a, b, c \in R_e$ is called a *system of linear inequalities in two variables.* Since the graph of a linear inequality consists of all points in a half-plane, the graph of the simultaneous system of inequalities will be the intersection of the half-planes corresponding to each of the inequalities.

For example, let us consider the simultaneous system of inequalities

$$\begin{cases} x + y - 2 < 0 \\ \quad \wedge \\ x - y + 1 < 0 \\ \quad \wedge \\ x > -3 \end{cases}$$

for which is obtained the equivalent system

$$\begin{cases} y < 2 - x \\ \quad \wedge \\ y > x + 1 \\ \quad \wedge \\ x > -3. \end{cases}$$

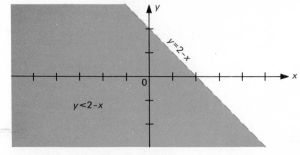

FIG. 14-19

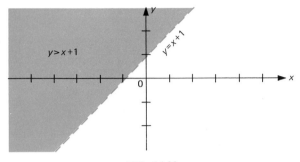

FIG. 14-20

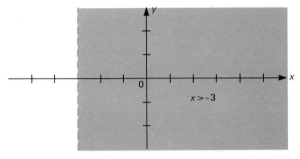

FIG. 14-21

The graphs of the three inequalities are shown by the shaded regions in Figs. 14-19, 14-20, and 14-21.

To obtain the graphical solution for the simultaneous system, we

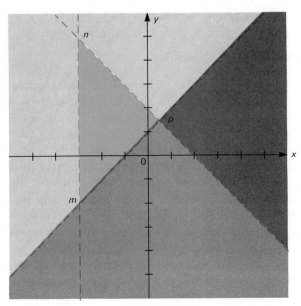

FIG. 14-22

sketch the graphs of the three inequalities on the same set of coordinate axes.

The graph of the system consists of all points of the plane that are located within the triangle with vertices M, N, and P. Since the solution set has infinitely many elements, a very effective means of representing it algebraically is to use set notation. The solution set is

$$\{(x, y) \mid y < 2 - x \wedge y > x + 1 \wedge x > -3\}.$$

Note that this example shows that the graphical solution is more meaningful than the algebraic solution.

Remember that when an inequality involves the equality sign $(=)$ as well as $>$ or $<$, such as $y \leq ax + b$ does, a heavy line is graphed for $y = ax + b$, otherwise a broken or dotted line is indicated as shown in Figs. 14-19–14-22.

EXERCISE 14-6

Given the sets $A = \{(x,y) \mid x + y = 6\}$, $B = \{(x,y) \mid 3x - 2y + 12 = 0\}$, and $C = \{(x,y) \mid y + 4 = 0\}$, interpret each set in Probs. 1–6 graphically by shading the corresponding region. It is understood that $(x,y) \in R_e \times R_e$.

1. $F = \{(x,y) \mid x + y \leq 6) \wedge x \geq 0 \wedge y \geq 0\}$
2. $G = \{(x,y) \mid y \in [-4,0]\}$
3. $H = \{(x,y) \mid 3x - 2y + 12 \geq 0 \wedge x \leq 0 \wedge y \geq 0\}$
4. $J = \{(x,y) \mid 3x - 2y + 12 \geq 0 \ \wedge x + y \leq 6 \wedge y \in [-4,0]\}$
5. $K = \{(x,y) \mid 3x - 2y + 12 \geq 0 \ \wedge x + y \geq 6 \wedge y \geq 0\}$
6. $L = \{(x,y) \mid y + 4 \leq 0 \wedge 3x - 2y + 12 > 0 \wedge x + y \leq 3\}$

14-11. LINEAR PROGRAMMING

Linear programming is an application of mathematics that is concerned with finding a solution set of a simultaneous system of inequalities in two or more variables which will maximize (or minimize) a specified function of the variable. The geometric technique (for the case of two variables) consists in graphing the solution sets of the inequalities of the simultaneous system and finding their intersection set. If this intersection set produces a set of points within some closed geometric figure bounded by straight lines, called a *polygon*, it provides a means for obtaining a maximum or minimum value of the given specified function. *It is stated here without proof that the maximum or minimum of this specified function will occur at one of the vertices of the polygon, if it exists.*

The ideas expressed above can perhaps best be appreciated by considering an illustration.

Example 1. Fine the maximum and minimum value of a specified function determined by $f = x - 2y + 4$, where we are working in an $R_e \times R_e$ space, which must satisfy the given simultaneous system of inequalities, namely,

$$x + y \leq 4$$
$$\wedge$$
$$x + 2y \geq -2$$
$$\wedge$$
$$x - y \geq -2$$
$$\wedge$$
$$x \leq 3$$

Solution. Graph $x + y = 4$, $x + 2y = -2$, $x - y = -2$, and $x = 3$, and shade the region as dictated by the system of inequalities. The indicated polygon is illustrated by the quadrilateral $ABCD$ in Fig. 14-23.

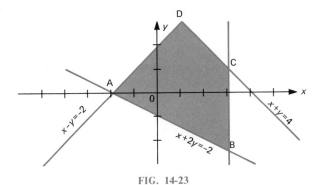

FIG. 14-23

Find the points of intersection of the appropriate pair of bounding lines involved at each of the vertices A, B, C, and D. For example, to find the vertex A, solve simultaneously $x - y = -2$ and $x + 2y = -2$:

$$\begin{cases} x - y = -2 \\ x + 2y = -2. \end{cases}$$

By subtraction (to eliminate the x variable)

$$-3y = 0$$
$$y = 0.$$

Then

$$x - 0 = -2$$
$$x = -2$$

Hence the point A is $(-2,0)$. Similarly $B = \left(3, -\dfrac{5}{2}\right)$, $C = (3,1)$ and $D = (1,3)$.

We now evaluate $f = x - 2y + 4$ at each of the vertices:

At $A, f = -2 - 2(0) + 4 = 2$

At $B, f = 3 - 2\left(-\dfrac{5}{2}\right) + 4 = 12$

At $C, f = 3 - 2(1) + 4 = 5$

At $D, f = 1 - 2(3) + 4 = -1$.

Thus the maximum of $f = x - 2y + 4$ over the region indicated by the system of inequalities is 12 and occurs at B, while the minimum is -1 and occurs at D.

Example 2. The ABC Textbook Company manufactures both hard-cover and paperback books. They have two assembly lines for the books. On one line, it takes 3 minutes for each hard-cover book to be produced and 1 minute for each paperback. On the second line, a hard-cover book and a paperback book require 1 minute each. The first production line works 40 hours each week, but the second line works only $26\dfrac{2}{3}$ hours each week. The profit expected on a hard-cover book is 5 cents and on a paper-back book, 1 cent. Assuming that the company can sell all of each type of book that it produces, how many books of each kind should be printed to maximize profit?

Solution. Let

$$x = \text{number of hard-cover books}$$
$$y = \text{number of paperback books.}$$

Each type to be produced must be a nonnegative number; thus $x \geq 0$ and $y \geq 0$. For the first assembly line, the total time for hard-cover books is $3x$ minutes, and for paperback books is y minutes. The sum $3x + y$ cannot exceed 40 hours (or 2,400 minutes) per week. Thus

$$3x + y \leq 2400.$$

For the second assembly line,

$$x + y \leq 1600. \qquad \left(26\dfrac{2}{3} \text{ hours} = 1600 \text{ minutes}\right)$$

The profit expected is given by

$$f = 5x + y \qquad \text{(in cents)}$$

and this is to be maximized.

The problem can now be expressed as follows: Maximize $f = 5x + y$

over the simultaneous system of inequalities

$$x \geq 0$$
$$\wedge$$
$$y \geq 0$$
$$\wedge$$
$$3x + y \leq 2400$$
$$\wedge$$
$$x + y \leq 1600.$$

Graph $x = 0$, $y = 0$, $3x + y = 2400$, and $x + y = 1600$ and shade the region dictated by the system of inequalities. The vertices of the polygon

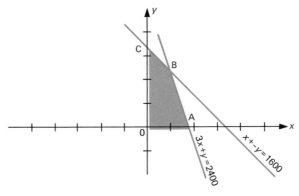

FIG. 14-24

represented by the shaded region in Fig. 14-24 are easily found to be $O = (0,0)$, $A = (800,0)$, $B = (400,1200)$, and $C = (0,1600)$. Then

$$f \text{ evaluated at } 0 \text{ is } f = 0$$
$$\text{at } A \text{ is } f = 4000$$
$$\text{at } B \text{ is } f = 3200$$
$$\text{at } C \text{ is } f = 1600.$$

Thus the maximum profit is $40.00 and is achieved by producing 800 hard-cover books and no paperback books.

EXERCISE 14-7

1. Find the maximum and minimum value of a specified function determined by $f = 3x + 4y - 2$ which must satisfy the simultaneous system of inequalities

$$x + y \leq 2$$
$$\wedge$$
$$x + 2y \geq -1$$
$$\wedge$$
$$x - y \geq -1$$
$$\wedge$$
$$x \leq 6.$$

2. A manufacturer has two warehouses: warehouse A containing 40 units of his product and warehouse B containing 50 units. He has orders to fill, one from Akron, Ohio, for 30 units and the other from Cleveland, Ohio for 40 units. Should he fill the order for Akron from one warehouse and that for Cleveland from the other, or is there a more economical distribution.

3. A couple decides to start a record collection. They can purchase records of musical shows for $6 apiece and records of a vocalist for $4 apiece. There are only 4 records of musical shows in which they are currently interested and 6 of their favorite vocalist. They have $40 to invest and decide that 8 records should be their limit.
   (a) Write two inequalities which express the number of records of musical shows which they can buy.
   (b) Write two inequalities which express the number of vocalist records which they can buy.
   (c) Write an inequality which shows they have $40 to invest.
   (d) Write an inequality which shows that 8 records should be their limit.
   (e) Graph the above system of inequalities.
   (f) They give a popularity rating of 3 to each record of a musical show and 2 to each record of the vocalist. How many records of each type should they buy to give their collection the highest rating?

4. A toy factory is planning to produce two types of toys—boats and cars. Each boat requires 3 hours on Machine I and 2 hours on Machine II. Each car requires 1 hour on Machine I and 4 hours on Machine II. Machine I has a maximum of 15 hours available. Machine II has a maximum of 20 hours available. The profit on each boat is $7. The profit on each car is $9. Determine the best combination of boats and cars that should be produced in order to maximize profits.

chapter 15

Ratios, Proportions, and Variations

15-1. RATIOS

A *ratio* is a fraction which compares two things in terms of the same unit. Its value is determined by the relative sizes of the things compared, and *not* by the unit chosen. Thus the ratio of 6 inches to 3 feet is $\frac{1}{6}$, since

$\frac{6 \text{ (inches)}}{36 \text{ (inches)}} = \frac{1}{6}$, and also $\frac{\frac{1}{2} \text{ (foot)}}{3 \text{ (foot)}} = \frac{1}{6}$. The ratio $\frac{1}{6}$ is a dimensionless

unit number. It merely means that one distance is $\frac{1}{6}$ of the other. It doesn't tell us what each distance is. It indicates that if a first distance is 12 feet, the second distance is 72 feet. If the second distance is 5 miles, then the first distance is $\frac{5}{6}$ miles, etc.

Ratios are of great importance in the branch of mathematics known as *trigonometry*. One of its uses is to measure the distance to an inaccessible object, such as the top of a mountain or a spot on the moon, by equating the ratios of corresponding measures of sides of similar triangles.

15-2. PROPORTIONS

A proportion is an equation whose two members are ratios. Thus to find the height *CD* of a cliff, a sight is taken at *O* (Fig. 15-1), and the lengths, *OA* = 5 feet, *AB* = 3 feet, and *OC* = 200 yards, are measured directly. (The representation in Fig. 15-1 shows *OA* and *AB* too large in comparison with *OC* and *CD*. Such a figure is called a *diagram* rather

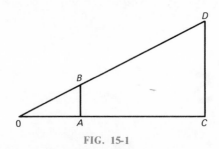

FIG. 15-1

than a *scale drawing*.) Then, from similar triangles,

(1) $$\frac{CD \text{ (in yards)}}{200 \text{ (yards)}} = \frac{3 \text{ (feet)}}{5 \text{ (feet)}} = \frac{3}{5}. *$$

From (1) it follows that

(2) $$CD = \left(\frac{3}{5}\right)(200 \text{ yards}) = 120 \text{ yards},$$

the height of the not necessarily climbed cliff.

The proportion

(3) $$\frac{a}{b} = \frac{c}{d}$$

is sometimes written

(4) $$a:b = c:d,$$

and is read, "*a* is to *b* as *c* is to *d*." Here *b* and *c* are called *means*, and *a* and *d* are *extremes*. There would, however, be no point in the new symbol replacing the division sign were it not for the gain effected by extending the notation in (4). For example,

(5) $$a:b:c = d:e:f,$$

which is read "*a* is to *b* is to *c* as *d* is to *e* is to *f*," states in briefer form the three proportions: $\frac{a}{b} = \frac{d}{e}, \frac{b}{c} = \frac{e}{f}$, and $\frac{a}{c} = \frac{d}{f}$. Evidently the notation of (5) can be extended indefinitely with as many letters as desired on each side of the equality sign.

Since the equation

(6) $$ad = bc$$

obtained by clearing fractions in (3), is linear in each of the letters involved, the solution for any one of them is simple. Evidently $a = \frac{bc}{d}$, $d = \frac{bc}{a}$, $b = \frac{ad}{c}$, and $c = \frac{ad}{b}$.

---

*Note that the indicated units in parentheses merely tell what the numbers represent, and that all algebraic operations are upon *numbers* (as represented by digits or letters).

EXERCISE 15-1

Find in each of Probs. 1–9 the ratio of the first to the second quantity.

1. 3 feet, 2 yards.
2. 7 feet, 3 miles.
3. 2 miles, 50 yards.
4. 6 ounces, 4 pounds.
5. 1 ton, 100 ounces.
6. 4 hours, 13 seconds.
7. $x, \dfrac{1}{x}$.
8. $x - 2, 2 - x$.
9. $a^2 + 1, a + \dfrac{1}{a}$.

Solve for the unknowns in Probs. 10–15.

10. $x:(x - 1) = (x - 1):(x - 3)$.
11. $x:(x + 1) = (x + 2):(x + 4)$.
12. $(x + 2):(x + 5) = (3x - 1):(2x + 2)$.
13. $(3x + 1):(2x - 3) = (x + 1):(2 - 4x)$.
14. $(-3x):(6x + 1) = (4x + 2):(12x + 9)$.
15. $(2 - 3x):(4x) = (x + 7):(3x + 1)$.

From the proportions in Probs. 16–22 get pairs of simultaneous equations, and solve for the unknowns.

16. $1:x:3 = x:4:5y$.
17. $(x + y):(2x + 3y):1 = 1:2:3$.
18. $(x + y + 1):(x - y - 2):(2x + 3y - 1) = 1:2:3$.
19. $(2x - y + 1):(x + y - 2):(3x - y + 1) = 1:2:3$.
20. $(x + 1):(2x + 3):(3x + 5) = 2y:(3y + 2):(5y + 3)$.
21. $(x + y):(y + z + 1):(x + y + 1):z = 1:2:3:4$.
22. $(x + 1):(y + 2):(z + 3):(x + y + z) = 1:2:3:4$.

15-3. CONSEQUENCES OF A PROPORTION

Some results following from

(1)
$$\frac{a}{b} = \frac{c}{d}, \quad abcd \neq 0$$

are given in equations (2) to (7) below.

When the members of (1) are multiplied by bd we learn that

(2)
$$ad = bc,$$

or *the product of the means equals the product of the extremes.*

When the members of (2) are divided by dc we find that

(3)
$$\frac{a}{c} = \frac{b}{d},$$

or, referring to (1), *the ratio of the numerators equals the ratio of the corresponding denominators.*

If the divisor is ac, we find that

(4)
$$\frac{b}{a} = \frac{d}{c},$$

or *the reciprocals of equal ratios are equal.*

Again, adding 1 to both members of (1) and writing each new member as a fraction, we have

(5)
$$\frac{a + b}{b} = \frac{c + d}{d}.$$

Similarly,

(6)
$$\frac{a - b}{b} = \frac{c - d}{d}.$$

Dividing corresponding members of (5) and (6), (as justified by the axiom: "When equals are divided by equals, the quotients are equal"), we have

(7)
$$\frac{a + b}{a - b} = \frac{c + d}{c - d}$$

The student may find further consequences of (1) by getting equations from (3) and (4) corresponding with (5), (6), and (7) as derived from (1), by inverting all members, and by combining members in various ways. Evidently an unending series of equations of an endless degree of complexity stems from the simple equation (1).

Results such as (2) to (7) were formerly given more prominence in algebra texts than at present. Probably one reason for the decrease in emphasis is the fact that such results are merely what one gets by applying to (1) the guiding principle for work with equations, namely: "Always do to the right-hand side what is done to the left-hand side." Nevertheless, the processes here suggested may lead to results which are interesting, useful, and far from self-evident. It is also important to observe that number values represented by letters must be such that division by zero is not a possibility in any ratios formed.

Hint. If, in launching out for himself, the interested student should arrive at a complicated result of (1) such as, say

(8)
$$\frac{a^2 + ab + ac + bc}{a^2 - ab - ac + bc} = \frac{d^2 + bd + cd + bc}{d^2 - bd - cd + bc},$$

he should not forget the value of frequent arithmetic tests to guard against errors. For instance, when $a = 1$, $b = 2$, $c = 3$, and $d = 6$, (1) is true and so is (8). However, the choice of $a = b = c = d = 1$ is meaningless, since division by zero would result.

EXERCISE 15-2

(The numbers in this exercise refer to proportions in Sec. 15-3.)

1. Noting that (5), (6), and (7) are consequences of (1), get three similar consequences of (3).

2. Get consequences of (4) similar to those of Prob. 1.

3. By inverting the members of (5), (6), and (7), as well as of the proportions obtained in Probs. 1 and 2, get nine more consequences of (1).

Test the proportions in Probs. 4–15 with numerical values which satisfy (1), such as $a = 1, b = 2, c = 3, d = 6$, or $a = 2, b = 3, c = 4, d = 6$. If the tests indicate that a given proportion may be a true consequence of (1), try to prove that this is so.

4. $\dfrac{a + b}{a} = \dfrac{c + d}{c}.$

5. $\dfrac{a + b}{a} = \dfrac{c + d}{d}.$

6. $\dfrac{a - b}{a} = \dfrac{c - d}{c}.$

7. $\dfrac{2a - b}{a} = \dfrac{2c - d}{c}.$

8. $\dfrac{a^2}{a + b} = \dfrac{c^2}{c + d}.$

9. $\dfrac{a + 2b}{b} = \dfrac{c + 2d}{d}.$

10. $\dfrac{(a + b)^2}{ab} = \dfrac{(c + d)^2}{cd}.$

11. $\dfrac{a^2 + b^2}{ab} = \dfrac{c^2 + d^2}{cd}.$

12. $\dfrac{a^2 - b^2}{ab} = \dfrac{c^2 - d^2}{cd}.$

13. $\dfrac{a^2 - b^2}{a^2} = \dfrac{c^2 - d^2}{c^2}.$

14. $\dfrac{a^3 + b^3}{ab} = \dfrac{c^3 + d^3}{cd}.$

15. $\dfrac{(a + b)^3}{a^2 b} = \dfrac{(c + d)^3}{c^2 d}.$

Solve Probs. 16–19 by means of proportions.

16. A light is on the top of a 20-foot pole. If a 6-foot man casts an 8-foot shadow, how far is he from the pole?

17. In Prob. 16, if the man is 30 feet from the pole, how long will his shadow be?

18. If a light is on top of a pole and a 6-foot man 30 feet away casts a shadow 10 feet long, how high is the pole?

19. A model, 3 feet high, is made from photographs of a mountain. If two villages known to be 5 miles apart are 7 feet apart on the model, how high is the mountain?

15-4.   VARIATION

Two quantities which behave so that their ratio remains fixed may be compared mathematically by use of the symbol $\propto$, read "varies as."

Thus, if C and d represent respectively the circumference and diameter of a circle, then C is doubled when d is doubled, tripled when d is tripled, and so on. This is expressed in English by saying that "C varies directly as d," or, "C is directly proportional to d." More simply, we may say that "C varies as d," or "C is proportional to d." In symbols,

(1) $$C \propto d.$$

The statement (1) can be put in a form more suitable for algebraic operations as the equation

(2) $$C = kd, \text{ or } \frac{C}{d} = k,$$

where k is called the *constant of proportionality*, or the *variation constant*. In this case, when C and d are measured in terms of the same linear unit, it is known that $k = \pi$ or (nearly) 3.1416, so that we have the formula

(3) $$C = \pi d.$$

In many problems, however, we must start with an undetermined k. Thus at a given time of day in a given place the length s of a man's shadow varies as his height h. We then have

(4) $$s \propto h, \quad \text{or} \quad s = kh,$$

where k remains to be found. If the shadow of a 6-foot man is 9 feet long, then

(5) $$9 = k6, \text{ or } k = \frac{9}{6} = \frac{3}{2}.$$

Hence, at the time and place in question,

(6) $$s = \frac{3}{2} h$$

for people or objects of various heights. In other words, the shadow will be $\frac{3}{2}$ as long as the height of the object.

Sometimes one quantity varies, not as a second one, but as some function of one or more quantities. Thus the equations

(7) $$y = kx^2, \quad \text{or} \quad \frac{y}{x^2} = k,$$

(8) $$y = kxz, \quad \text{or} \quad \frac{y}{xz} = k,$$

(9) $$y = \frac{k}{x}, \quad \text{or} \quad xy = k,$$

and

(10) $$y = \frac{kx}{z^2 w}, \quad \text{or} \quad \frac{yz^2 w}{x} = k$$

state in succession that y varies directly as x^2, xz, $\dfrac{1}{x}$, and $\dfrac{x}{z^2w}$. Sometimes it is said that, in (8), y varies *jointly* as x and z; and in (10), y varies *directly* as x and *inversely* as z^2 and w. More simply, however, *if y varies directly as any function of other letters, y is k times that function.*

Other common forms of expression for the variation law connecting y with the other variables in (7), (8), (9), and (10) can be used. In order to acquaint the student with some of these phrases, we shall list a few. In (7), it can be said that "y varies as x^2," or that "y is directly proportional to x^2," or simply that "y is proportional to x^2." All of these statements imply that $\dfrac{y}{x^2}$ is a constant.

Similarly, in (8), it can be said that "y varies directly as the product of x and z," or that "y is directly proportional to the product of x and z," or, more simply, that "y is proportional to x and z." All of these statements imply that $\dfrac{y}{xz}$ is a constant.

In (9), it can be said that "y varies inversely as x" or that "y is inversely proportional to x." These statements imply that xy is a constant.

In (10), it can be said that "y varies directly as x and inversely as the product of z^2 and w" or that "y is directly proportional to x and inversely proportional to z^2 and w." These statements imply that $\dfrac{yz^2w}{x}$ is a constant.

It should be observed that the words "directly" and "jointly" are frequently omitted, "directly" being understood when the dependence of one quantity on another is referred to, and "jointly" when there is more than one other quantity involved.

A problem in variation usually consists of the following steps:

1. The variation relation is stated as an equation involving the constant k. In this step all the quantities involved in the variation law should be described clearly. When any quantity is referred to by name, we shall adopt the plan of using the initial letter of the name as an abbreviation. For example, the word "pressure" would be described by the letter p or P. When the quantities are not named, the letters x, y, z, etc., are used.

2. One set of values of all the variables involved is inserted in the equation, leaving k as the only unknown. It is advisable in a problem where Step 5 is to be carried out later, to make a box scheme as indicated in Example 4, solution 3. This box should be filled in before going through any numerical work, as it will clearly show what quantities are given, the units being used respectively, and what quantities are to be found.

3. The resulting equation is solved for k.

4. The value of k is inserted in the original equation.
5. By means of the equation obtained in Step 4, the value of any specified variable is found when the values of the others are given. However, the same set of units must be used throughout the problem as were employed in Steps 2 and 3 to find the value of k. This point is very important, and is illustrated in the two versions of Example 4.

Example 1. y varies directly as $\dfrac{x^2}{zw}$. One set of values is: $x = 2$, $y = 4$, $z = -3$, and $w = -2$. Find z when $x = 3$, $y = -1$ and $w = 4$.

Solution.   The five steps in order yield the following equations.

(11) $$y = \frac{kx^2}{zw}.$$

(12) $$4 = \frac{4k}{(-3)(-2)}.$$

(13) $$k = 6.$$

(14) $$y = \frac{6x^2}{zw}.$$

(15) $$-1 = \frac{6(3)^2}{z(4)}, \quad \text{or} \quad z = \frac{-27}{2} \quad (Ans.)$$

Example 2.   State in words the law of variation for x in terms of the variables related to it in (8) and (10).

Solution.   If we use the second forms in (8) and (10), where the left-hand members include all the variables present, it becomes apparent that in a direct variation between two variables, one appears as a divisor of the numerator while the second appears as a divisor of the denominator. For inverse variation, both variables will appear in the same position either as divisors of the numerator or as divisors of the denominator. Thus, in (8)

"x varies directly as y and inversely as z."

Similarly in (10)

"x varies directly as y, z^2, and w."

It should be noted here that there are other forms of expression as well as those given. They are left to the student.

Example 3.   If the original value of x is 10 units in (8) and (10), what would its new value become if y is doubled, z is tripled, and w is halved?

Solution.   In (8), since x varies directly as y and inversely as z, it means that if y is doubled, so is x, but if z is tripled, x becomes one-third of its former measure. Carrying out these changes simultaneously, we get for x

$$2\left(\frac{1}{3}\right)(10) = \frac{20}{3} = 6\frac{2}{3} \text{ units.}$$

In (10), since x varies directly as y, z^2, and w, it means that if y is doubled, so is x; if w is halved, so is x; but if z is tripled, x becomes nine times its former measure. Carrying out these changes simultaneously, we get for x

$$2\left(\frac{1}{2}\right)(9)(10) = 90 \text{ units.}$$

Example 4.   Boyle's law in physics states that at a given temperature the volume of a given quantity of gas is inversely proportional to the pressure on the walls of the container. If for a given sample the volume is one cubic foot when the pressure is 20 pounds per square inch, what is the volume when the pressure is increased to 60 pounds per square inch?

Solution 1.   Let

(16)
$$V = \frac{k}{P} \quad \text{or} \quad VP = k,$$

where V and P represent units of volume and pressure respectively. In this first solution let P be measured in pounds per square inch, and V in cubic feet. Then

(17)
$$1 = \frac{k}{20}.$$

(18)
$$k = 20.$$

(19)
$$V = \frac{20}{P}.$$

(20)
$$V = \frac{20}{60} = \frac{1}{3}.$$

Solution 2.   Now let P be measured in pounds per square foot, with V unchanged in meaning. Then the first and second values of P in the problem are respectively $\frac{20}{144} = \frac{5}{36}$, and $\frac{60}{144} = \frac{5}{12}$. Equations (17) to (20) are replaced by the following.

(21)
$$1 = \frac{k}{\frac{5}{36}}.$$

(22)
$$k = \frac{5}{36}.$$

(23) $$V = \frac{5}{36P}.$$

(24) $$V = \frac{5}{36\left(\frac{5}{12}\right)} = \frac{1}{3}, \text{ as before.}$$

Thus, we see that the value determined for k, the so-called "proportionality constant," depends upon the choice of units; but *the same final result* is obtained in any case.

Solution 3. Simple problems in variation may often be worked more easily as problems in proportion; for if one quantity varies as another, corresponding values are proportional. When using the proportion method, it is better to write the variation equation in the second form illustrated in (7), (8), (9), and (10), where all variables are contained in one member of the equation. Thus, using the second form of (16) with V_1, P_1 indicating one set of values for V and P, while V_2, and P_2 a second set, etc., it follows that $V_1 P_1 = V_2 P_2 = V_3 P_3$, etc. Arrange the given information in a box scheme as follows:

V (cubic feet)	P (pounds per square inch)
$V_1 = 1$	$P_1 = 20$
$V_2 = ?$	$P_2 = 60$

Boyle's law: $\qquad V_1 P_1 = V_2 P_2 = V_3 P_3 = \text{etc.}$

$\qquad\qquad\qquad 1 \cdot 20 = V_2(60).$

$\qquad\qquad \therefore\ V_2 = \frac{1}{3} \text{ cubic foot.}$

Example 5. Here we shall use without proof the following important and useful mathematical result:

THEOREM 1. *The areas of similar plane figures vary as the squares of corresponding dimensions.*

The areas of two similar rectangles are 15 and 20 square units respectively. Find the length of the diagonal of the larger rectangle if the diagonal of the smaller one is 10 units long.

Solution. Let A and d stand for area and diagonal length respectively. The mathematical statement of the theorem here used is

(25) $$A = kd^2, \quad \text{or} \quad \frac{A}{d^2} = k.$$

From the smaller rectangle we have

(26) $15 = k(10)^2$,   or $k = \dfrac{15}{100} = \dfrac{3}{20}$.

This value, substituted in (25), gives

(27) $A = \dfrac{3d^2}{20}$.

Inserting the area of the larger rectangle, or $A = 20$, in (27), and remembering that in this case d must be positive, we have

(28) $d = 20\,\dfrac{\sqrt{3}}{3} = 11.5$ linear units (*Ans.*)

Note. If the student will try to solve this problem by means of simultaneous equations, as is possible, he will appreciate the simplicity and power of this method. In addition to the required answer he has in (27) a formula applying to *any* rectangle similar to the first one.

In Exercise 15-3 we shall use, in addition to Theorem 1,

THEOREM 2.   *The volumes of similar figures vary as the cubes of corresponding dimensions.*

EXERCISE 15-3

In each of Probs. 1–8, (a) express the given relation as an equation; (b) write the equation so that the left member will contain all the variables; and then (c) write an equivalent statement in words for the variation involving x as related to the other variables present.

1. $y \propto x^3$.   2. $z \propto xy$.   3. $w \propto \dfrac{x^2 y}{z}$.   4. $y \propto \dfrac{w}{x^2 z}$.

5. $z \propto \dfrac{1}{xy}$.   6. $w \propto \dfrac{x}{yz^3}$.   7. $x^2 \propto \dfrac{y}{z^2 w}$.   8. $y^3 \propto \dfrac{xz}{w}$.

9. If z varies as $\dfrac{x^2 y}{w}$ and is 4 when $x = -2, y = 3$, and $w = -4$, find the value of

    (a) y when $x = 3, w = -2$, and $z = 4$;
    (b) x when $z = 5, y = 10$, and $w = 8$;
    (c) w when $x = -3, y = 4$, and $z = -5$;
    (d) z when $x = -3, y = 4$, and $w = -2$.

10. If y varies as $\dfrac{z}{wx^2}$ and is -2 when $z = 3, w = 2$, and $x = -4$, find the value of

    (a) y when $z = -3, w = -4a$, and $x = -b$;
    (b) z when $y = -5, x = 2a$, and $w = -3c$;

(c) w when $y = -2$, $z = -3$, and $x = 2a$;

(d) x when $y = a$, $z = b$, and $w = c$.

Solve Probs. 11–15 by use of Theorems 1 and 2, Sec. 12-4.

11. The bases of 6 similar triangles are 2, 3, 4, 7, 8, and 9 inches long respectively. If the area of the smallest triangle is 5 square inches, what are the other areas?

12. A sign painter finds that a pint of paint is used in painting the words, "Chicken Dinner. Dine and Dance." How much paint will be used in making a similar sign, with letters of the same type and proportions but three times as high?

13. The heights of three similarly-proportioned men are $5, 5\frac{1}{2}$, and 6 feet respectively. If the tallest man weighs 200 pounds, about what would be the expected weights of the other two?

14. The weights of various aerial bombs in pounds are as follows: 100, 200, 500, 1,000, 2,000, 6,000, and 12,000. Assuming that all are similarly proportioned and made of the same materials in like proportions, what are the lengths of the other bombs if the 100-pound one is 2 feet long?

15. The perimeters of 6 similar plane figures are 4, 5, 10, 20, 50, and 100 inches, respectively. If the area of the figure with a 20-inch perimeter is 10 square inches, what are the other areas?

16. The weight of any given object on a planet varies directly as the mass of the planet and inversely as the square of its radius. For reference let the mass of the earth be one unit and its radius one unit. If a boy weighs 100 pounds on the earth, how much would he weigh on each of the following bodies?

Name	Radius	Mass
Moon	.27	.012
Mercury	.39	.04
Venus	.97	.81
Mars	.53	.11
Jupiter	11.2	317.
Saturn	9.4	95.
Sun	109.	330,000

17. The weight of a body within the earth, as in a mine, varies directly as its distance from the center. Assuming the radius of the earth to be 4,000 miles, how much would a 200-pound man weigh when 10 miles below the surface?

18. If S varies directly as the cube of x and inversely as the square of y, what change in S results when x is doubled and y is tripled?

19. The force of attraction between two bodies varies directly as the product of their masses and inversely as the square of the distance between them.

When two masses of 6 units and 24 units are separated by 192 inches, the force is 72 units. (a) If the distance between them is diminished by 24 inches and the smaller mass is doubled, what change in the larger mass will increase the force by 18 units? (b) At what distance will the two given masses have twice the force of attraction that they have at 192 inches?

20. Kepler's law states that the square of the time of a planet's revolution about the sun varies as the cube of its mean distance from the sun. The mean distances of Mars and the earth are in the ratio $3:2$. Find in days the time of revolution of Mars (i.e., the Martian year).

21. The volume V of a gas varies directly as the absolute temperature T and inversely as the pressure P. If a certain amount of gas occupies 100 cubic feet at a pressure of 16 pounds per square inch and at $T = 200°$, find its volume when the pressure is 20 pounds per square inch and $T = 420°$.

22. The mass of a spherical body varies directly as its density and the cube of the radius. Compare the masses of Jupiter and the earth if the diameter of Jupiter be taken as 11 times that of the earth and its density $\dfrac{5}{22}$ that of the earth.

23. Given that $y \propto x$, prove that $2x^2 + y^2 \propto xy$. $\left(Hint.\ \text{Let } y = kx.\ \text{Show that } \dfrac{2x^2 + y^2}{xy} = \text{const.}\right)$

24. If $y \propto x$, prove that $3x^4 + y^2x^2 \propto 3x^2y^2$.

chapter 16

Progressions

16-1. SEQUENCES

A succession of numbers of which one number is designated as the first, another as the second, and so on, is called a *sequence*. Each number of the sequence is called a *term*. For example, the ordered set of natural numbers $1, 2, 3, 4, \ldots$, used for counting, forms a sequence.

Since the terms of a sequence have a positional order of first term, second term, third term and so on, we see that there is a one-to-one correspondence between a set of positive consecutive integers, starting with 1, and the various terms of a sequence. *Hence the terms of the sequence constitute the range of a function whose domain is the set of positive integers.*

A finite sequence of n (natural number) terms is defined as a function whose domain is the ordered set of natural numbers $1, 2, 3, \ldots, n$ and whose range may, if desired, be represented theoretically as the ordered set $a(1), a(2), a(3), \ldots, a(n)$, also written as $a_1, a_2, a_3, \ldots, a_n$.

An *infinite* sequence is defined as a function whose domain is the ordered set of natural numbers $1, 2, 3, \ldots, n$, ad infinitum and whose range is $a(1), a(2), a(3), \ldots, a(n)$, ad infinitum, also written as

$$a_1, a_2, a_3, \ldots, a_n, \ldots.$$

The expression "ad infinitum" means that the terms continue without end.

If we represent the function by the letter a, then the sequence function could be described theoretically by its ordered pairs as follows:

$$a = \{(1, a(1)), (2, a(2)), (3, a(3)), \ldots\}$$

Examples.

1. $a = \{(1,1), (2,2), (3,3), \ldots, (n,n)\}$

This is a finite sequence where $a(n) = n$,

2. $a = \{(1,1), (2,4), (3,9), (4,16), \ldots\}$

This is an infinite sequence, where $a(n) = n^2$.

Since the domain of a sequence is always fixed as the ordered set of natural numbers 1, 2, 3, ..., n or 1, 2, 3, ..., n, ad infinitum, a sequence can be conveniently described by listing only the members of its range in the order of the natural numbers with which they are associated. For example, the sequence

$$a = \{(n, a(n))\}$$

might be written simply as

$$a(1), a(2), a(3), \ldots, a(n), \ldots.$$

The three dots after $a(n)$ takes the place of "ad infinitum," and henceforth will be understood to imply this fact. The simpler notation

$$a(1) = a_1, a(2) = a_2, a(3) = a_3, \ldots, a(n) = a_n, \ldots$$

is often used and a sequence is then denoted by

$$\{a_n\} = a_1 a_2, a_3, \ldots, a_n, \ldots.$$

a_1 is called the *first term* of the sequence, a_2 the second term, a_3 the third term, a_n the nth term or general term. Thus if $a_n = n^2$, we write

$$\{a_n\} = \{n^2\} = 1, 4, 9, 16, \ldots, n^2, \ldots,$$

which is read "a is the sequence of numbers whose nth term a_n is n^2." If we wish to write the tenth term of the sequence, we substitute $n = 10$ into the formula $a_n = n^2$ and get $a_{10} = 10^2 = 100$, the value of the sequence function. The tenth term of the sequence is 100, that is, (10, 100) is an ordered pair belonging to the sequence function. We may thus speak of

$$\{a_n\} = a_1, a_2, a_3, \ldots$$

and understand that it replaces

$$a = \{(1, a_1), (2, a_2), (3, a_3), \ldots\},$$

the sequence function.

Examples of sequences:

1. $\{a_n\} = \{a(n)\} = \{2n\} = 2, 4, 6, 8, \ldots$
2. $\{a_n\} = \{a(n)\} = \{2n - 1\} = 1, 3, 5, 7, \ldots$
3. $\{a_n\} = \{a(n)\} = \{3^{n-1}\} = 1, 3, 9, 27, 81, \ldots$
4, $\{a_n\} = \{a(n)\} = \left\{\dfrac{1}{n}\right\} = 1, \dfrac{1}{2}, \dfrac{1}{3}, \dfrac{1}{4}, \dfrac{1}{5}, \ldots$

The braces { } as used here should not be interpreted in the same sense as used with set notation, representing the phrase "the set of." However, when used with sequences, it is to be interpreted as described and symbolized in the preceding paragraphs. The a_n enclosed with the braces as $[a_n]$ specifies that a_n is the nth term of a sequence and when the terms are spelled out as $a_1, a_2, a_3, \ldots$, they are not to be enclosed within braces. In fact, it is possible that an a_j and a_k, $(j \neq k)$, may be equal to one another, but for different positioned terms of the sequence. For example if $\{a_n\} = \{n^2 - 3n + 2\}$, then $a_1 = 0$, and $a_2 = 0$. In a set, as was pointed out in Chapter 1, the same element is not repeated more than once when the elements are listed, irrespective of order. However, in a sequence, *order is most important*, and if the same-valued term appears in the sequence, it must be repeated in its appropriate ordered position. *Thus when the terms in a sequence are written as $a_1, a_2, a_3, \ldots$; no braces should be used to enclose them. However, when the sequence is represented as $\{a_n\}$, the term a_n is enclosed in braces.*

Another method for defining a sequence is to specify the first term and express a formula for the nth term as a defining condition involving the preceding terms. The formula for the nth term is called a recursion formula. For example, let $\{a_n\}$ be a sequence where $a_1 = 3$ and $a_n = 3a_{n-1} + 2$ where $n > 1$. Then the first four terms of the sequence are

$a_1 = 3$ (given).   We note that even though when $n = 1$, $a_1 = 3a_0 + 2$, its value is already defined here as being 3. The a_0 is not being included as a term in the sequence. Hence n is chosen as $2, 3, 4, \ldots$, to produce $a_2, a_3, a_4, \ldots$.

$a_2 = 3a_1 + 2 = 3(3) + 2 = 11$
$a_3 = 3a_2 + 2 = 3(11) + 2 = 35$
$a_4 = 3a_3 + 2 = 3(35) + 2 = 107$.

Another example would be the specification of a formula for a_n as an expression in n, where the successive terms of the sequence are obtained by putting $n = 1, 2, 3, 4, \ldots$. When such is the case, we usually, for simplicity, write a_n as the expression in n without necessarily enclosing each in parentheses.

EXERCISE 16-1

Write the first four terms of the sequence whose nth term is given in Probs. 1–8. Also write the tenth term.

1. $a_n = 2n + 1$.

2. $a_n = \dfrac{1}{n + 1}$.

3. $a_n = \dfrac{2n}{n + 3}$.

4. $a_n = \dfrac{1}{n(n + 1)}$.

5. $a_n = \dfrac{2^n}{n^2 + 1}$.

6. $a_n = \dfrac{(-1)^n}{n + 1}$.

7. $a_n = (-1)^n 2^n$

8. $a_n = 3 \left(-\dfrac{1}{2}\right)^n$

Among the following specific a_n's there is at least one that fits each of the sequences in Probs. 9–15. Make the proper choice for a_n in each and from it write the three terms following the last one given.

$$n^2 + 1; \quad 3n - 2; \quad 4n; \quad 2n; \quad \frac{(-1)^n}{n}; \quad \frac{n}{n + 1}; \quad (-1)^{n+1}$$

9. $2, 5, 10, 17, 26, \ldots$

10. $2, 4, 6, 8, 10, \ldots$

11. $1, 4, 7, 10, 13, \ldots$

12. $\dfrac{1}{2}, \dfrac{2}{3}, \dfrac{3}{4}, \dfrac{4}{5}, \dfrac{5}{6}, \ldots$

13. $-1, \dfrac{1}{2}, -\dfrac{1}{3}, \dfrac{1}{4}, -\dfrac{1}{5}, \ldots$

14. $4, 8, 12, 16, 20, \ldots$

15. $1, -1, 1, -1, 1, \ldots$

Write the first five terms of the sequences in Probs. 16–20:

16. $a_1 = 1, \quad a_n = a_{n-1} + 2$.

17. $a_1 = 5, \quad a_n = \dfrac{a_{n-1}}{2}$.

18. $a_1 = 100, \quad a_n = \dfrac{5 - 3a_{n-1}}{2}$.

19. $a_1 = 2, \quad a_n = \dfrac{(-1)a_{n-1}}{2}$.

20. $a_1 = -3, \quad a_n = 2a_{n-1} + 4$.

16-2. SERIES

For each sequence, there is an associated series which can be formed by replacing the commas in the ordered set of terms by plus signs. Thus a series is the algebraic sum of the corresponding terms of a sequence.

The finite series $a_1 + a_2 + a_3 + \cdots + a_n$ is obtained by summing the terms of the finite sequence $a_1, a_2, a_3, \ldots, a_n$.   The infinite series

$a_1 + a_2 + a_3 + \cdots + a_n + \cdots$ is obtained by summing the terms of the infinite sequence $a_1, a_2, a_3, \ldots, a_n, \ldots$. The nth term, or general term, of a series is the nth term of the corresponding sequence.

For a finite series, there is always a finite number which is the sum obtained by adding the terms of the series. Thus the sum of the series $2 + 4 + 6 + 8 + 10$ is 30. However, there is no finite number that can be designated as the sum of the infinite series

$$1 + 4 + 9 + 16 + \cdots + n^2 + \cdots.$$

There are, however, some infinite series which can be assigned a number, called the *sum*. Infinite series of the latter type play an important part in computer science and advanced mathematics.

16-3. SUMMATION NOTATION

In the study of many branches of mathematics, we will often be concerned with sums of elements, and it will be conveinent to be able to express such sums in compact form. For example, the finite series

$$1 + 4 + 9 + 16$$

can be written as

$$\sum_{k=1}^{4} k^2$$

where it is understood that k is to be replaced by each of the numbers 1, 2, 3, 4 in the expression k^2, and then the resulting values are to be summed. Thus

$$\sum_{k=1}^{4} k^2 = 1^2 + 2^2 + 3^2 + 4^2 = 1 + 4 + 9 + 16 = 30.$$

The Greek letter Σ (capital sigma) is called the *summation symbol* and is read "summation of." The letter k is called the *index of summation*, and the replacement set of consecutive integers for k is called the *range of summation*. The letter k is called a *dummy index*, or *variable*, since any other letter could be used and the same sum would still be indicated. The numbers 1 and 4 appearing below and above the summation symbol are called the *lower* (tells us where the sum starts) and *upper* (tells us where the sum ends) *limits of summation*. Thus

$$\sum_{k=1}^{4} k^2 = \sum_{i=1}^{4} i^2 = \sum_{j=1}^{4} j^2 = 1^2 + 2^2 + 3^2 + 4^2.$$

The sum of the first n terms of the series $a_1 + a_2 + a_3 + \cdots + a_n + \cdots$

can be represented by the symbol $\sum\limits_{i=1}^{n} a_i$, that is,

$$\sum_{i=1}^{n} a_i = a_1 + a_2 + a_3 + \cdots + a_n.$$

Examples:

(a) $\sum\limits_{i=1}^{3} a_i = a_1 + a_2 + a_3$

(b) $\sum\limits_{j=4}^{7} a_j = a_4 + a_5 + a_6 + a_7$

(c) $\sum\limits_{j=1}^{3} 2x_j = 2x_1 + 2x_2 + 2x_3$

(d) $\sum\limits_{k=2}^{5} (2k - 1) = [2(2) - 1] + [2(3) - 1] + [2(4) - 1] + [2(5) - 1]$

$$= 3 + 5 + 7 + 9$$
$$= 24$$

(e) $\sum\limits_{i=1}^{\infty} i = 1 + 2 + 3 + 4 + \cdots + n + \cdots$

(f) $\sum\limits_{i=1}^{4} x_i y_i z_i = x_1 y_1 z_1 + x_2 y_2 z_2 + x_3 y_3 z_3 + x_4 y_4 z_4.$

Three theorems that provide basic rules in dealing with the summation symbolism are given below.

THEOREM 1.

$$\sum_{i=1}^{n} (x_i + y_i) = \sum_{i=1}^{n} x_i + \sum_{i=1}^{n} y_i.$$

Proof: Expand the left-hand side and regroup terms.

$$\sum_{i=1}^{n} (x_i + y_i) = (x_1 + y_1) + (x_2 + y_2) + \cdots + (x_n + y_n)$$

$$= (x_1 + x_2 + \cdots + x_n) + (y_1 + y_2 + \cdots + y_n)$$

$$= \sum_{i=1}^{n} x_i + \sum_{i=1}^{n} y_i.$$

This theorem states that we can distribute a Σ over addition. In fact, it can easily be shown that the Σ is distributive over the operations of addition and subtraction.

THEOREM 2: If c is a constant,

$$\sum_{i=1}^{n} cx_i = c \sum_{i=1}^{n} x_i.$$

This theorem states that we can remove a constant factor from inside a Σ to the outside.

Proof: Expand the left-hand side and factor.

$$\sum_{i=1}^{n} cx_i = cx_1 + cx_2 + \cdots + cx_n$$

$$= c(x_1 + x_2 + \cdots + x_n)$$

$$= c \sum_{i=1}^{n} x_i.$$

THEOREM 3: If c is a constant,

$$\sum_{i=1}^{n} c = nc.$$

Proof: In Theorem 2 set all the x_i's equal to 1. Then

$$\sum_{i=1}^{n} c = \underbrace{c + c + \cdots + c}_{n \text{ terms}} = nc.$$

This theorem states that if we have n terms each equal to a constant c, its Σ is nc.

EXERCISE 16-2

From among the following:

(a) $\displaystyle\sum_{k=1}^{\infty} (-1)^{k+1} \frac{2k-1}{2^{k-1}}$

(b) $\displaystyle\sum_{k=1}^{\infty} (2k)$

(c) $\displaystyle\sum_{i=1}^{\infty} (-1)^{i+1} 4^i$

(d) $\displaystyle\sum_{k=1}^{6} 1$

(e) $\displaystyle\sum_{i=1}^{4} x_i^2$

(f) $\displaystyle\sum_{i=1}^{7} (2i-1)$

choose the appropriate Σ that serves each of Probs 1–6. There is at least one choice that fits the given series.

1. $1 + 3 + 5 + 7 + 9 + 11 + 13$
2. $4 - 4^2 + 4^3 - 4^4 + \cdots$
3. $1 - \dfrac{3}{2} + \dfrac{5}{4} - \dfrac{7}{8} + \cdots$
4. $x_1^2 + x_2^2 + x_3^2 + x_4^2$
5. $2 + 4 + 6 + 8 + 10 + \cdots$
6. $1 + 1 + 1 + 1 + 1 + 1$

Express each of Probs. 7–16 in expanded notation.

7. $\displaystyle\sum_{k=1}^{6} \frac{k(k+1)}{2}$

8. $\displaystyle\sum_{k=0}^{4} \frac{k}{k+1}$

9. $\displaystyle\sum_{k=0}^{5} (6 - 5k)$

10. $\displaystyle\sum_{k=0}^{4} \frac{(-1)^k}{2^k + 1}$

11. $\displaystyle\sum_{k=5}^{10} (k^2 + k)$

12. $\displaystyle\sum_{k=1}^{7} 2$

13. $\displaystyle\sum_{k=1}^{4} (3k)^k$

14. $\displaystyle\sum_{k=1}^{4} (3k^k)$

15. $\displaystyle\sum_{k=1}^{\infty} (3k)^k$

16. $\displaystyle\sum_{k=1}^{\infty} (3k^k)$

16-4. ARITHMETIC SEQUENCES OR PROGRESSIONS

If the difference between two adjacent terms in a sequence is the same, regardless of the pair chosen, the sequence is called an *arithmetic progression*.

Example. $1, 3, 5, 7, 9, 11, \ldots$

The abbreviation "A.P." stands for *arithmetic progression*. The letters a, d, n, l, and S_n are used to represent the *elements* of an A.P., where

a = first term

d = *common difference*, or what must be added to any term to get the next one

n = number of terms

l = last, or nth, term

S_n = sum of all the n terms

It may aid the memory to note that the elements are the letters in the word "lands."

These elements are so related that if any three of them are known the remaining two can be found by use of the proper formulas.

Consider first the progression:

(1) $a, a + d, \quad a + 2d, \quad a + 3d, \quad a + 4d, \quad a + 5d, \quad a + 6d, \ldots$

Here any term after the first term is found by adding d to the term which precedes it. Note that the second term is $a + 1d$, the third term is $a + 2d$, etc., so that the coefficient of d in any term is one less that the ordinal number of the term. From this we see that the nth term, designated by l, is $a + (n - 1)d$. Stated in symbols, this yields an important result which we shall call Formula 1, namely,

1. $l = a + (n - 1)d$.

A progression having a definite number of terms may be written out in full, but usually some dots are inserted to indicate that some of the terms are omitted. Dots coming after the last precise term stand for "ad infinitum" as explained in previous sections..

Example 1.   2, 5, 8, ... to 8 terms.

Example 2.   1, 3, 5, ..., 19, 21, ...

16-5.   ARITHMETIC MEANS AND EXTREMES

The first and last terms of a specified portion of a progression are called the *extremes*, and all the terms between the extremes are called *means*.

In the special case of an A.P. having only three terms, the middle term is called *the arithmetic mean*, or average.

Example.   Find the arithmetic mean of a and l.

Solution.   Let m be the desired mean in the A.P.: a, m, l. Since $m - a = d$, and also $l - m = d$, it follows that

(1) $m - a = l - m$

Solving for m we have, as Formula 2,

2. $m = \dfrac{a + l}{2}.$

In words, *the arithmetic mean of two numbers is their arithmetic average*.

If there is more than one mean to be inserted between two given extremes, we substitute the known values of a, l, and n in Formula (1) and solve for d. The entire set can then be written by adding d to each successive term, beginning with the first, until the last term (the second extreme) is reached.

Example 1. Find the arithmetic mean of 2 and 8.

Solution. By Formula (2) (here, and in the other examples to follow, the student should *first of all* write out the formula in question),

(2) $$m = \frac{2 + 8}{2} = \frac{10}{2} = 5.$$

Example 2. Find the arithmetic mean of 7 and -15.

Solution.

$$m = \frac{7 + (-15)}{2} = \frac{-8}{2} = -4.$$

Example 3. Insert three arithmetic means between 3 and 11.

Solution. Here $a = 3$, $l = 11$, and $n = 5$. By Formula 1, $[l = a + (n - 1)d]$,

(3) $$11 = 3 + 4d,$$

whence

(4) $$d = 2.$$

The progression, then, as obtained by adding 2 to each successive term, is 3, 5, 7, 9, 11; and the required means are 5, 7, and 9 (*Ans.*).

Example 4. Insert four arithmetic means between 1 and -14.

Solution. Here $a = 1$, $l = -14$, and $n = 6$. By Formula 1,

(5) $$-14 = 1 + 5d,$$

whence

(6) $$d = -3.$$

The progression is 1, -2, -5, -8, -11, -14; and the required means are -2, -5, -8, and -11 (*Ans.*).

Example 5. Find the 7th term of the progression: 2, 5, 8, ...

Solution. From the given terms we see that $a = 2$ and $d = 3$. Also

$n = 7$. By Formula 1,

(7) $l = 2 + (6)(3) = 20$ (*Ans.*)

Example 6.   The first 3 terms of an A.P. having 8 terms are 2, -1, and -4. Find the last term.

Solution. Here $a = 2$, $d = -3$, and $n = 8$. By Formula 1,

(8) $l = 2 + 7(-3) = -19$ (*Ans.*).

EXERCISE 16-3

Find the arithmetic mean of the numbers given in Probs. 1–5.

1. 3 and 19.
2. 2 and -12.
3. $3x$ and $8x$.
4. -3 and -9.
5. $5y^2$ and $4y^2$.
6. Insert 2 means between 3 and 15.
7. Insert 3 means between 2 and -22.
8. Insert 5 means between 10 and -2.
9. Find the 10th term of the progression: $3, 5, 7, \cdots$.
10. If $l = 21$, $n = 7$, and $d = 3$, find a.
11. if $n = 8$, $l = 30$, and $a = 2$, find d.
12. There are 5 apple trees in a row. Each tree, after the first, produces 10 more apples than the one that precedes it. If the first tree produces 75 apples, how many are obtained from the last tree?
13. The first term of an A.P. is 21. If $d = -3$ and $l = 0$, how many terms are there?
14. Find the 10th term of the progression: $3, 5, 7, \cdots$.
15. A group of boys, counting their marbles, found that one had 27, the next had 24, and so on to the last boy, who had 12. How many boys were there?
16. A man travels 50 miles on January 1, 55 miles on January 2, and so on through the month. How far did he travel on the last day of January?
17. A man traveled 100 miles on Monday, 85 miles Tuesday, and so on through the week. How far did he travel on Saturday?
18. A man invested $10 more each month, after the first one, than he invested in the preceding month. His investment for the 10th month was $110. What was the first month's investment?

16-6. THE SUM OF AN A.P.

We could find the sum of n terms of an A.P. by adding them; but that would be a long process in many cases. It is shorter and more convenient to use the formula for the sum derived from the general expressions for S_n in the two equations below. The second one is obtained by reversing the order of the terms in the first one.

(1) $S_n = a + (a + d) + (a + 2d) + \cdots + (l - 2d) + (l - d) + l$.

(2) $S_n = l + (l - d) + (l - 2d) + \cdots + (a + 2d) + (a + d) + a$.

Adding corresponding members of (1) and (2), we have

(3) $2S_n = (a + l) + (a + l) + (a + l) + \cdots$
$$+ (a + l) + (a + l) + (a + l).$$

Noting that $a + l$ occurs n times in this sum, we may write

(4) $$2S_n = n(a + l),$$

and solving (4) for S_n we have Formula 3:

3. $S_n = \dfrac{n}{2} (a + l)$.

A second formula for the sum may be obtained by replacing the l in Formula 3 by $a + (n - 1)d$, its value by Formula 1. Thus,

$$S_n = \frac{n}{2} [a + a + (n - 1)d] \text{ so that Formula 4 is}$$

4. $S_n = \dfrac{n}{2} [2a + (n - 1)d]$.

To find S_n we use Formula 3 when n, a, and l are given, and Formula 4 when we know n, a, and d.

Example 1. Find the sum of the first 6 terms of the progression: $1, 3, 5, \ldots$.

Solution. Here $a = 1$, $d = 2$, and $n = 6$. By Formula 4,

(5) $S_n = \dfrac{6}{2} [2(1) + (6 - 1)2] = 3(2 + 10) = 36$ (*Ans.*).

Example 2. Find the sum of the first 5 terms of an A.P. in which $a = 2$ and $l = 14$.

Solution. By Formula 3, with $a = 2$, $l = 14$, and $n = 5$,

(6) $S_n = \dfrac{5}{2} [(2 + 14)] = \dfrac{5}{2} (16) = 40$ (*Ans.*)

EXERCISE 16-4

1. Find the sum of the first 6 terms of the A.P.: $3, 5, 7, \ldots$.
2. Find the sum of the first 10 terms of the A.P.: $32, 29, 26, \ldots$.
3. Find the sum of the first 8 terms of the A.P.: $-25, -21, -17, \ldots$.
4. Find the sum of the first 12 terms of the A.P.: $-7, -4, -1, \ldots$.
5. Find the sum of the A.P.: $\displaystyle\sum_{k=1}^{10} (4k - 1)$.
6. Find the sum of the A.P.: $\displaystyle\sum_{k=0}^{n} (k + 1)$.
7. The first term of an A.P. is 5 and the 7th term is 17. Find the sum of the first 7 terms.
8. If $a = 4, l = 23$, and $S_n = 243$, find n and d.
9. If $a = 5, n = 12$, and $d = 2$, find S_n and l.
10. If $a = 12, d = 3$, and $l = 30$, find S_n and n.
11. If $a = 101, S_n = 1457$, and $l = -7$, find n and d.
12. If $S_n = 24, d = -2$, and $l = -4$, find a and n.
13. If $n = 13, d = \dfrac{3}{2}$, and $l = 33$, find S_n and a.
14. If $a = 17, n = 15$, and $l = -25$, find S_n and d.
15. If $S_n = 171, n = 9$, and $d = 2$, find a and l.
16. If $a = 5, d = 3$, and $S_n = 98$, find n and l.
17. If $n = 10, l = 43$, and $S_n = 250$, find a and d.
18. If $a = -6, n = 11$, and $S_n = 99$, find d and l.

19. How many boys are required for a triangular formation having 6 boys in the first row, 5 in the next, and so on to the last row, in which there is only one boy?

20. A ball falls and bounced to a height of 25 feet. It continues bouncing 5 feet less each time. How far does it travel between the first and sixth time it strikes the ground?

21. Ten bales of hay are lying 4 feet apart in a row. The first is 4 feet from a truck, the second is 8 feet, etc. How far must a man travel if he starts at the truck and carries it all, one bale at a time, to the truck?

22. A boy starts at the first one of 11 marks that are 5 yards apart and touches each of the other ten marks in order. If he returns to his starting point after each touch, what is the total distance he travels?

23. Five boys inherit an estate. Each one after the first receives $200 less than the one before him. If the value of the estate was $13,000, how much did each boy receive?

24. A man invests $100 at 5 per cent simple interest at the beginning of each year. Find the value of his investments at the end of 10 years.

25. A man invests $1,000 at 4 percent simple interest at the beginning of each year. Find the value of his investments at the end of 6 years.

26. A man invests $500 at 6 percent simple interest at the beginning of each year. Find the value of his investments at the end of 5 years.

16-7. GEOMETRIC PROGRESSIONS

The following sequence is called a *geometric progression*, or as abbreviated, a G.P.:

$$(1) \qquad a, ar, ar^2, ar^3, \ldots, l, \ldots$$

From (1) we note that any term after the first is found by multiplying the term preceding it by r. Or again, if any term after the first is divided by the preceding term, the quotient is r. This quantity r is called the *common ratio*.

Aside from r, which replaces the d of an A.P., the elements of a G.P. are the same as those of an A.P. The word "snarl" (replacing "lands"), here might be used as a memory aid.

The exponent of r in any term is one less than the position of the term. It follows that if there are n terms in a G.P., the last term is ar^{n-1}. Thus we have Formula 5:

  5. $l = ar^{n-1}$.

The sum S_n of n terms of a G.P., called more briefly the sum of the G.P., may be indicated as follows:

$$(2) \qquad S_n = a + ar + ar^2 + \cdots + ar^{n-2} + ar^{n-1}.$$

If we multiply each member of (2) by r, we have

$$(3) \qquad rS_n = ar + ar^2 + ar^3 + \cdots + ar^{n-1} + ar^n.$$

When the left- and right-hand sides of (3) are subtracted from the corresponding sides of (2), all terms in the right-hand members drop out except a in (2) and ar^n in (3). Thus we get

$$(4) \qquad S_n - rS_n = a - ar^n,$$

or

$$(5) \qquad S_n(1 - r) = a(1 - r^n).$$

The solution of (5) for S_n yields Formula 6:

  6. $S_n = \dfrac{a(1 - r^n)}{1 - r}, (r \neq 1)$.

Note that if $r = 1$, Formula 6 gives S_n the meaningless value $\dfrac{0}{0}$, whereas actually $S_n = na$ in that case.

Since $l = ar^{n-1}$ by Formula 5, it follows that $rl = ar^n$. Replacing ar^n by rl in Formula 6, we get Formula 7:

7. $S_n = \dfrac{a - rl}{1 - r}$ $(r \neq 1)$.

If any three of the elements $a, r, n, l,$ and S_n are given, the other two can be found by use of Formulas 5, 6, and 7.

Example 1. Find the 10th term of the progression: $1, 2, 4, \ldots$.

Solution. Here $a = 1, r = 2,$ and $n = 10$. By Formula 5,

(6) $l = 1(2)^9 = 512$ (*Ans.*).

Example 2. Find the sum of the first 8 terms of the progression $2, 6, 18, \ldots$.

Solution. By Formula 6, with $a = 2, r = 3,$ and $n = 8$,

(7) $S_n = \dfrac{2(1 - 3^8)}{1 - 3} = \dfrac{2(3^8 - 1)}{3 - 1} = 3^8 - 1 = 6560$ (*Ans.*).

Example 3. Insert 3 geometric means between $\dfrac{1}{2}$ and 8.

Solution. Here $a = \dfrac{1}{2}, l = 8,$ and $n = 5$. By Formula 5,

(8) $8 = \dfrac{1}{2} (r)^4,$

or

(9) $16 = r^4.$
$$r^4 - 16 = 0$$
$$(r^2 - 4)(r^2 + 4) = 0$$
$$r = 2 \quad \text{or} \quad r = -2$$

The G.P. is then either $\dfrac{1}{2}, 1, 2, 4, 8$ or $\dfrac{1}{2}, -1, 2, -4, 8$, and hence the geometric means are 1, 2, and 4 or $-1, 2,$ and -4.

(It should be noted that in this chapter we are disregarding any solutions in which the value of r involves the imaginary unit i.)

Example 4. Find the geometric mean of x and y, assuming that either both x, y are positive or both are negative.

Solution. Here $a = x, l = y,$ and $n = 3$. By Formula 5,

(10) $y = x(r)^2,$

whence

(11) $r^2 = \dfrac{y}{x},$

or

$$r = + \sqrt{\frac{y}{x}} = + \frac{\sqrt{xy}}{x}.$$

(12)

∨

$$r = - \sqrt{\frac{y}{x}} = - \frac{\sqrt{xy}}{x}.$$

The G.P., then, is either x, $\sqrt{xy}$, y or x, $-\sqrt{xy}$, y. Thus, we find that there are actually two geometric means of any two numbers with like signs. If we denote both of these by M_g, we have, as Formula 8,

8. $M_g = + \sqrt{xy}$, or $M_g = - \sqrt{xy}$

Example 5. Find the geometric means of 4 and 16.

Solution. By Formula 8,

$$M_g = + \sqrt{(4)(16)} = + \sqrt{64}.$$

(13)

∨

$$M_g = - \sqrt{(4)(16)} = - \sqrt{64}.$$

Thus the answers are 8 and -8.

Example 6. If $a = 32$, $l = 1$, and $r = \frac{1}{2}$, find n and S_n.

Solution. By Formula 5,

(14)
$$1 = (32)\left(\frac{1}{2}\right)^{n-1},$$

whence

(15)
$$\frac{1}{32} = \left(\frac{1}{2}\right)^{n-1}.$$

But $\left(\frac{1}{2}\right)^5 = \frac{1}{32}$, so that $n - 1 = 5$, and hence

(16)
$$n = 6 \quad (Ans.).$$

Also, by Formula 7,

(17)
$$S_n = \frac{32 - \frac{1}{2}(1)}{1 - \frac{1}{2}} = \frac{32 - \frac{1}{2}}{\frac{1}{2}} = \frac{64 - 1}{1} = 63 \quad (Ans.).$$

Example 7. Given $S_n = 126$, $r = 2$, and $l = 64$, find a and n.

Solution. By Formula 7,

(18)
$$126 = \frac{a - 2(64)}{1 - 2} = \frac{a - 128}{-1} = -a + 128.$$

Hence

(19) $$a = 128 - 126 = 2 \quad (Ans.).$$

Also, by Formula 5,

(20) $$64 = (2)(2)^{n-1} = 2^{1+n-1} = 2^n.$$

But $2^6 = 64$, and hence

(21) $$n = 6 (Ans.).$$

EXERCISE 16-5

1. Find the 5th term of the G.P.: $2, 4, 8, \ldots$
2. Find the 6th term of the G.P.: $1, 3, 9, \ldots$
3. Find the 7th term of the G.P.: $32, 16, 8, \ldots$
4. Find the 8th term of the G.P.: $1, -2, 4, \ldots$
5. Find the 9th term of the G.P.: $16, -8, 4, \ldots$
6. Insert 3 geometric means between 2 and 32.
7. Insert 4 geometric means between 32 and 1.
8. Insert 2 geometric means between 16 and -2.
9. Insert 4 geometric means between 1 and -243.
10. Insert 3 geometric means between 81 and 1.
11. Find the geometric means of 2 and 8.
12. Find the geometric means of 1 and 9.
13. Find the geometric means of -3 and -27.
14. Find the geometric means of -5 and -20.
15. Find the geometric means of $4a$ and $9a$.
16. If $a = 2, r = 2$, and $l = 16$, find n and S_n.
17. If $a = 32, l = -1$, and $r = -\dfrac{1}{2}$, find n and S_n.
18. If $a = 81, l = 1$, and $r = \dfrac{1}{3}$, find n and S_n.
19. If $a = 1, r = -2$, and $l = -32$, find n and S_n.
20. If $a = 16, r = \dfrac{1}{2}$, and $l = \dfrac{1}{2}$, find n and S_n.
21. If $S_n = 63, r = 2$, and $l = 32$, find n and a.
22. If $S_n = 121, r = 3$, and $l = 81$, find n and a.
23. If $a = 128, n = 8$, and $l = 1$, find r and S_n.
24. If $a = 16, n = 6$, and $l = \dfrac{1}{2}$, find r and S_n.

25. Find the sum of the areas of 5 squares if the side of the first is 12 inches, the side of the second is 6 inches, the next 3 inches, and so on to the last one.

26. A man buys 10 candies paying 1¢ for the first, 2¢ for the second, 4¢ for the third and so on. Find the total cost.

27. Four men divide $5,625 profit. Each one after the first receives half as much as the one before him. Find the amount each one receives.

28. An estate of $11,808 is divided among 4 people so that each one after the first receives $\frac{4}{5}$ as much as the one before him. How much does each one receive?

29. Each person has 2 ancestors of the first preceding generation (parents), 2^2, or 4, of the second (grandparents), etc. How many ancestors has he in the twelfth preceding generation?

30. Assuming that a patriarch has 6 children (first following generation), that each of these has 6 children (second generation) and so on, find the total number of descendants of the patriarch through and including the fourth generation.

16-8. INFINITE GEOMETRIC PROGRESSIONS

The sum of a finite geometric progression, $S_n = \dfrac{a - ar^n}{1 - r}$ can also be written as

(1)
$$S_n = \frac{a}{1 - r} - \frac{ar^n}{1 - r}.$$

If $|r| < 1$ (or $-1 < r < 1$), then r^n becomes numerically smaller and smaller as n becomes larger and larger. For example, if $r = \dfrac{1}{10}$ or $r = -\dfrac{1}{10}$, then

$$r^2 = \left(\frac{1}{10}\right)^2 = \frac{1}{100}; \quad \text{or} \quad r^2 = \left(-\frac{1}{10}\right)^2 = \frac{1}{100}$$

$$r^3 = \left(\frac{1}{10}\right)^3 = \frac{1}{1000}; \quad \text{or} \quad r^3 = \left(-\frac{1}{10}\right)^3 = -\frac{1}{1000}$$

$$r^4 = \left(\frac{1}{10}\right)^4 = \frac{1}{10,000}; \quad \text{or} \quad r^4 = \left(-\frac{1}{10}\right)^4 = \frac{1}{10,000}$$

and so on. By taking n large enough, r^n can be made numerically as close to zero as desired. As a consequence, $1 - r^n$ will be close to 1, and Formula (1) becomes $S_\infty = \dfrac{a}{1 - r}$, since $\lim\limits_{n \to \infty} \dfrac{ar^n}{1 - r} = 0$ when $|r| < 1$.

The statement $\lim\limits_{n \to \infty} \dfrac{ar^n}{1 - r} = 0$ is a conventional way in mathematics of saying that as n gets very large with $|r| < 1$, $(-1 < r < 1)$, the value of $\dfrac{ar^n}{1 - r}$ can be made as close to zero as is desired. In English it reads "the limit, as n approaches a positive integer however large in the expression $\dfrac{ar^n}{1 - r}$ with $|r| < 1$, is zero." It is noted and emphasized that the word "sum" is not being used in the ordinary sense, but implies a new concept described as a "limit of a sum." It is beyond the scope of this text to explore the concept of limit any further than to use it in an intuitive sense in what follows. Therefore, S (usually symbolized S_∞), the sum of an infinite geometric progression with $|r| < 1$, is defined as the value $\dfrac{a}{1 - r}$. An infinite geometric progression is often referred to as an infinite geometric series.

Example 1. Find the sum of the infinite geometric series

$$1, \frac{1}{2}, \frac{1}{4}, \frac{1}{8}, \ldots.$$

Solution. Here $a = 1$, $r = \dfrac{1}{2}$, and $S_\infty = \dfrac{1}{1 - \dfrac{1}{2}} = 2$

Example 2. Find the sum of the infinite geometric series

$$12, 3, \frac{3}{4}, \ldots.$$

Solution. Here $a = 12$, $r = \dfrac{1}{4}$, and $S = \dfrac{12}{1 - \dfrac{1}{4}} = \dfrac{12}{\dfrac{3}{4}} = 16.$

Example 3. Express the repeating decimal fraction $2.363636 \ldots$ as a common fraction.

Solution. Note that $2.363636 \ldots$ can be written as

$$2 + 0.36 + 0.0036 + 0.000036 + \cdots,$$

an infinite geometric series with $a = 0.36$ and $r = 0.01$. Thus

$$S = \frac{a}{1-r} = \frac{0.36}{1-0.01} = \frac{36}{100-1} = \frac{36}{99} = \frac{4}{11}$$

Hence $2.363636\ldots = 2 + \dfrac{4}{11} = \dfrac{26}{11}$

It should be observed from Examples 2 and 3, that repeating decimals, when treated this way, produce rational numbers. A most important difference between a rational and irrational real number is that the latter when converted into a decimal form will never produce a repeating decimal representation. For example, $\sqrt{3}$, π, etc., can never be represented as repeating decimals whereas $\dfrac{1}{3}, \dfrac{1}{7}$, or even $\dfrac{2}{5}$, $(0.40000\ldots)$, can. It is also of interest to know that $\dfrac{2}{5}$ may be represented as $0.39999\ldots$ as well as $0.40000\ldots$. This follows from the fact the

$$
\begin{aligned}
0.39999\ldots &= 0.3 + [0.09 + 0.009 + 0.0009 + \cdots] \\
&= 0.3 + \frac{0.09}{1-0.1} \\
&= \frac{3}{10} + \frac{9}{100-10} \\
&= \frac{3}{10} + \frac{1}{10} \\
&= \frac{2}{5}.
\end{aligned}
$$

EXERCISE 16-6

If the sum exists, find same for the infinite geometric series in Probs. 1–5. If the sum does not exist, state why.

1. $50 + 40 + 32 + \cdots$.

2. $12 - 2 + \dfrac{1}{3} + \cdots$.

3. $\displaystyle\sum_{k=1}^{\infty} 10\left(\frac{1}{4}\right)^{k}$.

4. $\displaystyle\sum_{k=1}^{\infty} 32\left(-\frac{5}{8}\right)^{k}$.

5. $(2)^{-1/2} + (6)^{-1/2} + \cdots$.

Convert the following to a common fraction.

6. $0.222\ldots$

7.   0.545454...
8.   0.215215215...
9.   4.132132132...
10.   10.1111...

11.   Show that 0.59999... is another way of representing 0.6 which in turn is $\frac{3}{5}$.

12.   Write the repeating decimal representations for $\frac{1}{7}, \frac{2}{7}, \frac{3}{7}, \frac{4}{7}, \frac{5}{7}, \frac{6}{7}, \frac{8}{7}, \frac{9}{7}$, etc., and make a very important observation. What is this observation?

13.   Obtain repeating decimal representations for $\frac{1}{19}, \frac{2}{19}, \frac{3}{19}, \ldots, \frac{18}{19}, \frac{20}{19}$, etc., and observe what happens.

14.   The owner of a fleet of trucks finds that if used motor oil is refined so that it can be used over again, 15 percent of the oil is lost in the process. If he starts with 200 gallons of refined oil and refines this oil each time it becomes dirty, determine the total amount of oil he has used before the 200 gallons have been lost.

15.   A ball is dropped from a height of 5 feet. On each rebound it bounces back to $\frac{3}{4}$ of the height from which it last fell. Assuming that this bouncing continues indefinitely, find the distance the ball travels in coming to rest. How far has it traveled after bouncing 5 times?

16.   Find the value of the following geometric series
      (a) $1 + (1.03) + (1.03)^2 + (1.03)^3 + (1.03)^4$ [*Hint*: $(1.03)^5 = 1.1593$].
      (b) $1 + (1.03) + (1.03)^2 + \cdots$.

chapter **17**

Introduction to Logic

17-1. DEDUCTIVE AND INDUCTIVE REASONING

The segment of mathematics commonly accepted as algebra is like high school geometry—it is a *deductive discipline.* By a deductive discipline we mean that it is dependent for its conclusions on agreed meanings for words, phrases, symbols, postulates, rules of logical inference, and the like. When a conclusion is obtained deductively, it follows from an hypothesis and is obtained through standardized rules of logic. It is a conclusion that does not change, a permanent conclusion that can be used to arrive at other conclusions in mathematics. It is for this reason that both algebra and geometry are said to follow deductive patterns in their respective reasoning procedures. Conclusions by inductive methods are usually based on observed or experimental data, and do not necessarily have to be permanent. For example, if it has been raining on each of ten successive days and the conclusion is drawn that, based on these observations, it will be raining on the eleventh day, it becomes evident that this may not happen. As a result the conclusion thus obtained will have to be modified as new observational information is recorded. Conclusions of the inductive type do not assure the consistent stability that is attributed to those obtained by deductive methods.

The intent of this text is to borrow certain connectives and operational rules from logical inference in order to initiate important ideas in algebra. The introduction and exploration of techniques for understanding and doing algebra requires a reasonable amount of material borrowed from the discipline of logic.

In Sec. 1-11 set-builder notation was introduced, wherein descriptions were made for replacing variables in open sentences which became either true or false. Such open sentences which are definitely either true or false, but not both, are referred to as *tf-statements or propositions* as defined in Sec. 17-2. The customary letters used to specify propositions are p, q, r, s, ..., which will be adopted here to clarify other ideas. In algebra these propositions become the language for communicating the working tools with which we are able to carry out our thinking. Each $p, q, r, s, \ldots$ is assigned a truth value of being either "a truth" designated as T or "a falsity" designated as F, but not both at the same time. Accordingly the algebra discipline borrows such "statements of logic" and is able to advance itself by deductive reasoning. In logic or in algebra many different symbols are used to carry out operations among the propositions $p, q, r, s, \ldots$. These operative symbols are called *connectives*, and in order to introduce them, the following context and example material will reinforce their meaning and usage.

17-2. TF-STATEMENTS

The word *calculus* appears in many mathematical discussions. According to the dictionary, the word *calculus* means "a method of computation." In the sentential or statement calculus, we attempt to compute the truth-value of a sentence. The only statements which are subjected to truth-value computation in the sentential calculus are those to which we can assign the value "true" or "false," but not both. Any sentence that leads to a variance of opinion will not be considered. Hence the sentential calculus may be considered, in part, as an infinite set of statements, each of which corresponds to one and only one of the following words—true, false.

Definition. A tf-statement is a statement which can be classified as "true" or "false" but not both at the same time.

The following sentences are examples of tf-statements.

1. Columbus is the capital of Ohio.
2. $4 + 2 = 8$.
3. John will carry the luggage.
4. $\log_{10}(100) = 2$.

We shall not attempt to compute the truth value of such sentences as the following:

1. Walk slowly.
2. Do you enjoy working with numbers?
3. Halt!
4. He is going to Boston on Tuesday.

Example (4) is called an open sentence, and its truth value cannot be computed until "he" is specified. Sentences such as (4) are examined in the phase of logic called the restricted predicate calculus.

EXERCISE 17-1

1. Which of the following are tf-statements?

    (a) Today is Thursday.
    (b) Jane is the prettiest girl at the University of Akron.
    (c) Five is greater than 3.
    (d) Jim is always busy.
    (e) Be careful!
    (f) I always lie.
    (g) You will meet many interesting people in Italy.
    (h) $2x + 1 = 7$.
    (i) Mathematics is fun.

2. Write three sentences which would be considered as tf-statements and three sentences which would not be considered as tf-statements.

17-3. CONNECTIVES, COMPOSITE STATEMENTS, AND SYMBOLS

Most of the sentences which are significant in any chain of logical reasoning are composite statements. That is, they consist of tf-statements and such connectives as "or," "and," "if...then," "not," and "if and only if."

We shall be using the letters p, q, r, s, t, and w to represent tf-statements. For example, consider the following statement, p: It is raining. This statement means that we are going to let p represent the sentence "It is raining." The connectives mentioned above will be represented by the following symbols:

$\wedge$ and
$\vee$ or
$\rightarrow$ if...then
$\sim$ not
$\leftrightarrow$ if and only if

Hence if p and q represent tf-statements, then

$p \wedge q$ is read "p and q,"
$p \vee q$ is read "p or q,"
$p \rightarrow q$ is read "if p, then q,"
$\sim p$ is read "it is not true that p" or simply "not p,"
$p \leftrightarrow q$ is read "p if and only if q."

The student will soon find that it is much easier to analyze a composite statement if the statement is first put into skeleton form, i.e., letters and symbols.

In Sec. 7-1 the connectives $\vee$ and $\wedge$ were introduced and it was explained therein how they were to be used with defining conditions. Even though defining conditions are not actually tf-statements until replacement values are made, it has become conventional in mathematics to use $\vee$ and $\wedge$ as was illustrated there. However, in the logic discipline the connectives $\vee$ and $\wedge$ as well as the others are used only with tf-statements.

Definition.   If p and q represent tf-statements, then the sentence represented by $p \wedge q$ is called a *conjunction*.

The conjunction of the statements

John enjoys classical music

and

Bob enjoys classical music

produces

John enjoys classical music and Bob enjoys classical music.

We will also consider "John and Bob enjoy classical music" as a conjunction since it has the same meaning as the preceding sentence. If r: John enjoys classical music, and w: Bob enjoys classical music, then $(r \wedge w)$: John and Bob enjoy classical music.

Definition.   If p and q represent tf-statements, then the sentence represented by $p \vee q$ is called a *disjunction*.

For example, if p: $2 + 3 = 5$, and q: $4 = 5$, then $p \vee q$ represents the disjunction $2 + 3 = 5$ or $4 = 5$.

Definition.   If p and q represent tf-statements, then the sentence represented by $p \rightarrow q$ is called a *conditional*.

If r: John works hard, and s: John will get a promotion, then $r \rightarrow s$ represents the conditional—If John works hard, then John will get a promotion, or simply, John will get a promotion if he works hard.

Definition.   If p and q represent tf-statements, then the sentence represented by $p \leftrightarrow q$ is called a *biconditional*.

If w: Today is Thursday, and r: Tomorrow is Friday, then $w \leftrightarrow r$ represents Today is Thursday if and only if tomorrow is Friday. We will establish in a later section that a biconditional has the same meaning as a *conjunction* of two *conditionals*. For example, "Today is Thursday if and only if tomorrow is Friday" has the same meaning as "Today is Thursday if tomorrow is Friday and today is Thursday only if tomorrow is Friday" or simply, "If tomorrow is Friday, then today is Thursday and if today is Thursday, then tomorrow is Friday."

Definition. If *p* represents a tf-statement, then the sentence represented by ~ *p* is called a *negation*.

For example, if *p*: The sun is shining, then ~ *p*: It is not true that the sun is shining, or simply, The sun is not shining.

As mentioned at the beginning of this section, composite statements consist of tf-statements and some combination of the five connectives defined in this section. The question now is, are composite statements tf-statements? That is to ask, can we assign a truth value to a composite statement? The answer to this question is *yes* as is discussed in Sec. 17-4.

EXERCISE 17-2

1. Categorize each of the following sentences as a conjunction, a disjunction, a conditional, a biconditional, or a negation.

    (a) John will pass if and only if he receives a 75 on the final examination.
    (b) There is no easy road to success.
    (c) Jane will attend college if she wins the scholarship.
    (d) No one saw the crack in the dam.
    (e) Mr. Smith is going to Cleveland or he is not going to Cleveland.
    (f) James and Frank are good students.
    (g) If David wins he loses and if he loses he wins.
    (h) Three is greater than two but five is less than seven.
    (i) If Thomas is willing to spend the time, he can become a great violinist.
    (j) Bob or Sam will carry the luggage.

2. Write each of the statements in the preceding exercise in symbolic form using *p*, *q*, etc., to represent the tf-statements and using the logical symbols $\vee$, $\wedge$, $\rightarrow$, $\leftrightarrow$, and ~ to represent the connectives.
    Hint. When writing a statement in symbolic form, it is best to let *p*, *q*, etc., represent "positive" tf-statements. For example, consider the following sentence: Jane will pass the examination or she will be unhappy. Let *p*: Jane will pass the examination, and let *q*: She will be happy. Hence, the symbolic form for the statement is $p \vee \sim q$.

17-4. SENTENTIAL STATEMENT PATTERNS AND TRUTH TABLES

If *p*, *q*, and *r* represent tf-statements, then $p \wedge q$, $p \rightarrow q$, $\sim p \leftrightarrow q$, $(p \vee q) \rightarrow r$, etc., are called *sentential statement patterns*.
    If *p*: Bob will go to the movies,
        q: Joe will go to the movies,
    and *r*: Harold will go to the movies,

then the sentential statement pattern $(p \lor q) \rightarrow r$ represents "If Bob or Joe goes to the movies, then Harold will go to the movies.

In this section we will define, by the use of *truth tables*, that any sentence which can be represented symbolically by one of the five basic sentential statement patterns $(p \land q;\ p \lor q;\ p \rightarrow q;\ p \leftrightarrow q;\ \sim p)$ is a tf-statement. The letters T and F as already explained will be used to represent true and false, respectively.

Definition.

Conjunction

p	q	$p \land q$
T	T	T
T	F	F
F	T	F
F	F	F

The definition of conjunction truth-value relates that a sentence represented by $p \land q$ will have the truth-value true assigned to it only if both p and q represent true statements. For example, consider the following sentence: $3 + 1 = 4$ and $5 = 6$. If we let $p:3 + 1 = 4$ and $q:5 = 6$, then the statement "$3 + 1 = 4$ and $5 = 6$" is an *instance* of the second row of the truth-table and hence, it is a false statement.

Definition.

Disjunction

p	q	$p \lor q$
T	T	T
T	F	T
F	T	T
F	F	F

The student should note that the above truth table attaches a somewhat different interpretation to the disjunction "or" than is common in everyday speech. The truth-table disjunction is referred to as *inclusive disjunction*. The everyday-speech disjunction is referred to as *exclusive disjunction*. Inclusive disjunction means "p or q, or both," while exclusive disjunction means "p or q, but not both."

Definition.

Conditional

p	q	$p \rightarrow q$
T	T	T
T	F	F
F	T	T
F	F	T

If a sentence has the sentential statement pattern $p \rightarrow q$, then the statement represented by p is called the *hypothesis* of the conditional and the statement represented by q is called the *conclusion* of the conditional. The definition of conditional truth value states that a conditional will be assigned truth value *false* only when the hypothesis is true and the conclusion is false. Rows 3 and 4 of the above truth table may be somewhat bewildering to the student. Let us attempt to clear the air. Consider the following statement: "If the sun shines, then the game will be played." Suppose that the sun does not shine but the game is played, or suppose the the sun does not shine and the game is not played. Since the given statement makes *no* reference to these occurrences, it is considered as being a true statement with respect to the mentioned possible occurrences. In other words, it is a case of "innocent until proven guilty."

As a second example consider the following statement: "If Mary receives a B on the examination, then she will pass the course." This statement would be assigned truth value F only if Mary does receive a B on the examination but she does not pass the course.

Definition.

Biconditional

p	q	$p \leftrightarrow q$
T	T	T
T	F	F
F	T	F
F	F	T

As mentioned earlier, a biconditional is a double conditional and therefore it is evident that the biconditional $p \leftrightarrow q$ will be true if and only if p and q are both true or both false.

Since "p" and "not p" cannot occur simultaneously, the truth-value definition for negation is quite simple.

Definition.

Negation

p	$\sim p$
T	F
F	T

The preceding truth tables can be synthesized into the following table:

p	q	$\sim p$	$\sim q$	$p \wedge q$	$p \vee q$	$p \rightarrow q$	$p \leftrightarrow q$
T	T	F	F	T	T	T	T
T	F	F	T	F	T	F	F
F	T	T	F	F	T	T	F
F	F	T	T	F	F	T	T

Having discussed the truth value of the five basic types of composite statements, we can now turn to more complex statements.

Example 1.   If *p*: September has 30 days, and *q*: Akron is the capital of Ohio, then the statement represented by *p* ∧ ~*q* has truth-value T.

Example 2.   Consider the following sentence: "If it is snowing or raining, then Bob will not go to Dayton."

If we let *p*: It is snowing,
          q: It is raining,
   and *r*: Bob will go to Dayton,
then (*p* ∨ *q*) → ~*r* represents the given sentence. Notice that the parentheses are necessary. *p* ∨ *q* → ~*r* is an ambiguous sentential statement pattern and (*p* ∨ *q*) → ~*r* is different from *p* ∨ (*q* → ~*r*). For example, if *p*, *q*, and *r* are all true, then *p* ∨ *q* is true and ~*r* is false, and therefore (*p* ∨ *q*) → ~*r* is false because of a true hypothesis and a false conclusion. On the other hand, *p* ∨ (*q* → ~*r*) is true since *p* is true.

Example 3.   Given *p*: John's work is hard,
               q: John's rewards are few,
               r: John should seek another position.
(*p* ∧ *q*) ∧ ~*r* represents "John's work is hard and his rewards are few, and he should not seek another position."

The preceding statement would sound better if it were written as follows: "John's work is hard and his rewards are few but he should not seek another position." Notice that at times the word "but" may be employed in place of "and."

Example 4.   When does the sentential statement pattern (*p* ∧ *q*) ↔ *r* represent a true statement and when does it represent a false statement? The following truth table gives the answer.

p	*q*	*r*	*p* ∧ *q*	(*p* ∧ *q*) ↔ *r*
T	T	T	T	T
T	T	F	T	F
T	F	F	F	T
T	F	T	F	F
F	F	F	F	T
F	F	T	F	F
F	T	T	F	F
F	T	F	F	T

For example, the table relates that (*p* ∧ *q*) ↔ *r* represents a true statement for the instance when *p* is true and *q* and *r* are both false.

EXERCISE 17-3

1. Determine the truth-value of each of the following symbolic statements given
   that

   p: 3 + 5 = 8.
   q: A triangle has two sides.
   r: Lake Erie is one of the Great Lakes.
   s: 0 is an odd integer.
   w: Three-fifths of ten is six.

   (a) $p \wedge q$.
   (b) $q \rightarrow w$.
   (c) $s \leftrightarrow q$.
   (d) $p \vee r$.
   (e) $\sim w$.
   (f) $\sim p \vee \sim q$.
   (g) $s \vee (r \wedge w)$.
   (h) $\sim (p \wedge q) \rightarrow \sim w$.
   (i) $\sim (r \rightarrow s) \leftrightarrow (r \wedge \sim s)$.

2. Write an English equivalent to each of the symbolic statements in the preceding exercise.

3. (a) What is the truth value of $u \rightarrow t$ if t is true?
   (b) What is the truth value of $q \vee s$ if $\sim s$ is false?
   (c) What is the truth value of $(p \wedge r) \rightarrow \sim r$ if p is false?
   (d) What is the truth value of $(p \wedge r) \leftrightarrow q$ if $(p \vee q)$ has truth value F?

4. Show, by means of a truth table, when the following sentential statement
   pattern has truth value T.

   $$(p \vee \sim q) \rightarrow \sim p.$$

chapter 18

Mathematical Induction—The Binomial Theorem

18-1. INTRODUCTION

This chapter is designed to bring attention to two very important techniques in mathematics, namely, the uses and application of the "principle of mathematical induction," and that of the Binomial Theorem with its expansion. The following points will be stressed: (1) the procedural approach for proof as suggested by the mathematical induction principle; (2) the interpretation of the truth tables for the logic pattern $p \wedge q \leftrightarrow r$ as it relates to mathematical induction; and (3) that proof by the induction principle is *deductive in character and not inductive* as might be suggested erroneously from its descriptive title. The remainder of the chapter points up the importance of the binomial theorem and its expansion.

18-2. MATHEMATICAL INDUCTION

To best introduce this very important principle of mathematical induction, a few illustrative examples should conveniently serve the purpose.

Example 1. Suppose that some means, such as a formula, is under consideration wherein an infinite number of tf-statements (or propositions) are created. Each of these tf-statements has a truth value of being either true (T) or false (F), and now it becomes our objective to prove that all these tf-statements are true. How would one proceed to accomplish this in a logically accepted fashion? To be specific, let us investigate the situation as it concerns the formula $3^n + 5$, where n is a natural number. By substituting $n = 1, 2, 3, 4, \ldots$, ad infinitum, tf-statements such as $3^1 + 5, 3^2 + 5, 3^3 + 5, \ldots$, arise with the common property that each of them represents an even integer. It seems to be that way as is supported by the values 8, 14, 32,..., when evaluated from the formula $3^n + 5$. Is this a general statement of fact, or does the formula stop doing this at some stage that has not yet been reached? This is the problem that we attempt to resolve, and this is where "the principle of mathematical induction" enters the scene of action. It offers a *deductive procedure* for either verification or denial of our assertion concerning the tf-statements under study. It does this in the following fashion which consists of two parts. In the first part, actual testing of a few values such as $n = 1, 2$, etc. is made where the formula can be checked by observation. In our example, the testing of $n = 1, 2,\ldots$, resulted in evidence that indicated "even integers" were being produced by "$3^n + 5$." This now gives one confidence to proceed farther with other values of n, but the mere satisfaction that may come by testing a few values for n is not in itself enough for a general conclusion. For the sake of simplicity, we will adopt the scheme of symbolizing statements produced by $n = 1$, as $P(1)$, $n = 2$, by $P(2)$, $n = 3$, by $P(3)$, etc. Hence $P(5)$ would represent $3^5 + 5 = 248$ which evidently is an even integer.

The second part of a mathematical induction proof attempts to remove doubts that a precise n will ever be reached to destroy the fact that an even number cannot be produced. To do this, the following "if" hypothesis is introduced, namely—If $P(k)$ is an even integer, does it follow that $P(k + 1)$ will also be such? Here k is a fixed value of n, but not specified at this point of the reasoning. This "if hypothesis" is important as the discussion will show. To continue with the example, $3^n + 5$, we now proceed as follows:

If $P(k) = 3^k + 5$ is assumed to be an even integer, then we must show that, on this basis, $P(k + 1) = 3^{k+1} + 5$ is also even. To do this we endeavor to express $P(k + 1)$ in terms of $P(k)$ so that a conclusion can be obtained based on the assumed truth of $P(k)$. It is observed that

$$3^{k+1} = 3(3^k) = 3(3^k + 5 - 5)$$
$$= 3(3^k + 5) - 15$$
$$= 3P(k) - 15$$

Hence $P(k + 1) = 3^{k+1} + 5 = [3P(k) - 15] + 5 = 3P(k) - 10$. Since $P(k)$ is an accepted even number, $P(k + 1)$ will follow suit and also be even, as is evident from $3P(k) - 10$.

The mathematical induction principle now comes into action by combining both parts of our discussion. This is done by removal of the "if hypothesis" stated in part 2 of the reasoning by use of the fact that in part 1 of the reasoning, when $k = 1$, $P(1)$ is actually known to be an even integer. Hence with $k = 1$ chosen for the necessary k in the discussion of part 2 in our reasoning, there is no more need for the "if" as used therein and $P(2)$ is true. This can now be carried on ad infinitum by choosing successive values of k where $P(k)$ is known to be true and producing $P(k + 1)$ sequentially. When one carries out this procedure, *by a combination of the parts 1 and 2 of the reasoning*, the tf-statements are said to be true for all choices of n, through induction on n, where n is a natural number. This reasoning is said to be based on "the mathematical induction principle," a property possessed by the set of natural numbers $N = 1, 2, 3, \ldots$. When reasoning involves this principle, it is indeed deductive in character.

To point out the importance of parts 1 and 2 in a proof by mathematical induction, the following example is worthy of attention.

Example 2. Suppose we use the formula $3^n + 5$ of Example 1, but this time propose to show that $3^n + 5$ produces numbers which are always odd, when n is a natural number. If the results expressed in Example 1 are accepted as valid, then it is evident that what is being proposed here for $3^n + 5$ cannot be true.

However, for the sake of discussion and stressing a vital point, let us bypass part 1 of the induction procedure and proceed directly to part 2 for the proposed condition. In this part the assumption that if $P(k) = 3^k + 5$ is an odd integer for a precise k, does it then mean from this fact that $P(k + 1) = 3^{k+1} + 5$ is also an odd integer? As in the previous example, $P(k + 1) = 3(3^k + 5) - 10 = 3P(k) - 10$; and now, since $P(k)$ is assumed to be an odd integer, it is evident that the product of 3 times an odd integer minus 10 is still an odd integer. Hence it becomes conclusive that "if $P(k)$" is an odd integer, then $P(k + 1)$ is also one.

Our intelligence is immediately challenged, and rightfully so. What has happened here? Confidence is restored when we recall that in order for part 2 to become operative there must be a starting k produced in part 1. In this example such a k has not and cannot be established. As a consequence, the "induction principle" asserts that if part 1 does not hold, and even though part 2 did, the original formula $3^n + 1$ *does not* turn out odd integers for choices of n, a natural number, and never will.

This should convince the user of "the principle of mathematical induction" that both parts 1 and 2 in the reasoning are essential.

18-3.   THE TRUTH TABLE FOR $(p \wedge q) \leftrightarrow r$

In Example 4, Sec. 17-4, the truth table for the logic pattern $(p \wedge q) \leftrightarrow r$ is spelled out. It is most interesting to note that each of "the eight lines" in this biconditional table is a pattern of reasoning that can occur when mathematical induction is being used.

If p, q, r are replaced by the following tf-statements, namely:

p: The formula, (tf-statement, proposition), holds true for $n = 1$; i.e., $P(1)$ is true,

q: The formula holds true for $n = k + 1$, if it holds true for $n = k$; i.e., $P(k + 1)$ is true if $P(k)$ is true,

r: The formula holds true for all natural number choices of n; i.e., $P(n)$ is true for all choices of n, where n is a natural number,

each line in the truth table for $(p \wedge q) \leftrightarrow r$ will now represent either a valid or invalid pattern of thinking in an induction proof.

For example, the entries in line 3 of the table show that if both p and q are false, and if the arrived conclusion is for r to be true, the truth value for $(p \wedge q) \leftrightarrow r$ shows that this cannot be so. This truth table may be used effectively to test the eight distinct possible situations involved when the "principle of mathematical induction" is applied in a proof.

It is left as a student exercise to test out the eight distinct patterns suggested in the truth tables for "$(p \wedge q) \leftrightarrow r$" and verify the consistency with actuality where mathematical induction is involved.

18-4. THE MATHEMATICAL INDUCTION PRINCIPLE

We shall spell out the mathematical induction principle in two forms in what follows:

Form 1. If S is a subset of the set of natural numbers and if

(a) $1 \in S$, and if

(b) $k + 1 \in S$ whenever $k \in S$, then

(c) $S = N = \{1, 2, 3, \ldots\}$.

This states that the natural numbers possess the property that if any subset S of natural numbers is chosen and if it can be shown that (a) 1 is a member of this subset, (b) and that "$k + 1$" belongs to this subset whenever k does, then this subset from which we started must itself be the set of all the natural numbers.

If a formula is being studied for verification by the induction procedure and if $P(1), P(2), P(3), \ldots$, are the resulting tf-statements, a function is actually involved in the discussion. The set of natural numbers is the domain of the function, the rule of correspondence is the formula to be verified, and its range is made up of tf-statements

$$P(1), P(2), \ldots, P(n), \ldots$$

In set notation this could be represented as

$$\{(1, P(1)), (2, P(2)), (3, P(3)), \ldots\}.$$

Since our proofs concern the range of this function, we concentrate attention upon the set made up of the tf-statements $P(1)$, $P(2)$, $P(3), \ldots$, and divorce ourselves from set communication symbolism.

As a consequence Form 2 for the induction principle may be stated as follows.

Form 2.   Suppose that a formula, say $P(n)$, about a natural number n produces tf-statements (propositions) for every natural number n. Then if

    (a) $P(1)$ is true   and if

    (b)   the truth of $P(k)$ implies the truth of $P(k + 1)$, it
          then can be said that

    (c) $P(n)$ is true for every natural number n.

More examples follow to compliment those already discussed so that the important features of the "principle of mathematical induction" are reinforced in the mind of the student.

Example 1.   Prove by mathematical induction that

$$P(n) = 1 + 2 + 3 + 4 + \cdots + n = \frac{n(n + 1)}{2}$$

for all natural numbers n.

Solution.   Let S be a subset of natural numbers for which the statement $P(n)$ is true.

1.   If $n = 1$, then $P(1) = \dfrac{1(1 + 1)}{2} = 1$.   The left-hand member is also 1, and thus $1 \in S$ or $P(1)$ is true.   This verifies Step (a) of the mathematical induction procedure.

2.   Assume the formula true for $n = k$, or that $P(k)$ is true.   Then

$$P(k) = 1 + 2 + 3 + \cdots + k = \frac{k(k + 1)}{2}$$

is true.   The additional term $k + 1$ is now added:

$$\begin{aligned}
P(k + 1) &= P(k) + (k + 1) \\
&= 1 + 2 + 3 + \cdots + k + (k + 1) \\
&= \frac{k(k + 1)}{2} + (k + 1) \\
&= (k + 1)\left(\frac{k}{2} + 1\right) \\
&= (k + 1)\left(\frac{k + 2}{2}\right) \\
&= \frac{(k + 1)(k + 2)}{2}.
\end{aligned}$$

or

$$P(k + 1) = \frac{(k + 1)(k + 2)}{2}.$$

The expression in the right-hand member is now precisely the result obtained by substituting $n = k + 1$ in the given formula $\frac{n(n + 1)}{2}$. Combining (1) and (2), S is the set of *all* natural numbers, or correspondingly all propositions $P(n)$, where n is a natural number, are true.

Example 2. If the formula in the preceding example had been specified as

$$P(n) = 1 + 2 + 3 + \cdots + n = \frac{n(n + 1)}{2} + 3,$$

and if for the sake of argument the second procedural step in the mathematical induction proof is carried out without first attempting to see whether the theorem holds for $n = 1$, then if

$$P(k) = 1 + 2 + 3 + \cdots + k = \frac{k(k + 1)}{2} + 3$$

is accepted as true, it follows that

$$P(k + 1) = 1 + 2 + 3 + \cdots + k + (k + 1)$$

$$= \frac{k(k + 1)}{2} + 3 + (k + 1)$$

$$= (k + 1)\left(\frac{k}{2} + 1\right) + 3$$

$$= \frac{(k + 1)(k + 2)}{2} + 3,$$

which is what the formula $\frac{n(n + 1)}{2} + 3$ would produce when $n = k + 1$. Consequently, if the assumed formula for the sum of the integers is valid for the choice $n = k$, it is also valid for $n = k + 1$. However, the formula cannot be verified for $n = 1, 2, 3, \ldots$. Although the second part of the proof by mathematical induction indicates the truth, the first part does not hold. Thus, the assumed formula is not a true formula. Compare this with $(p \wedge q) \leftrightarrow r$, where p, q, and r have the truth values F, T, and F respectively.

Example 3. If we consider the proof of

$$P(n) = 1 + 2 + \cdots + (n - 1) + n = \frac{n}{2}(n + 1)$$

$$+ (n - 1)(n - 2) \cdots (n - 1000),$$

it is evident from the discussion in Example 1, that when $n = 1$, $P(1) = 1$;

$n = 2$, $P(2) = 3$; ... to $P(1000) = 500,500$.   However, when $n > 1000$, this formula does not hold.   Hence, the formula being tested provides a starting point as it should in accord with the mathematical induction procedure, but it is evident that this is not enough to assume the validity of the given formula.   If Part 2 of the induction procedure is attempted,

$$P(k + 1) = P(k) + (k + 1)$$

$$= \frac{k}{2}(k + 1) + (k + 1) + (k - 1)(k - 2) \cdots (k - 1000)$$

$$= \frac{(k + 1)(k + 2)}{2} + (k - 1)(k - 2) \cdots (k - 1000),$$

it will be observed that if the given formula

$$P(n) = 1 + 2 + \cdots + n = \frac{n}{2}(n + 1) + (n - 1)(n - 2) \cdots (n - 1000),$$

were to be used directly with $n = k + 1$, then

$$P(k + 1) = \frac{k + 1}{2}(k + 2) + k(k - 1)(k - 2) \cdots (k - 999),$$

which is not what was obtained in the previous step.   Thus $P(k + 1)$ does not follow from $P(k)$ being accepted as true.   This shows that part 2 of the induction procedure, even though a starting point in part 1 was established, is not valid.

The formula does not hold for all n, where n is a natural number.

Compare this with the logic pattern $(p \land q) \leftrightarrow r$, where p, q, and r are respectively T, F, F.

EXERCISE 18-1

By "the principle of mathematical induction" prove the specified formulas in each of Probs. 1–7. (*Note:* It should not be assumed that because you will find each formula is correct that a proof for same has not been achieved.   It is a *deductive proof* based on the axiomatic property of mathematical induction possessed by the natural numbers.   For this reason a question mark has been placed above each equality sign questioning the validity of the formula.)

1. $2 + 4 + 6 + \cdots + 2n \overset{?}{=} n(n + 1)$.

2. $1^2 + 2^2 + 3^3 + \cdots + n^2 \overset{?}{=} \dfrac{n(n + 1)(2n + 1)}{6}$.

3. $1^3 + 2^3 + 3^3 + \cdots + n^3 \overset{?}{=} \dfrac{n^2(n + 1)^2}{4}$.

4. $(1)(2) + (2)(3) + (3)(4) + \cdots + (n)(n + 1) \overset{?}{=} \dfrac{n(n + 1)(n + 2)}{3}$.

5. $\dfrac{1}{(1)(2)} + \dfrac{1}{(2)(3)} + \dfrac{1}{(3)(4)} + \cdots + \dfrac{1}{(n)(n+1)} \overset{?}{=} \dfrac{n}{n+1}$.

6. $\displaystyle\sum_{k=1}^{n} 2^k \overset{?}{=} 2(2^n - 1)$.

7. $\displaystyle\sum_{k=1}^{n} (2k - 1) \overset{?}{=} n^2$.

Prove or disprove the following formulas in Probs. 8–10.

8. $1 + 2 + 2^2 + 2^3 + \cdots + 2^{n-1} \overset{?}{=} 2^n - 1$.

9. $4 + 8 + 12 + \cdots + 4n \overset{?}{=} 2n(n+1)$.

10. $1 \cdot 4 + 2 \cdot 5 + 3 \cdot 6 + \cdots + n(n+3)$

    $\overset{?}{=} \dfrac{n(n+1)(n+5)}{3} + (n-1)(n-2) \cdots (n-10)$.

Prove by induction on n (a natural number) that:

11. $2 + 4 + \cdots + 2n \overset{?}{=} n(n+1)$.

12. $2 + 2^2 + \cdots + 2^n \overset{?}{=} 2^{n+1} - 2$.

13. $1 + 2 \cdot 2 + 3 \cdot 2^2 + 4 \cdot 2^3 + \cdots + n \cdot 2^{n-1} \overset{?}{=} (n-1)(2^n + 1)$.

14. Prove by induction on n that

    $$2n + 2 < 2^n \text{ for } n \geq 4.$$

    [*Hint:* Here part 1 of the induction starts with $P(4)$ where

    $$P(n) = 2n + 2 - 2^n.]$$

15. Show that $x^{2n} - 1$ is divisible by $x - 1, n = 1, 2, 3, \ldots$.
    [*Hint:* $x^{2(k+1)} - 1 = (x^{2(k+1)} - x^{2k}) + (x^{2k} - 1)$.]

18-5. FACTORIAL AND BINOMIAL COEFFICIENT SYMBOLISM

In order to facilitate the writing of such products as $1 \cdot 2 \cdot 3 \cdots 1000$; or $1 \cdot 2 \cdot 3 \cdot 4 \cdot 5 \cdots 50{,}000{,}000$, we adopt a symbolism (called *factorial notation*) and write these successive products starting with the positive integer 1 and ending with the positive integer n as $n!$ In the specific examples illustrated $1000!$, $50{,}000{,}000!$ would replace the indicated products. More formally, the definition which follows introduces the symbolism for future use.

Definition. If n is a positive integer, the symbol $n!$, which is read "n factorial," is used to denote the product of the first n positive integers

$$n! = n(n-1)(n-2) \cdots 3 \cdot 2 \cdot 1.$$

As a special case we include 0! obtained when $n = 0$ and define it as being $0! = 1$. In particular,

$$1! = 1$$
$$2! = 2 \times 1 = 2$$
$$3! = 3 \times 2 \times 1 = 6$$
$$4! = 4 \times 3 \times 2 \times 1 = 24$$
$$5! = 5 \times 4 \times 3 \times 2 \times 1 = 120$$

Note that

$$10! = 10 \times 9! \text{ (and not } 10! \times 9!)$$
$$100! = 100 \times 99!$$
$$(n + 1)! = (n + 1) \times n!$$
$$(3!)^2 = 3! \times 3! = 6 \times 6 = 36$$
$$(3 + 3)! = 6! = 720 \text{ (not } 3! + 3! \text{ which equals 12)}$$

The division of one factorial by another is carried out by dividing common factors in both the numerator and denominator. For example,

$$\frac{6!}{4!} = \frac{6 \times 5 \times 4 \times 3 \times 2 \times 1}{4 \times 3 \times 2 \times 1} = \frac{6 \times 5 \times 4!}{4!} = 6 \times 5 = 30.$$

In the case of very large numbers, the fact that

$$n! = n(n - 1)! = n(n - 1)(n - 2)!, \text{ etc.,}$$

is important to remember. For example, 50! and 48! are both large numbers but their ratio

$$\frac{50!}{48!} = \frac{50 \times 49 \times 48!}{48!} = 50 \times 49 = 2450$$

is easily calculated.

Factorials as illustrated were first defined for positive integers, and then for $n = 0$, namely 0! A reason for choosing 1 to represent 0! follows. For any positive integer n, it is found convenient to have available the formula $(n + 1) \times n! = (n + 1)!$ We are already aware that $1! = 1$. It is observed that when $n = 0$, the formula

$$(0 + 1)! = (0 + 1) \times 0!$$
$$1! = 1 \times 0!$$
$$1 = 1 \times 0!$$
$$1 = 0!$$

To make this statement true, and include 0! in factorial symbolism, a reasonable definition for 0! is 1. Hence

$$(n + 1) \times n! = (n + 1)!$$

holds for n a positive integer or n equal to zero.

In close association with "factorial notation" is a second type referred to either as "combination, or binomial coefficient symbolism." For example,

$$\frac{5 \cdot 4 \cdot 3}{1 \cdot 2 \cdot 3} \text{ is replaced by } \binom{5}{3}$$

$$\frac{10 \cdot 9 \cdot 8 \cdot 7 \cdot 6}{1 \cdot 2 \cdot 3 \cdot 4 \cdot 5} \text{ is replaced by } \binom{10}{5}$$

$$\frac{5 \cdot 4 \cdot 3 \cdot 2 \cdot 1}{1 \cdot 2 \cdot 3 \cdot 4 \cdot 5} \text{ is replaced by } \binom{5}{5}$$

$$\frac{n(n - 1)(n - 2)}{1 \cdot 2 \cdot 3} \text{ is replaced by } \binom{n}{3}$$

Accordingly,

$$\binom{5}{4} \text{ is the same as } \frac{5 \cdot 4 \cdot 3 \cdot 2}{1 \cdot 2 \cdot 3 \cdot 4}$$

$$\binom{25}{23} \text{ is the same as } \frac{25 \cdot 24 \cdot 23 \cdots 3}{1 \cdot 2 \cdot 3 \cdots 23}$$

$$\binom{n}{5} \text{ is the same as } \frac{n(n - 1)(n - 2)(n - 3)(n - 4)}{1 \cdot 2 \cdot 3 \cdot 4 \cdot 5}$$

A formal definition for this notation is now given.

Definition: The symbol $\binom{n}{r}$ where n and r are integers, $0 \leq r \leq n$, is called the *binomial coefficient symbol* (or combination symbol) and is

equal to $\dfrac{\overbrace{n(n - 1)(n - 2) \cdots (n - r + 1)}^{r \text{ factors}}}{r!}$.   "$\binom{n}{r}$" is read "the binomial co-

efficient n over r," or simply "n over r."

More will be said about this symbol in Sec. 18-6.

18-6.   THE BINOMIAL THEOREM

The expansions of the following powers of the binomial $(f + s)$ may be obtained by performing the indicated multiplications.

$$(1) \begin{cases} (f + s)^1 = f + s \\ (f + s)^2 = f^2 + 2fs + s^2 \\ (f + s)^3 = f^3 + 3f^2s + 3fs^2 + s^3 \\ (f + s)^4 = f^4 + 4f^3s + 6f^2s^2 + 4fs^3 + s^4 \\ \quad \vdots \qquad \qquad \vdots \quad \vdots \qquad \quad \vdots \qquad \qquad \vdots \\ (f + s)^n = f^n + nf^{n-1}s + \dfrac{n(n-1)}{1 \cdot 2} f^{n-2}s^2 + \dfrac{n(n-1)(n-2)}{1 \cdot 2 \cdot 3} f^{n-3}s^3 \\ \qquad \qquad + \cdots + \dfrac{n(n-1)(n-2)\cdots(n-r+1)}{1 \cdot 2 \cdot 3 \cdots r} f^{n-r}s^r + \cdots + s^n \end{cases}$$

The right-hand member in each of equations (1) is said to be the *binomial expansion* of its corresponding left-hand member. The expansion of $(f + s)^n$ is called the *binomial formula*; and the full equation is the algebraic statement of *the binomial theorem dealing with a positive integral index, n*. The proof of the binomial formula is given in more advanced discussions, but the student may verify it for various integral values of n.

It will be noted that if n represents the exponent of $f + s$ in the left-hand member of any of the equations of (1), then the following statements are true:

1. The number of terms in the expansion is $n + 1$.
2. The first term is f^n and the last term is s^n. Note that $f^n = f^n s^0$ and $s^n = f^0 s^n$.
3. The exponent of f decreases by one in each succeeding term of the expansion, while that of s increases by one. Furthermore, the sum of the exponents of f and s in any term is n.
4. The coefficient of the first term is 1, while the coefficient of the second term is n. If we multiply the coefficient of any term by the exponent of f in that term, and then divide the product by one more than the exponent of s in the same term, the result is the coefficient of the next term in the expansion.
5. The coefficients equidistant from both ends of the expansion are equal.

Example 1.   Expand $(x + y)^7$.

Solution.

$$(x + y)^7 = x^7 + 7x^6y + 21x^5y^2 + 35x^4y^3 + 35x^3y^4$$
$$+ 21x^2y^5 + 7xy^6 + y^7.$$

The first coefficient is 1. Since $n = 7$ in this case, the second coefficient is 7. The coefficient of the third term is $\dfrac{(7)(6)}{2}$ or 21. The coefficients of the fourth to eighth terms, as found in succession, are

$$\frac{(21)(5)}{3} = 35$$

$$\frac{35(4)}{4} = 35$$

$$\frac{(35)(3)}{5} = 21$$

$$\frac{(21)(2)}{6} = 7$$

and

$$\frac{(7)(1)}{7} = 1.$$

Example 2. Expand and simplify $(x - 2y)^5$.

Solution. Comparing the binomial $x - 2y$ with $f + s$, we find that x corresponds with f and $-2y$ with s. By the binomial formula,

$$[x + (-2y)]^5 = x^5 + 5(x)^4(-2y) + 10x^3(-2y)^2 + 10x^2(-2y)^3$$
$$+ 5x(-2y)^4 + (-2y)^5$$
$$= x^5 - 10x^4y + 40x^3y^2 - 80x^2y^3 + 80xy^4 - 32y^5.$$

Example 3. Expand and simplify $\left(3\sqrt{x} + \frac{y}{2}\right)^4$.

Solution. Here $f = 3\sqrt{x}$ and $s = \frac{y}{2}$. Again using the binomial formula, we have

$$\left(3\sqrt{x} + \frac{y}{2}\right)^4 = (3\sqrt{x})^4 + 4(3\sqrt{x})^3\left(\frac{y}{2}\right) + 6(3\sqrt{x})^2\left(\frac{y}{2}\right)^2 + 4(3\sqrt{x})\left(\frac{y}{2}\right)^3 + \left(\frac{y}{2}\right)^4$$

$$= 81x^2 + 54x^{3/2}y + \frac{27xy^2}{2} + \frac{3x^{1/2}y^3}{2} + \frac{y^4}{16}.$$

By including $(f + s)^0 = 1$, the coefficients of the terms of the binomial expansion form an interesting pattern, known as *Pascal's triangle* (see Fig. 18-1). The first and last numbers in each row are 1, while each of the numbers different from 1 may be obtained by adding the number to the left of it and the one to the right of it in the row which precedes it. Thus 15 in the 7th row is equal to the sum of 5 and 10 in the 6th row, while 10 in the 6th row is equal to the sum of 4 and 6 in the 5th row, etc.

An examination of a few of the first terms at the beginning of the binomial expansion reveals the following properties of the *r*th term:

$$(f + s)^0 : \qquad\qquad 1$$

$$(f + s)^1 : \qquad\qquad 1 \quad 1$$

$$(f + s)^2 : \qquad\qquad 1 \quad 2 \quad 1$$

$$(f + s)^3 : \qquad\qquad 1 \quad 3 \quad 3 \quad 1$$

$$(f + s)^4 : \qquad\quad 1 \quad 4 \quad 6 \quad 4 \quad 1$$

$$(f + s)^5 : \qquad 1 \quad 5 \quad 10 \quad 10 \quad 5 \quad 1$$

$$(f + s)^6 : \quad 1 \quad 6 \quad 15 \quad 20 \quad 15 \quad 6 \quad 1$$

FIG. 18-1

(a) The exponent of s is $r - 1$, that is, 1 less than the number position of the term.

(b) The exponent of f associated with the s is $n - r + 1$; hence, the sum of the exponent of f and of s is equal to n.

(c) The coefficient of the term is represented as a fraction whose denominator is $1 \cdot 2 \cdot 3 \cdots (r - 1)$ equal to $(r - 1)!$ while the numerator is $n(n - 1)(n - 2) \cdots (n - r + 2)$, the number of factors in the numerator being $r - 1$ and equal to the number of factors in the denominator.

It follows that, in the expansion of $(f + s)^n$, the rth term takes on the form

$$\overbrace{\frac{n(n - 1)(n - 2) \cdots (n - r + 2)}{1 \cdot 2 \cdot 3 \cdots (r - 1)}}^{r - 1 \text{ factors}} f^{n-r+1} s^{r-1}$$

Accordingly, the $(r + 1)$st term in the expansion of $(f + s)^n$ is

$$\overbrace{\frac{n(n - 1)(n - 2) \cdots (n - r + 1)}{1 \cdot 2 \cdot 3 \cdots r}}^{r \text{ factors}} f^{n-r} s^{r}.$$

It is of interest to note the comparison of the coefficients for the terms in the binomial expansion of $(f + s)^n$ in terms of the formulas learned in connection with the binomial coefficient or combination symbolism $\binom{n}{r}$. By use of this symbolism, the expansion for $(f + s)^n$ can be restated with the change in the coefficients as follows.

The coefficient of $f^n s^0$ is $\binom{n}{0} = 1$,

The coefficient of $f^{n-1} s$ is $\binom{n}{1} = n$,

The coefficient of $f^{n-2}s^2$ is $\binom{n}{2} = \dfrac{n(n-1)}{1 \cdot 2}$,

$\vdots$

The coefficient of $f^{n-r}s^r$ is $\binom{n}{r} = \dfrac{n(n-1)(n-2)\cdots(n-r+1)}{1 \cdot 2 \cdot 3 \cdots r}$.

The expansion of $(f+s)^n$ can now be specified as

$$(f+s)^n = \binom{n}{0}f^n + \binom{n}{1}f^{n-1}s + \binom{n}{2}f^{n-2}s^2 + \cdots$$

$$+ \binom{n}{r}f^{n-r}s^r + \cdots + \binom{n}{n}s^n.$$

In general, the rth and $(r+1)$th terms in the expansion of $(f+s)^n$ are

$$\binom{n}{r-1}f^{n-r+1}s^{r-1},$$

and

$$\binom{n}{r}f^{n-r}s^r$$

respectively.

The property of equality between the binomial coefficients equidistant from either end of any specified row in Pascal's triangle is due to the identity

$$\binom{n}{r} = \binom{n}{n-r}$$

This may be proven by realizing that

$$\binom{n}{r} = \overbrace{\frac{n(n-1)(n-2)\cdots(n-r+1)}{r!}}^{(r \text{ factors})}$$

$$= \frac{n(n-1)(n-2)\cdots(n-r+1)}{r!} \cdot \frac{(n-r)!}{(n-r)!}$$

$$= \frac{n(n-1)(n-2)\cdots(n-r+1)(n-r)(n-r-1)\cdots 2 \cdot 1}{r!(n-r)!}$$

$$= \frac{n!}{r!(n-r)!}.$$

This means that $\binom{n}{r} = \dfrac{n!}{r!(n-r)!}$. If we now compare $\binom{n}{n-r}$ by replacing n and r respectively by n and $n-r$ in the right-hand side of this latter equation, we obtain

$$\binom{n}{n-r} = \frac{n!}{(n-r)![n-(n-r)]!}$$

$$= \frac{n!}{(n-r)!r!}$$

Thus it follows that

$$\binom{n}{0} = \binom{n}{n},$$

$$\binom{n}{1} = \binom{n}{n-1},$$

$$\binom{n}{2} = \binom{n}{n-2},$$

and so on. In each row of Pascal's triangle, the first and last numbers are equal, as are the second and next to the last, and so on.

Pascal's triangle is repeated in Fig. 18-2 with the use of the combina-

$(f+s)^0$: $\binom{1}{0}$

$(f+s)^1$: $\binom{1}{0}$ $\binom{1}{1}$

$(f+s)^2$: $\binom{2}{0}$ $\binom{2}{1}$ $\binom{2}{2}$

$(f+s)^3$: $\binom{3}{0}$ $\binom{3}{1}$ $\binom{3}{2}$ $\binom{3}{3}$

$(f+s)^4$: $\binom{4}{0}$ $\binom{4}{1}$ $\binom{4}{2}$ $\binom{4}{3}$ $\binom{4}{4}$

FIG. 18-2

tion symbolism, so as to exhibit the convenient form for binomial coefficients.

The rule for finding each binomial coefficient, in the *n*th row other than its first and last numbers, is given by the formula

$$\binom{n}{r} = \binom{n-1}{r-1} + \binom{n-1}{r}$$

which can be verified by writing out the binomial coefficients in their alternate forms and simplifying the algebra involved.

Example 4. Expand $(x + y)^5$.

Solution.

$$(x+y)^5 = \binom{5}{0}x^5 + \binom{5}{1}x^4y + \binom{5}{2}x^3y^2 + \binom{5}{3}x^2y^3 + \binom{5}{4}xy^4 + \binom{5}{5}y^5$$

$$= x^5 + 5x^4y + 10x^3y^2 + 10x^2y^3 + 5xy^4 + y^5.$$

Since $\binom{n}{r} = \binom{n}{n-r}$, it is only necessary to compute $\binom{5}{0}$, $\binom{5}{1}$, and $\binom{5}{2}$.

Example 5. Find the coefficient of the term containing $x^5 y^7$ in the expansion of $(x + y)^{12}$.

Solution. In the notation of the binomial expansion the $(r + 1)$st term is $\binom{n}{r} f^{n-r} s^r$. Hence, $n = 12$, $r = 7$, $n - r = 5$, and its coefficient is $\binom{12}{7}$ which equals $\binom{12}{5}$ for evaluation purposes.

Example 6. Write the fifth term in the expansion of $(a - 3x)^{21}$.

Solution. In the notation of the binomial expansion $n = 21$, $r = 5$, $f = a$, $s = -3x$, the exponent of f is $n - r + 1 = 17$, and the exponent of s is $r - 1 = 4$. Hence, the fifth term is

$$\binom{21}{4} a^{17}(-3x)^4 = \binom{21}{4} a^{17}(-3)^4 x^4 = 484{,}785 a^{17} x^4.$$

18-7. AN EXTENSION OF THE BINOMIAL FORMULA

It is interesting to note that if n is either negative or fractional in $(f + s)^n$, the binomial formula still holds when proper restrictions have been placed on the numerical values of f and s. Further, the expansion is not limited to $n + 1$ terms as before, but is made up of an infinite number of terms. It is beyond the scope of this text to discuss these restrictions on the binomial expansion when n is not a positive integer. However, it may be stated in general that the expansion is useful when s is numerically smaller than f, and when the successive terms approach zero so rapidly that the sum of the first three or four terms of the expansion serves as a good approximation for $(f + s)^n$. Example 3 below shows an application to the extraction of roots.

Example 1. Expand $(x + y)^{-2}$ to five terms and simplify.

Solution.

$$(x + y)^{-2} = x^{-2} + (-2)x^{-3}y + \frac{(-2)(-3)}{2} x^{-4}y^2 + \frac{(-2)(-3)(-4)}{2 \cdot 3} x^{-5}y^3$$

$$+ \frac{(-2)(-3)(-4)(-5)}{2 \cdot 3 \cdot 4} x^{-6}y^4 + \cdots$$

$$= x^{-2} - 2x^{-3}y + 3x^{-4}y^2 - 4x^{-5}y^3 + 5x^{-6}y^4 - \cdots$$

If real-number values were substituted for x and y, say $x = 1$ and $y = 25$, the right-hand side would give an erroneous result. However, if $x = 25$ and $y = 1$, a value for $(26)^{-2} = \frac{1}{(26)^2}$ would follow correct to as many decimal places as desired. It is left as an exercise for the student to verify this statement.

Example 2. Expand $(x - y)^{-1/2}$ to four terms and simplify.

Solution.

$$(x - y)^{-1/2} = x^{-1/2} + \left(-\frac{1}{2}\right)x^{-3/2}(-y) + \frac{\left(-\frac{1}{2}\right)\left(-\frac{3}{2}\right)}{2}x^{-5/2}(-y)^2$$

$$+ \frac{\left(-\frac{1}{2}\right)\left(-\frac{3}{2}\right)\left(-\frac{5}{2}\right)}{2 \cdot 3}x^{-9/2}(-y)^3 + \cdots$$

$$= x^{-1/2} + \frac{x^{-3/2}y}{2} + \frac{3x^{-5/2}y^2}{8} + \frac{5x^{-9/2}y^3}{16} + \cdots$$

Example 3. Find $\sqrt[3]{1002}$ to three decimal places.

Solution. Write

$$\sqrt[3]{1002} = (1000 + 2)^{1/3}$$
$$= [1000(1 + .002)]^{1/3}$$
$$= 10(1 + .002)^{1/3}$$
$$= 10\left[1^{1/3} + \frac{1}{3}(1)^{-2/3}(.002) + \frac{\frac{1}{3}\left(-\frac{2}{3}\right)(1)^{-5/3}(.002)^2}{2} + \cdots\right]$$
$$= 10(1 + .00067 - .0000004 + \cdots)$$
$$= 10.0000 + .0067 - .0000 + \cdots$$
$$= 10.0067 \quad \text{or} \quad 10.007.$$

Note that for accuracy to three decimal places we write successive terms to four decimal places until a term is reached which yields zeros in the four places. Then the answer is "rounded off" to three places. This is a good working rule, though a much more extended discussion would be needed for a rigorous treatment of problems of this type. An incorrect result would be obtained if the above binomial expansion had been written as $(2 + 1000)^{1/3}$.

EXERCISE 18-2

Expand and simplify each of the expressions in Probs. 1–12.

1. $(x + y)^3$.   2. $(x - y)^3$.   3. $(2x - y)^6$.

4. $(3a^2 + b)^3$.   5. $\left(2x - \frac{3}{y}\right)^3$.   6. $(2\sqrt{x} + y)^4$.

7. $\left(3x - \dfrac{y}{2}\right)^6$.   8. $\left(a^2 + \dfrac{b}{3}\right)^4$.   9. $(2x - y^2)^5$.

10. $(3\sqrt{x} - y)^5$.   11. $\left(\dfrac{x}{2} + \dfrac{y^2}{3}\right)^4$.   12. $\left(\dfrac{x^{1/3}}{2} - y\right)^3$.

Find the first four terms in each of the indicated expansions in Probs. 13–15, and simplify the terms obtained.

13. $(x^{1/2} - 2y)^{10}$.   14. $\left(\dfrac{2}{x} - \dfrac{x}{4}\right)^8$.   15. $\left(\sqrt{x} + \dfrac{\sqrt[3]{y}}{2}\right)^{12}$.

Find and simplify the required terms in the indicated expansions in Probs. 16–18.

16. 5th term of $\left(\dfrac{x}{y} - \dfrac{y}{x}\right)^8$.

(*Hint.* Let t_5 represent the fifth term, with $\dfrac{x}{y}$ corresponding to f and $\dfrac{-y}{x}$ to s.)

Then $t_5 = \dfrac{8 \cdot 7 \cdot 6 \cdot 5}{1 \cdot 2 \cdot 3 \cdot 4} \left(\dfrac{x}{y}\right)^4 \left(\dfrac{-y}{x}\right)^4$.

17. 6th term of $\left(ab - \dfrac{b^2}{a}\right)^{12}$.

18. 8th term of $(\sqrt{x} - x^{-1/2})^{14}$.

Assuming that all restrictions have been taken into account, expand each of the expressions in Probs. 19–24 to four terms and simplify.

19. $(x + y)^{-3}$.   20. $(x - y)^{1/2}$.   21. $(2x + y)^{-1/2}$.

22. $(a^{1/2} + 2b^{1/2})^{-1}$.   23. $(1 + 3x)^{-2/3}$.   24. $(1 - 2x)^{-1}$.

By grouping terms, express as binomials and expand by use of the binomial formula the expressions in Probs. 25–30.

25. $(a + b + c)^2$ or $[(a + b) + c]^2$.   26. $(a + b - c - d)^2$.

27. $(a + b - c)^2$.   28. $(a - b - c)^2$.

29. $(a + b + c)^3$.   30. $(a + b - c)^3$.

Use the method of illustrative Example 3, Sec. 18-7, to find the values of the roots in Probs. 31–40 to three decimal places.

31. $\sqrt{101}$.   32. $\sqrt{110}$.   33. $\sqrt[3]{1.005}$.   34. $\sqrt[3]{1010}$.

35. $\sqrt{26}$.   36. $\sqrt{24}$ (or $\sqrt{25 - 1}$).   37. $\sqrt[3]{10}$ (or $\sqrt[3]{8 + 2}$).

38. $\sqrt[3]{28}$.   39. $\sqrt[3]{26}$.   40. $\sqrt[5]{31}$.

chapter 19

Logarithmic and Exponential Functions

19-1. EXPONENTIAL FUNCTIONS

In Chapter 9 the number symbol b^x was defined and described as an exponential number for any positive real number b and for any real number x. Thus the equation $y = b^x$ defines a function

$$f = \{(x,y) \mid y = b^x \wedge b \neq 0\}$$

whose domain is the set of real numbers R_e. This function f is called the *exponential function with base b*.

Example: Graph the exponential function given by

$$f = \{(x,y) \mid y = 2^x\}$$

Assigning, arbitrarily, convenient values of x and calculating their corresponding values of y, the following table results:

x	-3	-2	-1	0	1	2	3
y	$\dfrac{1}{8}$	$\dfrac{1}{4}$	$\dfrac{1}{2}$	1	2	4	8

Plotting this sample representative number of points (x,y) whose coordinates satisfy the equation $y = 2^x$, and drawing a smooth curve through them, we obtain the graph of Fig. 19-1.

If $b > 1$, the graph of any function of the form $\{(x,y) \mid y = b^x\}$ looks similar to that of the graph for $y = 2^x$. For every function of this form, the following properties hold:

(a) The range R of the function is the set of positive real numbers.

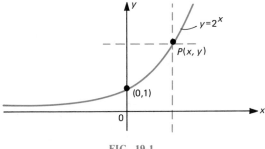

FIG. 19-1

(b)   If $x < 0$, $0 < b^x < 1$; if $x = 0$, $b^x = 1$; and if $x > 0$, then $b^x > 1$.
(c)   As x increases, b^x increases.

If $0 < b < 1$, the graph of a function $\{(x,y) \mid y = b^x\}$ will take on the graphical appearance in Fig. 19-2. For example, let us consider the case where $b = \dfrac{1}{2}$ or the graph of the equation $y = \left(\dfrac{1}{2}\right)^x = 2^{-x}$. By plotting a sample number of points whose coordinates satisfy the equation $y = \left(\dfrac{1}{2}\right)^x$, which are presented in the accompanying table, we obtain the curve shown in Fig. 19-2.

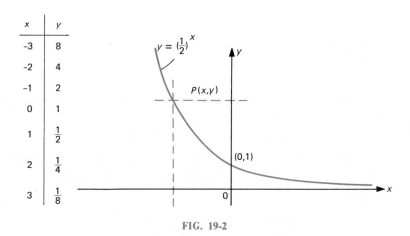

x	y
-3	8
-2	4
-1	2
0	1
1	$\dfrac{1}{2}$
2	$\dfrac{1}{4}$
3	$\dfrac{1}{8}$

FIG. 19-2

Each function of the form $\{(x, y) \mid y = b^x \wedge 0 < b < 1\}$ will have the same general appearance as the graph of $y = \left(\dfrac{1}{2}\right)^x$, and will satisfy the following properties:

(a)   The range R of the function is the set of positive real numbers.

(b) If $x < 0$, $b^x > 1$; if $x = 0$, $b^x = 1$; and if $x > 0$, $0 < b^x < 1$.

(c) As x increases, b^x decreases.

If $b = 1$, then $b^x = 1^x = 1$ for all $x \in R_e$.

There is one more significant property that is immediately apparent in the graphs of the equation $y = b^x$ which must be taken into account before proceeding further.

It is observed in Figs. 19-1 and 19-2 that if any line is drawn parallel to and above the x-axis, the curve is intersected in exactly one point. Consequently, if b is any real number with $b > 0$ and $b \neq 1$, there exists for every positive number y, one and only one real number x such that $y = b^x$.

We interpret this graphical fact by stating that if $b > 0$ and s and t are any real numbers, then $b^s = b^t$ if and only if $s = t$. For example, the solution set of the equation $3^x = 9$ is the set $\{2\}$, since $3^x = 9$ can be written as $3^x = 3^2$. Hence $x = 2$ agrees with the statement relating to $b^s = b^t$.

19-2. LOGARITHMIC FUNCTIONS

In the previous section, we discussed the exponential $y = b^x$ and based on its graph agreed that if b is a positive number other than 1, and if N is any given positive number, then there exists a unique real number L, such that

(1)
$$N = b^L.$$

The number L is said to be the logarithm of the number N to the base b, and is symbolically represented as

(2)
$$L = \log_b N.$$

Hence if N and b are positive numbers with $b \neq 1$, the important basic fact results:

(3) $\log_b N = L$ if and only if $N = b^L$ or $N = b^{\log_b N}$

The two equations in (3), namely, $\log_b N = L$ and $N = b^L$ are interchangeable, and the form which best serves convenience is used.

Examples:

(a) $3^2 = 9$ and thus $\log_3 9 = 2$; or $3^{\log_3 9} = 9$

(b) $4^1 = 4$ and thus $\log_4 4 = 1$; or $4^{\log_4 4} = 4$

Example. Find $\log_2 \dfrac{1}{16}$.

Solution. Let $L = \log_2 \dfrac{1}{16}$. Then $2^L = \dfrac{1}{16}$. Here $L = -4$ since $2^{-4} = \dfrac{1}{16}$. Hence $\log_2 \dfrac{1}{16} = -4$.

Example. If $\log_x 27 = \dfrac{3}{2}$, find x.

Solution. If $\log_x 27 = \dfrac{3}{2}$, then $x^{3/2} = 27$ which implies that

$$(x^{3/2})^{2/3} = 27^{2/3}$$

or

$$x = (\sqrt[3]{27})^2.$$

Thus

$$x = 3^2$$

or

$$x = 9.$$

Our attention is now centered on the logarithmic equation $y = \log_b x$. If b is a positive number other than 1, then this equation associates with each positive number x a unique real number y. Thus the equation $y = \log_b x$ defines a function $f = \{(x,y) \mid y = b^x \wedge b > 0 \wedge b \neq 1\}$. *Note that the domain for this logarithmic function is the set of all positive real numbers.*

Example. Graph the logarithmic function given by

$$f = \{(x, y) \mid y = \log_2 x\}.$$

Solution. Since $\{(x,y) \mid y = \log_2 x\} = \{(x,y) \mid x = 2^y\}$, we can graph the equation $y = \log_2 x$ by graphing the equation $x = 2^y$. Here we arbitrarily choose convenient sample values for y and calculate the corresponding values for x, which are exhibited in the following table.

x	$\dfrac{1}{8}$	$\dfrac{1}{4}$	$\dfrac{1}{2}$	1	2	4	8
y	-3	-2	-1	0	1	2	3

The graph of the sampled representative points joined by a smooth curve through them produces the sketch in Fig. 19-3.

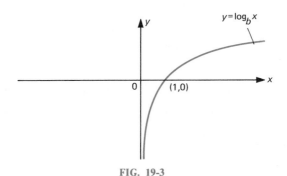

FIG. 19-3

The general shape, characteristics, and properties for the graph of a logarithmic function having base b greater than 1 are typical of the graph in Fig. 19-3. For example, its range R is always the set of real numbers R_e. If $0 < x < 1$, then $\log_b x < 0$ (is negative); if $x = 1$, $\log_b x = 0$; and if $x > 1$, then $\log_b x > 0$ (is positive).

EXERCISE 19-1

State the value for the logarithms in Probs. 1–10.

1. $\log_2 64$.

2. $\log_5 \dfrac{1}{25}$.

3. $\log_4 8$.

4. $\log_{1/3} 3$.

5. $\log_2 8$.

6. $\log_7 1$.

7. $\log_{36} 6$.

8. $\log_3 27$.

9. $\log_{10} 10$.

10. $\log_{10} 1$.

State the base b in Probs. 11–17.

11. $\log_b 16 = -\dfrac{4}{3}$.

12. $\log_b 4 = \dfrac{1}{2}$.

13. $\log_b 10 = 1$.

14. $\log_b \dfrac{1}{3} = -1$.

15. $\log_b 8 = -\dfrac{1}{2}$.

16. $\log_b 100 = 2$.

17. $\log_b 0.0001 = -4$.

Write the equations in Probs. 18–22 in an equivalent form and then solve for x.

18. $\log_2 8 = x$.

19. $\log_{10} 100 = x$.

20. $\log_{1/2} 4 = x$.

21. $\log_{10} 0.000001 = x.$

22. $\log_5 25 = x.$

Write the following exponential equations in Probs. 23–32 as a logarithmic statement.

23. $(5)^3 = 125.$ (*Solution:* $\log_5 125 = 3.$)

24. $2^{-2} = \dfrac{1}{4}.$

25. $0.00001 = 10^{-5}.$

26. $3^4 = 81.$

27. $4^3 = 64.$

28. $2^6 = 64.$

29. $8^2 = 64.$

30. $3^3 = 27.$

31. $9^{3/2} = 27.$

32. $(2.3)^0 = 1.$

Solve Probs. 33–38 for x.

33. $2^{2x} = 16.$

34. $2^{x+1} = 16.$

35. $4^{3x-1} = 2^3 \cdot 2^{x-1}.$

36. $2^{3x-1} = \left(\dfrac{1}{4}\right)^{x+2}.$

37. $3^{x^2-4x} = \dfrac{1}{27}.$

38. $(2^{x+3})(4^{1-2x}) = 16.$

Select six convenient sampling points in each of Probs. 39–42 and graph.

39. $f = \{(x, y) \mid y = 3^x\}.$

40. $f = \{(x, y) \mid y = 3^{-x}\}.$

41. $f = \{(x, y) \mid x = 3^y\}.$

42. $f = \{(x, y) \mid x = 3^{-y}\}.$

19-3. REMARKS AND DEFINITION—LOGARITHMS

The computation of a numerical quantity such as, for example, $\dfrac{\sqrt[3]{(38.4)(48.7)^5}}{\sqrt[7]{81.2}}$, would be a slow and tedious task were it not for the invention* called *logarithms*. This is a device which uses the laws of exponents to simplify calculations involving multiplication, division, *involution* [or evaluation of powers such as $(1.05)^{10}$], and *evolution* (or extraction of roots such as $\sqrt[4]{2321}$). Such laws are applicable because the definition indicated in Sec. 19-2 shows clearly that a logarithm is essentially an exponent.

Definition. The logarithm of the number N with respect to the base b, designated as "$\log_b N$," is the exponent which must be applied to b in order to produce N.

Today, the widespread use of electronic computers and desk calculators has almost eliminated the need for performing calculations of the above type by use of logarithms. Nevertheless basic logarithmic computations still have practical values. The theoretical aspects of logarithms are most important and will be explored in the succeeding sections.

19-4. FOUR LAWS OF LOGARITHMS

Since logarithms are exponents, the laws applying to both are similar. We shall now derive the basic laws for logarithms, where M, N, P, and b are positive numbers with $b \neq 1$.

1. $\log_b MNP = \log_b M + \log_b N + \log_b P$

In words, *the logarithm of a product is the sum of logarithms of its factors.*

Example.

$$\log_{10}[(58.4)(73.6)(86.4)] = \log_{10} 58.4 + \log_{10} 73.6 + \log_{10} 86.4.$$

Proof. Let $\log_b M = x$, $\log_b N = y$, and $\log_b P = z$. Then

$$M = b^x, N = b^y, \text{ and } P = b^z.$$

Multiplying,

$$MNP = b^x b^y b^z = b^{x+y+z} \qquad \text{(Law 1, Sec. 9-1)}$$

Changing the last equation to the logarithmic form, we have

$$\log_b MNP = x + y + z = \log_b M + \log_b N + \log_b P.$$

2. $\log_b \dfrac{M}{N} = \log_b M - \log_b N.$

In words, *the logarithm of a fraction is equal to the logarithm of the numerator minus the logarithm of the denominator.*

---

*Note: The inventor was John Napier (1550–1617), and the one who applied the invention to practical computation was Henry Briggs (1556–1631).

Example. By Law 2,

$$\log_{10} \frac{(58.4)(61.7)}{(15.6)(387)} = \log_{10}[(58.4)(61.7)] - \log_{10}[(15.6)(387)]$$

$$= (\log_{10} 58.4 + \log_{10} 61.7) - (\log_{10} 15.6 + \log_{10} 387)$$

$$= \log_{10} 58.4 + \log_{10} 61.7 - \log_{10} 15.6 - \log_{10} 387.$$

(by Law 1)

Proof. Let $\log_b M = x$ and $\log_b N = y$.
Then

$$M = b^x \quad \text{and} \quad N = b^y.$$

Dividing,

$$\frac{M}{N} = \frac{b^x}{b^y} = b^{x-y}. \qquad \text{(Law 2, Sec. 9-1)}$$

Hence,

$$\log_b \frac{M}{N} = x - y = \log_b M - \log_b N.$$

3. $\log_b M^n = n \log_b M.$

In words, *the logarithm of the nth power of any number equals n times the logarithm of the number.*

Example. $\text{Log}_{10}(873.4)^3 = 3 \log_{10} 873.4.$

Proof. Let $\log_b M = x$, so that $M = b^x$.
Then

$$M^n = (b^x)^n = b^{nx}. \qquad \text{(Law 5, Sec. 9-1)}$$

Hence,

$$\log_b M^n = nx = n \log_b M.$$

4. $\log_b \sqrt[n]{M} = \dfrac{1}{n} \log_b M.$

In words, *the logarithm of the nth root of a number equals $\dfrac{1}{n}$ times the logarithm of the number.*

Example. $\text{Log}_{10} \sqrt[3]{57.6} = \dfrac{1}{3} \log_{10} 57.6.$

Proof. Let $\log_b M = x$, so that $M = b^x$.
Then,

$$\sqrt[n]{M} = \sqrt[n]{b^x} = b^{x/n}. \qquad \text{(Def. 4, Sec. 9-5)}$$

Hence,

$$\log_b \sqrt[n]{M} = \frac{x}{n} = \frac{1}{n}(x) = \frac{1}{n}\log_b M.$$

The following law is a corollary of Laws 3 and 4.

Corollary, or Law 5.

$$\log_b \sqrt[n]{M^m} = \frac{m}{n}\log_b M.$$

For example,

$$\log_{10} \sqrt[5]{(0.084)^3} = \frac{3}{5}\log_{10}(0.084).$$

The proof is left to the student.

EXERCISE   19-2

Given $\log_{10} 2 = 0.30$ and $\log_{10} 3 = 0.48$, use the laws of logarithms to find the logarithms of the numbers in Probs. 1–16.

Examples.

(a) $\log_{10} 6 = \log_{10}(2 \cdot 3) = \log_{10} 2 + \log_{10} 3 = 0.30 + 0.48 = 0.78.$

(b) $\log_{10} 9 = \log_{10} 3^2 = 2\log_{10} 3 = 2(0.48) = 0.96.$

(c) $\log_{10} 24 = \log_{10}(3 \cdot 2^3) = \log_{10} 3 + 3\log_{10} 2 = 0.48 + 0.90 = 1.38$

(d) $\log_{10} \frac{3}{4} = \log_{10} 3 - 2\log_{10} 2 = 0.48 - 2(0.30) = -0.12.$

1. 12.   2. 18.   3. 27.   4. 8.   5. 16.

6. 32.   7. $\frac{2}{3}$.   8. $\frac{3}{2}$.   9. $\frac{8}{3}$.   10. $\frac{9}{4}$.

11. 5. HINT. $5 = \frac{10}{2}$.   12. 25.   13. 125.

14. .3 $\left(\text{or } \frac{3}{10}\right)$.   15. .2.   16. .12 $\left(\text{or } \frac{3}{25}\right)$.

Solve for x the equations in Probs. 17–34.

Examples.

(e) If $\log_2 x = 3$, $x = 2^3 = 8.$

(f) If $\log_2 8 = x$, $2^x = 8$, and hence $x = 3.$

(g) If $\log_x 8 = \frac{3}{2}$, $x^{3/2} = 8$, and hence $x = 4.$

17. $\log_3 x = 2.$ 18. $\log_4 x = -1.$ 19. $\log_8 x = \frac{2}{3}.$

20. $\log_2 x = -3.$ 21. $\log_5 x = 3.$ 22. $\log_9 x = -\frac{1}{2}.$

23. $\log_4 64 = x.$ 24. $\log_9 3 = x.$ 25. $\log_4\left(\frac{1}{2}\right) = x.$

26. $\log_9\left(\frac{1}{9}\right) = x.$ 27. $\log_8\left(\frac{1}{4}\right) = x.$ 28. $\log_4 8 = x.$

29. $\log_x 8 = 2.$ 30. $\log_x 9 = \frac{1}{2}.$ 31. $\log_x 3 = -\frac{1}{2}.$

32. $\log_x 8 = \frac{1}{3}.$ 33. $\log_x\left(\frac{4}{7}\right) = -1.$ 34. $\log_x 4 = -\frac{3}{2}.$

In each of Probs. 35–47 state whether the equation is true or false. If it is false, change one member so that it will be true.

Examples.

(h) $\log_a\left(\frac{A}{BC}\right) = \frac{\log_a A}{\log_a B + \log_a C}.$

False. Change right-hand side to $\log_a A - \log_a B - \log_a C.$

(i) $\log_a\left(\frac{x^3 y^2}{\sqrt[4]{z^3}}\right) = 3\log_a x + 2\log_a y - \frac{3}{4}\log_a z.$ True.

(j) $\frac{x}{y} = \log_a x - \log_a y.$

False. Change left-hand side to $\log_a\left(\frac{x}{y}\right).$

35. $\log_a \sqrt{A} = \frac{1}{2}\log_a A.$

36. $\sqrt[3]{\log_a B} = \frac{1}{3}\log_a B.$

37. $(\log_a A)^{2/3} = \frac{2}{3}\log_a A.$

38. $\log_a (xy)^{10} = (\log_a x + \log_a y)^{10}.$

39. $\log_a\left(\frac{A}{B}\right)^3 = 3(\log_a A - \log_a B).$

40. $\log_a \sqrt[4]{\frac{x^3}{y^3}} = \frac{3}{4}(\log_a x - \log_a y).$

41. $\log_{10} \sqrt{\frac{xy}{z}} = \frac{1}{2}\left(\frac{\log_{10} x + \log_{10} y}{\log_{10} z}\right).$

42. $\log_{10}\sqrt[3]{\frac{A^2}{B}} = (2\log_{10} A - \log_{10} B)^{1/3}.$

43. $\sqrt[5]{C} = \frac{1}{5}\log_a C.$

44. $10 = (\log_{10} 100)(\log_2 32)$.   45. $\log_{10}(\log_{10} 10) = 0$.

46. $a^{2\log_a x} = x^2$.   47. $\log_a a^3 = 3$.

19-5. SYSTEMS OF LOGARITHMS

There are two standard systems of logarithms in general use in elementary mathematics. They are:

(a) The *Briggs* or *common* system, in which 10 is used as the base. This system is used extensively in numerical calculations, and will be used hereafter in this text. Thus, whenever the base is omitted, the base is to be understood as 10. For example, "log 58" will mean "$\log_{10} 58$."

(b) The *Naperian* or *natural* system, in which the base is an irrational number approximately equal to 2.718. This so-called *natural* base, usually designated by the letter *e*, is used extensively in advanced mathematics.

19-6. CHARACTERISTICS AND MANTISSAS

In the following table, the two equations on the same line result one from the other, or, in other words, are corresponding exponential and logarithmic statements.

$$10^0 = 1; \qquad \log 1 = 0.$$
$$10^1 = 10; \qquad \log 10 = 1.$$
$$10^2 = 100; \qquad \log 100 = 2.$$
$$10^3 = 1000; \qquad \log 1000 = 3 \text{ (and so on).}$$

Note that if we apply integral (whole number) exponents to 10 we produce only numbers having 1 and 0 as digits. It is clear that most numbers are omitted from this group. Hence it becomes necessary to use some exponents for 10 that contain decimal fractions in order to write all numbers as powers of 10.

For example, 25 lies between 10 and 100. The exponent that must be applied to 10 to produce 25 is therefore between 1 and 2. Actually,

(1) $10^{1.3979} = 25$ (nearly),

or

(2) $\log 25 = 1.3979$.

That is, the exponent 1.3979, applied to the base 10, produces the number 25. This exponent consists of the integer 1 and the decimal fraction .3979. In general, the whole number part of any logarithm is called the *characteristic*, and the decimal part, if and when it is *positive*, is called the

mantissa. For example, while log .25 $= \log\left(\dfrac{25}{100}\right) = \log 25 - \log 100 =$
$1.3979 - 2 = -1 + .3979 = -.6021$, the mantissa of log .25 is .3979 rather than $-.6021$ (for convenience of use in tables).

19-7. OPERATIONS WHICH LEAVE THE MANTISSA UNCHANGED

When a new number is obtained from a given number by moving the decimal point to the right or left, the first number is in effect multiplied or divided by a power of 10. For example,

(1) $$2500 = 25.00 \times 10^2,$$

and

(2) $$.025 = 25 \div 10^3.$$

From (1) and Law 1 we have

(3) $$\begin{aligned} \log 2500 &= \log 25 + \log 10^2 \\ &= \log 25 + 2 \log 10 \quad \text{(by Law 3)} \\ &= 1.3979 + 2(1) \\ &= 3.3979 \end{aligned}$$

From (2) and Law 2 it follows that

(4) $$\begin{aligned} \log .025 &= \log 25 - \log 10^3 \\ &= 1.3979 - 3(1) \\ &= -2 + .3979. \end{aligned}$$

In equations (3) and (4) we see *why* the mantissas of the logarithms of the three numbers: 25, 2500, and .025 are the same.

In general, when the decimal point in the number is moved n places to the right, the logarithm is increased by the integer n (or log 10^n); and when it is moved n places to the left the logarithm is decreased by n. Hence in either case the mantissa remains unchanged. This very convenient result makes it possible to have compact tables of logarithms, since, for example, only one mantissa (.3979) need be recorded to apply to such various numbers as 25, 250, 2500, 2.5, .25, .025, etc.

19-8. RULES ABOUT THE CHARACTERISTIC

Since log 10 = 1 and log 100 = 2, it is evident that 1 is the characteristic of the logarithm of 10 and of all numbers between 10 and 100; or, in other words, of all numbers having two significant* digits to the

---

*The *significant* digits in a number include the first nonzero digit, as read from left to right, plus all the digits that follow it. For example, each of the numbers 10.732 and 00030.21 has two significant digits to the left of the decimal point.

left of the decimal point. Similarly, for numbers with three digits to the left of the decimal point, the characteristic is 2. In general, the following rule applies.

Rule 1. The characteristic of the logarithm of a number greater than one is one less than the number of significant digits to the left of the decimal point.

The logarithm of a number less than one is negative, but there is still a characteristic and a (positive) mantissa. For example, it was noted in (4) Sec. 19-7 that $\log 0.025 = -2 + .3979$, with the characteristic -2 and mantissa .3979. For convenience, this result is usually written in the form

(1) $$\log 0.025 = 8.3979 - 10$$

since the right-hand member of (1) is easy to use and preserves the positive mantissa.

Continuing the table in Sec. 19-6 in the reverse direction, we have

$$10^{-1} = \frac{1}{10} = .1; \qquad \log .1 \quad = -1.$$

$$10^{-2} = \frac{1}{10^2} = .01; \qquad \log .01 \quad = -2.$$

$$10^{-3} = \frac{1}{10^3} = .001; \qquad \log .001 = -3 \quad \text{(and so on)}.$$

With a little study of the table above we can arrive at a second rule about characteristics, namely,

Rule 2. The characteristic of the logarithm of a number less than one is negative, and is equal numerically to one plus the number of zeros between the decimal point and the first nonzero digit on the right.

Examples.

THE NUMBER	THE CHARACTERISTIC OF THE LOGARITHM
.8003	$-(1 + 0) = -1$
.00207	$-(1 + 2) = -3$
.00000000004	$-(1 + 10) = -11$

In practice we may count the decimal point as well as the proper zeros, getting at once for the sum the correct negative characteristic. Thus the latter is obtained first as a negative integer, after which it is rewritten in the conventional form when the mantissa is known.

Example 1. $\log .00025 = -4 + .3979 = 6.3979 - 10.$

Example 2. $\log .000000000025 = -11 + .3979 = 9.3979 - 20.$

19-9. SCIENTIFIC NOTATION AND A SECOND METHOD FOR DETERMINING CHARACTERISTICS

It is possible to find the characteristic of the logarithm of a number N to base 10 by taking advantage of what is called the "scientific notation" method for representing N. For example, if 583.4 is written as $(5.834)(10^2)$; 0.000208 as $(2.08)(10^{-4})$; 3.08 as $(3.08)(10^0)$; 100,000 as $(1)(10^5)$; 0.3141 as $(3.141)(10^{-1})$; 0.000,000,000,108 as $(1.08)(10^{-10})$, etc., each of the numbers is said to be written in scientific notation. In other words, N is in scientific notation if it is represented as $(M)(10^k)$, where $1 \le M < 10$ (M is equal to or greater than 1 but less than 10).
For example, in 0.00208, $M = 2.08$, and $k = -3$.

Rule 3. *To determine the characteristic of a logarithm of a number to base 10, it is merely necessary to write (or think of) the given number in scientific notation, and the exponent of the 10 in this representation is the characteristic.*

Example. Since, in scientific notation.

(a) $5870 = (5.87)(10^3)$;
(b) $3.4 = (3.4)(10^0)$;
(c) $0.0004108 = (4.108)(10^{-4})$;
(d) $0.01287 = (1.287)(10^{-2})$;
(e) $1,000,000 = (1)(10^6)$;
(f) $15 = (1.5)(10^1)$; and
(g) $0.000,000,000,012 = (1.2)(10^{-11})$;

it follows that the characteristics of the respective logarithms are the exponents of the 10 in the right members of the above equations. Thus the characteristics are (a) 3, (b) 0, (c) −4, (d) −2, (e) 6, (f) 1, and (g) −11.

EXERCISE 19-3 (Oral)

Find the characteristic of the logarithms of each of the numbers in Probs. 1–20 by both methods.

1. 36.	2. 407.	3. 8.	4. 2573.
5. 3.2.	6. 8.05.	7. 0.6.	8. 0.058.
9. 62.05.	10. 932.5.	11. 0.002.	12. 0.00015.
13. 2.75.	14. 0.235.	15. 0.056.	16. 0.0058.
17. 283.5	18. 0.08276.	19. 3258.	20. 865432.

19-10. FINDING THE MANTISSA; FOUR-PLACE TABLES

The mantissa of the logarithm of a given number is found by use of a table, such as Table 2 at the end of the text. The first column on the left with the heading N contains the first two digits of the number. For example, if the number is 157, the digits 15 are found in the sixth row beneath N. The third digit, 7, is found on the line across the top of the table which contains N and the digits 0, 1, 2, etc. In the sixth row, under 7 and in line with the first two digits 15, we find the entry 1959. This means that the mantissa of the logarithm of 157, or .157, or 15,700, or .000157, etc. is .1959 (the decimal being omitted for brevity).

If the number whose logarithm is sought has two digits it is found in the column under N. Its mantissa will then be on the same line and in the column beneath the digit 0. If the number has one digit, we multiply it by 10 and use the mantissa of the product. For example, the mantissa of $\log 7 =$ the mantissa of $\log 70 = .8451$.

When we find the logarithm of a number we first write its characteristic by inspection (it is very important to get this habit) and *then* find the entry in the table which gives the digits in the mantissa.

Examples.

(a)   log 4.3 = 0 plus the mantissa.   Here the student may be tempted to omit the characteristic; but this is a very bad practice, which often results in errors. *The characteristic should always be written first, even when it is zero.* In the table, in line with 43 and in the column under the digit 0, is the entry 6335. Hence log 4.3 = 0.6335.

(b)   log 564 = 2 plus the mantissa. In line with 56 in the table, and in the column under the digit 4, is the entry 7513, so that log 564 = 2.7513.

(c)   log 0.0108 = −2 plus the mantissa. The latter, according to the entry in the table in line with 10 and under 8, is .0334. Writing the characteristic −2 in the recommended form, we have log 0.0108 = 8.0334 − 10.

19-11.   ANTILOGARITHMS

If log $A = B$, then A is said to be the *antilogarithm of B* and may be found from the table by reversing the operation of finding the logarithm.

Examples.

(a)   log N = 3.8102. Find N.

We now look *inside* the table for the entry 8102. This is found in line with 64 and under the digit 6, so that N has the digits 646 with the decimal point yet to be fixed. Looking next at the characteristic, 3, we see that there are four digits to the left of the decimal point in N. Hence N = 6460.

(b)   Log N = 7.3979 − 10. Find N.

Inspection of the table shows that N has the digits 250. Since the characteristic is $7 - 10$ or -3, N is written with a decimal point followed by two zeros. Hence $N = .0025$.

(c) $\log N = 0.4133$. Find N.

The table shows that N has the digits 259. The characteristic 0 shows that N has one place to the left of the decimal point. Hence $N = 2.59$.

EXERCISE 19-4

Find the logarithm of each of the numbers in Probs. 1–20.

1. 183.	2. 347.	3. 526.	4. 235.
5. 621.	6. 420.	7. 360.	8. 924.
9. 32.5.	10. 52.6.	11. 3.72.	12. 8.28.
13. 0.062.	14. 0.735.	15. 0.0083.	16. 0.00091.
17. 0.0006.	18. 0.00584.	19. 0.000641.	20. 0.0000596.

Find N in each of Probs. 21–33.

21. $\log N = 1.0607$.	22. $\log N = 2.1303$.
23. $\log N = 1.3541$.	24. $\log N = 2.6335$.
25. $\log N = 1.6444$.	26. $\log N = 3.5933$.
27. $\log N = 9.4609 - 10$.	28. $\log N = 8.4983 - 10$.
29. $\log N = 7.3636 - 10$.	30. $\log N = 8.2455 - 10$.
31. $\log N = 0.7388$.	32. $\log N = 0.0043$.
33. $\log N = 6.0000 - 10$.	

19-12. INTERPOLATION

When a given number, or a given mantissa, is not found directly in the table, it is necessary to use a process called *interpolation*, as illustrated in the following examples.

Example 1. Find $\log 2576$.

Solution. Here the characteristic is 3. To obtain the mantissa, we observe that 2576 lies between the numbers 2570 and 2580, whose associated mantissas are the same as those for 257 and 258 respectively. Schematically the work is arranged as follows:

$$
\text{Number} \qquad\qquad\qquad\qquad \text{Mantissa digits}
$$

$$
10 \left[\begin{array}{c} 6 \left[\begin{array}{c} 2570 \\ 2576 \end{array}\right. \\ 2580 \end{array}\right. \qquad \left.\begin{array}{c} 4099 \\ \\ 4116 \end{array}\right] \quad 17 \text{ (the difference)}
$$

Now $4099 + \dfrac{6}{10}(17) = 4109.2$, but since four digits only are retained, the desired mantissa is .4109. Hence

$$\log 2576 = 3.4109.$$

Evidently the process of interpolation would not have been changed if the decimal point had been differently placed in the digit sequence 2576. For example,

$$\log .0002576 = 6.4109 - 10.$$

It should be realized that interpolation uses the principle of proportional parts, which assumes that for a small change in the number there corresponds a proportional change in the mantissa. This is only approximately true, but in order to use interpolation this assumption will be accepted when the logarithm table does not contain directly the information desired.

Example 2.   Find N if $\log N = 9.4177 - 10$.

Solution.   The digits 4177 are not found among the mantissa digits inside the table; but they are seen to lie between the adjacent entries 4166 and 4183. The schematic arrangement follows:

Number   Mantissa digits

$$10 \begin{bmatrix} 2610 \\ \\ 2620 \end{bmatrix} \qquad \left.\begin{matrix} \begin{bmatrix} 4166 \\ 4177 \end{bmatrix} 11 \\ 4183 \end{matrix}\right] 17$$

Hence the significant digits in N are

$$2610 + \dfrac{11}{17}(10) = 2616 \text{ (nearest four digit number).}$$

Thus, taking into account the characteristic of $\log N$, it follows that

$$N = 0.2616.$$

When first learning this process, the student should put the work in table form as illustrated in the examples. However, with enough practice and a clear understanding of the principle of proportional parts, he may often learn to interpolate mentally.

EXERCISE   19-5

Find the logarithm of each of the numbers in Probs. 1–12 by use of Table 2.

1. 2536.	2. 728.6	3. 0.08352.
4. 35.27.	5. 839.6.	6. 0.005706.
7. 5.732.	8. 294.3.	9. 0.0007085.
10. 6.325×10^8.	11. 9.246×10^{-12}.	12. 2.318×10^{20}.

Find N in each of Probs. 13–24 by use of Table 2.

13. $\log N = 2.2226$.
14. $\log N = 6.3641$.
15. $\log N = 3.1145$.
16. $\log N = 7.2883 - 10$.
17. $\log N = 9.1463 - 10$.
18. $\log N = 0.7714$.
19. $\log N = 8.1633 - 10$.
20. $\log N = 7.4161 - 20$.
21. $\log N = 2.3146 - 10$.
22. $\log N = 0.4923 - 10$.
23. $\log N = 10.8143$.
24. $\log N = 15.0129$.

19-13. COMPUTATION WITH LOGARITHMS

It should be clearly understood that the usefulness of logarithms lies in the fact that they shorten computations involving multiplication, division, involution, and evolution (though not addition and subtraction). Furthermore, these operations could be performed in other ways, so that if time is not saved, the point in the use of logarithms is missed. It is important, therefore, to take note of the details and practices which do save time. Chief among them are the following.

(a) The quantity to be evaluated should be written directly above the details of computation, and should be designated by some letter, as N.

(b) The computation should be outlined in full, *with the left members of all equations filled in before the logarithm table is used at all.*

(c) The logarithms should be arranged in neat column form, with the decimal points and the preceding equality signs in vertical lines.

The student should study carefully the illustrative examples below before attempting the problems in the subsequent exercise.

Example 1. Evaluate $\dfrac{324}{618}$.

Solution. Let $N = \dfrac{324}{618}$.

Then,

$$\log N = \log 324 - \log 618 \quad \text{(by Law 2).}$$

Outline.
$$\log 324 = 2.\underline{\quad}$$
$$\log 618 = 2.\underline{\quad} \ (-)$$
$$\log N = \underline{\quad}.$$
$$N = \underline{\quad}. \ (Ans.).$$

Note 1. In what follows we have repeated the outline to show how the mantissas should be entered. The student, however, should understand that after the complete outline is made, which includes all characteristics obtained by inspection, he should make his entries from the logarithm table in *that same outline*.

Turning next to Table 2 in the text, we fill in the outline as follows.

$$
\begin{aligned}
\log 324 &= 12.5105 - 10 \\
\log 618 &= \underline{\quad 2.7910 \quad} \qquad (-) \\
\log N &= 9.7195 - 10 \\
N &= .5242 \text{ (Ans.)}.
\end{aligned}
$$

Note 2. Since in the details above we are obliged to subtract a larger from a smaller number it is helpful, as soon as this fact becomes apparent, to rewrite the characteristic of log 324 as $12 - 10$ instead of 2. Remember that the decimal part of the logarithm is not the mantissa unless it is positive.

Note 3. In actual life many numbers used in computations are approximations with a limited number of significant digits. In this case the computed result should not have more significant digits than has any of the numbers which enter into the computation, and in the case above N should be written as .524. In the subsequent exercise, however, all numbers are assumed to be exact values rather than approximations.

In the following examples the values found in the table will be included along with the outline, though actually they should be filled in *after* the outline is made.

Example 2. Evaluate

$$
\frac{(.2764)(3.268)^4}{\sqrt[3]{210,700}}.
$$

Solution. (Here interpolation *is* in order. The arrangement below suggests a compact, efficient way of recording all logarithms found, so that no details looked up are omitted in the final form of the result.) Let

$$
N = \frac{(2764)(3.268)^4}{\sqrt[3]{210,700}}.
$$

Then,

$$
\log N = \log 2764 + 4 \log 3.268 - \frac{1}{3} \log 210,700.
$$

$$
\begin{aligned}
\log 2764 &= 3.4415 \\
4 \log 3.268 = 4\,(0.5142) &= \underline{2.0568} \quad (+) \\
\log \text{numerator} &= 5.4983 \\
\frac{1}{3} \log 210,700 = \frac{1}{3}\,(5.3237) &= \underline{1.7746} \quad (-) \\
\log N &= 3.7237 \\
N &= 5292 \ (Ans.).
\end{aligned}
$$

Note 4. In the preceding example we found that the antilog of 3.7237 is halfway between 5292 and 5293. In cases of this type, we shall agree to use the *even* one of the two numbers between which the interpolated result lies.

Example 3. Evaluate $N = \sqrt[3]{0.01084} + (0.5136)^4$.

Solution. Let $A = \sqrt[3]{0.01084}$ and $B = (0.5136)^4$. Then,

$$\log A = \frac{1}{3} \log 0.01084$$
$$\log B = 4 \log (0.5136)$$

and

$$N = A + B.$$

Details.

$$\log A = \frac{1}{3}(8.0350 - 10) = \frac{1}{3}(28.0350 - 30) = 9.3450 - 10.$$
$$\log B = 4(9.7106 - 10) = 38.8424 - 40 = 8.8424 - 10.$$
$$B = 0.06957$$
$$A = \underline{0.2213} \quad (+)$$
$$N = 0.2909 \ (Ans.).$$

Note 5. Since we have no formula for the logarithm of a sum, it is necessary to find A and B separately.

Note 6. By a second method of finding $\log A$ we have $\frac{1}{3}(8.0350 - 10) = \frac{1}{3}(1.0350 - 3) = 0.3450 - 1$. However, the form indicated in the solution is customary.

Note 7. It is not necessary to take the final step indicated in the calculation of $\log B$, since the characteristic, -2, is obtained from $38 - 40$ as easily as from $8 - 10$.

Example 4. Evaluate $N = (0.008402)^{2/7}$.

Solution.

$$\log N = \frac{2}{7} \log (0.008402)$$
$$= \frac{2}{7}(7.9244 - 10)$$
$$= \frac{1}{7}(15.8488 - 20)$$
$$= \frac{1}{7}(65.8488 - 70)$$
$$= 9.4070 - 10$$
$$N = 0.2553.$$

Example 5. Evaluate $N = (27.84)^{-3} = \dfrac{1}{(27.84)^3}$.

Solution.

$$\log N = \log 1 - 3 \log (27.84)$$

$$\begin{aligned}
\log 1 &= 10.0000 - 10 \quad \text{(or 0)}\\
3 \log (27.84) = 3(1.4446) &= \underline{4.3338} \qquad\quad (-)\\
\log N &= 5.6662 - 10\\
N &= 0.00004637.
\end{aligned}$$

EXERCISE 19-6

By use of Table 2 compute the value of each of the quantities in Probs. 1–37. (It is agreed* that $21 = 21.00$, $.031 = .0310$, etc.)

1. $\dfrac{(25)(76)}{83}$.

2. $\dfrac{(0.283)(41.6)}{388}$.

3. $\dfrac{(127.4)(32.6)}{0.0827}$.

4. $\dfrac{(576)(340)}{(228)^2}$.

5. $(213.4)(0.529)$.

6. $(3247)(6.97)(0.0844)$.

7. $3(41.62)^3(87.2)^2$.

8. $(0.732)^2$.

9. $(925.6)\sqrt{387.8}$.

10. $(0.00274)^{1/3}$.

11. $(0.009082)^{1/2}$.

12. $(327)^{2/3}$.

13. $(0.0528)^{3/4}$.

14. $(928)^{5/2}$.

15. $\sqrt[3]{(67.41)^2}$.

16. $\dfrac{1}{(387)^3}$.

17. $(5.76)^{-2}$.

18. $\sqrt{5298}$.

19. $\sqrt[3]{807.6}$.

20. $(8.37)^{-3}$.

21. $\sqrt[3]{3256}$.

22. $\sqrt[3]{8.362}$.

23. $\dfrac{4}{3}(3.142)(37.6)^3$.

24. $\sqrt{(23.8)(47.6)(39.8)(524)}$.

25. $\dfrac{1}{(58.4)(9.836)}$.

26. $\dfrac{1}{\sqrt{0.8846}}$.

27. $\dfrac{54.8}{(-1.06)^3}$ (*Hint.* First find $-N$, which is positive.)

28. $\sqrt[3]{\dfrac{(35.21)(568)}{-4.84}}$.

29. $\sqrt{\dfrac{(4.728)(175.3)}{(584)(755)}}$.

30. $\dfrac{(-4.76)(0.8138)}{(43.6)(-0.084)^2}$.

31. Given $S = \dfrac{3WPA^2}{43}$, find S if $W = 347.2$, $P = 6.7$, and $A = 0.7840$.

*See Note 3 in Sec. 19-13.

32. Given $T = \pi \sqrt{\dfrac{l}{g}}$, find T if $l = 733$, $g = 32.2$, and $\pi = 3.142$.

33. Given $M = \dfrac{b^2 + c^2 - a^2}{2bc}$, find log M if $a = 11.20$, $b = 43.43$, and $c = 48.38$.

34. $\dfrac{\sqrt[3]{10.20}}{0.45} - \sqrt[3]{41.3}$.

35. The volume of a right circular cone is given by $V = \dfrac{1}{3}\pi r^2 h$. If $V = 350$, $h = 10.5$, $\pi = 3.14$, find r to the nearest tenth.

36. If $\log_a P = .8672$ and $\log_a Q = 9.3108 - 10$, find $\log_a [P^3 Q^2]$.

37. If $\log_{10} 2 = .3010$ and $\log_{10} 5 = .6990$, find without use of tables,
    (a) $\log_{10} .025$
    (b) $\log_{10}(\sqrt[4]{20})$.

19-14.   NATURAL LOGARITHMS

Common logarithms, or logarithms to the base 10, are the most convenient for numerical computation. However, for more advanced mathematics, natural logarithms, or logarithms to the base e (approximately equal to 2.7182818284590...) are more appropriate for theoretical discussions.

The logarithm of a number to the base a can be obtained from the logarithm of the number to the base b by use of the following theorem:

THEOREM: *Conversion of bases:*

(1)
$$\log_a N = \frac{\log_b N}{\log_b a}$$

Proof:

(2)
$$\log_a N = \log_a(b^{\log_b N}), \text{ since } N = b^{\log_b N}$$
$$= (\log_b N)(\log_a b), \text{ by Law 3}$$

Substitute for N the number a in (2) and

$$\log_a a = (\log_b a)(\log_a b)$$

or

(3)
$$1 = (\log_b a)(\log_a b), \text{ since } \log_a a = 1.$$

Thus, substituting,

$$\log_a b = \frac{1}{\log_b a}$$

in the second step of the right-hand side of (2) it follows that

$$\log_a N = \frac{\log_b N}{\log_b a} \text{, a very useful formula.}$$

Since base 10 and base e are important in mathematics, the following example is significant. For these special cases where

$$a = e = 2.7182818284590 \ldots \text{ and } b = 10, \text{ from (1):}$$

$$\log_e N = \frac{\log_{10} N}{\log_{10} e} = \frac{\log_{10} N}{\log_{10} 2.718}$$

$$= \frac{\log_{10} N}{0.4343}$$

$$= 2.3026 \log_{10} N.$$

Hence the natural logarithm of a number is obtained by multiplying its common logarithm by 2.3026.

Example. Find $\log_e 2$ from your knowledge of $\log_{10} 2$.

Solution. Since $\log_{10} 2 = .3010$, it follows that

$$\log_e 2 = (.3010)(2.3026)$$

$$= .6930$$

EXERCISE 19-7

By use of the logarithmic Table 2 to base 10, evaluate the quantities in Probs. 1–5.

1. $\log_e 508$.   2. $\log_e 25$.

3. $\log_e .413$.   4. $\log_e .001$.

5. $\log_e 3.54$.

6. Since $(\log_b a)(\log_a b) = 1$, where a, b are positive real numbers greater that 1, how does one find the logarithm of a number to base 10, if the corresponding logarithm of the number to base e is known?

7. Given that $\log_e 800 = 6.68461$, find the $\log_{10} 800$ by using the conversion factor found in Prob. 6. Check your result by finding the $\log_{10} 800$ by use of a table.

8. If $\log_7 x = 2$; $\log_8 y = \frac{1}{3}$; $\log_z 27 = 3$; evaluate (a) $\frac{3y^2}{z}$, (b) xyz, (c) $\log_7 \frac{1}{x}$

    (d) $\log_z \frac{1}{27}$.

19-15. LOGARITHMIC AND EXPONENTIAL EQUATIONS

The properties of logarithmic and exponential functions can be applied to obtain solution sets for certain types of equations that otherwise would be quite difficult.

This is particularly true in an exponential equation where the variable appears as an exponent. This type of equation can be solved by the procedure illustrated in the following example.

Example. Solve $2^x = 12$.

Solution. $2^x = 12$. Since 2^x is not an integral power of 2 which equals 12, we proceed to equate the logarithms of both members of the equation $2^x = 12$ and obtain

$$\log_{10} 2^x = \log_{10} 12$$

or

$$x \log_{10} 2 = \log_{10} 12$$
$$x = \frac{\log_{10} 12}{\log_{10} 2}$$
$$= \frac{1.0792}{0.3010}$$
$$= 3.585 \text{ (approx.)}$$

Note: Any permissible logarithmic base might have been used, but in this case, it is evident that base 10 is most practical.

19-16.   LOGARITHMIC EQUATIONS

A *logarithmic equation* is an equation which contains logarithms among its terms. The solution of such an equation is illustrated in the following examples.

Example 1. Solve $2 \log_{10} x + \log_{10} 3 - \log_{10} (x + 1) = \log_{10} 4$.

Solution.

(1)
$$\log_{10}(x^2) + \log_{10} 3 = \log_{10} 4 + \log_{10}(x + 1)$$
$$\log_{10}(3x^2) = \log_{10}[4(x + 1)] \qquad \text{Why?}$$
$$3x^2 = 4x + 4$$
$$3x^2 - 4x - 4 = 0$$
$$(3x + 2)(x - 2) = 0$$
$$x = -\frac{2}{3} \quad \text{or} \quad x = 2$$

Check. When $x = 2$,

$$2 \log_{10} 2 + \log_{10} 3 - \log_{10} 3 = 2 \log_{10} 2$$
$$= \log_{10}(2^2)$$
$$= \log_{10} 4,$$

a true statement is obtained. Hence $x = 2$ is a solution.

When $x = -\dfrac{2}{3}$,

$$2 \log_{10} x = 2 \log_{10}\left(-\dfrac{2}{3}\right)$$

which is undefined. Thus $-\dfrac{2}{3}$ is not a root, and is extraneous.

Since the domain of the logarithmic function is the set of positive real numbers, the original equation (1) requires the restriction that $x > 0$ and $x + 1 > 0$. It is important to check all possible solutions in the original logarithmic equation as is evident in this example.

Example 2. Solve $x = \log_2 12$.

Solution. Rewriting this equation in exponential form involves the equation $2^x = 12$, which was solved in Sec. 19-15. This type of logarithmic equation arises when logarithms of numbers are desired with respect to bases that aren't in common use. The idea of changing bases was discussed in Sec. 19-14. For example, the $\log_{7.3} 28$ leads to the exponential equation $(7.3)^x = 28$ or $x \log_{10} 7.3 = \log_{10} 28$ or

$$x = \frac{\log_{10} 28}{\log_{10} 7.3}$$

which can now be completed by use of a table of logarithms to base 10.

Example 3. Solve for x without using a table of logarithms: $\log_{10}(x^2 - 15x) = 2$.

Solution. Rewriting this equation in exponential form,

$$x^2 - 15x = 10^2 = 100$$

or

$$x^2 - 15x - 100 = 0$$

and

$$(x - 20)(x + 5) = 0$$
$$x = 20 \text{ or } x = -5.$$

After checking $x = 20$ and $x = -5$ in the original equation

$$\log_{10}(x^2 - 15x) = 2,$$

it is found that they satisfy it. Hence the solution set is $\{20, -5\}$.

EXERCISE 19-8

In Probs. 1–10 where tables are involved use Table 2. Solve by logarithms.

1. $8^x = 143$.   2. $(2.16)^{2x-1} = 23.1$.

3. $7^x = (5^{2x})(3.8)^{x-1}$.

4. By use of a table of logarithms to base 10, find $\log_7 37$; $\log_3(.4)$; $\log_{21} 8.6$.

5. Solve for x if $2 \log_{10} x + \log_{10} 2 - \log_{10}(2x - 5) = \log_{10} 10$.

6. Solve for x:

$$3 \log_{10}(x + 2) = 2 \log_{10} 53.1 - 2.43.$$

7. In the formula $l = ar^{n-1}$, find n if $l = 62.3$, $a = 5.12$, $r = 2.41$.

8. In the formula $A = P(1 + r)^n$, find n if $P = 1650$, $A = 2500$, $r = .04$.

9. By logarithmic computation, evaluate

   (a) $\dfrac{(.734)(\sqrt[3]{17.8})}{4.32}$.

   (b) $\dfrac{(2.94)^6(\sqrt[3]{29.1})}{.7631}$.

10. Evaluate for x, given that $x = \dfrac{\sqrt[3]{58.1} + (\sqrt{101.3})(41.1)}{\sqrt[3]{68.4} + 3.7}$.

Tables

Table 1. Squares, Cubes, Roots

n	n^2	$\sqrt{n}$	n^3	$\sqrt[3]{n}$	n	n^2	$\sqrt{n}$	n^3	$\sqrt[3]{n}$
1	1	1.000	1	1.000	51	2,601	7.141	132,651	3.708
2	4	1.414	8	1.260	52	2,704	7.211	140,608	3.732
3	9	1.732	27	1.442	53	2,809	7.280	148,877	3.756
4	16	2.000	64	1.587	54	2,916	7.348	157,464	3.780
5	25	2.236	125	1.710	55	3,025	7.416	166,375	3.803
6	36	2.449	216	1.817	56	3,136	7.483	175,616	3.826
7	49	2.646	343	1.913	57	3,249	7.550	185,193	3.848
8	64	2.828	512	2.000	58	3,364	7.616	195,112	3.871
9	81	3.000	729	2.080	59	3,481	7.681	205,379	3.893
10	100	3.162	1,000	2.154	60	3,600	7.746	216,000	3.915
11	121	3.317	1,331	2.224	61	3,721	7.810	226,981	3.936
12	144	3.464	1,728	2.289	62	3,844	7.874	238,328	3.958
13	169	3.606	2,197	2.351	63	3,969	7.937	250,047	3.979
14	196	3.742	2,744	2.410	64	4,096	8.000	262,144	4.000
15	225	3.873	3,375	2.466	65	4,225	8.062	274,625	4.021
16	256	4.000	4,096	2.520	66	4,356	8.124	287,496	4.041
17	289	4.123	4,913	2.571	67	4,489	8.185	300,763	4.062
18	324	4.243	5,832	2.621	68	4,624	8.246	314,432	4.082
19	361	4.359	6,859	2.668	69	4,761	8.307	328,509	4.102
20	400	4.472	8,000	2.714	70	4,900	8.367	343,000	4.121
21	441	4.583	9,261	2.759	71	5,041	8.426	357,911	4.141
22	484	4.690	10,648	2.802	72	5,184	8.485	373,248	4.160
23	529	4.796	12,167	2.844	73	5,329	8.544	389,017	4.179
24	576	4.899	13,824	2.884	74	5,476	8.602	405,224	4.198
25	625	5.000	15,625	2.924	75	5,625	8.660	421,875	4.217
26	676	5.099	17,576	2.962	76	5,776	8.718	438,976	4.236
27	729	5.196	19,683	3.000	77	5,929	8.775	456,533	4.254
28	784	5.291	21,952	3.037	78	6,084	8.832	474,552	4.273
29	841	5.385	24,389	3.072	79	6,241	8.888	493,039	4.291
30	900	5.477	27,000	3.107	80	6,400	8.944	512,000	4.309
31	961	5.568	29,791	3.141	81	6,561	9.000	531,441	4.327
32	1,024	5.657	32,768	3.175	82	6,724	9.055	551,368	4.344
33	1,089	5.745	35,937	3.208	83	6,889	9.110	571,787	4.362
34	1,156	5.831	39,304	3.240	84	7,056	9.165	592,704	4.380
35	1,225	5.916	42,875	3.271	85	7,225	9.220	614,125	4.397
36	1,296	6.000	46,656	3.302	86	7,396	9.274	636,056	4.414
37	1,369	6.083	50,653	3.332	87	7,569	9.327	658,503	4.431
38	1,444	6.164	54,872	3.362	88	7,744	9.381	681,472	4.448
39	1,521	6.245	59,319	3.391	89	7,921	9.434	704,969	4.465
40	1,600	6.325	64,000	3.420	90	8,100	9.487	729,000	4.481
41	1,681	6.403	68,921	3.448	91	8,281	9.539	753,571	4.498
42	1,764	6.481	74,088	3.476	92	8,464	9.592	778,688	4.514
43	1,849	6.557	79,507	3.503	93	8,649	9.643	804,357	4.531
44	1,936	6.633	85,184	3.530	94	8,836	9.695	830,584	4.547
45	2,025	6.708	91,125	3.557	95	9,025	9.747	857,375	4.563
46	2,116	6.782	97,336	3.583	96	9,216	9.798	884,736	4.579
47	2,209	6.856	103,823	3.609	97	9,409	9.849	912,673	4.595
48	2,304	6.928	110,592	3.634	98	9,604	9.899	941,192	4.610
49	2,401	7.000	117,649	3.659	99	9,801	9.950	970,299	4.626
50	2,500	7.071	125,000	3.684	100	10,000	10.000	1,000.000	4.642
n	n^2	$\sqrt{n}$	n^3	$\sqrt[3]{n}$	n	n^2	$\sqrt{n}$	n^3	$\sqrt[3]{n}$

Table 2. Common Logarithms

FOUR-PLACE LOGARITHMS

N	L.0	1	2	3	4	5	6	7	8	9	Proportional Parts				
											1	2	3	4	5
10	0000	0043	0086	0128	0170	0212	0253	0294	0334	0374	4	8	12	17	21
11	0414	0453	0492	0531	0569	0607	0645	0682	0719	0755	4	8	11	15	19
12	0792	0828	0864	0899	0934	0969	1004	1038	1072	1106	3	7	10	14	17
13	1139	1173	1206	1239	1271	1303	1335	1367	1399	1430	3	6	10	13	16
14	1461	1492	1523	1553	1584	1614	1644	1673	1703	1732	3	6	9	12	15
15	1761	1790	1818	1847	1875	1903	1931	1959	1987	2014	3	6	8	11	14
16	2041	2068	2095	2122	2148	2175	2201	2227	2253	2279	3	5	8	11	13
17	2304	2330	2355	2380	2405	2430	2455	2480	2504	2529	2	5	7	10	12
18	2553	2577	2601	2625	2648	2672	2695	2718	2742	2765	2	5	7	9	12
19	2788	2810	2833	2856	2878	2900	2923	2945	2967	2989	2	4	7	9	11
20	3010	3032	3054	3075	3096	3118	3139	3160	3181	3201	2	4	6	8	11
21	3222	3243	3263	3284	3304	3324	3345	3365	3385	3404	2	4	6	8	10
22	3424	3444	3464	3483	3502	3522	3541	3560	3579	3598	2	4	6	8	10
23	3617	3636	3655	3674	3692	3711	3729	3747	3766	3784	2	4	6	7	9
24	3802	3820	3838	3856	3874	3892	3909	3927	3945	3962	2	4	5	7	9
25	3979	3997	4014	4031	4048	4065	4082	4099	4116	4133	2	4	5	7	9
26	4150	4166	4183	4200	4216	4232	4249	4265	4281	4298	2	3	5	7	8
27	4314	4330	4346	4362	4378	4393	4409	4425	4440	4456	2	3	5	6	8
28	4472	4487	4502	4518	4533	4548	4564	4579	4594	4609	2	3	5	6	8
29	4624	4639	4654	4669	4683	4698	4713	4728	4742	4757	1	3	4	6	7
30	4771	4786	4800	4814	4829	4843	4857	4871	4886	4900	1	3	4	6	7
31	4914	4928	4942	4955	4969	4983	4997	5011	5024	5038	1	3	4	5	7
32	5051	5065	5079	5092	5105	5119	5132	5145	5159	5172	1	3	4	5	7
33	5185	5198	5211	5224	5237	5250	5263	5276	5289	5302	1	3	4	5	7
34	5315	5328	5340	5353	5366	5370	5391	5403	5416	5428	1	2	4	5	6
35	5441	5453	5465	5478	5490	5502	5514	5527	5539	5551	1	2	4	5	6
36	5563	5575	5587	5599	5611	5623	5635	5647	5658	5670	1	2	4	5	6
37	5682	5694	5705	5717	5729	5740	5752	5763	5775	5786	1	2	4	5	6
38	5798	5809	5821	5832	5843	5855	5866	5877	5888	5899	1	2	3	5	6
39	5911	5922	5933	5944	5955	5966	5977	5988	5999	6010	1	2	3	4	5
40	6021	6031	6042	6053	6064	6075	6085	6096	6107	6117	1	2	3	4	5
41	6128	6138	6149	6160	6170	6180	6191	6201	6212	6222	1	2	3	4	5
42	6232	6243	6253	6263	6274	6284	6294	6304	6314	6325	1	2	3	4	5
43	6335	6345	6355	6365	6375	6385	6395	6405	6415	6425	1	2	3	4	5
44	6435	6444	6454	6464	6474	6484	6493	6503	6513	6522	1	2	3	4	5
45	6532	6542	6551	6561	6571	6580	6590	6599	6609	6618	1	2	3	4	5
46	6628	6637	6646	6656	6665	6675	6684	6693	6702	6712	1	2	3	4	5
47	6721	6730	6739	6749	6758	6767	6776	6785	6794	6803	1	2	3	4	5
48	6812	6821	6830	6839	6848	6857	6866	6875	6884	6893	1	2	3	4	5
49	6902	6911	6920	6928	6937	6946	6955	6964	6972	6981	1	2	3	4	4
50	6990	6998	7007	7016	7024	7033	7042	7050	7059	7067	1	2	3	3	4
51	7076	7084	7093	7101	7110	7118	7126	7135	7143	7152	1	2	3	3	4
52	7160	7168	7177	7185	7193	7202	7210	7218	7226	7235	1	2	3	3	4
53	7243	7251	7259	7267	7275	7284	7292	7300	7308	7316	1	2	2	3	4
54	7324	7332	7340	7348	7356	7364	7372	7380	7388	7396	1	2	2	3	4
N	L.0	1	2	3	4	5	6	7	8	9	1	2	3	4	5

FOUR-PLACE LOGARITHMS (*Continued*)

N	L.0	1	2	3	4	5	6	7	8	9	1	2	3	4	5
55	7404	7412	7419	7427	7435	7443	7451	7459	7466	7474	1	2	2	3	4
56	7482	7490	7497	7505	7513	7520	7528	7536	7543	7551	1	2	2	3	4
57	7559	7566	7574	7582	7589	7597	7604	7612	7619	7627	1	1	2	3	4
58	7634	7642	7649	7657	7664	7672	7679	7686	7694	7701	1	1	2	3	4
59	7709	7716	7723	7731	7738	7745	7752	7760	7767	7774	1	1	2	3	4
60	7782	7789	7796	7803	7810	7818	7825	7832	7839	7846	1	1	2	3	4
61	7853	7860	7868	7875	7882	7889	7896	7903	7910	7917	1	1	2	3	3
62	7924	7931	7938	7945	7952	7959	7966	7973	7980	7987	1	1	2	3	3
63	7993	8000	8007	8014	8021	8028	8035	8041	8048	8055	1	1	2	3	3
64	8062	8069	8075	8082	8089	8096	8102	8109	8116	8122	1	1	2	3	3
65	8129	8136	8142	8149	8156	8162	8169	8176	8182	8189	1	1	2	3	3
66	8195	8202	8209	8215	8222	8228	8235	8241	8248	8254	1	1	2	3	3
67	8261	8267	8274	8280	8287	8293	8299	8306	8312	8319	1	1	2	3	3
68	8325	8331	8338	8344	8351	8357	8363	8370	8376	8382	1	1	2	3	3
69	8388	8395	8401	8407	8414	8420	8426	8432	8439	8445	1	1	2	3	3
70	8451	8457	8463	8470	8476	8482	8488	8494	8500	8506	1	1	2	3	3
71	8513	8519	8525	8531	8537	8543	8549	8555	8561	8567	1	1	2	3	3
72	8573	8579	8585	8591	8597	8603	8609	8615	8621	8627	1	1	2	3	3
73	8633	8639	8645	8651	8657	8663	8669	8675	8681	8686	1	1	2	2	3
74	8692	8698	8704	8710	8716	8722	8727	8733	8739	8745	1	1	2	2	3
75	8751	8756	8762	8768	8774	8779	8785	8791	8797	8802	1	1	2	2	3
76	8808	8814	8820	8825	8831	8837	8842	8848	8854	8859	1	1	2	2	3
77	8865	8871	8876	8882	8887	8893	8899	8904	8910	8915	1	1	2	2	3
78	8921	8927	8932	8938	8943	8949	8954	8960	8965	8971	1	1	2	2	3
79	8976	8982	8987	8993	8998	9004	9009	9015	9020	9025	1	1	2	2	3
80	9031	9036	9042	9047	9053	9058	9063	9069	9074	9079	1	1	2	2	3
81	9085	9090	9096	9101	9106	9112	9117	9122	9128	9133	1	1	2	2	3
82	9138	9143	9149	9154	9159	9165	9170	9175	9180	9186	1	1	2	2	3
83	9191	9196	9201	9206	9212	9217	9222	9227	9232	9238	1	1	2	2	3
84	9243	9248	9253	9258	9263	9269	9274	9279	9284	9289	1	1	2	2	3
85	9294	9299	9304	9309	9315	9320	9325	9330	9335	9340	1	1	2	2	3
86	9345	9350	9355	9360	9365	9370	9375	9380	9385	9390	1	1	2	2	3
87	9395	9400	9405	9410	9415	9420	9425	9430	9435	9440	1	1	2	2	3
88	9445	9450	9455	9460	9465	9469	9474	9479	9484	9489	0	1	1	2	2
89	9494	9499	9504	9509	9513	9518	9523	9528	9533	9538	0	1	1	2	2
90	9542	9547	9552	9557	9562	9566	9571	9576	9581	9586	0	1	1	2	2
91	9590	9595	9600	9605	9609	9614	9619	9624	9628	9633	0	1	1	2	2
92	9638	9643	9647	9652	9657	9661	9666	9671	9675	9680	0	1	1	2	2
93	9685	9689	9694	9699	9703	9708	9713	9717	9722	9727	0	1	1	2	2
94	9731	9736	9741	9745	9750	9754	9759	9763	9768	9773	0	1	1	2	2
95	9777	9782	9786	9791	9795	9800	9805	9809	9814	9818	0	1	1	2	2
96	9823	9827	9832	9836	9841	9845	9850	9854	9859	9863	0	1	1	2	2
98	9868	9872	9877	9881	9886	9890	9894	9899	9903	9908	0	1	1	2	2
98	9912	9917	9921	9926	9930	9934	9939	9943	9948	9952	0	1	1	2	2
99	9956	9961	9965	9969	9974	9978	9983	9987	9991	9996	0	1	1	2	2
N	L.0	1	2	3	4	5	6	7	8	9	1	2	3	4	5

Proportional Parts

Answers

EXERCISE 1-1, PAGE 4

1. {m,a,t,h,e,i,c,s}. **3.** {1,2,3,4}. **5.** {January, March, May, July, August, October, December}. **7.** The positive integers less than 10. **9.** The positive odd integers less than or equal to 9. **11.** False. **13.** True. **15.** False. **17.** False. **19.** True. **21.** False. **23.** False. **25.** False. **27.** $A \notin B$. **29.** $A \not\subseteq B$. **31.** $\{3,1,2\} = A$. **33.** $B \subseteq C$. **35.** $\{7,3,5,1\} = B$.

EXERCISE 1-2, PAGE 8

1.

3.

$n(A) = 5$.

5. (a) infinite; (c) infinite; (e) finite. **9.** $9 = 3 \cdot 3$; $24 = 2 \cdot 2 \cdot 2 \cdot 3$; $36 = 2 \cdot 2 \cdot 3 \cdot 3$; $60 = 2 \cdot 2 \cdot 3 \cdot 5$.

EXERCISE 1-3, PAGE 10

1. {2,4,6,8,10}. **3.** {4,6,8,10}. **5.** {4,6,8,10}. **7.** {4}. **9.** {13}. **11.** {4,7,9}. **13.** {3,4,7}. **15.** {3,4,9}. **17.** $\{x \in N \mid x$ is positive odd integer$\}$. **19.** $\{x \in N \mid x = 3\}$.

EXERCISE 1-4, PAGE 12

3. False. **5.** False. **7.** True. **9.** False. **13.** {0,1,2,3,4,5,6,7}. **15.** {4,5,6,7}. **17.** ϕ. **19.** {0,1,2,3,4,5}. **21.** {4}. **23.** {0,1,2,3,4,5}. **25.** {4,5}. **27.** (a) $\{y \in N \mid y = 5\}$; (b) {5}. **29.** (a) $\{x \in N \mid x \in \phi\}$; (b) ϕ. **31.** $n(A) = 3, n(B) = 4, n(C) = 4$. **33.** Yes.

EXERCISE 1-5, PAGE 14

1. Fig. 1-4; 3, 4; Fig. 1-5; 2, 3, 4; Fig. 1-6; 3, 4, 5; Fig. 1-7; 3, 6, 7, 8. **3.** Fig. 1-4; 2; Fig. 1-5; ϕ; Fig. 1-6; 2; Fig. 1-7; 2, 5. **15.** True. **17.** True. **19.** True. **21.** False. **23.** True. **25.** False.

EXERCISE 2-1, PAGE 18

1. $3x$. **3.** $\frac{1}{2}x + 3$. **5.** $\frac{1}{3}(x - 2)$. **7.** $3(x + 1)$ miles; $40 - 3(x + 1)$ miles.
9. $(40 - x - y)$ miles. **11.** $P = bh$. **13.** $C = 2\pi r$. **15.** $3x + 7 = \frac{1}{3}(x + 8)$.
17. $\frac{1}{3}(x + 2y) = \frac{1}{2}(y + 3x)$. **21.** $x, 3x$. **23.** $x, \frac{2}{5}x + 3$.
25. $x - 10, x + 20, x + y$.

EXERCISE 2-2, PAGE 26

1. $-15, -5, -4, -2, -1, -\frac{1}{2}, 0, \frac{2}{3}, 5, 6$. **2.** $0, -\frac{1}{2}, \frac{2}{3}, -1, -2, -4, \pm 5$,
$6, -15$. **3.** -4. **4.** -3. **6.** -10. **7.** -7. **8.** 12. **9.** -5. **11.** -7.
12. -17. **13.** 32. **14.** -15. **16.** -4. **17.** -9. **18.** -7. **19.** 3. **21.** 3.
22. -5. **23.** 10. **24.** -17. **26.** 31. **27.** -3. **28.** -12. **29.** -7. **31.** -13.
32. 4. **33.** 3. **34.** 5. **36.** -17. **37.** 20. **38.** 31. **39.** 40. **41.** 8. **42.** -8.
43. -40. **44.** 12. **46.** 0. **47.** 0. **48.** 0. **49.** 0. **51.** -42. **52.** 0. **53.** 0.
54. 180. **56.** -30. **57.** -21. **58.** -1. **59.** -4. **61.** 0. **62.** -14. **63.** 5.
64. -3. **66.** -10. **67.** -2. **68.** 6. **69.** -5. **71.** 5. **72.** 0. **73.** 0.
74. Not a number. **76.** 0. **77.** 0. **78.** 0. **79.** Not a number. **81.** 0.
82. Not a number. **83.** 1. **84.** 2. **86.** 1. **87.** 0.

EXERCISE 2-3, PAGE 30

1. (Sample answers) $2x^2yz^3$; $5x^2yz^3$; $-x^2yz^3$. **2.** (Sample answers):
Monomials: $2x$; $3y$. Binomials: $3x + y$, $4m + 3n$. Trinomials: $2x + 3y + 5$;
$m^2 + 2mn + 5n^2$. **3.** $6x - 4$. **4.** $7 - 5x$. **6.** $5ax^2 - 5x + 9$.
7. $4x^3 - 3x^2 - 2ax - 1$. **8.** $3x^3 - 6ax + 2$. **9.** $-3x^4 + x^2 + 4x -$
$2a - 1$. **11.** $x^3 + 3x^2 - 3x + 13$. **12.** $x^4 + 2x^2 - 2x + 3$. **21.** No.
22. $2x - 10$. **23.** $9x - 1$. **24.** $ax^2 + 8x - 5$. **26.** $-2x^3 - 7x^2 +$
$4ax - 3$. **27.** $-x^3 - 4x^2$. **28.** $-7x^4 + 5x^2 - 2x - 2a + 1$.
29. $-2x^4 + 3x^3 + 3x^2 + 2x - 4a + 3$. **31.** $-9x + 1$. **32.** $-ax^2 -$
$8x + 5$. **33.** $-ax^2 + x - 1$. **34.** $2x^3 + 7x^2 - 4ax + 3$. **36.** $7x^4 -$
$5x^2 + 2x + 2a - 1$. **37.** $2x^4 - 3x^3 - 3x^2 - 2x + 4a - 3$. **38.** $-a -$
$b + d$. **39.** $7x - 2y - 1$. **41.** $-4a - b + 4$. **42.** $5a - 2b - c$.

43. $-a + 2b + 4c + 1.$ **44.** $-4x + 7.$ **46.** $-x^2 + 3ax^2 + 3bx.$
47. $-3x^2 - 2ax^2 + 2x.$ **48.** $2x - (3a - b).$ **49.** $4x - (2a + 3y).$
51. $3a - (-4b + c + 1).$ **52.** $-3b - 5c.$ **53.** $2x^3 - x^2 + 7x - 3.$
54. $4a^3 - 10a^2 + 12ab + 3.$

EXERCISE 2-4, PAGE 34

1. $12a^4x^3.$ **2.** $-15bx^4.$ **3.** $24a^3x^5.$ **4.** $-6ay^3.$ **6.** $-3x.$ **7.** $4xy^5.$
8. $[(x + 1)(x - 1)](2x + 1) = (x^2 - 1)(2x + 1) = 2x^3 + x^2 - 2x - 1.$
$(x + 1)[(x - 1)(2x + 1)] = (x + 1)(2x^2 - x - 1) = 2x^3 + x^2 - 2x - 1.$
9. $12x^8 + 22x^3 - 2x^2 - 10x.$ **11.** $9x^5 - 24x^4 + 13x^3 - 29x^2 + 18x - 3.$
12. $2x^6 - 11x^5 + 19x^4 - 5x^3 - 17x^2 + 16x - 4.$ **13.** $12x^6 + 32x^5 -$
$5x^4 - 47x^3 - x^2 + 11x - 2.$ **14.** $x^7 - 2x^6 - 7x^5 + 21x^4 - 16x^3 - 9x^2 +$
$10x - 2.$ **16.** $18x^6 - 6x^5 - 13x^4 + 9x^3 + 15x^2 + 2x - 4.$ **17.** $3x^5 +$
$14x^4 + 15x^3 - 7x^2 - 8x + 3.$ **18.** $8x^5 + 12x^4 - 32x^3 - 20x^2 + 48x - 16.$
19. $3x^6 - 2x^5 - 42x^4 + 6x^3 + 45x^2 - 13x.$ **21.** $18x^5 + 39x^4 - 4x^3 -$
$32x^2 - x + 6.$ **22.** $3x^6 + \dfrac{11x}{2} - \dfrac{1}{2} - \dfrac{5}{2x}.$ **23.** $x^4 - \dfrac{11x^3}{3} + \dfrac{7x}{3} - \dfrac{5}{3} + \dfrac{2}{3x}.$
24. $x^3 - 2x^2 - 3.$ **26.** $3x^2 - x - 2.$ **27.** $x^3 + 4x^2 + 6x + 19 +$
$\dfrac{55x - 21}{x^2 - 3x + 1}.$ **28.** $3x^3 - x^2 + 2.$ **29.** $2x^2 - 2x + 1 + \dfrac{5 - x}{3x^2 + x - 1}.$
31. $2x - 3 + \dfrac{x + 2}{2x^2 + 3x - 2}.$ **32.** $3x^2 - 20x + 57 + \dfrac{57 - 178x}{x^2 + 3x - 1}.$
33. $x + 2 - \dfrac{1}{4x^2 - 3x + 1}.$ **34.** $2x + 3 + \dfrac{3}{3x^2 + x - 2}.$
36. $a^2 - ab + b^2.$ **37.** $a^2 + ab + b^2.$ **38.** $-3x^2 + 2ax + 5a^2.$
39. $-3x^2 - x + 11.$ **41.** $-3x + \dfrac{1}{3} + \dfrac{5}{3(1 - 3x)}.$

GENERAL REVIEW LIST, PAGE 35

1. $4x.$ **2.** $\dfrac{3x}{4}.$ **3.** $\dfrac{x}{5}.$ **4.** $x - 7$ or $7 - x.$ **6.** $3x - 9.$ **7.** $5 - \dfrac{5x}{2}.$
8. $10x + y.$ **9.** $10y + x.$ **11.** $2(10x + y) + 36.$ **12.** $4x$ yds.; $10x$ yds.;
$4x^2$ sq. yds.   **13.** $(2x - 9)$ yds.; $(6x - 18)$ yds.; $(2x^2 - 9x)$ sq. yds.
14. $600x$ ft.   **16.** $7200(x + 1)$ ft.   **17.** $V = \dfrac{4}{3}\pi R^3.$ **18.** $A = \dfrac{h(a + b)}{2}.$
19. $T = 0.10m + 0.40x.$ **21.** $D = 2x - y; D = y - 2x.$ **22.** $x = y + 10.$
23. $I = 50x.$ **24.** $I = .07R.$ **26.** $x = 26,400x.$ **27.** $24.$ **28.** $-9.$
29. $-9.$ **31.** $-20.$ **32.** Not a number.   **33.** $0.$ **34.** Not a number.
36. $-18.$ **37.** $-8.$ **38.** $30.$ **39.** $-2.$ **41.** $-32.$ **42.** $-\dfrac{1}{2}.$ **43.** $76.$

44. -1.   **46.** 9.   **47.** $-8b^2$.   **48.** 0.   **49.** $2(a + b) = 2a + 2b$.   **51.** $3y$.
52. $8a^2 - 9ab + c$.   **53.** $-8n^2 - mn + 10$.   **54.** $6a - 10b + c$.   **56.** $-x +$
$2y - 6z$.   **57.** $2x^2 + 10xy - 17$.   **58.** $-8ab - 11c^2 + 2d + 6$.   **59.** $x + 4$.
61. $-3a + 12b + 24$.   **62.** $x + 5y + 8$.   **63.** $-3x^2 - y -$
$(2x - z + 3w)$.   **64.** $a^2 - b^2 - (2a^2b^2 - 4a^4)$.   **66.** $y - 5 - (x + 3z^2)$.
67. $-6xy$.   **68.** $21x^7y^6$.   **69.** $-15m^3n^3$.   **71.** $-10m^3n^2 + 15m^2n - 10mn^2$.
72. $-3x^4 - 9x^3 - 6x^2 + 4x^2y + 7xy - y^2$.   **73.** $4a^2 + 26ab - 14b^2$.
74. $x^3 - x^2y + xy^2 - y^3$.   **76.** $3x^5 + x^4y - 6x^2y - 2x^3y^2 + 4xy^2 + x^3y +$
$x^2y^2 - 2y^2$.   **77.** $x^2 + 7x + 12$.   **78.** $x^2 - 7x + 10$.   **79.** $x^2 + 4x - 21$.
81. $-3a^2 + 3$.   **82.** $2a^2 - 5a - 12$.   **83.** $6a^2 - 19a + 10$.   **84.** $-30a^2 -$
$4a + 2$.   **86.** $4x^2 - y^2$.   **87.** $-9x^2 + y^2$.   **88.** $y^2 - 4x^2$.   **89.** $-45x^4 + 5y^2$.
91. $9 - 12x + 4x^2$.   **92.** $-32 + 16x - 2x^2$.   **93.** $-3x^2 - 12x - 12$.
94. $100x^2 + 60x + 9$.   **96.** $16x^2 + 40xy + 25y^2$.   **97.** $-8y$.   **98.** $25m$.
99. $9ab^2$.   **101.** $3x^2 + 2x + \dfrac{3}{2x - 1}$.   **102.** $3x - 4y$.   **103.** $\dfrac{2x^2}{3} + \dfrac{7x}{9} -$

$\dfrac{52}{27} + \dfrac{25}{27(3x + 1)}$.

EXERCISE 3-1, PAGE 42

2. (Sample answers) (a) $2x^2 + x + 5$. (b) $2x^{1/2} - 3$.   **3.** $10x^2 - 5ax - 5x$.
4. $-3y^2 + 6xy^2$.   **6.** $-6x^3 + 4ax^3 - 2bx^2 - 4x^2$.   **7.** $-12ax - 6a^2$.
8. $3p^3 + 3pq^2$.   **9.** $x^2 + 10x + 25$.   **11.** $-9x^2y^2 - 12xy - 4$.
12. $-18m^4 - 24m^2n - 8n^2$.   **13.** $4a^4 - 4a^2b + b^2$.   **14.** $16m^4 - 24m^2x +$
$9x^2$.   **16.** $4 - 4y^2 + y^4$.   **17.** $9a^4c^2 - 3a^2c + \dfrac{1}{4}$.   **18.** $9x^2 - 4y^2$.

19. $4x^4 - 16y^4$.   **21.** $\dfrac{a^2}{b^2} - \dfrac{b^2}{a^2}$.   **22.** $x^2 + 2ax + a^2 - 4$.   **23.** $9x^2 - 12x +$
$4 - 9y^2$.   **24.** $x^2 + 2xy + y^2 - 4r^2 + 4rs - s^2$.   **26.** $27a^3 + b^3$.   **27.** $8p^6 +$
$27m^3p^3$.   **28.** $a^3 - y^3$.   **29.** $-24a^3 + 3b^3$.   **31.** The square of a trinomial
equals the sum of the squares of the terms plus twice the product of each pair of
terms.   **32.** $x^2 + y^2 + 4z^2 + 2xy + 4xz + 4yz$.   **33.** $9x^2 + 4y^2 + z^2 -$
$12xy + 6xz - 4yz$.   **34.** $4a^2 + b^2 + 9c^2 - 4ab - 12ac + 6bc$.   **36.** $x(a +$
$b + 1)$.   **37.** $y(2ay - 1)$.   **38.** $(2x + 1)^2$.   **39.** $(x - 3y)^2$.   **41.** $(2y - 1)$
$(2y + 1)$.   **42.** $(a + b - c - d)(a + b + c + d)$.   **43.** $(1 - 2x + y)(1 +$
$2x - y)$.   **44.** $(2 - 3y)(4 + 6y + 9y^2)$.   **46.** $(3x^2 - 2y^2)(9x^4 + 6x^2y^2 +$
$4y^4)$.   **47.** $(a + b - 2)(a^2 + 2ab + b^2 + 2a + 2b + 4)$.   **48.** $(8 - x -$
$2y)(8 + x + 2y)$.   **49.** $(x + y)(x + y - 1)$.   **51.** $(x - y)(x + y)(x^2 +$
$xy + y^2)(x^2 - xy + y^2)$.   **52.** $(x^2 + y^2)(x^4 - x^2y^2 + y^4)$.   **53.** $(4a -$
$5b)(4a + 5b)$.   **54.** $(x - y - a - b)(x - y + a + b)$.   **56.** $(k + 1 -$
$x + y)(k + 1 + x - y)$.   **57.** $25x^3y(2xy - 1)(2xy + 1)$.   **58.** $12(a^4b^5 - 3)$.
59. $16xy^3(2xy - 1)(2xy + 1)$.

EXERCISE 3-2, PAGE 44

1. $(x + 1)^2$. **2.** $(2x + 3)^2$. **3.** $(4x + 5)^2$. **4.** $(a - 5)^2$. **6.** $(x - 2)^2$.
7. $(3x - 2)^2$. **8.** $(5x - 4)^2$. **9.** $(2m - 1)^2$. **11.** $(x - 3)(x - 2)$.
12. $(x - 3)(x + 1)$. **13.** $(x + 2)(x + 1)$. **14.** $(x - 6)(x + 1)$. **16.** $(x + 6)$
$(x - 1)$. **17.** $(x - 2)(x - 1)$. **18.** $(x - 7)(x + 1)$. **19.** $(x + 2)(x - 1)$.
21. $(x - 6)(x - 5)$. **22.** $(x - 12)(x + 1)$. **23.** $(x + 12)(x - 1)$.
24. $(x - 5)(x + 1)$. **26.** $(x - 7)(x - 3)$. **27.** $(x + 8)(x + 4)$.
28. $(x + 13)(x - 1)$. **29.** $(x - 13)(x + 1)$. **31.** $(2x + 1)(x + 2)$.
32. $(2x + 1)(x - 2)$. **33.** $(3x - 1)(x + 2)$. **34.** $(5x + 2)(x - 1)$.
36. $(3x - 2)(2x + 3)$. **37.** $(3x + 2)(2x - 3)$. **38.** $(5x - 3)(2x - 1)$.
39. $(5x - 3)(2x + 1)$. **41.** $(3x + 5)(2x - 1)$. **42.** $(5x - 3)(3x - 2)$.
43. $(3x - 2)(3x + 1)$. **44.** $3(x + 2)(3x - 1)$. **46.** $(8x - 3)(3x + 2)$.
47. $(9x + 4)(3x - 2)$. **48.** $(10x + 3)(2x + 1)$. **49.** $(12x - 5)(3x + 2)$.

EXERCISE 3-3, PAGE 46

1. $(a + b)(x - y)$. **2.** $(b - c)(x + y)$. **3.** $(x + y)(a + b)$. **4.** $(m - n)$
$(k - 1)$. **6.** $(x + y)(a + b)$. **7.** $(x - y)(b + c)$. **8.** $(x - 2)(x^2 + 1)$.
9. $(x - 1)(x + 1)(2x + 3)$. **11.** $(x + y + 1)(x - y)$. **12.** $(x - y)$
$(x + y - 1)$. **13.** $(2x + 3y + 1)(2x - 3y)$. **14.** $(3x + 4y)(3x - 4y - 1)$.
16. $(2x - y + 1)(2x + y - 1)$. **17.** $(x + y - 3)(x + y + 3)$. **18.** $(4 - x + y)$
$(4 + x - y)$. **19.** $(x - y + 5)(x - y - 5)$. **21.** $(y + 1 - x)(y + 1 + x)$.
22. $(2x - 1 - y)(2x - 1 + y)$. **23.** $(x - 3 - y)(x - 3 + y)$. **24.** $(x -$
$a - b + 1)(x - a + b - 1)$. **26.** $(x^4 - x^2 + 1)(x^2 - x + 1)(x^2 + x + 1)$.
27. $(x^2 + x - 1)(x^2 - x - 1)$. **28.** $(x^2 - x + 2)(x^2 + x + 2)$. **29.** $(x^2 +$
$3 - x)(x^2 + 3 + x)$. **31.** $(x^2 + x - 3)(x^2 - x - 3)$. **32.** $(x^2 - 2x + 3)$
$(x^2 + 2x + 3)$. **33.** $(x^2 + 4 - 2x)(x^2 + 4 + 2x)$. **34.** $(2x^2 - x + 1)$
$(2x^2 + x + 1)$. **36.** $(x + y)(1 - x + y)$. **37.** $(2x - y + 2)(2x + y - 2)$.
38. $(2x^2 - 2x + 1)(2x^2 + 2x + 1)$. **39.** $(5x^2 - 3x + 1)(5x^2 + 3x + 1)$.
41. $(3x - 1)(3x + 1)(x + 1)(x - 1)$. **42.** $(3x - 2)(3x + 2)(x - 2)(x + 2)$.

EXERCISE 3-4, PAGE 48

1. 3; 180. **2.** 6; 72. **3.** 9; 108. **4.** 1; 252. **6.** 15; 450. **7.** 16; 480. **8.** 18;
540. **9.** 13; 3640. **11.** $5a^2x^2$; $30a^4x^4$. **12.** $3x^2y^2$; $180x^4y^4$. **13.** $x - y$;
$x^3 - xy^2$. **14.** $x + y$; $x^3 - xy^2$. **16.** $x + y$; $x^2(x - y)(x + y)^2$. **17.** $x - 2$;
$(x - 2)(x + 2)(x - 1)(x - 3)$. **18.** $2x - 1$; $(2x - 1)(x - 1)(x + 3)(2x + 1)$.
19. $3x - 1$; $(3x - 1)(x + 2)(x - 1)(x + 1)$. **21.** $3x - 1$; $(3x - 1)(2x + 1)$
$(x - 1)(2x - 1)$. **22.** $5x + 4$; $(5x + 4)(x - 1)(3x - 2)(2x - 3)$. **23.** $2y - x$;
$x^2(2y - x)^3$. **24.** $(x - y)^2$; $y^4(x - y)^3$.

GENERAL REVIEW LIST, PAGE 48

1. $4y^2(y - 3)$.   **2.** $3b^2(a + 2b)$.   **3.** $mn(m - n)$.   **4.** $ab(3a^2 + 5b - 1)$.
6. $(x - 3y)(y + 2)$.   **7.** $(c - 2a)(3a - b)$.   **8.** $(2m - n)(3 - x^2 - y^2)$.
9. $(m + c)(x + y)$.   **11.** $(x - 1)^2(x + 1)$.   **12.** $(3b - 1)(2a + 1)$.
13. $(x - 4y)(x^2 - 2y^2)$.   **14.** $(2q - 3)(3p + 2)$.   **16.** $(x - 3y)(x + 3y + 1)$.
17. $(y - 4)(y + 3)$.   **18.** $(2x + 1)(x + 2)$.   **19.** $(x + 7)(x + 3)$.
21. $(x + 4y)(x - 3y)$.   **22.** $(p^2 + 18)(p^2 - 2)$.   **23.** $(4a + 1)(3a - 1)$.
24. $(5r + 3s)(5r - s)$.   **26.** $(3x - 1)(4x + 25)$.   **27.** $(10 - x)(2 + x)$.
28. $(x^4 + 2y^4)^2$.   **29.** $(2c - d)^2$.   **31.** $(2 - 5x)^2$.   **32.** $(3x^2 - yz)^2$.
33. $(2x - 11y)(2x + 11y)$.   **34.** $(3 - x)(3 + x)(9 + x^2)$.   **36.** $(3x - y - 3)$
$(3x - y + 3)$.   **37.** $(x - 2y - z)(x + 2y + z)$.   **38.** $(x + 2y - 3m + 3n)$
$(x + 2y + 3m - 3n)$.   **39.** $(1 - x - y)(1 + x + y)$.   **41.** $(3 - a + 4b)$
$(3 + a - 4b)$.   **42.** $(2x - a - b + y)(2x - a + b - y)$.   **43.** $(p + q - a)$
$(p + q + a)$.   **44.** $(x + 2)(x^2 - 2x + 4)$.   **46.** $(ay + 4)(a^2y^2 - 4ay + 16)$.
47. $(x^2 + a^2)(x^4 - a^2x^2 + a^4)$.   **48.** $(2x - 3)(4x^2 + 3)$.   **49.** $(3y + a + 2b)$
$(9y^2 - 3ay - 6by + a^2 + 4ab + 4b^2)$.   **51.** $(x^2 - 4x + 8)(x^2 + 4x + 8)$.
52. $(x^2 + 2y^2 - 2xy)(x^2 + 2y^2 + 2xy)$.   **53.** $(x^2 - xy + y^2)(x^2 +$
$xy + y^2)$.   **54.** $(x^2 - 4 - 4x)(x^2 - 4 + 4x)$.   **56.** $(a^2 - 8b^2)(a^2 - 2b^2)$.
57. $r^2(2y - 5)(2y + 5)$.   **58.** $y^2(y - 2)^2(y + 2)^2$.   **59.** $(x - a)(x + a)$
$(x^2 + a^2)$.   **61.** $(a + 2)(a - 2)(a + 1)$.   **62.** $(y - a)^2(y + a)^2$.   **63.** $(m - 2)$
$(n + 1)(n - 1)$.   **64.** $(x + 3m)(x^2 - 3mx + 9m^2)$.   **66.** $(2x - 3y - 6)$
$(2x + 3y - 2)$.   **67.** $a(3x + y)(x - y)$.   **68.** $8rm(rx - 2 - 6r^2m^2)$.
69. $(1 - b)(1 + b)(x + y)$.   **71.** $(pq - 1)(pq + 1)$.   **72.** $(2x + 7c)^2$.
73. $(x - a - 2)(x^2 + ax + 2x + a^2 + 4a + 4)$.   **74.** $(2x + 1)(x - 1)^2$.

EXERCISE 4-1, PAGE 54

1. (a) $1; 3$. (b) $3; 1$. (c) $2; 2$.   **2.** In case (b).   **3.** $\dfrac{a}{b + 1}$.   Canceling not per-

missible in Probs. 4, 5, 7, 9, 10, and 12.   **6.** $\dfrac{x - 1}{3}$.   **8.** a.   **11.** $\dfrac{1}{3(x + y)}$.

13. $\dfrac{x - y}{a}$.   **18.** $\dfrac{1}{3}$.   **19.** $\dfrac{2}{3}$.   **21.** $\dfrac{7}{5}$.   **22.** $\dfrac{x^2 + x + 1}{x + 1}$.   **23.** $\dfrac{2x}{3}$.   **24.** $\dfrac{x}{2}$.

26. $\dfrac{6(x + y)}{5}$.   **27.** $\dfrac{5(y + 1)}{2}$.   **28.** $\dfrac{7y(x + 3)}{3}$.   **29.** $\dfrac{x - 4}{x + 4}$.   **31.** $\dfrac{x + 3}{x - 3}$.

32. $\dfrac{x - 5}{x - 3}$.   **33.** $\dfrac{x - 2}{x + 2}$.   **34.** $\dfrac{x - 2}{x - 1}$.   **36.** $\dfrac{3x - 2}{x - 1}$.   **37.** $\dfrac{3x - 1}{2x - 1}$.   **38.** $\dfrac{3x - 1}{2x + 1}$.

39. $\dfrac{3x + 2}{2x + 3}$.   **41.** $\dfrac{x^2 - 4}{x^2 - 9}$.   **42.** $\dfrac{x^2 + 1}{x - x^3}$.   **43.** $\dfrac{x^2 + 2}{3 - x^2}$.

44. $\dfrac{5c^2 - 10cd + 5d^2 - x}{c + d}$. **46.** $\dfrac{x^2 + 2xy + 2y^2}{5}$. **47.** $\dfrac{x + y + 8}{x + y - 3}$.

48. $\dfrac{x - 4y}{x^2 + xy + y^2}$. **49.** $\dfrac{a^2 - 2ab + 4b^2 + a - 2b}{a - 2b}$.

EXERCISE 4-2, PAGE 57

1. -1. **2.** 1. **3.** -1. **4.** 1. **6.** 1. **7.** -1. **8.** -1. **9.** -1. **11.** $\dfrac{4x + 1}{4}$.

12. $\dfrac{x + 2}{6}$. **13.** $\dfrac{8x - 5}{5}$. **14.** $\dfrac{4x - 1}{8}$. **16.** $\dfrac{3x + 1}{x + 1}$. **17.** $\dfrac{x + 1}{2x - 1}$.

18. $\dfrac{7x + 3}{x - 9}$. **19.** $\dfrac{5x - 8}{x + 1}$. **21.** 0.

EXERCISE 4-3, PAGE 60

1. $\dfrac{5}{6}$. **2.** $\dfrac{14}{15}$. **3.** $\dfrac{19}{20}$. **4.** $\dfrac{20}{21}$. **6.** $\dfrac{61}{60}$. **7.** $\dfrac{1}{280}$. **8.** $\dfrac{41}{40}$. **9.** $\dfrac{47}{36}$.

11. $\dfrac{x}{2 - x}$. **12.** $\dfrac{4x - 7}{2x - 3}$. **13.** $\dfrac{14x - 3}{12}$. **14.** $\dfrac{21x + 40}{60}$. **16.** $\dfrac{20x - 15}{18}$.

17. $\dfrac{9x - 30}{20}$. **18.** $\dfrac{6 - x}{10}$. **19.** $\dfrac{12 - 5x - 2x^2}{6x}$. **21.** $\dfrac{9 + 6x - 2x^2}{6x}$.

23. $\dfrac{3x^2 + 15x - 3}{5x}$. **23.** $\dfrac{6x^2 - 20x + 7}{4x}$. **24.** $\dfrac{6x^2 - 28x + 3}{7x}$.

26. $\dfrac{5x^2 + 2x + 15}{x^2 - 9}$. **27.** $\dfrac{7x + 5}{2x - 1}$. **28.** $\dfrac{5x^2 - 3x - 19}{6x^2 + 5x - 6}$.

29. $\dfrac{2x^2 + 31x - 43}{6x^2 + x - 12}$. **31.** $\dfrac{14x^2 + 14x + 1}{4x^2 - 1}$. **32.** $\dfrac{x^2 - 13x}{x^2 + 4x + 3}$.

33. $\dfrac{8x^2 - 7x + 12}{3x^2 - 2x - 1}$. **34.** $\dfrac{3x^2 - 18x - 28}{6x^2 + 5x - 6}$. **36.** $\dfrac{6x^2 + 3x - 41}{6x^2 + 13x - 5}$.

37. $\dfrac{9x - 7y}{3x - 2y}$. **38.** $\dfrac{8x - 32y}{7y - 5x}$. **39.** $\dfrac{23x^2 - 49xy + 15y^2}{6x^2 - 5xy + y^2}$. **41.** $\dfrac{8x + 2y}{2y - 3x}$.

42. $\dfrac{33x - 6y}{y - 7x}$. **43.** $\dfrac{x^3 + 3x^2 - 4xy + 8y^2 + y^3}{x^3 + y^3}$.

44. $\dfrac{x^3 + 3x^2 + 9xy + 9y^2 - y^3}{x^3 - y^3}$. **46.** $\dfrac{33 - 10x}{15x}$. **47.** $\dfrac{9x - 19}{15x}$.

48. $\dfrac{9x^2 - 10x + 10}{6x}$. **49.** $\dfrac{26x - 15 - 8x^2}{12x}$.

EXERCISE 4-4, PAGE 62

1. 5.   **2.** $\dfrac{14}{5}$.   **3.** $\dfrac{8}{3}$.   **4.** $-\dfrac{8}{25}$.   **6.** $-\dfrac{3}{14}$.   **7.** $\dfrac{3}{14}$.   **8.** -3.   **9.** $\dfrac{3}{2}$.

11. $\dfrac{2x^2 - 2x}{x + 2}$.   **12.** $-2x - 3$.   **13.** $\dfrac{15x^2 - 4x - 4}{3x - 1}$.   **14.** $6x - 14$.

16. $6x - 9$.   **17.** $39x + 9$.   **18.** $\dfrac{17x^2 - 3x}{3}$.   **19.** $\dfrac{2x - 13x^2}{7}$.

21. $\dfrac{21x^2 - 9x}{2x - 1}$.   **22.** $10x$.   **23.** $2x$.   **24.** 1.   **26.** 3.   **27.** $\dfrac{45x^2 + 15x - 30}{2x^2 - 13x + 15}$.

28. $\dfrac{3x - 1}{x}$.   **29.** $\dfrac{3x - 2}{x}$.   **31.** $\dfrac{7 - 5x}{2x}$.   **32.** $-\dfrac{4x + 3}{5x}$.

33. $\dfrac{6x^2 - 13x + 6}{x^2 - 9}$.   **34.** $\dfrac{10x^2 - x - 21}{x^2 + 2x - 35}$.   **36.** $\dfrac{x - 3}{2x + 6}$.

EXERCISE 4-5, PAGE 63

1. $\dfrac{1}{3x - 4}$.   **2.** $\dfrac{3}{5x + 3}$.   **3.** $\dfrac{4}{7x + 10}$.   **4.** $\dfrac{2}{2x + 3}$.   **6.** $-\dfrac{x + 2}{x^2 + 4}$.

7. $\dfrac{x - 2}{x^2 + x - 2}$.   **8.** $\dfrac{2x - 1}{2x^2 - x - 3}$.   **9.** $\dfrac{12x^2 - 7x - 12}{36x^3 + 9x^2 - 43x + 12}$.

11. $\dfrac{3x^2 + 7x - 6}{x - 2}$.   **12.** $\dfrac{2x^2 + x - 10}{3x - 2}$.   **13.** $\dfrac{10x^2 - 31x + 15}{x + 4}$.

14. $5 - 3x$.   **16.** $\dfrac{6x^2 - 5x - 6}{x - 1}$.   **17.** $\dfrac{6x^2 - 11x - 2}{3x - 2}$.   **18.** $\dfrac{x^2 + 2x + 1}{3x^2 - 2x - 1}$.

19. $\dfrac{6x^3 + 7x^2 - 9x + 2}{2x - 3}$.   **21.** $\dfrac{1}{2 - x}$.   **22.** -2.   **23.** x^2.   **24.** $\dfrac{3y^2 + 3y}{2}$.

26. $\dfrac{9x + 6}{2}$.   **27.** $8x^2 - 12x + 4$.   **28.** $7(x^2 + 2x - 1)$.   **29.** 2.

31. $\dfrac{9x^2 + 6x + 1}{x + 1}$.   **32.** $\dfrac{(y - 3x)(x + y)}{(y - x)(3x + 2y)}$.   **33.** $\dfrac{2x + y}{4x - 2y}$.

34. $\dfrac{(3x - 2y)(x - 2)}{(x - y)(x + 2)}$.   **36.** $\dfrac{y - 1}{y - 2}$.

EXERCISE 4-6, PAGE 66

1. $\dfrac{y}{x}$.   **2.** $\dfrac{xy + 1}{xy - 1}$.   **3.** $\dfrac{x - 1}{x + 1}$.   **4.** $\dfrac{1 + x + y}{1 - x - y}$.   **6.** -1.   **7.** 1.   **8.** -1.

9. $x + y$.   **11.** $\dfrac{(3x - 2y)(x - 2)}{(x - y)(x + 2)}$.   **12.** $\dfrac{y - x}{2y + x}$.   **13.** $\dfrac{2x + y}{4y - 2x}$.

14. $-\dfrac{(x + y)^2}{(x - y)^2}$.   **16.** $\dfrac{x^2 + xy + y^2}{x^2 - y^2}$.   **17.** $\dfrac{3y - 3x}{10}$.   **18.** -1.   **19.** $\dfrac{5y - 3x}{5y + 2x}$.

21. $\dfrac{y - 2x - x^2 + 2xy - y^2}{2y - x + x^2 - 2xy + y^2}$.

22. $\dfrac{x - 1}{x - 4}$.

23. $\dfrac{x^2 - 3x}{x + 1}$.

24. $\dfrac{6x^3 - x^2 - 4x}{2x^2 - x - 1}$.

26. $\dfrac{5x + 2}{x + 1}$.

27. $\dfrac{1}{1 - x}$.

28. $\dfrac{6x^2 - 4x - 1}{(1 - 2x)(x + 1)}$.

29. $\dfrac{x + 3}{2x + 1}$.

REVIEW EXERCISES, PAGE 67

1. $\dfrac{4a - 2b}{a - 3b}$.

2. $\dfrac{3x - 2y}{9x^2 + 6xy + 4y^2}$.

3. $\dfrac{x^2 + 4xy + 4y^2 - xz - 2yz - z^2}{x + 2y - z}$.

4. $\dfrac{3n + c}{3n - c}$.

6. $\dfrac{4x^2 - 4xy + y^2 - 5}{2x + y}$.

7. $-\dfrac{3x + 23}{24}$.

8. $\dfrac{7a - 15y}{12y}$.

9. $\dfrac{9x^3 - 3x^2y + 8x^2y^2 - 4xy - 12xy^2 - 3y^2}{12x^2y^2}$.

11. $\dfrac{5x^2 - xy + x + y}{(x - y)^2(x + y)}$.

12. $\dfrac{2bc - a^2 - b^2}{(a - b)(b - c)(c - a)}$.

13. $\dfrac{2x^2 - 8x + 2}{3 - x}$.

14. $\dfrac{5x^2 - 4x + 11}{12x^2 - 12}$.

16. $\dfrac{x^2 - 1}{xy - 1}$.

17. $\dfrac{3a^2 - 6ab - b^2}{3a - b}$.

18. $\dfrac{2(x + y)}{z(x - y)^2}$.

19. $\dfrac{ab}{3b - 1}$.

21. $\dfrac{x^2 - 1}{x}$.

22. $\dfrac{ab}{a^2 + 2ab + 2b^2}$.

23. $\dfrac{(a^3 - 8)(a + 2)}{8}$.

24. $\dfrac{4x^2 + 2xy}{y^2}$.

26. $\dfrac{(x^2 + 1)(x^2 - 4)}{x^2 - 1}$.

27. $\dfrac{2x + 1}{2}$.

28. $\dfrac{(5 - 2a)(a + 1)}{a^2 + 3a}$.

29. $\dfrac{(y - x)(3 + xy - x^2)}{y - x + 2}$.

31. $\dfrac{x + y}{x - y}$.

32. $\dfrac{a + b}{a^2 + ab + b^2}$.

33. $\dfrac{5a + 5b - 3}{2a + 2b - 1}$.

34. $\dfrac{5ab - 3b - 3a}{2ab - b - a}$.

36. $\dfrac{(a^2 + 5)(2a^2 + 7)}{(a^2 + 4)^2}$.

37. $-\dfrac{(x + 3)(x + 5)}{(x + 2)^2}$.

38. $-\dfrac{3u^3 + 6u^2 + 2u}{(u + 2)^2}$.

39. $\dfrac{2ac}{(b - a - c)[(a - c)^2 - b^2]}$.

41. $-\dfrac{(a + b)^3}{a^3b}$.

42. $\dfrac{4ab + a - 2b}{a^2 - b^2}$.

43. $\dfrac{m^3 - mn^2 - 2n^3}{n^3}$.

44. $\dfrac{b^3c}{a}$.

GENERAL REVIEW LIST, PAGE 70

1. (a) False—incorrect division between numerator and denominator. (b) False—denominator omitted. (c) True. (d) False—incorrect procedure for adding fractions. (e) True. (f) False—if dc ≠ 0, then result is 1. (g) True. (h) False—only numerator should be multiplied by 5. (i) True. (j) False—denominator omitted. (k) True. (l) True. **3.** (a) $\dfrac{3x + 6}{x}$. (b) $\dfrac{3y^2 + y}{3y^2 - y}$. (c) $\dfrac{1}{2x}$.

(d) $\dfrac{(c - 3d)^2(c + d)}{(c + 2d)(c + 3d)}$. (e) 3. (f) $\dfrac{y - x}{xy}$. (g) $5xz$. (h) $2xy$. (i) $\dfrac{17}{10}$. (j) $\dfrac{-y^2}{x^2}$.

5. (a) $15x^2 - 2x - 1$. (b) $9z^2 - 4y^4$. (c) $15x^2 + 4xy - 4y^2$. (d) $49x^2 - 28x + 4$.
(e) $9x^4 + 12x^2y^3 + 4y^6$. (f) $x^2 - y^2 - 2yz - z^2$. (g) $a^2 + b^2 + c^2 - 2ab + 2ac - 2bc$. (h) $(100 - 2)(100 + 2) = 9996$. (i) $x^3 + 8y^3$. (j) $1 - x^3$.
7. (a) $11a + 5b$. (b) $-35x^2 + x$.

EXERCISE 5-1, PAGE 80

The equations in Probs. **3, 5, 7, 9** and **11** are identities. **1.** 5. **2.** −4. **4.** 2.
6. 2. **8.** −1. **12.** 5. **13.** $\dfrac{-3}{8}$. **14.** $\dfrac{19}{2}$. **16.** $\dfrac{10}{3}$. **17.** $\dfrac{7}{2}$. **18.** $\dfrac{73}{44}$.
19. $\dfrac{10}{3}$. **21.** $\dfrac{5}{2}$. **22.** $\dfrac{7}{2}$. **23.** −4. **24.** $\dfrac{22}{9}$. **26.** $\dfrac{43}{7}$. **27.** $\dfrac{-1}{8}$. **28.** $\dfrac{3}{5}$
29. −1. **31.** −1. **32.** $\dfrac{9}{46}$. **33.** $\dfrac{5}{2}$. **34.** −9. **36.** 3. **37.** 4. **38.** 4; 8.
39. 9; 3. **41.** \$500; 1000. **42.** 6 p.m.

EXERCISE 5-2, PAGE 82

1. No root. **2.** 1. **3.** No root. **4.** 2. **6.** 4. **7.** $-\dfrac{10}{13}$. **8.** $\dfrac{1}{2}$. **9.** $\dfrac{41}{6}$.
11. 9. **12.** 1. **13.** No root. **14.** $-\dfrac{1}{15}$. **16.** $-\dfrac{5}{12}$. **17.** −1. **18.** $-\dfrac{57}{14}$.
19. $-\dfrac{4}{3}$. **21.** 1. **22.** −1. **23.** 2. **24.** $\dfrac{1}{2}$. **26.** 10. **27.** $-\dfrac{8}{11}$. **28.** 1.
29. $-\dfrac{25}{2}$. **31.** $-\dfrac{2}{5}$. **32.** $\dfrac{1}{6}$. **33.** No root.

EXERCISE 5-3, PAGE 86

1. $\dfrac{6b + 2a}{6 - bc}$. **2.** $\dfrac{6bd}{5(4a + c - 4d)}$. **3.** $\dfrac{a + d}{2c}$. **4.** b. **6.** $-d$. **7.** $-c$.

8. $\dfrac{adm + adn + bc}{cm + cn + d}$. **9.** $-\dfrac{na}{b}$. **11.** $\dfrac{-bm}{n}$. **12.** $-\dfrac{an}{m}$. **13.** $\dfrac{6br + 2bn}{r - 3n}$.

14. $\dfrac{ar - 3an}{6r + 2n}$. **16.** $\dfrac{r(a - 6b)}{3a + 2b}$. **17.** $\dfrac{2r}{1 + 6rn - 4rm}$.

18. $\dfrac{2m - 2mn - 2m^2}{3m + 3n + 3}$. **19.** $\dfrac{3a}{2 - b}$. **21.** $l - nd + d$; $\dfrac{d - a + l}{d}$; $\dfrac{l - a}{n - 1}$.

22. $\dfrac{En - IRn}{I}$; $\dfrac{En - IR}{In}$; $\dfrac{Ir}{E - Ir}$. **23.** $\dfrac{fp}{p - f}$; $\dfrac{fq}{q - f}$; $\dfrac{pq}{p + q}$. **24.** $\dfrac{RR_2}{R_2 - R}$;

$$\frac{RR_1}{R_1 - R}; \frac{R_1 R_2}{R_1 + R_2}.$$ **26.** $\frac{aM}{v - a}; \frac{vm - am}{a}; \frac{aM + am}{m}.$ **27.** $\frac{Sr - S + a}{r};$

$rl + S - Sr, \frac{S - a}{S - l}.$ **28.** $\frac{Fd^2}{KM}; \frac{Fd^2}{Km}.$ **29.** $\frac{v - v_0}{g}; v - gt; \frac{v - v_0}{t}.$

31. $\frac{2A}{a + b}; \frac{2A - ha}{h}.$ **32.** $\frac{br^2 + V}{r^2}.$ **33.** $\frac{aW_2 - W_1}{a - 1}; \frac{W_1 + aW - W}{a}.$

34. $(a + b)$ years. **36.** $2a + 20.$ **37.** $(5x + 25)$ cents. **38.** $\frac{2a}{3}.$

39. $\frac{ac + bc}{2}$ miles. **41.** $\frac{100a}{c}$ dozens.

EXERCISE 5-4, PAGE 87

1. 15. **2.** 23. **3.** 12. **4.** 6; 9. **6.** 9; 12. **7.** 3. **8.** 5. **9.** 12. **11.** $\frac{3}{5}.$
12. 17. **13.** $\frac{2}{7}.$

EXERCISE 5-5, PAGE 90

1. $\frac{21}{5}$ ft.; $\frac{14}{5}$ ft. **2.** $\frac{5}{2}$ ft.; $\frac{3}{2}$ ft. **3.** 7 in.; 10 in. **4.** 6 in.; 8 in.; 12 in. **6.** 10 in. ×
10 in.; 15 in. × 10 in. **7.** 3 in.; 6 in. **8.** 4 in.; 8 in. **9.** 10 in. × 6 in.;
6 in. × 6 in. **11.** 1 in.; 4 in. **12.** 50; 40. **13.** 30°; 60°; 90°. **14.** 40°; 100°.
16. 20°; 60°; 100°.

EXERCISE 5-6, PAGE 92

2. 15 hr. after 12 o'clock. **3.** $\frac{90}{17}.$ **4.** $\frac{40}{17}.$ **6.** $\frac{440}{17}.$ **7.** 6 hrs. after 1st car
starts. **8.** $\frac{160}{3}$ mph. **9.** 6 mi.; 3 hr.; 2 hr. **12.** 10 mph. **13.** 20 mph.
14. $\frac{39}{5}$ mph. **16.** 2 mph. **17.** 100 mph. **18.** speed; 125 mph.; distance: 525
miles.

EXERCISE 5-7, PAGE 95

1. $30. **2.** 4%. **3.** 4%. **4.** $^{10}\!/_3$%. **6.** 2 yrs. **7.** $5000 @ 5%; $2500 @ 6%.
8. $5000 @ 4%; $3000 @ 5%. **9.** $5000 @ 4%; $4000 @ 5%. **11.** $9.00 per
day. **12.** $4.00; $8.00. **13.** $8.00; $16.00. **14.** 6 @ $6; 4 @ $8. **16.** $39.
17. $517.50. **18.** 6%. **19.** 2 yrs. **21.** $600; $90. **22.** $1000. **24.** 12 nks.;
24 dms. **26.** 2 qtrs.; 4 dms.; 8 nks. **27.** 5 nks.; 5 dms.; 10 qtrs. **28.** 6 nks.;
4 qtrs.; 10 dms.

EXERCISE 5-8, PAGE 98

1. 30 lb.   **2.** 30.   **3.** $58\frac{1}{3}$ oz.   **4.** $\frac{23}{17}$ oz.   **6.** $\frac{135}{16}$ oz.   **7.** 28 lb.   **8.** 21 lb @ 15¢; 9 lbs. @ 25¢.   **11.** 7 cases @ \$2.50; 8 cases @ \$3.

EXERCISE 5-9, PAGE 101

1. 4.8 ft from 90-lb boy.   **2.** $93\frac{1}{3}$ lb.   **3.** 640 lb.   **4.** $333\frac{1}{3}$ lb.   **6.** $\frac{7}{10}$ miles from fulcrum.   **7.** $\frac{32}{9}$ ft. from end.   **8.** 42 lb.   **9.** $\frac{56}{3}$ lb.   **11.** 500 lb. **12.** $396\frac{2}{3}$ lb.   **13.** 550 lb.   **14.** 28 lb; 42 lb.   **16.** 10 ft.   **17.** 3 ft.

EXERCISE 5-10, PAGE 103

1. $6\frac{6}{19}$ days.   **2.** 50 min.   **3.** A: 48 days; B: 192 days; C: 576 days.   **4.** 4 min. **6.** 40 hrs.   **7.** $9\frac{9}{20}$ min.   **8.** $\frac{ab}{a+b}$ days.   **9.** A: $\frac{5a+5}{a}$ days; B: $\frac{5a+5}{5}$ days.

EXERCISE 6-1, PAGE 115

1. $V = \frac{4}{3}\pi r^3$ or $f = \{(r,v) \mid V = f(r) = \frac{4}{3}\pi r^3\}$.   **3.** $f = \{(h,w) \mid w = f(h)\}$.

5. $f = \{(t,I) \mid I = f(t) = 100(.05)t\}$.   **7.** $f = \left\{(h,A) \mid A = f(h) = \frac{\sqrt{3}}{2}h^2\right\}$.

9. $S = \pi r(r+s)$ or $f = \{(r,s,S) \mid S = f(r,s) = \pi r(r+s)\}$.   **11.** When $x = 1$, $y = 6$; when $x = 0$, $y = -4$; when $x = -t$, $y = 3(-t)^2 + 7(-t) - 4 = 3t^2 -$

$7t - 4$.   **13.** $f(2) = 3$; $f(1+x) = \dfrac{1 - 2(1+x)}{1 - (1+x)} = \dfrac{1+2x}{x}$.

15. $\dfrac{6x^2 - x - 1}{6(1+x)}$.   **17.** $x^2 + 3x + 3$.   **19.** (a) $\dfrac{5}{xy}$.   **21.** $\dfrac{4t}{1 - 4t^2}$.

23. $\dfrac{10h}{(3 - 5x_0 - 5h)(3 - 5x_0)}$.   **27.** $f(1,2) = 12$; $f(0,0) = 0$.   **29.** (a) $-\dfrac{40}{9}$.

31. $A = \dfrac{1}{2} \times (2000 - x)$.   **33.** $A = \dfrac{x(200 - 2x)}{1 + (\pi/2)} - \dfrac{\pi}{2}\left(\dfrac{100 - x}{1 + (\pi/2)}\right)^2$.

35. $A = \pi x^2 + \dfrac{108}{x}$.

EXERCISE 6-2, PAGE 122

15. $D = R_e$. **17.** $D = R_e$. **19.** $D = R_e$. **21.** $D = R_e$. **23.** $D = R_e$.
25. $D = R_e$. **27.** $D = R_e$. **29.** $D = R_e$. **31.** $D = R_e$. **33.** $D = R_e$.
35. $D = \{x \in R_e \wedge x \neq 0\}$. **37.** $D = \{x \in R_e \wedge x \neq 0\}$. **39.** $D =$
$\{x \in R_e \wedge x \neq 1\}$. **41.** $D = \{x \in R_e \mid x \geq 0\}$. **43.** $D = \{x \in$
$R_e \mid -2 \leq x \leq 2\}$. **45.** (a), (e).

EXERCISE 6-3, PAGE 126

19. $y = x$; $x = y$. **21.** $y = 1 - x$; $x = 1 - y$. **22.** $y = x + 1$; $x = y - 1$.
23. $y = 2x - 2$; $x = \frac{1}{2}(y + 2)$. **24.** $y = 6 - 3x$; $x = \frac{6 - y}{3}$.
26. $y = \frac{2x + 6}{3}$; $x = \frac{3y - 6}{2}$. **27.** $y = \frac{6 - 3x}{2}$; $x = \frac{6 - 2y}{3}$.
28. $y = 2x + 4$; $x = \frac{y - 4}{2}$. **29.** $y = 4 - 2x$; $x = \frac{4 - y}{2}$. **31.** $(a) F = \frac{9}{5}C + 32$; (b) $C = \frac{5}{9}(F - 32)$; (c) $5(F + 40) = 9C + 360$. **32.** $(a) P = \frac{I}{rt}$;
$(b) r = \frac{I}{Pt}$; $(c) t = \frac{I}{Pr}$.

EXERCISE 7-1, PAGE 138

1. $(2,3)$. **2.** $(2,3)$. **3.** $(-3,2)$. **4.** $(-3,5)$. **6.** $\left(\frac{4}{5}, -\frac{6}{5}\right)$. **7.** $\left(-\frac{3}{2}, -\frac{5}{2}\right)$.
8. $(-3,-1)$. **9.** $(-2,6)$. **11.** $\left(\frac{1}{3}, \frac{1}{2}\right)$. **12.** $(2,-3)$. **13.** $(1,-4)$. **14.** $(3,2)$.
16. $(2,-3)$. **17.** $(2,0)$. **18.** $(-2,2)$. **19.** $(4,3)$. **21.** $\left(\frac{1}{3},1\right)$. **22.** $\left(-\frac{11}{2},4\right)$.

23. $(-7,5)$. **24.** $\left(\frac{2}{5},\frac{3}{2}\right)$. **26.** $(3,6)$. **27.** $(-7,3)$. **41.** $\left(\frac{11}{5},\frac{2}{5}\right)$. **42.** $\left(\frac{36}{5},-\frac{8}{5}\right)$.
43. $\left(\frac{19}{2},-\frac{1}{2}\right)$. **44.** $\left(\frac{35}{13},-\frac{55}{78}\right)$. **46.** $\left(-\frac{9}{29},-\frac{63}{58}\right)$. **47.** $\left(-\frac{10}{7},-\frac{33}{7}\right)$.
48. $\left(-\frac{25}{12},-\frac{4}{3}\right)$. **49.** $(b,0)$. **51.** $\left(\frac{a + b}{a}, \frac{a - b}{b}\right)$. **52.** $\left(a + b, \frac{a^2 - b^2}{b}\right)$.
53. $\left(\frac{4}{3},\frac{7}{5}\right)$. **54.** $\left(-\frac{2}{a},\frac{6}{b}\right)$. No solutions (inconsistent): 55, 58, 59, and 61. More

than one solution (dependent); 56, 57, 60, 62, and 63. **66.** (1,3). **67.** $\left(\frac{2}{5}, -\frac{3}{5}\right)$.
68. $\left(\frac{1}{2}, \frac{1}{3}\right)$. **69.** $\left(\frac{1}{4}, 2\right)$.

EXERCISE 7-2, PAGE 141

1. (1,2,3).   **2.** (1,−1,−2).   **3.** (3,3,4).   **4.** (1,−1,0).   **6.** $\left(\frac{1}{5}, -3, -\frac{22}{5}\right)$.
7. $\left(\frac{16}{29}, \frac{19}{29}, \frac{21}{29}\right)$.   **8.** $\left(\frac{17}{20}, -\frac{1}{20}, -\frac{9}{20}\right)$.   **9.** $\left(\frac{10}{11}, -\frac{3}{11}, \frac{3}{11}\right)$.   **11.** $\left(\frac{7}{3}, -\frac{2}{3}, \frac{4}{3}, \frac{5}{6}\right)$.
12. $\left(\frac{1}{3}, 2, \frac{4}{3}, \frac{4}{3}\right)$.   **13.** $\left(3, \frac{1}{2}, 2\right)$.   **14.** (1,3,4).   **16.** $\left(\frac{9}{4}, \frac{9}{2}, 18\right)$.

EXERCISE 7-3, PAGE 144

1. 2; 1. **2.** 3; 5. **3.** 7; 5. **4.** 8; 6. **6.** 4; 5. **8.** 3 mph.; 4 mph. **9.** 2 mph.;
3 mph. **11.** 335 mph.; 15 mph. **12.** 150 mph.; 50 mph. **14.** 25. **16.** 347.
17. 397. **18.** 9 in. × 5 in. **19.** 12 in. × 7 in. **21.** 10 ft. × 4 ft.
22. 16 in. × 9 in. **23.** $2,000 @ 5%; $4,000 @ 6%. **24.** $6,000 @ 5%;
$4,000 @ 6%. **26.** $3,000 @ 4%; $4,000 @ 6%. **27.** A: $10; B: $6. **28.** 10
dms.; 20 nks. **29.** 6 qtrs.; 10 dms.; 20 nks. **31.** 70 lb, 5%; 30 lb, 15%.

GENERAL REVIEW LIST, PAGE 179

1. (a) $\begin{bmatrix} 3 & 3 & 5 \\ 1 & 0 & 0 \\ 3 & 2 & 2 \\ 4 & 4 & 3 \end{bmatrix}$ (b) $\begin{bmatrix} 4 & -3 & 3 & 3 \\ 2 & -5 & -1 & -4 \end{bmatrix}$ **3.** $\begin{bmatrix} 8 & 4 & 4 \\ 16 & 12 & 12 \\ 17 & 11 & 11 \end{bmatrix}$

5. (a) [24]; (b) [8 1 −3].

7. (b) $A'A = \begin{bmatrix} 10 & -1 & 12 \\ -1 & 5 & -4 \\ 12 & -4 & 16 \end{bmatrix}$; $AA' = \begin{bmatrix} 5 & 1 \\ 1 & 26 \end{bmatrix}$

9. (b) $\begin{vmatrix} 3 & 1 & 4 \\ 14 & 0 & 14 \\ -9 & 0 & -15 \end{vmatrix} = -94$.

11. (a) $A^{-1} = \frac{1}{-16} \begin{bmatrix} 3 & -5 \\ -5 & 3 \end{bmatrix}$.   (c) $A^{-1} = \frac{1}{-17} \begin{bmatrix} 7 & -9 \\ -5 & 4 \end{bmatrix}$,

(e) $A^{-1} = \dfrac{1}{240} \begin{bmatrix} 93 & 42 & -3 \\ -78 & -12 & 18 \\ -3 & -22 & 13 \end{bmatrix}$.

EXERCISE 9-1, PAGE 186

26. $(ab^2c^3)^x$.　**29.** $(2a)^4$.　**44.** $\left(\dfrac{x}{y}\right)^2$.

EXERCISE 9-2, PAGE 189

1. (a) $1;\ -1$.　(b) $2;\ -2$.　(c) $\dfrac{1}{2};\ -\dfrac{1}{2}$.　(d) $\dfrac{2}{3};\ -\dfrac{2}{3}$.　(e) $\dfrac{5}{2};\ -\dfrac{5}{2}$.　(f) $x,\ -x$.
2. (a) 3. (c) 2. (d) -3. (g) 4. (h) -1. (i) 1. (k) -2.　**3.** (a) $\sqrt{5}$ in. (b) $\sqrt{13}$ in.
(c) 5 in. (d) $\sqrt{58}$ in. (e) 13 in. (f) $2\sqrt{13}$ in. (g) 17 in.　**4.** In cases (c), (e), and (g).

EXERCISE 9-3, PAGE 191

1. 2.　**2.** 2.　**3.** 27.　**4.** 32.　**6.** 125.　**7.** -6.　**8.** 16.　**9.** 25.　**11.** -9.
12. -16.　**13.** 4.　**14.** -4.　**16.** 3.　**17.** 16.　**18.** 8.　**19.** -8.　**21.** -4.　**22.** 9.
23. 9.　**24.** -27.　**26.** 4.　**27.** 1.　**28.** $\dfrac{1}{2}$.　**29.** 3.　**31.** $\dfrac{1}{4}$.　**32.** 2.　**33.** $\dfrac{1}{12}$.
34. $\dfrac{3}{4}$.　**36.** $-\dfrac{1}{27}$.　**37.** $\dfrac{9}{4}$.　**38.** $\dfrac{3}{2}$.　**39.** $\dfrac{1}{81}$.　**41.** $\dfrac{1}{3}$.　**42.** $-.3$.　**43.** -16.
44. $-\dfrac{1}{5}$.　**46.** $\dfrac{1}{3}$.　**47.** $\dfrac{8}{17}$.　**48.** $\dfrac{1}{y}$.　**49.** $\dfrac{3}{2x^3}$.　**51.** $\dfrac{2y^2}{x^3}$.　**52.** $-\dfrac{y^2}{3x}$.　**53.** $\dfrac{6y}{x^2}$.
54. $\dfrac{y^2}{2}$.　**56.** $\dfrac{2y^2}{x^2}$.　**57.** $\dfrac{5y^4}{x^2}$.　**58.** $\dfrac{xy^2}{4}$.　**59.** $\dfrac{x}{y}$.　**61.** $\dfrac{25y^8}{9x^8}$.　**62.** $\dfrac{x^8}{y^{12}}$.　**63.** $\dfrac{1}{18x^5y}$.
64. $\dfrac{x^7y^3}{16}$.　**66.** $\dfrac{xy^3}{12}$.　**67.** $\dfrac{125y^4}{3x^8}$.　**68.** $\dfrac{x^5}{2}$.　**69.** $\dfrac{729x}{2y}$.　**71.** $\dfrac{3a^4}{b^3}$.
72. $\dfrac{(x-y)^2}{x+y}$.　**73.** $\dfrac{a-b}{(a+b)^3}$.　**74.** $\dfrac{x+2y}{2x-y}$.　**76.** $\dfrac{1}{(2x-3y)^2}$.　**77.** $\dfrac{1}{x-y}$.
78. 1.　**79.** 1.　**81.** 1.　**82.** $\dfrac{1}{(a^2+x^2)^{1/4}}$.　**83.** $(x^2-a^2)^{1/4}$.　**84.** $\dfrac{2a^2b^2}{b^2+a^2}$.
86. $\dfrac{x^2y^2}{y^2-x^2}$.　**87.** $\dfrac{ab(b^2+2ab-a^2)}{(a-b)^2(a+b)}$.　**88.** $\dfrac{1}{x^2(a^2+x^2)^2}$.　**91.** $\dfrac{a^2-x^2+1}{(a^2-x^2)^{3/2}}$.
92. $\dfrac{a^2+x^2+1}{a^2+x^2}$.　**93.** $\dfrac{a^2-x^2-1}{a^2-x^2}$.　**94.** $\dfrac{a^2+x^2-1}{(a^2+x^2)^{3/2}}$.　**96.** $\dfrac{a^2}{(a^2+x^2)^2}$.

97. $\dfrac{a^2 - x^2}{1 - a^2}$.　　**98.** $\dfrac{a^2 + x^2}{x^2}$.　　**99.** $\dfrac{(a^2 - x^2)^{3/2}}{x^2 - 1}$.　　**101.** $\dfrac{(a^2 - x^2)^{3/2}}{2a^2 - x^2}$.

102. $-\dfrac{(a^2 + x^2)^2}{x^2}$.

EXERCISE 9-4, PAGE 196

1. 3.　**2.** 4.　**3.** 6.　**4.** 2.　**6.** 5.　**7.** $2\sqrt{3}$.　**8.** $2\sqrt{5}$.　**9.** $2\sqrt{7}$.　**11.** $3\sqrt{2}$.
12. $3\sqrt{3}$.　**13.** $3\sqrt{5}$.　**14.** $3\sqrt{6}$.　**16.** $6\sqrt{2}$.　**17.** $3\sqrt{10}$.　**18.** $-3\sqrt[3]{3}$.
19. $-4\sqrt[3]{2}$.　**21.** $4\sqrt{6}$.　**22.** $8x\sqrt{2x}$.　**23.** $5x\sqrt{5}$.　**24.** $5x\sqrt{2x}$.　**26.** $5\sqrt{6x}$.
27. $5x^2\sqrt{7}$.　**28.** $10x^2\sqrt{2x}$.　**29.** $5\sqrt{10x}$.　　**31.** $6x^3\sqrt{2}$.　**32.** $6x^6\sqrt{5x}$.
33. $6x^8\sqrt{6}$.　**34.** $7x^4\sqrt{2}$.　**36.** $7x^3\sqrt{5x}$.　　**37.** $2x\sqrt[3]{2x}$.　　**38.** $2x\sqrt[3]{3}$.
39. $2x\sqrt[3]{4x}$.　**41.** $2\sqrt[3]{6x^2}$.　　**42.** $2y\sqrt[3]{7}$.　**43.** $2y^2\sqrt[3]{9y}$.　**44.** $3b^2\sqrt[3]{2}$.
46. $3y\sqrt[3]{3y}$.　**47.** $3y^2\sqrt[3]{4y}$.　**48.** $5x\sqrt[3]{2x^2}$.　**49.** $5y^3\sqrt[3]{3}$.　**51.** $2y\sqrt[4]{3y^3}$.
52. $2x\sqrt[5]{x}$.　**53.** $2\sqrt[5]{2x^4}$.　**54.** $2x\sqrt[5]{3x}$.　**56.** 9.　**57.** $4\sqrt{10}$.　**58.** 10.
59. $9\sqrt{6}$.　**61.** $4\sqrt[3]{2}$.　**62.** 10.　**63.** $6\sqrt[3]{4}$.　**64.** 6.　**66.** 10.　**67.** 5.　**68.** 7.
69. $4x$.　**71.** $3x\sqrt[3]{x}$.　**72.** $3x\sqrt[3]{x^2}$.　**73.** $2\sqrt{1 - 2x^2}$.　**74.** $2\sqrt{1 + 3x^2}$.
76. $3\sqrt{1 + 3x^2}$.　**77.** $2\sqrt{1 - 4x^2}$.　**78.** $2\sqrt{4 - a^2}$.　**79.** $5\sqrt{1 + 4x^2}$.
81. $3\sqrt{x^2 + 4y^2}$.　**82.** $5\sqrt{y^2 + 4x^2}$.　**83.** 1.　**84.** $\dfrac{2}{xy}\sqrt{y^2 - x^2}$.　**86.** $\sqrt{3}$.
87. $\sqrt[3]{4}$.　**88.** 2.　**89.** 2.　**91.** $\sqrt[3]{6}$.　**92.** $\sqrt{5}$.　**93.** $\sqrt{3}$.　**94.** $3\sqrt{3}$.
96. $\sqrt{2}$.　**97.** $9\sqrt{3}$.　**98.** $(3a + 2b)\sqrt{3a}$.　**99.** $3 + \sqrt{2}$.　**101.** $-1 - \sqrt{2}$.
102. $13\sqrt{2}$.　**103.** $1 - \sqrt{2}$.　**104.** $2\sqrt{5x}$.　**106.** $2 - \sqrt{3}$.　**107.** $\sqrt{5} - \sqrt{2}$.
108. $\sqrt{3} - \sqrt{5}$.　**109.** $-\sqrt{7} + \sqrt{2}$.　**111.** $-3\sqrt{2}$.　　**112.** -12.
113. $2x + 50 + 20\sqrt{x}$.　**114.** 59.　**116.** $-4 + 2\sqrt{6}$.　**117.** $10\sqrt{3} -$
$18\sqrt{2} + 6\sqrt{5} + 3\sqrt{6} + 10\sqrt{10} - 60$.　　　**121.** $x = \dfrac{a}{3b}$ or $x = -2$.

122. $x = -1 + \sqrt{2}$ or $x = -1 - \sqrt{2}$.　　　**123.** $x = \dfrac{c + \sqrt{m + p}}{4}$ or

$x = \dfrac{c - \sqrt{m + p}}{4}$.

EXERCISE 9-5, PAGE 200

1. $\dfrac{\sqrt{2}}{2} = 0.707$.　**2.** $\dfrac{\sqrt{3}}{3} = 0.577$.　**3.** $\dfrac{\sqrt{6}}{2} = 1.224$.　**4.** $\dfrac{\sqrt{3}}{2} = 0.866$.

6. $\dfrac{\sqrt{15}}{5} = 0.775$.　**7.** $\dfrac{2\sqrt{5}}{5} = 0.894$.　**8.** $\dfrac{\sqrt{30}}{6} = 0.913$.　**9.** $\dfrac{\sqrt{6}}{4} = 0.612$.

11. $\dfrac{\sqrt{6}}{2} = 1.224$.　**12.** $\dfrac{\sqrt{15}}{3} = 1.291$.　**13.** $\dfrac{\sqrt{70}}{5} = 1.661$.

14. $\dfrac{\sqrt{115}}{5} = \dfrac{\sqrt{5}\sqrt{23}}{5} = 2.145.$ **16.** $\dfrac{\sqrt{45y^2 - 6xy}}{3y}.$ **17.** $\dfrac{\sqrt{75 + 10y}}{5}.$

18. $\dfrac{\sqrt{25x^2y^2 - 15}}{5xy}.$ **19.** $\dfrac{\sqrt[3]{4}}{2} = 0.794.$ **21.** $\dfrac{\sqrt[3]{18}}{3} = 0.874.$

22. $\dfrac{\sqrt[3]{6}}{2} = 0.908.$ **23.** $\dfrac{\sqrt{x^2 + x}}{x}.$ **24.** $\dfrac{\sqrt{2x^2 - 3x}}{x}.$ **26.** $\dfrac{\sqrt{x^3 - 2x}}{x}.$

27. $\dfrac{\sqrt{x^3 - x}}{x}.$ **28.** $\dfrac{\sqrt{3x^3 - x}}{x}.$ **29.** $\dfrac{\sqrt{3x - x^3}}{x}.$ **31.** $\dfrac{\sqrt{x - x^4}}{x}.$

32. $\dfrac{\sqrt{x^5 - 2x}}{x^2}.$ **33.** $\dfrac{\sqrt{x^6 + x}}{x^2}.$ **34.** $\dfrac{\sqrt{xz}}{z^2}.$ **36.** $\dfrac{\sqrt{3y}}{3}.$ **37.** $\dfrac{3\sqrt{xz}}{z^2}.$

38. $\dfrac{2y\sqrt{xy}}{3x^2}.$ **39.** $\dfrac{\sqrt{xy}}{3x^2}.$ **41.** $\dfrac{\sqrt{2} + 2}{2}.$ **42.** $\dfrac{\sqrt{3} - 3}{3}.$ **43.** $\dfrac{2\sqrt{5} + 5}{5}.$

44. $\dfrac{3\sqrt{2} - 2}{2}.$ **46.** $5 - 2\sqrt{6}.$ **47.** $5 + 2\sqrt{6}.$ **48.** $\sqrt{3} - 1.$

49. $-3 - 3\sqrt{2}.$ **51.** $\dfrac{3 - \sqrt{3}}{2}.$ **52.** $\dfrac{5(\sqrt{3} + 1)}{2}.$ **53.** $\dfrac{\sqrt{3x}}{3x}.$ **54.** $\dfrac{\sqrt{3ab}}{ab}.$

56. $\dfrac{2(\sqrt{a} - \sqrt{b})}{a - b}.$ **57.** $\dfrac{\sqrt[3]{9x}}{3x}.$ **58.** $\dfrac{\sqrt[4]{2x^3}}{2x}.$ **59.** $\dfrac{\sqrt[3]{25x^2}}{x}.$ **61.** $\dfrac{y^2\sqrt[3]{x^2y}}{x^2}.$

62. $\dfrac{x + y + 2\sqrt{xy}}{x - y}.$ **63.** $\dfrac{(\sqrt{x} - \sqrt{y})\sqrt{x - y}}{x - y}.$ **64.** $\dfrac{b + a}{b - a}.$ **66.** $\dfrac{3\sqrt{2a}}{2}.$

67. $\dfrac{\sqrt{a - b}}{a - b}.$ **68.** $\dfrac{5\sqrt{6} - 5\sqrt{3} - \sqrt{2} + 2}{3}.$ **69.** $\dfrac{\sqrt{6}}{2}.$ **71.** $\dfrac{1}{2 - \sqrt{2}}.$

72. $\dfrac{-2}{3 + \sqrt{3}}.$ **73.** $\dfrac{1}{5 - 2\sqrt{5}}.$ **74.** $\dfrac{7}{2 + 3\sqrt{2}}.$ **76.** $\dfrac{1}{5 + 2\sqrt{6}}.$

77. $\dfrac{1}{5 - 2\sqrt{6}}.$ **78.** $\dfrac{y^3}{x\sqrt[3]{xy^2}}.$ **79.** $\dfrac{x - y}{x + y - 2\sqrt{xy}}.$ **81.** $\dfrac{b + a}{b - a}.$

82. $\dfrac{3x - 1}{(\sqrt{3x} - 1)\sqrt{3x + 1}}.$ **83.** $\dfrac{3a}{\sqrt{2a}}.$ **84.** $\dfrac{1}{\sqrt{a - b}}.$ **86.** $\dfrac{\sqrt{2}}{4}.$ **87.** $\dfrac{\sqrt{5}}{25}.$

88. $\dfrac{3\sqrt{6}}{4}.$ **89.** $\dfrac{\sqrt[3]{4}}{4}.$ **91.** $\dfrac{3\sqrt[3]{12}}{4}.$ **92.** $\dfrac{3\sqrt[3]{75}}{25}.$ **93.** $\dfrac{2\sqrt{6}}{9}.$ **94.** $\dfrac{\sqrt{2}}{4}.$

96. $\dfrac{2\sqrt{10}}{25}.$ **97.** $\dfrac{3\sqrt{6}}{4}.$ **98.** $\dfrac{\sqrt[3]{4}}{4}.$ **99.** $\dfrac{2\sqrt[3]{18}}{9}.$ **101.** $\dfrac{3\sqrt[3]{12}}{4}.$

EXERCISE 9-6, PAGE 203

1. $\sqrt[4]{9}.$ **2.** $\sqrt[6]{8}.$ **3.** $\sqrt[6]{4}.$ **4.** $\sqrt[6]{9}.$ **6.** $\sqrt{2}.$ **7.** $\sqrt[10]{4}.$ **8.** $\sqrt{2}.$ **9.** $\sqrt[3]{3}.$

11. $\sqrt{3} > \sqrt[3]{5}.$ **12.** $\sqrt{5} > \sqrt[3]{11}.$ **13.** $\sqrt[4]{3} > \sqrt[3]{2}.$ **14.** $\sqrt[6]{5} > \sqrt[3]{2}.$

16. $\sqrt[6]{32}.$ **17.** $\sqrt[6]{243}.$ **18.** $\sqrt[6]{108}.$ **19.** $\sqrt[6]{8}.$ **21.** $\sqrt{6}.$ **22.** $1.$ **23.** $\dfrac{\sqrt[4]{8}}{2}.$

24. $\dfrac{\sqrt[3]{18}}{3}$. **26.** 1. **27.** $\sqrt[6]{3}$. **28.** $\dfrac{\sqrt[6]{x^5}}{x}$. **29.** $\sqrt[6]{x}$. **31.** $\sqrt[6]{x}$.

32. $\dfrac{x\sqrt{4-x^2}}{2}$. **33.** $\dfrac{a\sqrt{3a}}{3}$. **34.** $\dfrac{x\sqrt[3]{2a^2x}}{2a}$. **36.** $\dfrac{y\sqrt[3]{12x}}{2}$. **37.** $\dfrac{\sqrt[4]{6yz}}{3yz}$.

GENERAL REVIEW LIST, PAGE 204

1. $y^{2/3} - \dfrac{1}{a^2}$. **3.** $y + z$. **5.** $3^{-2} - 2^{-2} = \dfrac{-5}{36}$. **7.** $a^{1/4} - b^{1/4}$.

9. $a^{-2/3} + a^{-1/3}b^{-1/3} + b^{-2/3}$. **11.** $(3a^2)^3 = 27a^6$. **13.** $-27^{2/3} = -9$.

15. $(x-y)^2 = x^2 - 2xy + y^2$. **17.** True. **19.** $a^3 - 27 = (a-3)(a^2 + 3a + 9)$.

21. $\left(\dfrac{x^3}{3}\right)^2 = \dfrac{x^6}{9}$. **23.** $\dfrac{1}{-5^{-2}} = \dfrac{5^2}{-1} = -25$. **25.** $x^3 + 8 = (x+2)(x^2 - 2x + 4)$.

27. $a^6 \div a^2 = a^4$. **29.** $3(1 + 3^5) = 3 + 3^6$. **31.** 9. **33.** $\dfrac{4}{x+y}$. **35.** $\dfrac{24}{11}$.

37. xy^2. **39.** $\dfrac{1}{3}$. **41.** $-\dfrac{xy}{(x-y)^2}$. **43.** 81. **45.** $6^9 = ab$. **47.** $x = 1$.

49. $5\sqrt[3]{2} - 6\sqrt[3]{3} + 5\sqrt[3]{5}$. **51.** $0.45\sqrt{2}$. **53.** $\dfrac{(4d^2 + 2cd + 3)}{d}\sqrt[3]{d^2}$.

55. $(-2a - 7)\sqrt{5}$. **57.** $\dfrac{a-b}{ab}\sqrt{ab}$. **59.** 48. **61.** $.\ 150\sqrt{2}$.

63. $31 - 6\sqrt{2} - 4\sqrt{3} + 12\sqrt{6}$. **65.** $3x\sqrt{x} - 6\sqrt{xy} - xy + 2y\sqrt{y}$.

67. $a + \sqrt{b}$. **69.** $\dfrac{1}{6}$. **71.** $\dfrac{3}{8}$. **73.** 60. **75.** $\dfrac{3\sqrt{2} + 5\sqrt{3} + 4}{3}$. **77.** $\dfrac{10\sqrt{21}}{21}$.

79. $\dfrac{7\sqrt{2}}{6}$. **81.** $\dfrac{23 + 6\sqrt{10}}{13}$. **83.** $\dfrac{5\sqrt{6} - 6}{30}$. **85.** $\dfrac{a + b + 2\sqrt{ab}}{a-b}$.

87. $-3\sqrt{5}$. **89.** $r = \dfrac{\sqrt[3]{48\pi^2 V}}{4\pi}$, $r = 4\sqrt[3]{21}$ inches. **91.** $y = 12$ or

$y = -12$. **93.** $S = \pi r^2$; $r = 9$. **95.** (a) $18x^2\sqrt{2}$. (b) $-5x\sqrt[3]{90x^2}$. (c) $\sqrt{2x}$.

EXERCISE 10-1, PAGE 216

4. $6i$. **6.** $3i$. **7.** $7i$. **8.** $i\sqrt{47}$. **9.** $8i$. **11.** $12i$. **12.** $-2i$. **13.** $-3i$.

14. $-i\sqrt{11}$. **16.** $3ia$. **17.** $4ix$. **18.** $-5iy^2$. **19.** $x^2i\sqrt{17}$. **21.** $-ai\sqrt{23}$.

22. -1. **23.** $-i$. **24.** -1. **26.** i. **27.** $2i$. **28.** $-2i$. **29.** $3 + 4i$.

31. $-3 - 4i$. **32.** 13. **33.** 41. **34.** $9 + 7i$. **36.** 61. **37.** $-4 + 3i$.

38. $3 + 9i$. **39.** $16 - 12i$. **41.** $\dfrac{3+i}{5}$. **42.** $\dfrac{12-3i}{17}$. **43.** $\dfrac{6-4i}{13}$.

44. $\dfrac{15 + 10i}{13}$. **46.** $-i$. **47.** $\dfrac{3 + 11i}{10}$. **48.** $\dfrac{3 - 11i}{10}$. **49.** $\dfrac{8+i}{5}$.

51. i. **52.** $\dfrac{-3i}{2}$. **53.** $\dfrac{2i}{3}$. **54.** i. **56.** $\dfrac{7i}{3}$. **57.** $\dfrac{10i}{3}$. **58.** $-3i$. **59.** $\dfrac{5i}{3}$.

61. -6. **62.** $-10 + 10i$. **63.** $6i$. **64.** $5i\sqrt{3}$. **66.** $\sqrt{2}$. **67.** $i\sqrt{2}$.

68. $\dfrac{10 - 15i}{13}$. **69.** $\dfrac{1 - i}{6}$. **71.** $-1 - i$.

EXERCISE 11-1, PAGE 224

(The values of a, b, and c are listed in that order.) **2.** $4, -4, 1$. **3.** $2, 1, -6$.
4. $3, 2, -1$. **6.** $1, 2, -3$. **7.** $4, 5, -6$. **8.** $2, 1, -3$. **9.** $1, 3, 2$. **11.** $4, 4, -3$.
12. $4, 8, 3$. **13.** $1, -2, 0$. **14.** $1, -3, 0$. **16.** $3, 2, 0$. **17.** $2, 3, 0$.
18. $1, 0, -d^2$. **19.** $4, 0, -9e^4$. **21.** $4d^2, 0, -e^2$. **22.** $1, r - s. -rs$. **23.** $a^2,$
$0, -16b^2$. **26.** $2 - C, -A - B, A + 4$. **27.** $A - 3, 1 - B - C, 1$.
28. $A - B, A + C, B - C$. **29.** $A - C, -D, B$.

EXERCISE 11-2, PAGE 229

1. $2; -2$. **2.** $2; -2$. **3.** $2; -2$. **4.** $3; -3$. **6.** $5; -5$. **7.** $3i; -3i$. **8.** $2i; -2i$.
9. $2i; -2i$. **11.** $7i; -7i$. **12.** $5i; -5i$. **13.** $3\sqrt{2}; -3\sqrt{2}$. **14.** $2\sqrt{3}; -2\sqrt{3}$.
16. $\dfrac{4\sqrt{2}}{a}; \dfrac{-4\sqrt{2}}{a}$. **17.** $\dfrac{2\sqrt{3}}{b}; \dfrac{-2\sqrt{3}}{b}$. **18.** $\dfrac{4c\sqrt{6}}{a}; \dfrac{-4c\sqrt{6}}{a}$.

19. $3ai\sqrt{2}; -3ai\sqrt{2}$. **21.** $\dfrac{10bi}{a}; \dfrac{-10bi}{a}$. **22.** $4bi\sqrt{2}; -4bi\sqrt{2}$. **23.** $2ci\sqrt{6};$

$-2ci\sqrt{6}$. **24.** $\dfrac{4ib\sqrt{6}}{a}; \dfrac{-4ib\sqrt{6}}{a}$. **25.** $\dfrac{5i\sqrt{ab}}{a}; \dfrac{-5i\sqrt{ab}}{a}$. **26.** $\dfrac{10i\sqrt{c}}{a}; \dfrac{-10i\sqrt{c}}{a}$.

27. $\dfrac{2i\sqrt{5ab}}{a}; \dfrac{-2i\sqrt{5ab}}{a}$. **28.** $-4; 3$. **29.** $4; -3$. **31.** $4; -1$. **32.** $3; -2$.

33. $5; -2$. **34.** $\dfrac{1}{2}; -1$. **36.** $-\dfrac{1}{3}; 1$. **37.** $1; -\dfrac{1}{4}$. **38.** $\dfrac{1}{2}; \dfrac{1}{2}$. **39.** $-\dfrac{1}{3}; -\dfrac{1}{3}$.

41. $4a; 4a$. **42.** $-\dfrac{5}{3}; -\dfrac{5}{3}$. **43.** $0; \dfrac{1}{6}$. **44.** $0; \dfrac{1}{3}$. **46.** $0; -\dfrac{a}{10}$. **47.** $0; -\dfrac{b}{a}$.

48. $0; \dfrac{d}{c}$. **49.** $\dfrac{1}{2}; -\dfrac{2}{3}$. **51.** $\dfrac{3}{2}; -\dfrac{1}{5}$. **52.** $-\dfrac{2}{5}; \dfrac{1}{2}$. **53.** $\dfrac{1}{3}; -\dfrac{2}{5}$. **54.** $\dfrac{1}{3}; -\dfrac{2}{5}$.

56. $-\dfrac{2}{5}; -\dfrac{1}{2}$. **57.** $\dfrac{2}{5}; \dfrac{1}{2}$. **58.** $-\dfrac{2}{3}; -\dfrac{3}{7}$. **59.** $\dfrac{2}{3}; \dfrac{3}{7}$. **61.** $4; -\dfrac{5}{3}$.

62. $\dfrac{\sqrt{39}}{6}; -\dfrac{\sqrt{39}}{6}$. **63.** $20; -8$. **64.** $\dfrac{i\sqrt{15}}{3}; -\dfrac{i\sqrt{15}}{3}$. **66.** $\dfrac{\sqrt{6}}{4}; -\dfrac{\sqrt{6}}{4}$. **67.** $\dfrac{1}{7}$.

68. $0; \dfrac{7}{10}$. **69.** $0; \dfrac{11}{5}$.

EXERCISE 11-3, PAGE 234

1. $4; 2$. **2.** $-3; -2$. **3.** $-4; 2$. **4.** $5; -2$. **6.** $-5; 2$. **7.** $-\dfrac{1}{3}; \dfrac{3}{2}$. **8.** $-\dfrac{2}{3}; \dfrac{1}{2}$.

9. $\frac{1}{3}; -\frac{3}{2}.$ **11.** $\frac{3}{4}; -\frac{4}{3}.$ **12.** $\frac{3}{2}; -\frac{3}{4}.$ **13.** $\frac{1 \pm \sqrt{7}}{3}.$ **14.** $\frac{-3 \pm \sqrt{69}}{10}.$

16. $\frac{-2 \pm \sqrt{19}}{3}.$ **17.** $\frac{-3 \pm \sqrt{19}}{2}.$ **18.** $\frac{-1 \pm \sqrt{7}}{4}.$ **19.** $\frac{7 \pm 2\sqrt{7}}{7}.$

21. $\frac{-3 \pm i\sqrt{71}}{10}.$ **22.** $\frac{-5 \pm i\sqrt{23}}{6}.$ **23.** $\frac{-3 \pm i\sqrt{3}}{4}.$ **24.** $\frac{-3 \pm i\sqrt{71}}{20}.$

26. $1 \pm 2i.$ **27.** $\frac{3 \pm i\sqrt{15}}{2}.$ **28.** $2 \pm i\sqrt{2}.$ **29.** $3 \pm \sqrt{7}.$ **31.** $\frac{1 \pm \sqrt{21}}{2}.$

32. $\frac{-1 \pm i\sqrt{3}}{2}.$ **33.** $\frac{1 \pm \sqrt{53}}{2}.$ **44.** $\frac{3 \pm \sqrt{201}}{6}.$

EXERCISE 11-4, PAGE 238

1. $\frac{3 \pm i\sqrt{31}}{4}.$ **2.** $\frac{1}{3}; -2.$ **3.** $\frac{1}{2}; \frac{1}{2}.$ **4.** $\frac{3}{5}; -1.$ **6.** $3 \pm 3\sqrt{2}.$ **7.** $\frac{-1 \pm \sqrt{13}}{2}.$

8. $\frac{-3 \pm \sqrt{13}}{2}.$ **9.** $\frac{3 \pm \sqrt{5}}{2}.$ **11.** $\frac{1 \pm i\sqrt{11}}{2}.$ **12.** $\frac{5}{3}; \frac{5}{3}.$ **13.** $\frac{-1 \pm i\sqrt{3}}{2}.$

14. $\frac{5 \pm \sqrt{17}}{4}.$ **16.** $\frac{-1 \pm \sqrt{17}}{8}.$ **17.** $5 \pm 2\sqrt{6}.$ **18.** $\frac{1 \pm i\sqrt{39}}{20}.$

19. $\frac{5 \pm \sqrt{13}}{6}.$ **21.** $1; \frac{1}{4}.$ **22.** $1; \frac{1}{7}.$ **23.** $\frac{1 \pm i\sqrt{7}}{6}.$ **24.** $\frac{1}{2}; \frac{1}{3}.$ **26.** $1; -\frac{1}{8}.$

27. $\frac{9 \pm \sqrt{57}}{6}.$ **28.** $1; -\frac{1}{5}.$ **29.** $\frac{1}{2}; -\frac{1}{5}.$ **31.** $\frac{3 \pm \sqrt{65}}{14}.$ **32.** $\frac{1}{2}; \frac{1}{6}.$

33. $\frac{3 \pm \sqrt{7}}{4}.$ **34.** $1; \frac{1}{11}.$ **36.** $\frac{1}{2}; \frac{1}{3}.$ **37.** $\frac{b \pm \sqrt{b^2 + 4ac}}{2a}.$

38. $\frac{-c \pm \sqrt{c^2 - 4ab}}{2b}.$ **39.** $\frac{-b^2 \pm \sqrt{b^4 - 4a^2c^2}}{2a^2}.$ **41.** $\frac{-b \pm \sqrt{b^2 - 3ac}}{3a}.$

42. $\frac{b \pm \sqrt{b^2 + 16ac}}{4a}.$ **43.** $\frac{3 \pm \sqrt{13}}{2}.$ **44.** $\frac{-1 \pm \sqrt{17}}{2}.$

46. $\frac{v_0 \pm \sqrt{v_0^2 - 2sg}}{g}; \frac{2s + gt^2}{2t}.$ **47.** $\frac{-2a + d \pm \sqrt{4a^2 - 4ad + d^2 + 8ds}}{2d}.$

48. $-1 \pm \sqrt{2 - x^2 - 4x}.$ **49.** $\frac{1 \pm \sqrt{1 - 4g^2x^2}}{2g}; \frac{\pm \sqrt{gR - g^2R^2}}{g}.$

EXERCISE 11-6, PAGE 244

1. $x^2 - 3x + 2 = 0.$ **2.** $x^2 - 2x - 3 = 0.$ **3.** $x^2 + 4x + 3 = 0.$
4. $x^2 - 2x = 0.$ **6.** $8x^2 - 10x + 3 = 0.$ **7.** $6x^2 - x - 2 = 0.$
8. $5x^2 - 2x = 0.$ **9.** $5x^2 - 2x - 3 = 0.$ **11.** $x^2 - 6x + 7 = 0.$

12. $4x^2 - 8x + 1 = 0$. **13.** $2x^2 - 2x - 1 = 0$. **14.** $x^2 + 1 = 0$.
16. $x^2 - 4x + 13 = 0$. **17.** $x^2 - 4x + 7 = 0$. **18.** $4x^2 - 8x + 5 = 0$.

EXERCISE 11-7, PAGE 246

1. -8, -5; 5, 8. **2.** 12. **3.** 150 ft. $\times$ 200 ft. **4.** 50 ft. $\times$ 120 ft.
6. 8 in. $\times$ 5 in. **7.** 6 in. $\times$ 3 in. **8.** $2 + 2\sqrt{2}$ ft. **9.** 15 in. $\times$ 8 in.
11. $(8 + 2\sqrt{17})$ in. **12.** $(4 + 2\sqrt{5})$ in. **13.** $-\dfrac{1}{2}$. **14.** $-\dfrac{c}{3}$. **16.** 8; -3.
17. $\pm 2\sqrt{6}$.

EXERCISE 12-1, PAGE 250

1. -1; $\dfrac{1 \pm i\sqrt{3}}{2}$. **2.** ± 1; $\pm i$. **3.** i; i; $-i$; $-i$. **4.** 0; 1; 1; -1; -1.

6. 0; 0; 3; -2 **7.** 1; 1; -1. **8.** 0; 1; i; $-i$. **9.** 2; $\dfrac{\pm i\sqrt{6}}{2}$.

11. $\sqrt{2}$; $-\sqrt{2}$; $i\sqrt{2}$; $-i\sqrt{2}$. **12.** $\dfrac{1 \pm i\sqrt{3}}{2}$; $\dfrac{-1 \pm i\sqrt{3}}{2}$.

13. $x^3 - 6x^2 + 11x - 6 = 0$. **14.** $x^3 + 4x^2 + x - 6 = 0$.
16. $x^3 + x^2 - 6x = 0$. **17.** $x^4 - 1 = 0$. **18.** $x^3 - 2x^2 - x = 0$.
19. $x^3 - 2x^2 + 3x = 0$. **21.** $8x^3 - 20x^2 + 18x - 5 = 0$.
22. $4x^4 - 16x^3 + 13x^2 + 6x - 1 = 0$. **23.** $6x^4 - 7x^3 - x^2 + 2x = 0$.
24. $x^4 - 6x^3 + 13x^2 - 12x + 4 = 0$. **26.** $x^3 = 0$.
27. $x^3 + 3x^2 + 3x + 1 = 0$. **28.** $x^4 - 2x^3 + x^2 = 0$.

EXERCISE 12-2, PAGE 253

1. $\pm\sqrt{2}$; $\dfrac{\pm i\sqrt{6}}{2}$. **2.** $\pm\dfrac{\sqrt{6}}{2}$; $\pm i\sqrt{2}$. **3.** $\pm\dfrac{\sqrt{3}}{3}$; $\pm\dfrac{i\sqrt{2}}{2}$. **4.** $\pm\dfrac{i\sqrt{3}}{3}$; $\pm\dfrac{\sqrt{2}}{2}$.

6. $\pm\dfrac{\sqrt{2}}{2}$; $\pm i$. **7.** -2; $1 \pm i\sqrt{3}$; 1; $\dfrac{-1 \pm i\sqrt{3}}{2}$. **8.** 2; $-1 \pm i\sqrt{3}$; -1; $\dfrac{1 \pm i\sqrt{3}}{2}$.

9. -3; $\dfrac{3 \pm 3i\sqrt{3}}{2}$; 1; $\dfrac{-1 \pm i\sqrt{3}}{2}$. **11.** 2; $-\dfrac{1}{2}$; $-1 \pm i\sqrt{3}$ $\dfrac{1 \pm i\sqrt{3}}{4}$.

12. $\dfrac{1}{2}$; -2; $1 \pm i\sqrt{3}$; $\dfrac{-1 \pm i\sqrt{3}}{4}$. **13.** 1; 3; $\dfrac{-1 \pm i\sqrt{3}}{2}$; $\dfrac{-3 \pm 3i\sqrt{3}}{2}$.

14. -1; $\dfrac{3}{2}$; $\dfrac{-3 \pm 3i\sqrt{3}}{4}$; $\dfrac{1 \pm i\sqrt{3}}{2}$. **16.** $\dfrac{-1 \pm \sqrt{7}}{2}$; $\dfrac{-1 \pm \sqrt{5}}{2}$.

17. $\dfrac{1 \pm \sqrt{7}}{2}$; $\dfrac{1 \pm i\sqrt{3}}{2}$. **18.** $\dfrac{1 \pm \sqrt{5}}{2}$; $\dfrac{1 \pm \sqrt{13}}{2}$. **19.** 1; -2; $\dfrac{-1 \pm \sqrt{13}}{2}$.

21. 1; $-\dfrac{1}{2}$; $\dfrac{1 \pm i\sqrt{15}}{4}$. **22.** 0; -1; $\dfrac{-1 \pm \sqrt{5}}{2}$. **23.** 1; 1; $\dfrac{1 \pm i\sqrt{15}}{4}$.

24. $1 \pm \sqrt{2}; \dfrac{-1 \pm \sqrt{17}}{4}$.

EXERCISE 12-3, PAGE 255

1. 14. **2.** 20. **3.** 0. **4.** 1; 2. **6.** -1. **7.** No root. **8.** -2. **9.** $\dfrac{1}{2}$.
11. 3; -3. **12.** 1. **13.** 2. **14.** 1. **16.** -1; -2. **17.** $-a$; $-b$. **18.** 1; -3.

EXERCISE 12-4, PAGE 261

1. $3x^2 + x + 5$. **2.** $5x^3 - 2x^2 + x - 2$. **3.** $2x^3 - 3x^2 + 2x - 3$.
4. $3x^3 - 2x + 1$. **6.** $x^4 - 1$. **7.** $3x^2 - 8$. **8.** $2x^3 - 3$.
9. $3x^2 + 4x + 14 + \dfrac{46}{x-3}$. **11.** $3x^3 + 3x^2 + x + 1 + \dfrac{6}{x-1}$.
12. $4x^4 - 4x^3 + x^2 + x - 1 - \dfrac{4}{x+1}$. **13.** $7x^2 - 34x + 141 - \dfrac{564}{x+4}$.
14. $3x^3 - 2x$. **16.** Yes. **17.** Yes. **18.** Yes. **19.** Yes. **21.** No.

EXERCISE 12-5, PAGE 264

1. ± 1; 3. **2.** 1; 1; -2. **3.** 1; $\dfrac{-1 \pm i\sqrt{11}}{2}$. **4.** 1. **6.** -1. **7.** ± 1; $\dfrac{1}{2}$.
8. -1; $-\dfrac{1}{6}$; -2. **9.** ± 2; $\dfrac{-3 \pm \sqrt{5}}{2}$. **11.** -1; 3; $\pm \sqrt{3}$. **12.** 1; $-\dfrac{1}{2}$; $\pm \dfrac{\sqrt{5}}{2}$.
13. $\dfrac{1}{2}$; -1; $\pm \dfrac{2\sqrt{3}}{3}$. **14.** No rational roots. **16.** 1; $\dfrac{-1 \pm i\sqrt{7}}{2}$.
17. -1; ± 4; $\dfrac{1}{3}$. **18.** 1. **19.** 2; 2; -2; $-1 \pm i\sqrt{3}$. **21.** 1; -9; $\pm \sqrt{3}$
22. No rational roots.

EXERCISE 13-2, PAGE 273

1. $(4, 3)$; $(-4, -3)$. **2.** $(5, 0)$; $(0, 5)$. **3.** $\left(\dfrac{5\sqrt{2}}{2}, \dfrac{5\sqrt{2}}{2}\right)$; $\left(\dfrac{-5\sqrt{2}}{2}, \dfrac{-5\sqrt{2}}{2}\right)$.
4. $(4, 3)$; $\left(\dfrac{-56}{13}, \dfrac{-33}{13}\right)$. **6.** (No real intersections.) $(i\sqrt{11}, 6)$; $(-i\sqrt{11}, 6)$.
7. $(5, 3)$; $(-5, -3)$. **8.** $(5, 3)$; $(-5, 3)$. **9.** $(4, 0)$. **11.** $(3, i\sqrt{7})$; $(3, -i\sqrt{7})$.
12. $(2, 4)$; $\left(-\dfrac{2}{3}, \dfrac{4}{9}\right)$. **13.** $(1, 1)$. **14.** $(1 + i, 2i)$; $(1 - i, -2i)$. **16.** $(4, 2)$;
$(4, -2)$. **17.** $(1, 1)$. **18.** $\left(-1, \dfrac{1}{2}\right)$; $\left(1, -\dfrac{1}{2}\right)$. **19.** $\left(1, -\dfrac{3}{4}\right)$; $\left(2, -\dfrac{1}{2}\right)$. **21.** (a, b);

$\left(\dfrac{b}{2}, 2a\right)$.   **22.** $\left(\dfrac{a}{2}, -2b\right)$; $(b, -a)$.   **23.** 10 rods × 2 rods.   **24.** 12 in. × 5 in.

EXERCISE 13-3, PAGE 277

1. $\left(\dfrac{\sqrt{58}}{2}, \dfrac{\sqrt{42}}{2}\right)$; $\left(\dfrac{-\sqrt{58}}{2}, \dfrac{-\sqrt{42}}{2}\right)$; $\left(\dfrac{\sqrt{58}}{2}, \dfrac{-\sqrt{42}}{2}\right)$; $\left(\dfrac{-\sqrt{58}}{2}, \dfrac{\sqrt{42}}{2}\right)$.

2. $(5, 0)$; $(-5, 0)$.   **3.** $\left(\dfrac{\sqrt{10}}{2}, \dfrac{i\sqrt{6}}{2}\right)$; $\left(\dfrac{\sqrt{10}}{2}, \dfrac{-i\sqrt{6}}{2}\right)$; $\left(\dfrac{-\sqrt{10}}{2}, \dfrac{i\sqrt{6}}{2}\right)$;

$\left(\dfrac{-\sqrt{10}}{2}, \dfrac{-i\sqrt{6}}{2}\right)$.   **4.** $(0, 2)$; $(0, -2)$.   **6.** $(1, 1)$; $(-1, 1)$.   **7.** $(2, -1)$; $(-2, 1)$.

8. $\left(-\dfrac{i\sqrt{2}}{2}, i\sqrt{2}\right)$; $\left(\dfrac{i\sqrt{2}}{2}, -i\sqrt{2}\right)$.   **9.** $\left(\dfrac{\sqrt{3}}{2}, \dfrac{2}{3}\right)$; $\left(-\dfrac{\sqrt{3}}{2}, \dfrac{2}{3}\right)$.   **11.** $\left(\dfrac{2}{3}, \dfrac{3}{2}\right)$.

12. $(3, 1)$.   **13.** $\left(i, -\dfrac{i}{2}\right)$; $\left(-i, \dfrac{i}{2}\right)$.   **14.** $\left(-\dfrac{i}{6}, 2i\right)$; $\left(\dfrac{i}{6}, -2i\right)$.   **16.** $\left(\sqrt{a}, \dfrac{b\sqrt{a}}{a}\right)$;

$\left(-\sqrt{a}, -\dfrac{b\sqrt{a}}{a}\right)$.

EXERCISE 13-4, PAGE 280

1. $(3, 4)$; $(3, -4)$; $(3, -4)$; $(-4, 3)$.   **2.** $(0, 0)$; $(4, 4)$; $\left(-1, \dfrac{1}{4}\right)$; $\left(-1, \dfrac{1}{4}\right)$.   **3.** $(5, 3)$;

$(-5, 3)$; $(5, 3)$; $(-5, -3)$.   **4.** $(5, 3)$; $(5, 3)$; $\left(-\dfrac{13}{3}, -\dfrac{5}{3}\right)$.   **6.** $\left(\dfrac{17}{2}, \dfrac{15}{2}\right)$; $\left(\dfrac{17}{2}, -\dfrac{15}{2}\right)$.

7. $\left(\dfrac{\sqrt{2}}{2}, -\dfrac{\sqrt{2}}{2}\right)$; $\left(-\dfrac{\sqrt{2}}{2}, \dfrac{\sqrt{2}}{2}\right)$; $\left(\dfrac{1}{2}, \dfrac{1}{2}\right)$; $\left(-\dfrac{1}{2}, -\dfrac{1}{2}\right)$.   **8.** $(1, 2)$; $(-1, -2)$; $(1, 2)$;

$(11, -8)$.   **9.** $(1, 1)$; $(1, 1)$; $\left(\dfrac{2}{3}, \dfrac{1}{3}\right)$; $\left(-\dfrac{5}{3}, \dfrac{11}{3}\right)$.   **11.** $(0, 0)$; $(0, 0)$; $(0, 0)$; $(0, 0)$.

12. $\left(\dfrac{2}{5}, -\dfrac{6}{5}\right)$; $\left(\dfrac{3}{2}, 1\right)$; $\left(-\dfrac{2}{5}, \dfrac{6}{5}\right)$; $\left(-\dfrac{3}{2}, -1\right)$.   **13.** $(-2, 6)$; $(4, -6)$; $(0, -2)$; $(-6, 10)$.

14. $\left(\dfrac{1}{3}, \dfrac{2}{3}\right)$; $\left(-\dfrac{1}{3}, -\dfrac{2}{3}\right)$; $\left(\dfrac{3}{2}, -\dfrac{1}{2}\right)$; $\left(-\dfrac{3}{2}, \dfrac{1}{2}\right)$.   **16.** $(1, 2)$; $(-1, -2)$; $\left(\dfrac{1}{2}\sqrt{10}, -\dfrac{1}{2}\sqrt{10}\right)$;

$\left(-\dfrac{1}{2}\sqrt{10}, \dfrac{1}{2}\sqrt{10}\right)$.   **17.** $(1, 1)$; $(-1, -1)$; $(1, 1)$; $(-1, -1)$.   **18.** $\left(\dfrac{\sqrt{14}}{7}, \dfrac{2\sqrt{14}}{7}\right)$;

$\left(-\dfrac{\sqrt{14}}{7}, -\dfrac{2\sqrt{14}}{7}\right)$.

GENERAL REVIEW LIST, PAGE 280

7. Circle with center at $(0, 0)$ and radius 3.   **9.** y-parabola with open end upward.
11. x-ellipse, center at $(0, 0)$ with $a = 3\sqrt{10}$, $b = 3$.   **13.** $\{(5, 2)\}$.   **15.** $\{(-3, 1)$,

$\left(\dfrac{21}{13}, -\dfrac{2}{13}\right)$.   **17.** $\{(4, -2), (-4, 2)\}$.   **19.** $\{(2, 0), (-2, 0)\}$.   **21.** $\{(3, 0)\}$ here $w = 3$ and $v = 0$.   **23.** $10' \times 12'$.   **25.** $12'$ and $16'$.

EXERCISE 14-1, PAGE 286

1. (a) False. (b) True. (c) True. (d) True. (e) False. (f) False.   **3.** (a) $[4, 22]$.
(b) $[-7, 3)$. (c) $[-6, 2]$. (d) $[6, 7]$. (e) $(-\infty, 4]$. (f) $[-7, 3)$.   **5.** (a) $(3, 7)$.
(b) $[-3, 8]$. (c) $[-4, -1)$. (d) $(0, 7)$. (e) $[-1, .6)$. (f) $(-\infty, 2)$.   **7.** (a)

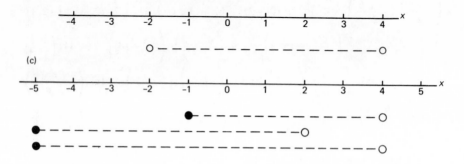

(c)

EXERCISE 14-2, PAGE 291

1. $\left(\dfrac{7}{3}, \infty\right)$.   **3.** $[3, \infty)$.   **5.** $x \in R_e \wedge x \neq 0 \wedge x \neq \dfrac{1}{4}$.   **7.** $\left(-\infty, \dfrac{3}{5}\right)$.
9. $\{-1, 0, 1\}$.   **11.** $x \in I^+$.

EXERCISE 14-3, PAGE 294

1. $(-1, 3)$.   **3.** $(-\infty, 4) \cup (4, \infty)$.   **5.** ϕ.   **7.** $(-\infty, -2) \cup (3, \infty)$.
9. $\left(-\dfrac{1}{2}, \dfrac{1}{3}\right)$.   **11.** $\{0, 1\}$.   **13.** $\{2, 3\}$.   **15.** $\{4, 5\}$.   **17.** ϕ.   **19.** (a) $[2, 6)$;
(b) $[4, 5]$.   **21.** $\left[-\dfrac{1}{3}, -\dfrac{1}{4}\right]$.   **23.** $(-\infty, 1] \cup [4, \infty)$.   **25.** $x \in R_e$.

EXERCISE 14-5, PAGE 305

1. $\left\{-\dfrac{4}{5}, \dfrac{2}{5}\right\}$.   **3.** ϕ.   **7.** $\left(-\infty, -\dfrac{1}{2}\right] \cup \left[\dfrac{13}{2}, \infty\right)$.

EXERCISE 14-7, PAGE 311

2. Ship all 30 units to Akron from warehouse A, and ship 10 units from warehouse A and 30 units from warehouse B to Cleveland.   **4.** The toy factory should produce 4 boats and 3 cars by using the available hours of machines 1 and 2.

EXERCISE 15-1, PAGE 315

1. $\dfrac{1}{2}$. **2.** $\dfrac{7}{15,840}$. **3.** $\dfrac{352}{5}$. **4.** $\dfrac{3}{32}$. **6.** $\dfrac{14,400}{13}$. **7.** x^2. **8.** -1. **9.** a. **11.** 2.

12. $-9; 1$. **13.** $\dfrac{5}{7}; -\dfrac{1}{2}$. **14.** $-\dfrac{1}{20}; -\dfrac{2}{3}$. **16.** $2, \dfrac{6}{5}; -2, -\dfrac{6}{5}$. **17.** $\left(\dfrac{1}{3}, 0\right)$.

18. $(-4, 0)$. **19.** $\left(\dfrac{2}{3}, 2\right)$. **21.** $\left(\dfrac{5}{2}, -2, 2\right)$. **22.** $(2, 4, 6)$.

EXERCISE 15-2, PAGE 317

1. $\dfrac{a+c}{c} = \dfrac{b+d}{d}$; $\dfrac{a-c}{c} = \dfrac{b-d}{d}$; $\dfrac{a+c}{a-c} = \dfrac{b+d}{b-d}$. **2.** $\dfrac{b+a}{a} = \dfrac{d+c}{c}$;

$\dfrac{b-a}{a} = \dfrac{d-c}{c}$; $\dfrac{b+a}{b-a} = \dfrac{d+c}{d-c}$. **3.** $\dfrac{b}{a+b} = \dfrac{d}{c+d}$; $\dfrac{b}{a-b} = \dfrac{d}{c-d}$;

$\dfrac{a-b}{a+b} = \dfrac{c-d}{c+d}$; $\dfrac{a}{b+a} = \dfrac{c}{c+d}$; $\dfrac{a}{b-a} = \dfrac{c}{d-c}$; $\dfrac{b-a}{b+a} = \dfrac{d-c}{d+c}$;

$\dfrac{c}{a+c} = \dfrac{d}{b+d}$; $\dfrac{c}{a-c} = \dfrac{b}{b-d}$; $\dfrac{a-c}{a+c} = \dfrac{b-d}{b+d}$. **16.** $18\dfrac{2}{3}$ ft. **17.** $12\dfrac{6}{7}$ ft.

18. 24 ft. **19.** $\dfrac{15}{7}$ mis.

EXERCISE 15-3, PAGE 323

1. $y = kx^3$; $\dfrac{y}{x^3} = k$; x varies directly as $\sqrt[3]{y}$.

2. $z = kxy$; $\dfrac{z}{xy} = k$; x varies directly as z and inversely as y.

3. $w = \dfrac{kx^2 y}{z}$; $\dfrac{zw}{x^2 y} = k$; x varies directly as $\sqrt{wz}$ and inversely as $\sqrt{y}$.

4. $y = \dfrac{kw}{x^2 z}$; $\dfrac{x^2 yz}{w} = k$; x varies directly as $\sqrt{w}$ and inversely as $\sqrt{yz}$.

6. $w = \dfrac{kx}{yz^3}$; $\dfrac{wyz^3}{x} = k$; x varies directly as w, y, and z^3 (or as wyz^3).

7. $x^2 = \dfrac{ky}{z^2 w}$; $\dfrac{x^2 z^2 w}{y} = k$; x varies directly as $\sqrt{y}$ and inversely as $z\sqrt{w}$.

8. $y^3 = \dfrac{kxz}{w}$; $\dfrac{y^3 w}{xz} = k$; x varies directly as wy^3 and inversely as z.

9. (a) $\dfrac{2}{3}$; (b) $\pm i\sqrt{3}$; (c) $\dfrac{48}{5}$; (d) 24. **11.** $\dfrac{45}{4}$ sq in.; 20 sq in.; $\dfrac{245}{4}$ sq in.;

80 sq in.; $\frac{405}{4}$ sq in. **12.** 9 pts. **13.** 115.74 lb.; 154.05 lb. **14.** $2\sqrt[3]{2}$ ft.; $2\sqrt[3]{5}$ ft.; $2\sqrt[3]{10}$ ft.; $2\sqrt[3]{20}$ ft.; $2\sqrt[3]{60}$ ft.; $4\sqrt[3]{15}$ ft. **16.** Moon: 16.46 lb; Mercury: 26.3 lb; Venus: 86.1 lb; Mars: 39.15 lb; Jupiter: 252.8 lb; Saturn: 107.5 lb; Sun: 2777.5 lb. **17.** 199.5 lb. **18.** S is decreased by $S/9$. **19.** (a) It is decreased to $11\frac{31}{64}$ units, (b) $96\sqrt{2}$ in. **21.** 168 cu ft. **22.** Mass of Jupiter = 302.5 (mass of earth).

EXERCISE 16-1, PAGE 328

1. 3,5,7,9. **3.** $\frac{1}{2},\frac{4}{5},1,\frac{8}{7}$. **5.** $1,\frac{4}{5},\frac{4}{5},\frac{16}{17}$. **7.** $-2,4,-8,16$. **9.** $n^2 + 1$; 37,50,65.

11. $3n - 2$; 16,19,22. **13.** $\frac{(-1)^n}{n}$; $\frac{1}{6},-\frac{1}{7},\frac{1}{8}$. **15.** $(-1)^{n+1}$; $-1,1,-1$.

17. $5,\frac{5}{2},\frac{5}{4},\frac{5}{8},\frac{5}{16}$. **19.** $2,-1,1,-\frac{1}{2},\frac{1}{4}$.

EXERCISE 16-2, PAGE 332

1. (f) $\sum_{i=1}^{7} (2i - 1)$. **3.** (a) $\sum_{k=1}^{\infty} (-1)^{k+1}\frac{2k - 1}{2^{k-1}}$. **5.** (b) $\sum_{k=1}^{\infty} (2k)$. **7.** $1 + 3 + 6 + 10 + 15 + 21$. **9.** $6 + 1 + (-4) + (-9) + (-14) + (-19)$. **11.** $30 + 42 + 56 + 72 + 90 + 110$. **13.** $3 + 36 + 729 + 20736$. **15.** $3 + 36 + 729 + 20736 + \cdots$.

EXERCISE 16-3, PAGE 336

1. 11. **2.** -5. **3.** $\frac{11}{2}x$. **4.** -6. **6.** 7,11. **7.** $-4,-10,-16$. **8.** 8,6,4,2,0. **9.** 21. **11.** 4. **12.** 115. **13.** 8. **14.** 21. **16.** 200 mis. **17.** 25 mis. **18.** $20.

EXERCISE 16-4, PAGE 338

1. 48. **2.** 185. **3.** -88. **4.** 114. **8.** 18; $\frac{19}{17}$. **9.** 192; 27. **10.** 147; 7. **11.** 31; -3.6. **13.** 312; 15. **14.** -60; -3. **15.** 11; 27. **16.** 7; 23. **18.** 3; 24. **19.** 21. **20.** 150 ft. **21.** 440 ft. **23.** $3,000; $2,800; $2,600; $2,400; $2,200. **24.** $1,275. **25.** $6,840. **26.** $2,950.

EXERCISE 16-5, PAGE 342

1. 32. **2.** 243. **3.** $\frac{1}{2}$ **4.** -128. **6.** 4,8,16, or $-4,8,-16$. **7.** 16,8,4,2.

8. $-8, 4.$ **9.** $-3, 9, -27, 81.$ **11.** $\pm 4.$ **12.** $\pm 3.$ **13.** $\pm 9.$ **14.** $\pm 10.$ **16.** 4;
30. **17.** 6; 21. **18.** 5; 121. **19.** 6; $-21.$ **21.** 6; 1. **22.** 5; 1. **23.** $\frac{1}{2}$; 255.

24. $\frac{1}{2}$; 31.5. **26.** \$10.23. **27.** \$3,000; \$1,500; \$750; \$375. **28.** \$4,000; \$3,200;
\$2,560; \$2,408. **29.** 4096.

EXERCISE 16-6, PAGE 345

1. 250. **3.** $\frac{10}{3}$. **5.** $\frac{\sqrt{3}}{\sqrt{2}(\sqrt{3}-1)}$. **7.** $\frac{6}{11}$. **9.** $4\frac{44}{333} = \frac{1376}{333}$.

EXERCISE 17-1, PAGE 349

1. (a), (c), (d).

EXERCISE 17-2, PAGE 351

1. (a) biconditional; (b) negation; (c) conditional; (d) negation; (e) disjunction;
(f) conjunction; (g) conjunction of conditionals or a biconditional; (h) conjunction;
(i) conditional; (j) disjunction.
2. (a) $p \leftrightarrow q$. (b) $\sim p$. (c) $q \to p$. (d) $\sim p$. (e) $p \vee \sim p$. (f) $p \wedge q$.
(g) $(p \to \sim p) \wedge (\sim p \to p)$ or $p \leftrightarrow \sim p$. (h) $p \wedge q$. (i) $p \to q$. (j) $r \vee s$.

EXERCISE 17-3, PAGE 355

1. (a) F. (b) T. (c) T. (d) T. (e) F. (f) T. (g) T. (h) F. (i) T.
2. (h) If it is not true that $3 + 5 = 8$ and a triangle has two sides, then three-
fifths of ten is not six.
 (i) It is not true that 0 is an odd integer if Lake Erie is one of the Great Lakes
if and only if Lake Erie is one of the Great Lakes and 0 is not an odd integer.
3. (a) T. (b) T. (c) T. (d) T.
4.

p	q	$\sim p$	$\sim q$	$p \vee \sim q$	$(p \vee \sim q) \to \sim p$
T	T	F	F	T	F
T	F	F	T	T	F
F	T	T	F	F	T
F	F	T	T	T	T

The truth-table reveals that the given pattern is true whenever p is false.

EXERCISE 18-2, PAGE 372

1. $x^3 + 3x^2y + 3xy^2 + y^3$. **2.** $x^3 - 3x^2y + 3xy^2 - y^3$. **3.** $64x^6 - 192x^5y + 240x^4y^2 - 160x^3y^3 + 60x^2y^4 - 12xy^5 + y^6$. **4.** $27a^6 + 27a^4b + 9a^2b^2 + b^3$.

6. $16x^2 + 32xy\sqrt{x} + 24xy^2 + 8y^3\sqrt{x} + y^4$.   **7.** $729x^6 - 729x^5y +$

$\dfrac{1215}{4}x^4y^2 - \dfrac{135}{2}x^3y^3 + \dfrac{135}{16}x^2y^4 - \dfrac{9}{16}xy^5 + \dfrac{y^6}{64}$.   **8.** $a^8 + \dfrac{4}{3}a^6b + \dfrac{2}{3}a^4b^2 +$

$\dfrac{4}{27}a^2b^3 + \dfrac{b^4}{81}$.   **9.** $32x^5 - 80x^4y^2 + 80x^3y^4 - 40x^2y^6 + 10xy^8 - y^{10}$.

11. $\dfrac{x^4}{16} + \dfrac{x^3y^2}{6} + \dfrac{x^2y^4}{6} + \dfrac{2xy^6}{27} + \dfrac{y^8}{81}$.   **12.** $\dfrac{x}{8} - \dfrac{3y\sqrt[3]{x^2}}{4} + \dfrac{3y^2\sqrt[3]{x}}{2} - y^3$.

13. $x^5 - 20x^{9/2}y + 180x^4y^2 - 960x^{7/2}y^3 + \cdots$.   **14.** $\dfrac{256}{x^8} - \dfrac{256}{x^6} + \dfrac{112}{x^4} -$

$\dfrac{28}{x^2} + \cdots$. **16.** 70. **17.** $-792a^2b^{17}$. **18.** -3432.   **19.** $x^{-3} - 3x^{-4}y +$

$6x^{-5}y^2 - 10x^{-6}y^3 + \cdots$.   **21.** $\dfrac{1}{\sqrt{2x}}\left(1 - \dfrac{y}{4x} + \dfrac{3y^2}{32x^2} - \dfrac{5y^3}{128x^3} + \cdots\right)$.

22. $\dfrac{\sqrt{a}}{a} - \dfrac{2\sqrt{b}}{a} + \dfrac{4b\sqrt{a}}{a^2} - \dfrac{8b\sqrt{b}}{a^2} + \cdots$. **23.** $1 - 2x + 5x^2 - \dfrac{40x^3}{3} + \cdots$.

24. $1 - 2x + 4x^2 - 8x^3 \cdots$.   **26.** $a^2 + b^2 + c^2 + d^2 + 2ab - 2ac -$
$2ad - 2bc - 2bd + 2cd$.   **27.** $a^2 + b^2 + c^2 + 2ab - 2ac - 2bc$.
28. $a^2 + b^2 + c^2 - 2ab - 2ac + 2bc$.   **29.** $a^3 + 3a^2b + 3ab^2 + b^3 +$
$3a^2c + 6abc + 3b^2c + 3ac^2 + 3bc^2 + c^3$.

EXERCISE 19-1, PAGE 378

1. 6. **3.** $\dfrac{3}{2}$. **5.** 3. **7.** $\dfrac{1}{2}$. **9.** 1. **11.** $\dfrac{1}{8}$. **13.** 10. **15.** $\dfrac{1}{64}$. **17.** 10.

19. $10^x = 100$; $x = 2$. **21.** $10^x = 0.000001$; $x = -6$. **25.** log $0.00001 =$

-5. **27.** $\log_4 64 = 3$. **29.** $\log_8 64 = 2$. **31.** $\log_8 27 = \dfrac{3}{2}$. **33.** 2. **35.** $\dfrac{4}{5}$.

37. $\dfrac{1}{3}$.

EXERCISE 19-2, PAGE 382

1. 1.08. **2.** 1.26. **3.** 1.44. **4.** 0.90. **6.** 1.5. **7.** -0.18. **8.** 0.18. **9.** 0.42.

11. 0.70. **12.** 1.4. **13.** 2.1. **14.** -0.52. **16.** -0.92. **17.** 8. **18.** $\dfrac{1}{4}$. **19.** 4.

21. 125. **22.** $\dfrac{1}{3}$. **23.** 3. **24.** $\dfrac{1}{2}$. **26.** -1. **27.** $-\dfrac{2}{3}$. **28.** $\dfrac{3}{2}$. **29.** $2\sqrt{2}$.

31. $\dfrac{1}{9}$. **32.** 512. **33.** $\dfrac{7}{4}$. **34.** $\dfrac{1}{2\sqrt[3]{2}}$.   **36.** Change left side to $\log_a \sqrt[3]{B}$.

37. Change left side to $\log_a A^{2/3}$.   **38.** Change right side to $10(\log_a x +$

$\log_a y$). **39.** True. **41.** Change right side to $\frac{1}{2}$ ($\log_{10} x + \log_{10} y - \log_{10} z$). **42.** Change right side to $\frac{1}{3}$ ($2 \log_{10} A - \log_{10} B$). **43.** Change left side to $\log_a \sqrt[5]{C}$. **44.** True. **46.** True. **47.** True.

EXERCISE 19-4, PAGE 389

1. 2.2625. **2.** 2.5403. **3.** 2.7210. **4.** 2.3711. **6.** 2.6232. **7.** 2.5563.
8. 2.9657. **9.** 1.5119. **11.** 0.5705. **12.** 0.9180. **13.** 8.7924 − 10.
14. 9.8663 − 10. **16.** 6.9590 − 10. **17.** 6.7782 − 10. **18.** 7.7664 − 10.
19. 6.8069 − 10. **21.** 11.5. **22.** 135. **23.** 22.6. **24.** 430. **26.** 3920.
27. 0.289. **28.** 0.0315. **29.** 0.00231. **81.** 5.48. **32.** 1.01. **33.** 0.000100.

EXERCISE 19-5, PAGE 390

1. 3.4041. **2.** 2.8625. **3.** 8.9218 − 10. **4.** 1.5474. **6.** 7.7563 − 10.
7. 0.7583. **8.** 2.4688. **9.** 6.8503 − 10. **11.** 8.9659 − 20. **12.** 20.3651.
13. 167.0. **14.** 2,313,000. **16.** 0.001942. **17.** 0.1401. **18.** 5.908.
19. 0.01456. **21.** 2.063×10^{-8}. **22.** 3.107×10^{-10}. **23.** 6.521×10^{10}.
24. 1.030×10^{15}.

EXERCISE 19-6, PAGE 394

1. 22.89. **2.** 0.03034. **3.** 50,220. **4.** 3.768. **6.** 1910. **7.** 1.307×10^9.
8. 0.5358. **9.** 18,220. **11.** 0.09530. **12.** 47.47. **13.** 0.1102.
14. 2.624×10^7. **16.** 1.725×10^{-8}. **17.** 0.03014. **18.** 72.79. **19.** 9.314.
21. 7.555. **22.** 1.529. **23.** 222,700. **24.** 4861. **26.** 1.063. **27.** −46.01.
28. −16.05. **29.** 0.04336. **31.** 99.75. **32.** 15.01. **33.** 9.9894 − 10.
34. 1.441.

EXERCISE 19-7, PAGE 396

1. 6.2305. **3.** −0.8843. **5.** 0.2641.

EXERCISE 19-8, PAGE 398

1. 2.3866. **3.** 0.55189. **5.** 5. **7.** 3.84074. **9.** 0.3246.